A GENERAL HISTORY OF THE SCIENCES

Edited by René Taton

Ancient and Medieval Science

FROM PREHISTORY TO AD 1450

·

The Beginnings of Modern Science

FROM 1450 TO 1800

·

Science in the Nineteenth Century

·

Science in the Twentieth Century

The Contributors to this Volume

ROGER ARNALDEZ
Faculté des Lettres, Lyons. *Arabic Science*

JEAN BEAUJEU
Faculté des Lettres, Lille. *Hellenistic and Roman Science*

GUY BEAUJOUAN
Archives Nationales, Paris. *Medieval Science in the Christian West*

RAYMOND BLOCH
École des Hautes Études. *Estruscan Science*

LOUIS BOURGEY
Faculté des Lettres, Algiers. *Hellenic Medicine*

PAUL DUPONT-SOMMER
Sorbonne. *Ancient Hebrew Science*

JEAN FILLIOZAT
Collège de France. *Indian Science*

RAYMOND FURON
Muséum National d'Histoire Naturelle. *Prehistoric Science*

ANDRÉ HAUDRICOURT
Centre National de la Recherche Scientifique. *Chinese Science*

JEAN ITARD
Lycée Henry IV. *Hellenistic and Roman Mathematics*

RENE LABAT
Collège de France. *Mesopotamia*

GUSTAVE LEFEBVRE
Institut Français. *Egyptian Science: general presentation and medicine*

LOUIS MASSIGNON
Collège de France. *Arabic Science*

P. H. MICHEL
Bibliothèque mazarine. *Hellenic Science*

J. NEEDHAM, F.R.S.
Gonville and Caius College, Cambridge. *Chinese Science*

I. SIMON
Society for the History of Jewish Medicine. *Medieval Jewish Science*

G. STRESSER-PÉAN
École des Hautes Études. *Pre-Columbian Science*

RENÉ TATON
Centre National de la Recherche Scientifique.
General co-ordination of the work

JEAN THÉODORIDÈS
Centre National de la Recherche Scientifique. *Byzantine Science*

JEAN VERCOUTTER
Director of Antiquities, Sudan. *Egyptian Mathematics and Astronomy*

CHARLES VIROLLEAUD
Institut Français. *Phoenician Science*

Ancient and Medieval Science

FROM PREHISTORY TO AD 1450

Edited and with a general Preface by
RENÉ TATON

Translated by A. J. Pomerans

With 53 black and white plates and 43 figures

THAMES AND HUDSON · LONDON

La Science Antique et Médiévale © 1957 by Presses Universitaires de France
English translation © 1963 by Basic Books Inc.
Printed in Great Britain by Western Printing Services Ltd, Bristol
Not for sale in the U.S.A. or Canada

CONTENTS

viii   *Contents*

ILLUSTRATIONS

TRANSLATOR'S NOTE

Throughout this work, I have followed Sarton in giving Greek endings to Greek names, thus distinguishing Greek writers like Celsos and Sallustios from Latin writers like Celsus and Sallustius.

Chinese names have been romanized in accordance with Needham's system, and I am greatly indebted to Dr Needham for his invaluable help in this matter.

My thanks are also due to the British Interlibrary Service, and particularly to the West Suffolk, Nottingham University, and National Central Libraries, from which I have obtained authoritative English renderings of several of the ancient inscriptions and the original texts of the English works quoted.

A. J. POMERANS

GENERAL PREFACE

WHILE THERE HAVE BEEN MANY HISTORIES of the various branches of science, there have been few attempts to present a comprehensive history of science as such. Yet the ever-increasing tempo of scientific and technological progress, which has had such profound repercussions on every aspect of our civilization, makes it imperative to study the role of science as a whole in the cultural life of man.

Seen in this light, the history of science cannot be the exclusive concern of scientists curious about the individual contributions of their great predecessors or about the sources of modern scientific trends. It affects all men who are interested in the world in which they live.

Since it impinges on science, philosophy, and general history, the history of science is a powerful means of combating the modern tendency to pigeon-hole all branches of knowledge into separate compartments. Hence it is surprising that, apart from specialized papers, the educated man has been so widely neglected by scientific historians. Even the exceptions, e.g., the unfinished writings of such eminent scientific historians as Aldo Mieli and George Sarton, do not entirely meet his requirements.

The present general history of science in four volumes aims to bridge this gap by giving an objective and accurate survey of the development of science, considered as an essential aspect of our culture.

In order to make this work accessible to the widest possible readership, footnotes, references, and critical discussions have been cut down to the absolute minimum. On the other hand, the bibliographies of the various sections are wide enough to enable interested readers to follow up the discussion. The plates, which have been carefully selected, aim at capturing the scientific atmosphere of the periods they portray. Finally, though they have not sacrificed their scientific standards, the authors have either avoided the use of specialized terms or taken pains to explain them.

The presentation of an objective and accurate survey of our present knowledge of the history of all the sciences, from antiquity to the middle of the twentieth century, has been entrusted to eminent scholars. All the authors who have agreed to participate in this work are acknowledged experts in their chosen fields, and their collaboration has ensured a far wider and deeper approach than any individual could hope to achieve by himself. While giving an unbiased account of current findings, these men have not been afraid to state their personal views on controversial problems, and this freedom of expression has added greatly to the liveliness of the discussion. The various chapters have, however, been carefully co-ordinated to ensure coherence and continuity.

Volume I deals with the long period spanning the first scientific gropings of prehistoric man and the middle of the fifteenth century, which heralded the beginnings of modern science. During that entire period, science developed along parallel paths in the various centres of civilization—science still differed from country to country. While we have few records of our scientific beginnings in prehistoric times, we know a great deal about the great Eastern civilizations—Egypt, Mesopotamia, Phoenicia, Israel, India, and China—which, while still imbued with magical and utilitarian concerns, nevertheless gave science its first great impetus.

From the sixth century B.C. onwards, Eastern science became eclipsed by the magnificent achievements of Greece which led to a far deeper and more abstract conception of the role and the structure of science. The diffusion of Greek ideas, which followed in the wake of Alexander's conquests, led to the rapid and brilliant development of Hellenistic science. Then came the expansion of the Roman empire, and the great barbarian invasions in the fifth century A.D. which marked the almost total extinction of Greco-Roman science in the west, and with it the end of the new scientific vision.

During the next period, known collectively as the Middle Ages, science began to stir again in the Arab world, India, China, Byzantium and Western Europe. As contacts between them grew more intimate and more numerous, Western Europe learned of the achievements of ancient and Arabic science.

The resulting upsurge from the middle of the fifteenth to the eighteenth century, culminating in modern science, and the less important contributions of other civilizations, will be discussed in Volume II.

Volumes III and IV discuss the development of contemporary science, from the beginning of the nineteenth century to our day. This period is marked by the accelerated tempo of advances in all fields of science, by the growing impact of science on everyday life, and by its increasingly international character.

So gigantic a task could never have been completed without the devotion of its many eminent contributors, nor without the prior spade work of such ardent pioneers as Paul Tannery and George Sarton, who were the first to plead the cause of the general history of science and to plead it so eloquently.

The Dawn of Science

PREHISTORIC BEGINNINGS

NO HISTORY OF SCIENCE can ignore the achievements of prehistoric man.

Though he appeared on the earth about a million years ago, we know next to nothing of his mental development during the first hundreds of millennia, when his only implements were chipped stone tools. Then, quite suddenly, during the last part of the Stone Age, man began to build burial grounds and to produce carvings, paintings, and sculptures. This period covers no more than the last 50,000 years. However, it was only in the course of the last 10,000 years that man discovered and perfected all his greatest skills: from the potter's wheel to the exploitation of nuclear energy.

Prehistoric man was the first creature to apply reason to the satisfaction of his everyday needs. Hence the history of science begins with the history of technology.

Clearly, scientific explanations cannot precede the actions which they attempt to interpret. Thus the earliest metallurgists, who melted copper some 8,000 years ago, had no idea of the distinction between oxides, carbonates, and sulphides, though they managed to find and to use the ore from which they could obtain pure copper.

The recorded history of science as such began only some 5,000 years ago—the date of the earliest monuments, works of art, and inscriptions that give us clues about the thinking of early civilized man.

On these clues, sparse though they are, we have to base our entire knowledge of the first gropings of nascent science. Some prehistoric men must have handed on their knowledge by word of mouth, and it is undoubtedly due to their teachings that proto-historical and ancient science was born.

GEOLOGICAL PERIODS
To gain any understanding of the beginnings and development of scientific thought, we must fit them into the history of human evolution.

I

Man, as we saw, has existed for the past million years or so, during which there was a marked fall in temperature and the consequent formation of a vast ice-cap over the Arctic regions.

In the Scandinavian (boreal) zone, an ice-sheet spread to Northern Germany, Holland and Great Britain, finally reaching Ireland and the Atlantic. Another enormous mass of ice covered Canada and north-east U.S.A., reaching to the Atlantic.

There were four main glacial periods, interrupted by inter-glacial periods during which the weather was warmer than it is today, so much so that elephants and hippopotami managed to survive in Western Europe. In the cold spells, however, mammoths and reindeer predominated. In detail, we can distinguish eight cold phases, during the last of which the warm-climate fauna and flora were driven out of Europe, including even Italy and Spain. It is only in the last 12,000 years that the Scandinavian ice-cap has begun to melt perceptibly and that the ocean level has risen sufficiently to invade the European mainland, including the English Channel.

In the equatorial zone, the ice of the high mountains in Eastern Africa descended some 3,250 to 4,750 feet lower than its present level.

It was under such climatic conditions that early humanity developed. All we know of its biological beginnings is based on a number of fossil men, animals, and plants, and on an examination of stone implements.

During the middle of the Pleistocene (about half a million years ago), lived those remarkable 'ape-men', Pithecanthropus (of Java), 'Sinanthropus' (of China), and Atlanthropus of Algeria. These early man-like creatures were familiar with fire and flint-chipping. Atlanthropus, in particular, whose fossil remains were discovered in 1954, was buried with a set of flint tools of the kind classified as belonging to the Acheulian and Chellian cultures of the Old Stone Age (corresponding with the first inter-glacial period).

The next stage in the development of man is represented by two fossils discovered respectively at Swanscombe (England) and Fontéchevade (France). Both had marked human characteristics, though their skull bones were much thicker than ours. The tools used by the Fontéchevade man represented a higher level of the lower Old Stone Age (2nd or 3rd inter-glacial period). According to current hypotheses, these two fossils represent man's mental development some 200,000 years ago. The capacity and convolutions of his brain were fairly similar to ours.

During the next phase of palaeolithic culture, which coincided with the end of the 3rd inter-glacial and the 4th glacial period, there appeared a quite distinctive and more primitive type of man,

Date	Archaeological classification		Human types	Human cultures
0 0 to −2500 −2500 to −5000	Beginning of our era Metals (copper, bronze, iron) Neolithic		Modern	Proto-histori-cal urban civilizations
−5000 to −8000	Mesolithic			Agriculture, cattle raising
−8000 to 30,000	Upper Palaeolithic	Magdalenian Solutrean Aurignacian	Chancelade Cro-Magnon	Carvings, paintings, and sculptures
−30,000 to −200,000	Middle Palaeolithic	Mousterian Lavalloisian	 Neanderthal	Burials and carvings
Before −200,000 *c.* −1,000,000	Lower Palaeolithic	Levalloisian Acheulian Chellian and Pre-Chellian	Swanscombe Fontéchevade Mauer Atlanthropus 'Sinanthropus' Pithecanthropus	None

fig. 1 Survey of the history of human cultures.

commonly called Neanderthal Man. His skull differed from modern human skulls in the marked development of its brow ridges, its receding forehead, and the flatness of its roof. Neanderthal Man, who inhabited Europe, Western Asia and Africa, used typical Middle Palaeolothic implements, and practised ceremonial burial. Neanderthal skeletons recovered at La Ferrassie (Dordogne) had been buried in a hollow covered with flat stones; another skeleton found at La Chapelle-aux-Saints (south-west France) which was also covered with stones, was dug up together with the leg of a bison; the Moustier skeleton (Dordogne) had been buried in a contracted position, its head resting on the right arm. In Drachenloch (Switzerland), archaeologists have unearthed a singular cave whose walls were studded with the bones and skulls of bears, while another chamber contained sarcophagi constructed of large flagstones and covered with bear skulls arranged in a pattern. Similar sarcophagi were discovered in Franconia and Styria.

During the next stage, the late Old Stone Age or Upper Palaeolithic, which covers the retreat of the Würm glaciation and a dry and rather cold spell (*c.* 30,000 years ago), we distinguish between the Aurignacian, the Solutrean and the Magdalenian cultures, and three corresponding types of Homo sapiens: Cro-Magnon Man (average height 6 feet) who inhabited Western Europe and Northern Africa, Chancelade Man (small stature and broad cheek-bones), remains of whom have been found as far afield as France and China, and Grimaldi Man, who is said to have had pronounced negroid features.

All these late Stone Age men practised complicated burial rites appropriate to a culture of hunters. Apart from flint and bone implements, they produced a host of decorated utensils, cave carvings and paintings.

From them, we pass on very quickly to historic man, whose civilization has left far more unmistakable traces. We distinguish between the Mesolithic (*c.* 10,000 years ago); the Neolithic (polished stone implements, cattle raising, and agriculture) and the various Metal Ages (copper, bronze and iron).

There is a close connection between classical antiquity and prehistory, during the last stages of which man had acquired a vast store of knowledge handed on by greatly respected 'wizards'.

Non-civilized man was very observant. He had time to gaze at the stars and follow their motions. He studied the behaviour of the wild animals which he hunted. Above all, he had learnt to distinguish between edible and poisonous plants, and to find suitable materials for his implements and weapons. Moreover, hunters and traders needed to count. Hence it was in prehistoric times that man acquired the first notions of geology, zoology, botany, medicine, astronomy, and mathematics.

GEOLOGY AND MINING

Most of the implements and weapons of prehistoric man were made of flint. Hence he must have discarded as unsuitable the countless varieties of other stones spread all over the surface of the world. True, in countries where flint was scarce, quartz, granite, shale, quartzite, and even ironstone were used, but flint was always the first choice, and remained so for hundreds of thousands of years— from the early untrimmed tools used in St. Prest and Abbeville until the discovery of metals.

Having exhausted their surface supplies, our prehistoric ancestors went digging for flint below ground. To do so, they had to 'prospect' for suitable deposits, and then dig into the earth. Thus, during the first four millennia before our era they founded geology and mining.

Belgian geologists have discovered a Neolithic mining centre, dating from 3000 to 2500 B.C., at Spiennes, near Mons. It had 25 bore-holes of average diameter 31 in., each going down to a depth of 40 feet or more. Shafts up to 6 feet high would be driven whenever a particularly rich vein was struck. Miners' implements of the time included flint or bone picks, polished axes, and flint sledge-hammers. In England, at Grime's Graves (Norfolk), archaeologists have discovered 250 workings, 40 to 43 feet deep, and in France similar workings were found in various places, from Meudon near Paris down to Mur-de-Barryz in Southern France. The most striking of all these sites was undoubtedly the flint mine at Grand Pressigny near Tours (2500–2000 B.C.). It extended for a number of miles and yielded flint cores the colour of wax, weighing many pounds each. Its cutting edges were famed throughout Western Europe. In Egypt, a kind of flint was obtained from Eocene rocks in the Nile valley.

Apart from flint, early man occasionally used implements made of obsidian (vitreous lava) which were extremely sharp but very fragile. They also collected various minerals of pleasing appearance or colour, which they turned into ornaments. Among them were agate, cornelian, turquoise, callainite, and haematite.

Later, *i.e.* from about 1000 B.C. onwards, miners began to dig for metals—first of all copper and then tin, which was needed for making bronze, and finally for iron.

ZOOLOGY AND THE STUDY OF ANIMAL HABITS

Prehistoric man lived in a world of profound climatic changes. As the ice spread through Europe and North America, warm-climate animals, including reindeer, were driven southwards. At other periods, animals from the steppes of Asia were attracted to Western Europe. We know of these successive migrations not only from fossils, but also from cave paintings.

When prehistoric men first drew pictures of animals they laid the foundations of descriptive zoology, for their rock paintings and carvings were accurate enough for modern scholars to identify the species they portrayed.

In Europe, such carvings are found particularly in caves in south-west France and in the French and Spanish Pyrenees, *viz.*, in Lascaux, Laussel, Les Combarelles, Font-de-Gaume, Rouffignac, Lespugne, Niaux, Mas d'Azil, Lourdes, Isturiz, and Altamira.

Some of the cave walls are covered with Aurignacian and Magdalenian drawings and carvings, and date back to between 12,000 and and 30,000 B.C. In the Magdalenian grotto of Les Combarelles, Capitan, Breuil, and Peyrony have discovered 291 clear representations, including 116 horses, 35 bison, 19 bears, 14 reindeer, 30 mammoths and 1 rhinoceros. In the Font-de-Gaume cave, the same workers came across 200 pictures of bison, horses, mammoths, reindeer, wolves, rhinoceros, cats, bears, etc. The Altamira caves, in the province of Santandér (Spain), are decorated with bison, horses and boars, but not with mammoths or reindeer. Cave paintings made in eastern Spain during the Mesolithic depict hunting and battle scenes. Many of the animals in them are wounded or trapped, from which we may infer that hunting was an important part of the economy.

In Africa, the Sahara may be called a treasure-trove of cave drawings going back to about 4000 B.C. While the drawings of camels are recent (beginning of our era) and horses did not appear before 100 B.C., the oldest Egyptian paintings represent the fauna of an earlier and more humid Sahara: elephants, rhinoceros, giraffes, hippopotami, oxen, rams, and antelopes.

Interest in wild animals and the study of their habits by hunters, were responsible for the first attempts at domestication. We know that the camel was domesticated in Central Asia at about 3000 B.C. and the horse at about the same time. E. Dechambre thinks that the deterioration of Egypt's climate about 4000 B.C. forced hunters to keep a closer watch on, and control over, the movements of their herds of antelope. This is borne out by numerous representations on pre- and proto-dynastic tombs. We have other evidence of the existence of an intermediate stage between hunting and rearing, namely 'controlled freedom', such as the protection of young hippopotami by the Sorko of the central Niger basin before the European invasion, studied by J. Rouch.

From cave drawings we know that prehistoric man had some ideas about anatomy. At Lespugne, a plate representing a fish shows the gills, the mouth, two eyes, the vertebral column and the fish-bones. Another fish, at Goudain, carved from a sliver of bone, bears a diagrammatic sketch of the digestive tract.

Primitive knowledge of animals was not limited to vertebrates; molluscs, too, played an important part in the diet, and later as utensils, ornaments and means of exchange. Upper Palaeolithic finds include clusters of shells: barnacles and mussels in Gibraltar; seapens at La Barma Grande (near Menton); barnacles, mussels, periwinkles, cockles, oysters and clams in the Santander caves. Mesolithic kitchen-middens in Europe included the shells of periwinkles, cockles, clams and snails.

The Aurignacians used sea-snails for making necklaces, belts, headgear, *etc*. Many, belonging to the genera *Littorina* and *Nassa* (periwinkles and dog-whelks) were pierced and threaded together. Even those prehistoric men who lived far from the sea-shore nevertheless obtained marine shells or dug them out of fossilized rock.

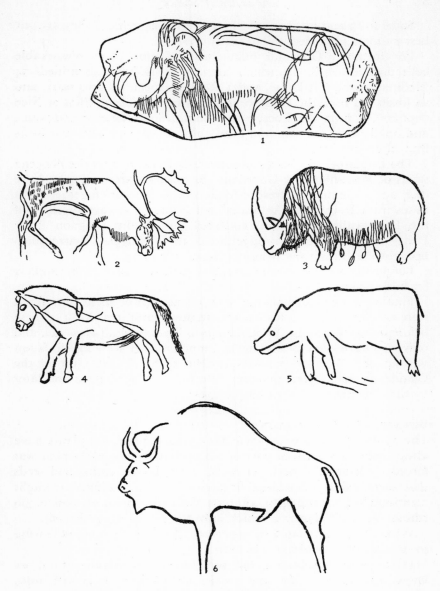

fig. 2 Cave painting and carvings of prehistoric animals.

1 Mammoth from La Madeleine
2 Grazing reindeer from Thaingen (after Heim)
3 Rhinoceros from La Colombière (after Mayer and Pissot)
4 Trapped horse from Combarelles (after Breuil, Capitan, and Peyrony)
5 Cave-bear carved on stone from Massat, Ariège
6 Bison from La Grèze, Dordogne (after H. Breuil)

Some fresh and fossilized shells were used as money; they are our best pointers to palaeolithic trade routes.

For instance, Grimaldi man (near Menton) had remarkable collections of shells in which archaeologists have identified 74 Mediterranean, 6 Atlantic, and 1 Red Sea species (*Cassis rufa*), and 24 fossils: 14 from the Pleistocene, 7 from the Pliocene (Biot or Nice deposits), 2 from the Eocene (nummulitic limestone of Garavan), and finally a rhyncholite and even an ammonite (*Acanthoceras lyelli*) from the Rhône valley.

The Bruniquel (S. France) fossilized shells came from the Pliocene sands of Roussillon. At Gourdant (S. France), archaeologists have dug up a mixture of fresh Mediterranean species together with fossils from Roussillon, Aquitaine and Anjou. The cave-dwellers of the Lesse valley (Belgium) collected fossils from Grignon (near Paris) and their eastern neighbours in Thaingen (Switzerland) brought fossils from the Miocene basin at Vienna.

Larger shells were carved into spoons, scrapers, knives, and sinkers for fishing-nets.

Finally, more than half the many thousands of shells discovered were neither 'kitchen refuse' nor were they perforated. Most of these belonged to the genera *Nassa*, *Cerithium*, *Trochus*, and *Columbella*, and may well have been used as money, much as they were in Africa not so long ago. Pearl oysters were caught in the Persian Gulf for the Chaldeans, and *Murex* was sought for first by the Cretans and later by the Phoenicians, for its purple dye.

BOTANY AND AGRICULTURE

The study of plants is as ancient as man himself, for plants have always been an essential part of man's diet. Hence early man was forced to distinguish between roots, stems, leaves, fruits, and seeds that were edible, worthless, or poisonous. In passing, we might mention that, according to botanists, the earth produces some 2,500 edible species of plants, of which only 700 are worth gathering.

When Neolithic man first conceived the brilliant idea of sowing seeds himself, agriculture was born.

From provisions buried and preserved in lacustrine strata, we know that amongst the wild species he stored were acorns, nuts, plums, apples, pears, walnuts, beechnuts, chestnuts, brome grass, wheat, mustard seeds, thistles, plantain leaves, dead-nettles, crowfoot, water lilies, *etc.*

Among the cultivated species were red and tender wheat, barley and flax. Rice has been cultivated in China since 5000 B.C. Date palms, which grow wild in a zone extending from the Sahara to Mesopotamia, have been fertilized artificially and propagated by cuttings since about 4000 B.C. Two hundred and fifty species of plants, in all, were cultivated by prehistoric man, including a number of graminaceous species, which helped to feed the constantly growing population.

MEDICINE AND SURGERY

From fossils, we can tell that prehistoric men suffered from a number of diseases, but we have no idea how they treated them.

On the other hand, we know that Neolithic surgeons performed skilful trepanations, for the bone tissue of many skulls shows that the patients survived the operation. A number of such skulls is kept in the Paris *Musée de l'Homme*, and Baron de Baye has discussed further specimens dug up from tombs in the valley of the Petit-Morin. Dr Lucas-Championnière has stressed the resemblance between pre-historic European trepanations and those performed by the American Indians and more recently by the Kabyles.

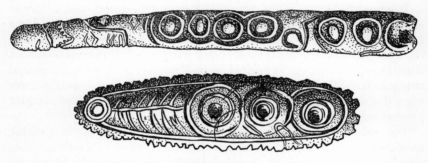

fig. 3 Upper Palaeolithic ivory carvings.

MATHEMATICS

The beginnings of arithmetic must go back to very early times, since man must have felt the need to count his livestock and stone implements almost as soon as he learned to value them. All we know about the subject is that in the Upper Palaeolithic men cut notches on rock faces and later on ivory rods. A Middle Palaeolithic tally-stick, dis-covered in 1937 in Vestonice (Moravia), was made of the radius of a wolf and contained fifty-five notches in two rows, arranged in groups of five. Mesolithic pebbles discovered in Mas d'Azil (S. France) were marked with red ochre strokes and are thought to have represented numbers. Counting must have become more complicated when commerce began to expand in the Neolithic, which is borne out by the mathematical developments in the urban civilizations which we shall be discussing in the following chapters.

From the Upper Palaeolithic, we also have a number of geometric inscriptions: points, lines, circles, spirals, squares, ovals and triangles, all of which were used for purely ornamental purposes. This trend was developed further in the copper age, when the first 'solar wheels' heralded the coming of astronomy.

ASTRONOMY

The beginnings of astronomy are lost in the dawn of prehistory. It began to make its first serious strides in the Neolithic, when agricultural needs demanded knowledge of the solar and lunar cycles and the seasons. Groups of stars, or 'constellations', had long since been observed.

When we discuss the beginnings of astronomy in the oldest civilizations, we shall see that, lunar and solar cults notwithstanding, the main interest was concentrated on the observation of the heliacal rising of certain stars which served as a kind of ritual calendar. A great deal of such knowledge was acquired by prehistoric man.

During the Megalithic age, the first astronomers made stone-carvings of some easily identifiable constellations: Ursa Major, Ursa Minor, and the Pleiades. Each star was represented by a small hollow in a stone. Representations of the Pleiades (at Pierres Folles, La Filouzière, and in the Vendée) have been the subject of a special study by Dr Marcel Baudouin. Some dozen such rock carvings have been discovered in France, especially in Brittany and in the Vendée Department.

Towards the end of the Neolithic, at the time of the Megalithic monuments, 75 per cent of the menhirs and dolmens faced East (*i.e.*, towards the rising sun), 15 per cent faced West (towards the setting sun) and 10 per cent towards the South. Not a single one faced North. Similarly, the *mastabas* of ancient Egypt and even the first Christian churches all faced East, while the funerary chambers in the Valley of the Pharaohs faced West.

It has been observed, however, that these directions were never exact, and that each of these monuments deviates by a number of degrees to the right from the true cardinal point. This suggests that prehistoric men assumed the pole star to be immovable and failed to appreciate the precession of the equinoxes, or else that they determined directions during the equinoxes or solstices, not from the rising of the sun but from the heliacal rising of a given star.

*   *   *

Such were the achievements of prehistoric man, and the state of science at the rising of the great urban civilizations of recorded antiquity: Egypt, Mesopotamia, Persia, India, and China.

BIBLIOGRAPHY

R. FURON, *Manuel de préhistoire générale*, Paris, 1958.

H. ALIMEN, *Atlas de préhistoire*, Paris, 1950–55.

K. LINDNER, *La chasse préhistorique*, Paris, 1941.

A.–L. GUYOT, *Origine des plantes cultivées*, Paris, 1942.

L. CAPITAN, H. BREUIL, D. PEYRONY, *La caverne de Font-de-Gaume*, 1906; *Les Combarelles*, 1924.

E. CARTAILHAC, H. BREUIL, *La caverne d'Altamira*, 1906.

G. GOURY, *Origine et évolution de l'homme*, Paris, 1948.

L. FROBENIUS, H. OBERMAIER, *Hadschra Maktuba*, 1925.

H. BREUIL, *L'Afrique préhistorique*, 1930.

TH. MONOD, *Gravures, peintures et inscriptions rupestres du Sahara occidental*, Paris, 1938.

H. LHOTE, Gravures, peintures et inscriptions rupestres du Kaouar, de l'Aïr et de l'Adrar des Iforas, *Bull. Inst. Fr. Afrique Noire*, 1952.

R. PERRET, *Les gravures rupestres et les peintures à l'ocre du Sahara français et du Fezzan*, Cahiers Ch. de Foucauld, 1948.

P. H. FISCHER, Rôle des coquillages dans les premières civilisations humaines, *J. Conchyliologie*, 1949, Vol. 89, pp. 82–93, 149–157.

J. W. JACKSON, *Shells as evidence of the migrations of early culture*, Manchester, 1917.

E. DECHAMBRE, Le Sahara, centre primitif de domestication, *C. R. Soc. Biogéographie*, 1950, pp. 147–151.

R. MAUNY, *Gravures, peintures et inscriptions rupestres de l'Ouest africain*, Inst. Fr. Afrique Noire, Dakar, 1954.

DR LUCAS-CHAMPIONNIÈRE, *Trépanation néolithique, trépanation précolombienne, trépanation des Kabyles, trépanation traditionelle*, Paris, 1912.

D. E. SMITH, *History of Mathematics*, Boston, 1923–25, 2 vols.

DR MARCEL BAUDOUIN, *La préhistoire par les étoiles*, Paris, 1926.

PART I

Ancient Science in the East

WE HAVE WITNESSED THE EMERGENCE, in prehistoric times, of that curiosity about nature which is the mainspring of all scientific activity. True, the approach was generally magical and based on mystical principles, but it was an essential step towards those great historical civilizations which were to flourish in the valleys of the Nile and Euphrates in 3000 B.C., and later on the eastern shores of the Mediterranean, in India, and in China.

It is the science of these great civilizations which we shall examine in Part I of this book. The first two chapters investigate the oldest scientific texts known to man—those of Egypt and Mesopotamia. The third chapter is devoted to Phoenician and Hebrew science, which, though far less brilliant and original, nevertheless exerted an appreciable influence over the Mediterranean world, and over ancient Greece in particular. The last two chapters examine the scientific achievements of ancient India and China. More recent than those of the Near East, they yet followed a course of their own. While the Near East civilizations were almost completely superseded by the Greek and Roman, the Indian and Chinese cultural developments continue to this day. We shall take up the thread in Part III of this book, and again in Volume II.

We may be blamed for having omitted to describe a host of other ancient civilizations, but as far as we can tell today they made few decisive contributions to the progress of science. We have, however, included relevant information about them in the various chapters of this book.

CHAPTER 1

Egypt

HISTORICAL INTRODUCTION

WHEN EGYPT ENTERED HISTORY at about 3000 B.C., she could look back on a long past, stretching at least as far as 4440 B.C. (Fayum Neolithic). Excavations in a number of burial places in Upper Egypt (Nagada, Hierakonpolis, el-Hadari) and in the southern delta (Meadi, Heliopolis) have brought to light a great many decorated objects—vases, mace-heads and slate palettes—from which we can vaguely reconstruct a picture of Egyptian civilization during the centuries immediately preceding the historical epoch. At that time Egypt was divided into two kingdoms, and so it remained until the day when, after an abortive attempt by one of the southern rulers, the 'Scorpion King', his successor, King Narmer, managed to unite the 'Two Lands'.

King Narmer (who is now identified with King Menes) must therefore be considered the founder of the first Pharaonic dynasty. The first and second dynasties make up the Thinite period (3000–2778), so-called after the town of This, the royal residence in the neighbourhood of Abydos. That period was followed, without any appreciable internal changes, by the Old Kingdom (3rd–6th dynasties) which saw the building of the pyramids of Sakkara and Giza, a remarkable upsurge of the plastic arts, and of great religious themes, and the brilliant creations of the first scientists. This is the period (2778–2263) associated with the names of the great Memphitic kings, Zoser, Sneferu, Cheops, Chephren, Mycerinus, Unas, and Teti.

If we neglect the next two and a half centuries, during which Egypt was laid waste by invasions and internal dissension, we come to the dawn of the second millennium, when the country was powerful and prosperous once again under the rule of the Amenemhets and the Sesostris (12th dynasty, 2000–1785). The end of that period, which is known as the Middle Kingdom, was again disrupted by civil wars and by the Hyksos invasion of Northern Egypt. It was under the reign of one of the Hyksos rulers, King Ahusser (seventeenth

13

century B.C.), that the mathematical document known as the Rhind
Papyrus must have been compiled.

A 'saviour king', Ahmes, restored Egyptian hegemony and founded
the 18th dynasty (1580–1314). His successors, the Amenhoteps and
Thotmes, upheld the dominant power of Egypt, and two further
dynasties of the New Kingdom, the 19th and 20th (1314–1085), also
produced kings of great repute, namely Seti I, Rameses II and
Rameses III.

Then came the period marking the decline of Egypt (1085–333).
The kings removed to Tanis or Bubastis (21st–23rd dynasties) and
part of Egypt was occupied, first by the 'Ethiopians' and then by the
Assyrians (24th–25th dynasties). After a temporary recovery under
Psammetic I and other kings of the 26th (Saite) dynasty (663–525),
there ensued a period of foreign overlordship which lasted for more
than a century (524–404), followed by a war of liberation, a last
period of autonomy (404–341), and a renewed period of Persian
domination (less than eight years) until Alexander the Great defeated
the Persians in 333. Egypt, however, simply changed her masters;
for the next three centuries she was governed by Macedonian
kings of the Ptolemaic dynasty, to fall under Roman control in
30 B.C.

The Old Kingdom was the most characteristic and the most
fruitful era of all Egyptian history. It was in that period that all the
basic discoveries of Egyptian mathematics, astronomy, and medicine
were made. All the mathematical papyri of the Middle Kingdom
indicate that they were based on earlier works, on a long and gradual
development of the science of numbers. Similarly, isolated indications from very early times (for example, a 3rd-dynasty inscription
on a Mechen *mastaba* tomb) show that the area of a house or a vine-
yard was already expressed in much the same way as in the much
later Rhind Papyrus. Moreover, the great 18th-dynasty medical
anthologies, the Papyrus Ebers and the Edwin Smith Surgical
Papyrus, are undoubtedly copies or adaptations of documents dating
back to the Old Kingdom.

Egyptian medical science must therefore have stood still for centuries. Like Molière's doctors, Egyptian physicians kept rigidly to
their elders' opinions—either through indolence or through blind
faith in the past. Diodoros of Sicily (a contemporary of Julius
Caesar) was well aware of this fact when he wrote of the Egyptians
(I, 82):

They treated diseases according to the written precepts of the famous
physicians of old. If, by following the rules of a sacred book, they failed
to save a patient's life, they felt free of any blame or reproach; if, on the

other hand, they ignored the written rule, they could be prosecuted and condemned to death. The law considered that few men could discover a better method of cure than that practised for so long, and one established by the best practitioners.

It is not really surprising that Egyptian medicine always remained what it had been in 2800 B.C. when we consider its necessary limitations and the great reputation it enjoyed throughout the East, despite its shortcomings. Thus it was to Egypt that Greek physicians, from Hippocrates to Galen, turned whenever they wanted to improve their locally acquired medical knowledge.

Herodotos (II, 109), who was a great Egyptophile, attributed to Egypt 'the invention of geometry which the Greeks brought back to their own country'. What did Herodotos mean by geometry, two centuries before Euclid? Did he include arithmetic in which, as the Rhind Papyrus clearly shows, the Egyptians went much further than in geometry? Or did he restrict his remarks to their acknowledged mastery of architecture? Imhotep, King Zoser's chief architect, managed to build a pyramid with four, and then six, steps, over a *mastaba*. 'Anxious to ensure the stability of the building, he constructed it quite unlike the *mastaba*; instead of arranging the layers horizontally, he set them at right angles to the faces, thus thrusting the weight to the centre of the structure'.[1] During the 4th to 6th dynasties all the pyramids were built with triangular sides; that of Cheops, with its perfect proportions, towered 481 feet above the ground. In later years, obelisks were hewn in quarries to be transported to, and set up in front of, the temples. One of these granite monoliths (18th dynasty) had a height of about 100 ft. The architects who accomplished these gigantic feats apparently had not studied the principles of their art from books of a scientific level superior to that of the Rhind Papyrus, in which facts are presented without any arguments and ready-made solutions without any proof. In fact, the geometry of this papyrus may be said to be purely eclectic.

But in the following centuries we might have expected the advent of a geometry not merely designed to provide useful information for architects and surveyors, *i.e.*, no longer the kind of estoeric geometry developed in the shade of the temple and jealously guarded by the priests. Unfortunately all the evidence we have for this 'new' geometry consists of a few pronouncements attributed to Democritos and to Aristotle, and if there was a geometrical papyrus with the scientific merit of the Smith Papyrus, it still remains to be dug up. The term 'scientific' requires elaboration. Egyptian science—as

[1] J. P. Lauer in *Bull. Eg. inst.* vol. 36 (1955) p. 357.

exemplified by the Smith Papyrus—though based on observation, and though presented lucidly and methodically, was not 'scientific' in the Greek sense of the word. Thus A. Rey[1] said that, 'Egyptian science is distinguished from the science which flourished in fifth-century Greece by its lack of theoretical or cosmological objectives, and by the utter absence of any metaphysical concepts. It was merely a technique, as Plato clearly showed when he contrasted Greek love of learning (science) with the Egyptians' love of riches'.[2]

Even so, Greek science did not object to borrowing from Egypt whatever it deemed useful. Thus, through the Greeks, Egypt contributed greatly—in mathematics and also in medicine—to the progress of Western civilization.

The Western Aryans who, under the leadership of Alexander the Great, advanced to the Nile valley and later settled there, were no strangers to the Egyptians, for the Greeks had been in close contact with them under the Saite dynasty. Mercenaries, mainly from Ionia, Caria and Rhodes, had fought in the armies of Psammetic II and his successors; Greek merchants had settled in the Delta, founding the Greek town of Naukratis in 585 B.C. Hecataeos of Miletos, who had visited Egypt during the reign of Darius I (end of sixth century), wrote an account of his journeys which is no longer extant, but which was consulted by Herodotos, 'the Father of History', when he travelled through Egypt about the middle of the fifth century B.C. A little later, 'the Father of Medicine', Hippocrates (born *c.* 460), was allowed to examine the library in the temple of Imhotep in Memphis, where he consulted Egyptian medical texts. Other Greek physicians followed suit, Dioscorides in the first century A.D. and Galen in the second.

Herodotos (II, 4) was right to say that the Egyptians 'were the first to have invented the year and to have divided it into twelve parts', though their year, with its twelve months of thirty days each and its holiday season of five epagomenic days, fell short by about a quarter of a day of the solar year. This defect was first tackled by the Ptolemies, who laid the foundations of Julius Caesar's calendar reform in 47 B.C.

Herodotos (II, 109) also mentions that the Greeks borrowed scientific ideas not only from Egypt but from Babylonia as well. Thus they took over the Babylonian gnomon (which was well-known to the Egyptians) and the polos, a Chaldean instrument marking the hours of the day and the periods of the year. In the fourth century B.C. Greek astronomers improved this instrument to enable them to tell solar time even at night. The clepsydra, an instrument used by

---

[1] A. Rey: *La Science Orientale avant les Grecs*, 1942, p. 335.
[2] Plato: The Republic, IV.

1 Lascaux cave painting

2 Counting the grain

the Greeks for measuring short time intervals by the discharge of water, was probably invented independently by the Egyptians and the Chaldeans, though the Phoenicians may have introduced it into Egypt from Chaldea. Conversely, the Chaldeans may have borrowed parts of their arithmetic from the Egyptians.

Generally speaking, however, there seem to have been few important cultural contacts between Babylonia and Egypt. In the exact sciences the honours are shared between both, Babylonia taking precedence in algebra and astronomy, and Egypt in arithmetic and geometry. In medicine, on the other hand, Egypt was head and shoulders above Babylonia.

To judge from the Bible, the Jews must have learnt their astronomy from the Chaldeans and much of their medicine from Egypt (*e.g.* the use of bile for treating eye diseases). To Egypt they also owe many hygienic measures, including circumcision, which they turned into a religious rite. Thus Herodotos (II, 104) reports that 'the Phoenicians and the Syrians of Palestine (*i.e.* the Jews) freely admit that they have learnt these customs from the Egyptians'. (The above remark must not be taken to mean that the Bible is based on gleanings from Egyptian scientific writings.)

All in all, the science—or, if we prefer it, the technology—of Egypt cannot have advanced very far into inner Asia. It is mainly through the West, by way of Greece, that most of the legacy of the Pharaohs has found its way to us.

MATHEMATICS AND ASTRONOMY

EVERY TRAVELLER who halts before the Great Pyramid of Giza or steps into the great pillared chamber at Karnak is bound to be filled with awe and astonishment. These great achievements of an ancient civilization readily persuade us that their creators were the scientific peers of our own master-builders.

The Greeks, like us, were deceived by the Egyptian mirage Aristotle and Democritos bowed before Egyptian science, and Herodotos, who appreciated the pre-eminence of Babylonian science, nevertheless claimed that Egypt taught Greece the laws of geometry. It needed the labours of three generations of scholars to bring home the fact that mathematics and astronomy played no more than a negligible role in the history of Egyptian science.

Our knowledge of Egyptian mathematics is based on papyrus or parchment manuscripts far smaller in number than the comparable Babylonian texts. Two very fragmentary papyri from the Middle Kingdom (1900–1800 B.C.), the Kahun and Berlin papyri, two somewhat longer and more recent papyri which are obvious copies of

earlier texts (the Rhind and Moscow Papyri), a very short leather
manuscript (the British Museum Leather Roll) and two wooden
tablets in the Cairo Museum are, in fact, all we have to go by. But
few and far between though they are, these mathematical texts are
profuse in comparison with Egyptian astronomical writings. Not a
single didactic 'treatise' comparable with those dealing with arithmetic or medicine is extant, and all our knowledge of Egyptian
astronomy is inferred from documents depicting funerary and mythological scenes in which the sky is shown only incidentally, from the
orientation of the faces of monuments and from calendars. Clearly,
any information obtained in this way is uncertain in the extreme.

Since scientific developments are generally limited by mathematical knowledge, we shall first of all take stock of Egyptian
arithmetic and geometry.

Egyptian Arithmetic

NOTATION

The decimal system was known to the Egyptians from the very
beginnings of their history, *i.e.* from the third millennium B.C. This
system contained special signs for all powers of 10 up to 1 million,
but apparently lacked a zero, although, in certain cases, the scribes
would intuitively leave an empty space where we should put a
nought (*see fig. 4*).

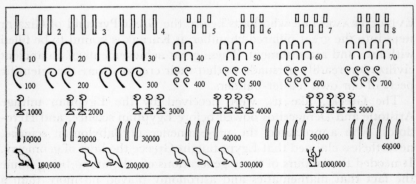

fig. 4 Egyptian hieroglyphic numerals.

As we see, a given symbol was repeated as often as it was needed,
the highest powers being written down first. Thus the Egyptians
wrote: ⟨hieroglyphs⟩ for 152,023 and ⟨hieroglyphs⟩ for 966.

This system, simple though it was, was not devoid of drawbacks, since even relatively small numbers required an enormous repetition of signs which caused the scribes to make many mistakes, particularly when it came to complicated astronomical calculations.

The Egyptian notation and its early adoption are the obvious results of economic and social conditions. Egypt, a unified and strongly centralized monarchy, stretched like a narrow ribbon for more than 600 miles from North to South. Each individual agricultural area may be said to have formed a cell in this huge body. In order to administer the country as a whole, and in order to assess its resources and to use them wisely, the central and provincial authorities of a country lacking a coin of the realm were dependent on a vast system of national book-keeping. Egyptian arithmetic and geometry never emerged from this bondage, and this remark applies to Egyptian science in general. The scribes, used as they were to interminable stock-takings, censuses *etc.*, must have had the greatest difficulty in looking beyond immediate facts; hence they failed to invent even the simplest operators, such as our plus and minus signs.

METROLOGY

Egyptian metrology, like all ancient metrologies, was unsystematic—capacity, length, weight, *etc.*, all had their own terminology and their own subdivisions. The chief measure of capacity was the *hekat* 〔hieroglyphs〕 ('bushel') which was equivalent to about 10 pints and had a number of subdivisions. Liquids were measured in *henu* 〔hieroglyphs〕, which modern research has shown to be equal to about seven-eighths of a pint.

For small lengths, the Egyptian standard measure was the *meh* (cubit). It would appear that according to the province, the period, and the nature of the work, different kinds of cubits were in use. The most frequently employed was the 'short' cubit (17.72 in.); another was the royal cubit (20.62 in.). The small cubit was divided into 6 palms (*shesep*), or into 24 digits (*jeba*). The multiples of the cubit were the 'rod', *khet* (literally 'log') equal to 100 cubits, and the *iteru* (literally 'river') 〔hieroglyphs〕, equal to 20,000 royal cubits or some 6 miles. The *iteru* is thus comparable to the Greek *schene*.

Areas were measured in *setats*, equal to one square *khet*, *i.e.* about half an acre; like the *hekat*, the *setat* was subdivided into fractions, of which the smallest was the 'land' cubit ($\frac{1}{100}$ *setat*) equal to 100 square cubits.

The most usual multiple of the *setat* was the *kha* (literally 'thousand') representing 10 *setats* or about 5 acres.

The most common weight was the *deben* of about 3.2 oz. which was subdivided into 10 *kites*.

All measurements were set down by writing first the name of the unit employed, followed by the number required, *e.g.*

𓏴𓏲𓏲𓏲 (hieroglyphs)	645 bushels of Upper Egyptian corn
(hieroglyphs)	4 cubits, 4 palms, 2 digits
(hieroglyphs)	22 *setats* of land
(hieroglyphs)	Silver: 761 *deben* and 2 *kites*

Clearly Egyptian metrology was most unsystematic. Multiples and submultiples might be expressed by decimals (weights) or by vulgar fractions (capacity and square measures). In other cases (linear measure) the multiples were part of the decimal system while the submultiples were derived from the septuagesimal system.

THE FOUR SIMPLE RULES

Egyptian arithmetic, like all others, was based on counting. However, Egyptian multiplication tables were much simpler to memorize than our own, since the Egyptians multiplied and divided exclusively by 2. To multiply by a larger number they had to perform a series of duplications:

(hieroglyphs)	Reckon with 3, 4 times
(hieroglyphs)	1 ($\times$), 3
(hieroglyphs)	2 ($\times$), 6
(hieroglyphs)	4 ($\times$), 12
(hieroglyphs)	Makes 12.

A further example will illustrate the process used even better. This is how an Egyptian scribe would have multiplied 13 × 7:

$$
\begin{array}{rr}
-1 & 7 \\
2 & 14 \\
-4 & 28 \\
-8 & 56 \\
\hline
\text{Total: } 91 &
\end{array}
$$

In other words, he would write the multiplier (7) in the right column, and the figure 1 in the left. He would then keep doubling both columns until, by addition, he could obtain the desired multiplicand. In our example, the multiplicand (13) is obtained by adding 1, 4, and 8. At this point the scribe would mark all the numbers adding up to 13 with a stroke, and then add up the corresponding numbers in the right column, *i.e.*, 7, 28, and 56. The sum of these numbers would then give him the correct result of the multiplication. These examples clearly show the (additive) character of Egyptian arithmetic.

Since the Egyptians used a decimal system, multiplications by 10, 100, and 1,000 were performed by simple changes of symbols. Thus while 36 was expressed by ∩∩‖ ∩‖‖, 36 × 10 became ℓℓ∩∩ ℓ∩∩∩, and

36 × 1,000 became ‖‖ 𝖎𝖎𝖎𝖎𝖎𝖎.

Division was performed by the same process in reverse. Thus to divide 168 by 8, the scribe would proceed as if he were multiplying:

— 1	8
2	16
— 4	32
8	64
—16	128

Having done that, he would look in the right column (and not in the left as in multiplication) for the numbers adding up to the dividend (168). In our example, he would choose 8, 32, and 128, and mark off the corresponding numbers in the left column, *i.e.* 1, 4, 16, the sum of which would give him the answer, *i.e.*, 21.

Clearly the Egyptian system of calculation seems very slow and laborious to us who are so accustomed to quick mental operations. However, it did not tax the memory, and it is astonishing to see with what ease even the most complicated calculations were solved by this primitive procedure. This explains why Egypt, unlike Mesopotamia, failed to introduce multiplication tables—the scribes were apparently quite content with what they had.

FRACTIONS

Now, division is not always as simple as in the example we have used. In fact, whenever the dividend is not exactly divisible by the divisor, fractions will appear. If, for example, the scribe had wished to divide sixteen by three, he would have had to write:

—1	3
2	6
—4	12

Thence he would have realized that it was impossible to find any combination of numbers in the right column to add up to sixteen.

The nearest sum is fifteen, which corresponds to $1+4=5$ in the left column. What is needed, therefore, is $16-15=1$, which can only be expressed by means of fractions.

Now with the exception of $\frac{2}{3}$, for which they had a special sign, the Egyptians knew only unit fractions, *i.e.*, $\frac{1}{2}$, $\frac{1}{3}$, $\frac{1}{4}$, $\frac{1}{5}$, *etc.* Fractions were expressed by means of writing the sign ⬯ meaning 'a part' above, or next to, the denominator. Thus:

$$\overset{\text{⬯}}{\text{𐎟𐎟}} = \frac{1}{5} \qquad \overset{\text{⬯}}{\text{∩∩∩∩}} = \frac{1}{40} \qquad \overset{\text{◁}}{\underset{\text{ℭℭ ∩∩ 𝄽}}{}} = \frac{1}{276}$$

This is the form of fractions found in most Egyptian mathematical texts. However, in measures of grain capacity and other agricultural quantities, the Egyptians also used a very ancient method of expressing fractions, obtained by subdividing the fraction $\frac{1}{2}$.

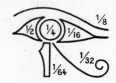

fig. 5 The eye of Horus representing fractions.

Fig. 5 shows the origins of this method. The symbols of the various fractions are all derived from the ancient myth, according to which the eye of the falcon-god, Horus, was torn out and cut up by Seth. The eye of Horus, called *ujat* (literally 'whole') was a combination of a human eye (iris, pupil, eyebrow), and the coloured markings of a falcon's eye. Each part of this magic eye represented a special fraction, *viz.*: ◁$\frac{1}{2}$ ○$\frac{1}{4}$ ◝$\frac{1}{8}$ ▷$\frac{1}{16}$ ◝$\frac{1}{32}$ ◖$\frac{1}{64}$

The sum of all of them is $\frac{63}{64}$, and the Egyptians believed that the missing $\frac{1}{64}$ was provided by Thoth, the ibis-god, who restored and returned the eye of Horus. Thus we find:

🌱 ○ 𓂧 𓏲 ◁◝ $1+\frac{1}{2}+\frac{1}{8}+\frac{1}{32}$ ($=1\frac{21}{32}$) bushels of wheat.

For land measurements, the Egyptians used yet a third system of expressing fractions: ᗡ𝅵a ✕b 𓅭c ᗡ✕ 𓅭d

(a$=\frac{1}{2}$ *setat*; b$=\frac{1}{4}$ *setat*; c$=\frac{1}{8}$ *setat*; d$=\frac{1}{2}+\frac{1}{4}+\frac{1}{8}$ ($=\frac{7}{8}$) *setat*).

But no matter which system they chose, the Egyptians used unit fractions only, *i.e.* fractions with numerator 1 (with very few exceptions). To the modern mind, this method is utterly inadequate, and we cannot but wonder why they did not improve it. We are astonished for instance to see that, when they divided one into seven-sevenths, they should have boggled at expressing the fact that $\frac{6}{7}$ is the complement of $\frac{1}{7}$. We touch here upon one of the most primitive aspects of Egyptian science. A. H. Gardiner, one of the foremost modern Egyptologists, has remarked that 'the Egyptians would have thought it both absurd and contradictory to write $r\ 7 \times 4$ or something of the kind to express $\frac{4}{7}$; to their eyes one part and one part only could be the seventh—to wit, the part occupying seventh place in a series of seven equal parts'. In other words, the Egyptians were never able to develop their mathematical arguments and to consider, as we do, such fractions as $\frac{2}{7}$, $\frac{3}{7}$, *etc.*, as numbers in their own right. It must be noted, however, that in some cases they did use such simple 'complementary' fractions as $\frac{2}{3}$ and, more rarely, $\frac{3}{4}$, $\frac{4}{5}$, and $\frac{5}{6}$.

MANIPULATIONS OF FRACTIONS

Hence, every operation with fractions involved Egyptian mathematicians in a multitude of fractions. Refusing *a priori* to conceive of a fraction like, say, $\frac{2}{5}$, they were forced to express it as $\frac{1}{3} + \frac{1}{15}$. No wonder that fractions take up the major part of Egyptian arithmetical texts.

In principle, fractions were manipulated in much the same way as integral numbers, *viz.*, by systematic duplication. When the denominator of the fraction was even, there was no difficulty. For instance, to multiply $\frac{1}{8} \times 7$, the Egyptian scribe would put:

$$
\begin{array}{cc}
-1 & \frac{1}{8} \\
-2 & \frac{1}{4} \\
-4 & \frac{1}{2}
\end{array}
$$

Since the sum of the numbers in the left column was seven, *i.e.* the multiplier of the fraction, the scribe would transcribe the result directly, thus:

$$7 \times \tfrac{1}{8} = \tfrac{1}{2} + \tfrac{1}{4} + \tfrac{1}{8}$$

But if the multiplication involved odd denominators, the system broke down, and a new means of overcoming the difficulty had to be found.

Now any fraction of the form $2/n$, in which n is an odd number, can always be broken down into a sum of two or more fractions with numerator 1. For instance, we saw that $\frac{2}{5}$ can be expressed as $\frac{1}{3} + \frac{1}{15}$. This is just what the Egyptians did, and to facilitate their work they set up a table of resolutions beginning with $\frac{2}{5}$ and running up to $\frac{2}{101}$. This table, which played a considerable role in their education, represents one of the most important sections of the Rhind Papyrus. We quote:

To divide 2 by 41: $1\frac{2}{3}(+)\frac{1}{24}$ (corresponds to) *$\frac{1}{24}$; $\frac{1}{6}$ to *$\frac{1}{246}$; $\frac{1}{8}$ to *$\frac{1}{328}$

Do it thus:	1	41
	$\frac{2}{3}$	$27\frac{1}{3}$
	$\frac{1}{3}$	$13\frac{2}{3}$
	$\frac{1}{6}$	$6\frac{2}{3}+\frac{1}{6}$
	$\frac{1}{12}$	$3\frac{1}{3}+\frac{1}{12}$
	$/\frac{1}{24}$	$1\frac{2}{3}+\frac{1}{24}$
Remainder		$\frac{1}{6}+\frac{1}{8}$
	1	41
	/2	82
	/4	164
	/6	246 $\frac{1}{6}$
	/8	328 $\frac{1}{8}$.

N.B. The scribe has marked the answer $(\frac{1}{24}+\frac{1}{246}+\frac{1}{328})$ by drawing red lines (asterisks) under the fractions to be retained.

Written in our way, the answer is: $\frac{2}{41}=\frac{1}{24}+\frac{1}{246}+\frac{1}{328}$.

Clearly this method was extremely laborious, and modern mathematicians still argue about the way in which answers were obtained by it. It is, in fact, quite possible that the scribes arrived at their results by simple trial and error. Even so, the ease and certainty with which they manipulated these tables are astonishing; Greeks and Romans alike continued to use their procedures.

PROPORTIONAL DIVISION

Undoubtedly the Egyptians owed their mastery in handling fractions to their economic and social system. Egypt had no currency until the time of the Persian conquest, and all commerce was based on barter. Moreover, there was hardly any private property; most of the land belonged to the king or to the priests. Under that social system, all individuals were completely dependent on their employers and, in the absence of money, on a vast book-keeping system. It was the scribe's task to divide the grain stored by the state or by various temples, and hence he concentrated on the problems of proportional division so typical of Egyptian arithmetic. This fact may well explain why the scribes adhered to their simple tables, rather than venture further into the slippery realm of vulgar fractions. For instance, to divide 7 loaves among 10 men:

You are to multiply $\frac{2}{3}(+)\frac{1}{30}$ by 10. Result (7).

Do it thus:	1	$\frac{2}{3}(+)\frac{1}{30}$
	—2	$1\frac{1}{3}(+)\frac{1}{15}$
	4	$2\frac{2}{3}(+)\frac{1}{10}(+)\frac{1}{30}$
	—8	$5\frac{1}{3}(+)\frac{1}{10}$

Total: 7 loaves. This is it. (Rhind Papyrus, probl. 4.)

Proportional division is given much prominence even in the Rhind Papyrus, the most 'theoretical' of all known mathematical papyri, so that we need not be surprised to find simple problems, like the above, treated side by side with long tables of unit fractions.

It must be stressed that the scribe was not content with presenting the results, but that he tried, however obscurely, to show how he arrived at them. The addendum 'this is it' may therefore be likened to our Q.E.D., and suggests an attempt to go beyond mere assertion.

OTHER ARITHMETICAL METHODS

In order to solve their many everyday problems, the Egyptians had to perform other arithmetical operations as well, such as squaring numbers or taking their square roots. The square root was called the 'corner'; this term was clearly derived from the notion of a square cut diagonally, and shows to what extent the Egyptians preferred concrete symbols to the abstractions of other peoples. In the Berlin Papyrus we find a scribe taking the square root of $6\frac{1}{4}$ and of $1\frac{1}{2}+\frac{1}{16}$ correctly, but we do not know whether he obtained his answers methodically or by trial and error.

Proportions, as we have seen, played a paramount role in Egyptian arithmetic. Now we know that Egyptian society had a rigid class structure. Differences of rank entailed rights to a greater share of goods, and scribes had often to solve problems of the following kind:

Divide 100 loaves among 5 men in such a way that $\frac{1}{7}$ of the sum of the largest shares shall be equal to the sum of the smallest two.

(Rhind Papyrus, probl. 40.)

From the solution, it appears that the problem amounted to a division into parts in arithmetic progression. The method employed is not explained, and the various steps seem to be based on trial and error. In any case, the solution is correct: the respective shares are shown to be $38\frac{1}{3}$, $29\frac{1}{6}$, 20, $10\frac{5}{6}$, $1\frac{2}{3}$. Egyptian mathematicians therefore had a confused but nevertheless correct idea of arithmetic progressions. Another problem shows that they were conversant with geometric progressions as well; these are presented in a somewhat sibylline way:

An Inventory of a Household.

		(Operations)
7 houses		
49 cats		—
343 mice	1	2,801
2,301 (*sic!*) grains of wheat	2	5,602
16,807 bushels	4	11,204
Total 19,607		Total 19,607

(Rhind Papyrus, probl. 79.)

The problem really amounted to the following: There were seven houses, each house had seven cats, each cat killed seven mice, each mouse would have eaten seven grains of wheat, and each grain of wheat would have produced seven bushels of corn. How many bushels would that make?

Without that explanation the total seems meaningless. Still, from the fact that it was obtained from the multiplication of 2,801 × 7, and from the series 7, 49, 343, . . ., we see clearly that the Egyptians were acquainted with geometric progressions.

DID THE EGYPTIANS KNOW ALGEBRA?

A series of problems with equally utilitarian objects raises the question of whether the Egyptians were familiar with algebra. Here is an example:

> A quantity when added to its fourth part, is 15. What is that quantity?
> (Answer): The quantity is 12; its quarter is 3. Total 15.
>> Do it thus: Reckon with 4.
>>> You are to make this quarter, namely 1. Total 5.
>>> Reckon with 5 to find 15.

−1	5
−2	10
The result is 3	
Multiply 3 by 4	
1	3
2	6
−4	12
The result is 12	
1	12
$\frac{1}{4}$	3
Total	15

(Rhind Papyrus, probl. 26.)

This problem is in fact expressed by the equation $x + 1/4x = 15$. In order to solve it, the scribe used a purely empirical method. He chose the number 4 for the obvious reason that it is the smallest number of which the fourth part is an integer. He then added that number to its fourth part to obtain 5, and divided 15, the given figure, by 5. Thence he obtained 3, which he multiplied by 4, his original number.

Problems of this type were known as *âha* problems, from the Egyptian word ⟨hieroglyphs⟩ meaning 'heap' or 'pile', which invariably accompanied the question, and obviously corresponded to 'unknown quantity' or 'number'. Hence the Egyptians adhered to their characteristically concrete terminology, even in highly theoretical problems.

It is because of *âha* problems that we have asked whether the Egyptians knew algebra. In effect, *âha* problems are comparable to modern equations of the first degree and even of the second degree. Some experts (Cantor and Neugebauer—in his original papers) were therefore convinced that the Egyptians, like the Babylonians with whom they had many contacts, had gone some way beyond pure arithmetic. However, it is best to suspend judgement since, for example, Problem 26 of the Rhind Papyrus (see above) was in fact solved by simple arithmetic, and the solution of other problems (*e.g.* Problem 6 of the Moscow Papyrus) was based on graphical methods.

The only known case in which an Egyptian mathematician may have used real algebra was a division problem involving an equation of the second degree, *viz.*:

Divide 100 into two parts, so that the square root of one be three fourths of that of the other.

(In algebra we should put: $x^2 + y^2 = 100$, and $y = \frac{3}{4}x$,

whence $x^2 + \frac{9}{16}x^2 = 100$.)

The Egyptian scribe, lacking our symbols, began quite arbitrarily with the numbers 1 and 3/4. He then squared these numbers and added their results: $1 + \frac{1}{2} + \frac{1}{16}(= 1\frac{9}{16})$. He then took the square root of $1\frac{9}{16}$ which came to $1\frac{1}{4}$, and that of 100, *i.e.*, 10, which is $1\frac{1}{4}$ multiplied by 8. Thereupon he assumed that his original numbers must be multiplied by 8 to give the correct answer, *i.e.*, 8×1 and $8 \times \frac{3}{4}$, or 8 and 6.

The Egyptian scribe, in fact, while proceeding like a modern mathematician, wrote 1 where we should put x. Scholars like O. Neugebauer, who are not otherwise given to overestimating the Egyptians' scientific approach, have taken this solution as proof positive of their ability to handle equations of the second degree. On the other hand, the translator of the Rhind Papyrus, Eric Peet, has pointed out that the scribe used this procedure simply because there was no other way of obtaining the answer! According to him, the Egyptian method, lacking abstract symbols, was not algebraic but merely eclectic. This would explain why the scribe left nothing to posterity except this one solitary solution.

CONCRETE ASPECTS OF EGYPTIAN ARITHMETIC

All the problems discussed so far have one common trait: they all dealt with material problems associated with the everyday affairs of an agricultural community. In fact, all the Egyptian mathematical manuscripts are nothing but collections of problems of this type. In addition to problems like the division of bread among individuals, arithmetic and geometric progressions, and the taking of square roots in land measurements, we also find problems of this type:

Example of reckoning a bag containing various precious metals. You are told: a bag containing gold, silver, and lead has been bought for 84 rings. What is the value of each metal?

In his solution the scribe assumed that one part of gold was worth as much as two parts of silver and four parts of lead and that the bag contained an equal weight of each of these metals. Or again

Example of reckoning out 100 loaves for 10 men, a sailor, a foreman, and a watchman who is entitled to twice as much (as the seven others) . . .

Example of reckoning the produce of a herdsman. The herdsman brought seventy oxen to the count. When the official asked him why he had brought so few, the cowherd replied: 'I have brought thee two thirds of one third of the herd thou hast entrusted to me; count and thou wilt find me complete!'

The Concept of 'Quality' in Egyptian Calculations

We have seen that the Egyptians were interested only in the practical aspects of science. This fact explains why, particularly with divisions, the scribes considered not only the number of parts involved but also the quality of the goods to be distributed. Hence they introduced the notion of *pefsu* (from *pefs* = to cook), which represented the number of units of a given product contained in one bushel of grain. Thus the *pefsu* of bread was twelve, *i.e.*, each loaf of bread was equal to one twelfth of a bushel, and the *pefsu* of beer, the other basic element of the Egyptian diet, varied with the number of jugs which could be brewed from one bushel of grain. The smaller the *pefsu*, the stronger was the beer, and the heavier or more compact the bread.

The introduction of a qualitative factor is essential in any society in which services are paid for in kind, and therefore crops up in a host of Egyptian problems. For example:

$3\frac{1}{2}$ bushels of flour are turned into eighty loaves. Tell me how much flour has gone into every loaf and what is its *pefsu*?

Or again:

If the fourth part of a measure of beer has been spilled, and the vessel filled with water, what is its *pefsu*?

Mastery of problems of this kind was absolutely essential for scribes who were charged with the distribution and exchange of produce and were constantly faced with such problems as:

Thou art told to change a hundred loaves of force 10 (*pefsu*) against loaves of force 15 (*pefsu*). (The answer was that a hundred loaves of 10 *pefsu* are equivalent to 150 loaves of 15 *pefsu*!!)

Clearly the nutritional value, the *pefsu*, of a given substance was not constant, and this involved additional complications, particularly when it came to exchanging liquids for solids or *vice versa*.

When we consider the real scope of the various problems treated by Egyptian scribes, we fully understand the disappointment which modern scholars feel in actual Egyptian mathematical achievements. This disappointment is all the greater because the title of the Rhind Papyrus promises us 'Rules for enquiring into nature, and for knowing all that exists, every mystery, every secret'.

Egyptian Geometry

WERE THE EGYPTIANS better geometers than they were arithmeticians? Herodotos, and later Strabo and Diodoros, assumed that the very character of their country was bound to have forced the Egyptians to solve geometrical problems from very early times. From their own observations the Greeks took it that the Egyptians had 'invented' geometry and that they had been its first exponents. Superficially, this assumption seems fully justified. For example, from the Middle Kingdom onward and probably in even earlier times, before the Greeks settled in Hellas, the Egyptians knew how to evaluate the areas of rectangles and probably of triangles as well, and they obtained good approximations of the areas of circles. But despite these achievements, Egyptian geometry, like Egyptian arithmetic, was above all practical. It did not reason but proceeded instead by trial and error (quite understandably in the case of the area of the circle) to the best solutions of concrete problems. In that respect, the Greeks were certainly right when they assumed that the need for evaluating the areas of fields for the correct assessment of taxes 'led to . . . the invention of geometry, which the Greeks brought to their own country'. (Herodotos II, 109.)

THE AREA OF THE TRIANGLE
This completely 'earthy' origin of Egyptian geometry is reflected in the manner in which even Middle Kingdom scribes posed their problems. Thus we read:

Example of reckoning a triangle of land. You are told a triangle of height (*meryt*) ten rods has a base of four rods. What is its area? Do it thus:

Take half of 4 (2), to form its rectangle. Multiply 10 by 2 to obtain its area.

Do it thus: 1   400   1   1,000
               1/2   200   2   2,000

(Answer) Its area is 2,000 cubits (2 *khâ*)=20 *setats*.

(Rhind Papyrus, probl. 51.)

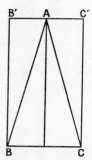

fig. 6 Egyptian method of calculating the area of a triangle.

The very succinct manner in which the problem is treated has been the cause of many scholarly discussions. Some experts think that the word *meryt*, which we have translated by height, actually means side, so that the very basis of the calculation would be wrong; other authors disagree and claim that the Egyptians were fully capable of calculating the area of triangles, a point of view which strikes us as being more plausible. In effect, the apparently mysterious injunction: 'Take one half of four to form its rectangle' can only mean that the Egyptian scribe must have used a graphical method to solve his problem. Having been given any triangle, he apparently constructed on the base a rectangle with side equal to the height of the triangle. Half the area of that rectangle was the required solution. Moreover, since the scribes also knew how to obtain the area of a trapezium (Rhind Papyrus, problem 52), they must have been able to find the area of triangles.

AREA OF THE CIRCLE

Egyptian geometers scored their greatest hit in their calculations of the areas of circles. We shall, therefore, examine their method in some detail:

Method for calculating (the area of) a circular piece of ground of diameter nine rods. What is its area?

Substract the ninth part of the diameter leaving 8 parts. Then multiply 8 by 8 times which will give you 64. Hence its area is six *khâ* and four *setat*.

Do it thus: 1   9

 $\frac{1}{9}$ of it   1

Remainder 8

1   8

2   16

4   32

/8   64

Its area is 6 *khâ* (60), 4 *setats*.

(Rhind Papyrus, probl. 50.)

As we can see the method is tantamount to squaring eight-ninths of the diameter. (A brief calculation will show that this method gives $\pi = 3.1605$.) The figure accompanying the problem shows that, once again, the Egyptians arrived at the solution by a graphical method; the circle was inscribed in a square, and the scribe apparently evaluated the difference of area by approximate triangulations. It must be emphasized that the value of π obtained in this empirical way was a much better approximation than the value of three, used by most other ancient peoples of the East.

CUBIC MEASURE
Starting from simple geometry, the Egyptians evaluated the volumes of the most familiar solids: pyramids, truncated pyramids, and cylinders. At the time of the Middle Kingdom, when the texts we have been examining were drawn up, the royal tomb was still a pyramid. Its construction, begun on the accession of the king, was continued during his entire reign, involving a host of workers and great quantities of materials. It was the scribe's task to survey the work, to assess the number of bricks that would be required, and to deal with such problems as supply routes, transport, *etc.* There is no text to show precisely how the scribes evaluated the volume of pyramids, but that they must have done so is borne out on the one hand by a problem involving the calculation of the slope of a pyramid of known base and height, and on the other hand by a satirical letter from which we gather that the scribes knew, or ought to have known, how to calculate the number of bricks needed for constructing an inclined plane of given dimensions. Finally, one of the problems of the Moscow Papyrus (No. 14) discusses the volume of the frustum of a pyramid.

This problem involves the determination of the volume of a truncated pyramid of known square bases and height. By calling the height h, and the sides of the lower and upper bases a and b respectively, we can explain the procedure of the scribes. They squared a, multiplied a by b, then squared b and added the results of the three operations. Thereupon they multiplied the final answer by $\frac{1}{3}h$, thus obtaining the desired volume. Generalizing their apparently incoherent method, we find, in fact, that they used the correct formula, namely:

$$V = \left(\frac{h}{3}\right)(a^2 + ab + b^2).$$

The scribe did not show how he arrived at the solution, and simply contented himself with setting out the necessary operations; in fact, like all other problems of this kind, he treated this geometric problem as an exercise in pure arithmetic.

The answer was of great practical importance since obelisks and most of the blocks used in the construction of temples—plinths, shrines, ornamental columns, *etc.*—were simply frusta of pyramids, the volume of all of which had to be calculated before they were quarried and transported.

This 'utilitarian' approach to solid geometry is also found in problems connected with the volumes of cylinders (evaluated by multiplying the area of the circular base by the height). In fact, the volumes of cylinders had to be known for assessing the capacity of cylindrical or near-cylindrical measures used in the state granaries.

What the treatment of all these problems, arithmetical and geometrical alike, had in common was the highly condensed form in which the solutions were presented. A series of figures and operations is all the reader is ever given. We may well wonder how Egyptian students ever made any sense of these texts. Undoubtedly the texts could not have been the sole sources of their knowledge; they must have been complemented by the oral explanations so characteristic of even modern teaching methods in the East. Can we take it, then, that all these texts merely represented specific examples of general geometrical problems? We have every reason to doubt it. The figures involved in the texts always lead to the simplest and quickest solutions, and could, at best, have served the student as mnemonic devices for *similar* problems. We must therefore take it that Egyptian mathematical problems 'ought to be considered, not as problems containing certain formulae, but rather as formulae to be applied to the solution of certain problems'.

Egyptian Astronomy

IN GENERAL, WE CAN SAY that Egyptian mathematics was rather primitive and hence bound to have an adverse effect on Egyptian astronomy. Because of its additive character, *i.e.* its tendency to reduce all mathematical operations to a series of additions (duplications), Egyptian arithmetic failed to provide astronomy with

3 Ox being led to the cattle count

4 Annals of Thotmes III

appropriate mathematical tools. Whenever the complexity of observed phenomena eluded their mathematics, the Egyptians would, in astronomy as in geometry, fall back on simplifications. Now, while such methods allowed them to estimate the area of the circle fairly well, they were far less successful when it came to astronomy.

Hence we look in vain for any Egyptian references to eclipses, of which, for instance, Mesopotamian texts mention a great number. True, our present state of knowledge about Egyptian astronomy does not entitle us to speak of ignorance or indifference on the part of the Egyptians, and it is quite possible that astronomical texts may have escaped the vigilant search of archaeologists or have been destroyed in the course of the ages. Clearly, Egyptian texts, written as they were on papyri, were much more vulnerable than Mesopotamian clay tablets—a fact we should do well to bear in mind whenever we compare the two civilizations.

EGYPTIAN ASTRONOMICAL SOURCES

For the study of Egyptian astronomy, we have nothing to compare with the mathematical and medical papyri. Hence Egyptian astronomical knowledge must be inferred from the legends behind astronomical representations on New Kingdom tombs, or on the 'diagonal calendars' adorning Middle Kingdom coffin-lids. Because of their funerary origins and also because they were copied from one another, these figures must be interpreted with the utmost circumspection.

However, the orientation of the faces of these tombs and the character of the diagonal calendars tell us a great deal about Egyptian astronomy, and have therefore been studied at length by many historians of science.

From the signs of the zodiac adorning the ceilings of certain temples built during the Greek period, early Egyptologists concluded that these temples must have been constructed according to the principles of Pharaonic astrology and astronomy. Nowadays, we know that these ornaments were largely based on Greek concepts, and that they reflected nothing of ancient Egyptian astrology except the notion of the decans. It was only towards the close of the history of Ancient Egypt that papyri were compiled from which we may gather what the Egyptians themselves contributed to astronomy (Demotic Carlsberg Papyri Nos. 1 and 9). Though written during the Roman period (after A.D. 144), the Carlsberg Papyrus No. 9, which describes a method for determining the phases of the moon, is based on very ancient sources. The same is true of the Carlsberg Papyrus No. 1, and we may therefore take it that, despite the absence of relevant documents, the authors must have consulted earlier astronomical texts or at least collections of practical hints, comparable to the mathematical and medical papyri. Chance finds or excavations may well fill the gap in our knowledge one day. What other Egyptian demotic texts we have on the position of the planets are all based on Greek astronomy. Moreover, it cannot be stressed enough that the astronomy of the Old, Middle, and New Pharaonic Kingdoms differed radically from Egyptian astronomy after the Persian conquest (end of sixth century B.C.), and was, in fact, an offshoot of Greek astronomy.

EGYPTIAN CALENDARS

Apparently the Egyptians first adopted an astronomical calendar in about the third millennium B.C., and many scholars have claimed that this calendar could have been adopted only on the basis of systematic astronomical observations during the preceding millennium, an assumption which has done a great disservice to the true evaluation of Egyptian history.

The Egyptians divided the year into twelve months of thirty days each, and into three equal 'seasons'. In addition to these 360 days the Egyptians also introduced five epagomenic days, so that their year consisted of a total of 365 days. The three seasons of four months each were called: 1, the Inundation (*akhet*); 2, Winter (*peret, i.e.,* the emergence of land from the water); and 3, Summer (*shemu*, probably 'lack of water'.) The Egyptians had no continuous era like ours or the Mohammedan Hegira. Instead, all their dates were referred to the accession to the throne of their reigning monarch, for instance:

Year 2, 3rd month of the Inundation, first day, under the reign of the King of Upper and Lower Egypt, Nemaat-Rē (Amenemhet III).

As far as we know, the Egyptians never attempted to intercalate an extra day to bring their civil year of 365 days into step with the astronomical year, as we do during leap years. As a result, the civil year would gain a whole month on the astronomical year every 120 years, and it took 1,456 years for the two to concide once again. The period of 1,456 years was called the Sothic cycle, after Sothis (*Sepedet*), our Sirius, from the heliacal rising of which the Egyptians fixed the beginning of their year. They were bound to have observed in fairly early times that the Nile began to rise almost at the very moment when Sothis, after having been invisible for a long time, reappeared above the horizon a little before sunrise. That event, which the Egyptians called the 'coming-out of *Sepedet*', was their New Year's Day, 'the first day of the first month of the Inundation'.

Had the Egyptians fixed the beginning of their civil calendar to coincide with the heliacal rising of Sirius, theirs would have been an exact calendar year, and the season of the Inundation would always have extended from mid-July to mid-November, when the Nile subsides; Winter would have extended from mid-November to mid-March, and Summer from mid-March to mid-July when the earth, crumbled by drought, required constant irrigation. Instead, the first month of the Inundation always followed the fifth epagomenic day, irrespective of whether Sothis had risen or not. Since the resulting year lagged behind the real year by a quarter of a day, the real summer might eventually come to concide with the winter of the civil calendar and *vice versa*.

Now since classical authors tell us that, in A.D. 139, the New Year's Day of the civil year coincided with the heliacal rising of Sirius, we know that the same event must have occurred in 1317, in 2773, and in 4229 B.C. There are also Egyptian references to the date of the heliacal rising of Sirius in terms of the civil year: the first during the reign of Tuthmosis III in 1469; the second during year 9 of the reign of Amenophis I (1545) and the third during year 7 of the reign of Sesostris III (1877 B.C.). Since the calendar must necessarily have been adopted before the last date, it probably goes back to 2773 B.C. or to 4229 B.C. (within approximately twelve years). According to whether we refer Egyptian history to one or the other of these dates, we accept the short or the long chronology, of which the former agrees more closely with what we know of Egyptian history from other sources.

Of course, the above remarks apply only if the Egyptians based their original calendar on long observation of Sirius. Now, the very premises of this assumption seem wrong. The Egyptian year of 365 days is not so much an astronomical year as an agricultural year (R. Parker). Though the Nile rises every year, its inundation, which depends on rainfall over the Abyssinian plateau, is an irregular meteorological phenomenon—fluctuations of more than six weeks between the beginnings of two consecutive inundations have been recorded. No doubt it is this very irregularity which prevented the Egyptians from basing their civil calendar on the annual inundations and caused them to look instead—though as an afterthought—for a less capricious celestial phenomenon apparently associated with the flooding.

This interpretation changes the entire problem. The year of 365 days, the best of all ancient calendars, would then not have been the result of Egypt's superiority in astronomy, but of observations of the yearly inundations. Hence the very idea of a precise astronomical science from the third millennium onwards must be rejected. Moreover, since it took 240 years for their New Year's Day to fall outside the Inundation, the calendar could have been initiated during any one of 240 years. Thus, we may take it that it was begun in 2880–2560 B.C., dates which are in closer agreement with what else we know of Egypt, rather than in 2777–2773 or in 4233–4229.

Apart from the civil calendar, the Egyptians also used other calendars, notably a ritual calendar based on the synodic month. The Carlsberg Papyrus No. 9 explains the method whereby they predicted the phases of the moon. It is based on the fact that 25 Egyptian years are equivalent to 309 lunations representing 9,125 days, grouped into mean lunar months of 29 or 30 days each. 'Ordinarily, two consecutive lunar months are given 59 days by the scheme. But every 5th year the last two months are made 60 days long. This gives the whole 25-year cycle the correct total of 9,125 days. In this way one had an exceedingly handy scheme for determining by simple rules the dates of all lunar festivals in such a way that no grave error could develop for many centuries, though the single new moon or full moon could deviate by $\pm$ 2 days or even more.' (O. Neugebauer.) The main object of the Carlsberg Papyrus No. 9 was to provide scribes and priests with a means of fitting the moving lunar festivals into the civil year, according to a division of the 309 months of the cycle into 16 ordinary years of 12 months and 9 'great' years of 13 months.

THE ORIENTATION OF TEMPLES AND PYRAMIDS

Ever since Napoleon's expedition, Europeans working in the Nile valley have been struck by the precise orientation of the faces of Egyptian monuments, and particularly of those pyramids which face the four cardinal points. In fact, the deflection from true north of the face of all the main pyramids is less than one degree. (Great Pyramid and Pyramid of Chephren: 2′ 28″; Pyramid of Mycerinus: 9′ 12″; Rhomboid Pyramid: 24′ 25″; Meidun Pyramid: 14′ 3″.)

In view of the gigantic dimensions of these structures, such errors are negligible, and the Egyptians must certainly have had a valid method of finding the true north. Lacking compasses, they must have relied on astronomical observations, though we do not know of what kind. The shortest-shadow method, for one, is not accurate enough.

Various other methods have been suggested, such as the direction of the Pole Star, the culmination of a fixed star, transit of two fixed stars, bisection of the angle between the positions of one and the same star after an interval of twelve hours, bisection of the angle between the rising and setting of a fixed star, and, more recently, the minimum displacement of a fixed star, probably Eta of Ursa Major (Z. Zaba).

But no matter which method they chose, the Egyptians certainly solved the problem in their characteristic, empirical way. Once their shadow-clocks had shown them that the shortest shadow always pointed north, they were bound to notice a fixed star lying in the same direction. As with their calendar, they probably started with simple observations, perfecting the results as they went along. We know, in any case, that the Egyptians had instruments for taking simple sightings, and it is probably from the inherent inaccuracy of these instruments that the slight variations in the orientation of the various buildings arose.

However, not all Egyptian buildings were oriented with the same precision as the Great Pyramid. In many cases, temples simply faced the Nile, which the Egyptians believed ran generally south to north, no matter how much it meandered on its way; needless to say, orientations based on that notion turned out to be rather crude.

In any case, the correct orientation of the faces of the pyramids does not imply that the Egyptians were accomplished astronomers, and our present state of knowledge certainly does not entitle us to assume, as many Egyptologists have done, that the Egyptians realized long before Hipparchos that the 'motion' of the fixed stars was due to the precession of the 'world's axis'.

THE EGYPTIAN CONSTELLATIONS

Though astronomy played no more than a subsidiary role in the adoption of the Egyptian calendar, it is nevertheless true to say that, from very early times onwards, the inhabitants of the Nile valley had noticed the passing of the stars and hence connected two independently discovered facts: the heliacal rising of Sothis and the annual overflow of the Nile. Among the tasks that fell to the vizier, the foremost state official, was the recording of observations of Sothis; it was to him that the rising of the star and the overflowing of the Nile had to be reported.

Representations of the sky on certain tombs have enabled scholars to identify some of the constellations known to the Egyptians—for example, the Great Bear (leg of beef), Boötes (crocodile and hippopotamus intertwined), Cygnus (man with outstretched arms), Orion (man running and looking over his shoulder), Cassiopeia (figure with extended arms), and Draco, the Pleiades, Scorpio and Aries, each represented by characteristic figures. This pictorial representation of the constellations is akin to that handed down to astrologers from the Middle Ages, though the modern signs of the zodiac, which are based on Babylonian models, differ from the Egyptians'.

Egyptian observers were in the habit of naming everything they saw in the sky. Thus the planets were 'stars which never rest'; Venus was the morning star and Jupiter the resplendent star; Saturn was 'Horus the Bull', Mars the 'Red Horus', while the circumpolar stars, *i.e.*, those stars which are visible all the year round, were called 'imperishable'.

THE DECANS

The twelve signs of the Zodiac were unknown in Egypt before the Greek period. However, the Egyptians used special constellations, the decans, to divide their year into 36 parts. The various decans had different names, of which only a few have been deciphered, such as the 'Eyebrow of the South', the 'Eyebrow of the North', the 'God who travels across the Sky'. These decans, which might be groups of stars or single bright stars, rose at particular hours of the night during thirty-six successive periods of ten days, thus making up the year. They lay within a wide equatorial belt and began with *Sepedet* (literally, 'the excellent'), *i.e.* Sirius, sometimes called the 'Mistress of the Year'. Pictures of decans account for most of the celestial representations of tombs and were often accompanied by hieroglyphic legends, the texts of which, though not very intelligible to us must have been understood by the Egyptians themselves, since the Carlsberg Papyrus No 1, written more than 1,000 years after the legends, is a commentary on them. The original hieratic text is followed by a literal translation in the demotic style, sometimes accompanied by glosses. In some cases, cryptic symbols have been substituted for the common hieroglyphic signs to hide the real sense from the uninitiated. The Carlsberg Papyrus has forced historians to beware of taking the astronomical funerary texts too literally, and to re-examine all previous accounts of the times of rising and setting of the stars, and hence all previous identifications of the constellations.

The extant tables giving the hours of the rising and setting of the stars and constellations are, moreover, rather inaccurate. It is doubtful, for instance, that each decan covered ten degrees of the great celestial circle exactly, and hence it is difficult to the use the relevant texts for mapping the Egyptian's sky. The decanal system, which can be traced back at least as far as the 3rd dynasty (*c.* 2800 B.C.), assumed historical importance only when the Greeks made the twelve signs of the Zodiac (derived from the Babylonians) an integral part of astrology.

ASTRONOMICAL INSTRUMENTS

To appreciate the true value of Egyptian astronomical observations, we must look more closely at their instruments and at their methods of observation.

The scribes and priests charged with making the observations on which the ritual life of the country depended worked mainly with a very simple instrument, called the *merkhet*. The *merkhet* was the rib of

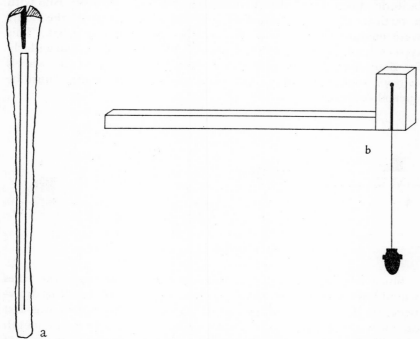

fig. 7 Egyptian astronomical instruments: (*a*) merkhet, (*b*) *straight-edge and plumb line.*

a palm leaf, split at its widest point (*fig. 7a*). The slot was held in front of the eye, and the observer looked through it at a lead weight suspended from a straight-edge held horizontally by an assistant, in such a way that the cord lay over a mark on the wood (*fig. 7b*). The two observers would face each other along a north–south line, and determine the precise hour from the transit of a given star directly over the heart, the right or left eye, or other parts of the assistant's body. The results were checked against existing diagrams, ruled into squares and depicting a man surrounded by stars. The legends of the diagrams explain, for instance, that the second hour begins when the star *Petef* is above the heart, the third hour when the star *Ary* is above the left eye, *etc.* Diagrams gave the positions of various stars during the twelve hours of night for the whole year, at intervals of fifteen days.

The *merkhet* was used chiefly for nocturnal observations. During the day, the Egyptians generally fixed the hour from the lengths of shadows—a practice that goes back to their early history. While they must have realized that these lengths varied from season to season, we do not know whether they also appreciated the effect of latitude. Their simplest instrument was a wooden or ivory rule with a vertical edge and plumb-line (*fig. 8a*). The names of the hours were engraved on the rule against the corresponding mark. This type of instrument is used in Upper Egypt to this day, particularly for determining when a team of oxen turning the water-wheels (*saggieh*) is due for relief, and when the irrigation sluices must be opened or shut.

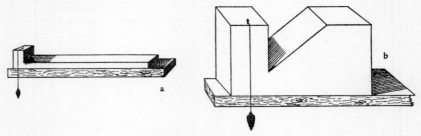

fig. 8 Egyptian shadow clocks.

Since morning and evening shadows are rather long, the rules would have had to be of awkward dimensions. To obviate this drawback, the Egyptians built instruments in which the shadow was cast on an inclined plane, and hence considerably reduced in length (*fig. 8b*). But all the instruments known to us—no matter of what type—have one thing in common: none of the hours marked on them is correct.

Apart from these instruments, the Egyptians also used sundials, divided into equal arcs, for measuring the *direction* of shadows. The oldest extant Egyptian sundial goes back to the thirteenth century B.C. However, that instrument, too, is inaccurate—only noon is marked correctly.

To determine the correct time during the day *and* the night, the Egyptians used water-clocks of the kind known to the Greeks as clepsydrae. Most of the specimens recovered are unfortunately in a very bad state of preservation. The oldest, which goes back to the thirteenth century B.C., is adorned with stars and constellations and bears the following inscription: 'Every figure is in its hour . . . to determine the hours of the night when the stars of the decans are invisible. Thus, the correct hour of the sacrifice may always be observed' (*fig. 9*). An inscription from the beginning of the 18th dynasty (*c.* 1580 B.C.) makes it clear that clepsydrae were used even at that earlier period.

According to the Egyptians, the complete day (24 hours) began at sunset. They distinguished night (*gereh*), characterized by the absence of the sun, from *heru*, which started at dawn. Each of the two parts of the full day was divided into twelve hours, the length of which varied from season to season. Thus *gereh* hours in winter were much longer than *gereh* hours in summer. In order to account for these seasonal differences, a table was engraved inside the clepsydra: each month had a vertical scale of twelve marks corresponding to the twelve hours of night during that month.

fig. 9 Egyptian clepsydra.

The instrument, which had the shape of a truncated cone, was filled with water, and a small opening at the bottom allowed the liquid to escape gradually. It was graduated on the false assumption that the water level would fall uniformly. In fact, the conical shape, ingenious though it was, was not enough to offset the effects of the gradual drop in pressure. Here we are face to face with the basic failure of Egyptian science; the construction of a reliable clepsydra would have demanded mathematical skills quite beyond their powers. The conical shape, adopted after many trials and errors, does admittedly mitigate the errors, but even so the results remained inaccurate. Towards the end of their history, the Egyptians tried to remedy this deficiency by using cylindrical clepsydrae filled from a reservoir with a constant head. We do not know whether, in this way, they managed to overcome the problem satisfactorily.

THE INADEQUACY OF EGYPTIAN METHODS
Our examination of Egyptian astronomical instruments has shown how rudimentary their observational methods really were. Thus, if the observer used two assistants of different build, the stars would

cross his eyes at appreciably different times, and the same was true
if he changed his distance from the assistant—surely a common
occurrence in a country with no uniform standard of length. Similarly, the instruments themselves were often far too rough and ready
to give accurate results. We have only to study the tables giving the
differences between the day and the night during the various seasons
to be struck forcefully by their lack of precision. The hours of daylight in them increase and decrease uniformly over the year, an
error which was undoubtedly due to 'imperfections of the instruments used for determining the hours' (J. J. Clère). Here is an
example taken from one of their tables:

First month of the Inundation: 1st day ... day 10¼ h. night 13¾ h.
  ,,   ,,   ,, ,,   ,,   15th day ...   ,, 11 h.   ,,   13 h.
Second ,,   ,, ,,   ,,   1st day ...   ,, 11½ h.   ,,   12½ h.

All the fractions in the table can be expressed in twelfths, so 'We may
therefore assume that the hours were divided on the duodecimal
system; in conformity, no doubt, with the fact that the year was
divided into twelve months, the day and the night were divided into
twelve hours' (J. J. Clère).

While the equinoxes were recorded correctly, the rest of the table
was not. Thus the fifteenth day of the third month of *shemu* (summer)
was shown to have 9 hr. 20 min. of daylight and 14 hr. 40 min. of night
(clearly, at that period the civil calendar was quite out of step with
the astronomical calendar). Now, in the latitude of Egypt the
shortest day can never have less than 10 hr. 5 min. Other tables are
even more incorrect. Thus a papyrus in the Cairo Museum bases all
its calculation on fluctuations of two hours per month, irrespective
of the season.

From all this we can see how poor the Egyptians' standard of
accuracy was, and with how little they were satisfied—doubtless one
of the reasons why their astronomy made so little progress.

RELIGIOUS AND RITUAL CHARACTER OF EGYPTIAN ASTRONOMY

We shall seek vainly for an astrological basis to Egyptian astronomy
before the Greek period. Even so, their celestial notions were strongly
affected by religious ideas. All the extant astronomical texts were
written with one single object—to determine the hour and season of
given religious festivals. It was this quest which must clearly be
considered to have been the starting-point of all Egyptian astronomy
—a contention which is also borne out by inscriptions on many
astronomical instruments. Now the punctilious performance of
temple rites involved the service of relays of priests (*phylae*) under a
'Priest in his Hour'. The priests had to be relieved at fixed times,

whence the inscription on a sighting instrument: 'Pointer . . . for allocating all men to their places.'

Even beyond the grave, time played a very important role. The dead had to know, hour by hour, what incantations were needed to avoid the snares set by their enemies on their nocturnal journey—hence the astronomical figures on coffin-lids and tombs.

Bearing these facts in mind, we have good reason to claim that Egyptian astronomy was above all ritual in character. Their concern with the passage of time, in exact orientations, and with seasonal festivals, led the Egyptians to a characteristic conception of existence: every day was influenced by a precedent that had occurred in mythological times. According to whether this event was good or evil, the day was judged favourable or unlucky. Entire papyri were devoted to this kind of calculation, whereby every day was divided into three equal parts, each with its own omens. Moreover, one of the lists of good and bad days gave the length of each day and night involved, so that the list might be used in conjunction with the civil calendar.

Since Herodotos, it has become common practice to claim that the Egyptians were a deeply religious people. Indeed, their ritual, their concern with the repetition of mythological events, day by day, and almost hour by hour, is the best explanation of Egyptian astronomy and of the importance of the calendar in it.

Conclusion

Before concluding our account of Egyptian mathematics and astronomy, we must say a word about what has been called the 'secret science' of the Pharaohs, the alleged inscription in the Great Pyramid of the correct value of π, of the radius of the earth, of the length of a meridian, *etc*. It must be stressed that if that science ever really existed, we have no evidence whatsoever of it. All the speculations about the meaning of the 'cyphers' on the Great Pyramid are pure childishness, and would be so even had their authors been correct in their other figures—which they were not. Moreover, since the Nile valley from the Delta to the Sudan can boast 150 pyramids, it is ridiculous to think that the Great Pyramid would be the sole repository of this secret knowledge. In any case, Egyptian science, secret or not, went hand in hand with elementary errors.

There have been many discussions about the scientific character of Egyptian mathematics and astronomy. We have seen that we cannot dismiss any discipline as unscientific simply because it is practical rather than theoretical. 'The scientific criterion of all mathematics must be the use of proofs; in astronomy, it is the rejection of all arguments not exclusively based on observation or on mathematical deductions from an original hypothesis. . . . Egyptian mathematics never rose to explanations that could be called proofs. . . . Egyptian astronomy was contented with a very summary qualitative description of phenomena, and lacked all traces of a scientific method. . . . It is a great error to bestow upon Egyptian mathematical or astronomical documents the glorious title of scientific works, or to assume the existence of an unknown, forgotten, or secret science yet to be discovered in extant texts.'

Though this judgement of O. Neugebauer is certainly fair comment, it strikes us as being a little too severe. True, the Egyptians never had any clear notion of what a scientific method was or could be; that knowledge had to await the coming of Greek civilization in the fifth century B.C. Nevertheless, the Egyptians had a love for truth, '*maāt*', in all senses of the word. This attitude of mind is borne out by their entire civilization—by their material and technical achievements in the construction of pyramids and temples, and by their artistic perfection. Admittedly, their mathematics and astronomy remained rudimentary, but what we must grant them is that they used these disciplines for introducing greater accuracy and efficiency into their everyday lives. They, like so many other primitive civilizations, might have been contented with the adoption of lunar months, vague years, and vague times for taking their meals, rising, or retiring. Instead, they tried to be more accurate, even though their final results were far from perfect. This concern for accuracy, and for results, while not being tantamount to a true scientific turn of mind, was nevertheless a step in the right direction. In this respect, the Egyptians were far superior to most contemporary and even to many later civilizations. No wonder, therefore, that the Greeks were such great admirers of their achievements.

EGYPTIAN MEDICINE

DOCUMENTATION

Champollion and his immediate successors acquired all their knowledge of Egyptian medicine from Greek writers. Theophrastos, Dioscorides and Galen constantly mention prescriptions obtained from Egyptian medical texts kept in the library of the Temple of Imhotep in Memphis. This library, which Hippocrates consulted about 480 B.C., was still visited by Greek scholars some seven centuries later.

It was not until 1875 that modern Egyptologists made direct contact with Egyptian medicine, thanks to the publication of more than half a dozen papyrus scrolls from Upper Egypt, of which the main ones are: the Papyrus Ebers (1875), the Kahun Papyrus (1898), the Berlin Papyrus (1909) and the Edwin Smith Surgical Papyrus (1930). These papyri differ in contents, methods of presentation, and in trend. The Papyrus Ebers and the Berlin Papyrus are mainly collections of medical prescriptions including magical incantations; the Smith Papyrus is devoted exclusively to surgery and is distinguished by its quasi-scientific approach, while the relatively short Kahun Papyrus is remarkable for its striking accuracy and sobriety. Though the Kahun Papyrus dates back to the twelfth, the Papyri Ebers and Smith to the 18th, and the Berlin Papyrus to the 19th dynasty, the originals from which all of them were copied or adapted must certainly be traced back to the Old Kingdom.

THE BEGINNINGS OF MEDICINE

The Egyptians held that all diseases—or rather all internal diseases—were caused by supernatural agents (gods, goddesses, and dead enemies) who took 'possession' of the bodies of the living. Clearly, supernatural ailments could be exorcized only by supernatural remedies. Thus, to loosen a bandage safely an Egyptian would have to recite a magical prayer:

Loosened was the loosened one by Isis, Horus was loosened by Isis from the evils done to him by his brother Seth.... Oh Isis, great in sorcery! Mayst thou loosen me, mayst thou deliver me from everything bad and evil and vicious, from afflictions (caused) by a god or goddess, from dead man or woman, from male or female adversary who will oppose me, like thy delivery with thy Son Horus. For I have entered into the fire and have come forth from the water, I will not fall into this day's snares. I have spoken and now I am young and refreshed. (Pap. Eb. I.)

Such incantations were assumed to be effective without any medical assistance, though others had to be accompanied with more tangible applications of ointments, potions, powders, *etc*. For instance, burns were cured by the following method:

My son Horus is burnt in the desert. Is water there? There is no water there. There is water in my mouth and a Nile between (my) thighs. I come to extinguish the fire. (Formula) recited over the milk of (a woman) who has borne a male child. (Pap. Eb. LXIX.)

In addition to this incantation, which was considered the main remedy, specific mixtures were also applied to the burn. Now, it must have happened quite often that patients, having forgotten the incantation, applied the mixture by itself, and were yet cured. In time, therefore, the mixture itself was retained while the magical formula gradually fell into oblivion—magic receded before medical science.

However, this process was never carried to its logical conclusions. Thus Egyptian physicians always stressed the value of certain remedies of 'celestial origin', given, for instance, in 'a writing found under Anubis' feet in Letopolis' (Pap. Eb. CIII). Moreover, there were some diseases which physicians refused to treat altogether and which they left entirely to magicians. Thus there was apparently no medical cure for scorpion bites, and only appeals to Isis or Thoth, or taking waters endowed with magical properties through previous contact with figures and legends of 'healing' statues, were thought to be effective.

Magicians and physicians worked in harmony. The 'Treatise of the Heart' tells us that magicians and the 'Sekhmet Priests' alike knew how to listen to the patient's heart-beat. Clearly the Egyptians made few distinctions between skilled practitioners, 'inspired' diviners, and the disciples of ancient magicians. Again, there were those, like Iri (Old Kingdom), who combined the skills of physician and magician, or like the official in charge of the Hatnub quarries whose title was 'Chief Priest of Sekhmet, Chief of Magicians, Physician-in-Chief to the King'. Even so, one may assume that the great reputation which Egyptian physicians enjoyed in the whole Orient was based on their professional skill rather than on their more transcendental powers.

PHYSICIANS
Medicine in Egypt was one trade among many. Trade secrets were handed down from father to son, and there were no medical schools other than the 'Houses of Life', where young practitioners could complete their paternal teaching by contact with physicians and surgeons, or with scribes engaged in copying out sacred medical texts. The 'Houses of Life' were responsible for compiling the medical papyri, while similar institutions published such religious works as the 'Book of the Dead'.

Assured of the protection of Thoth who 'shall be his guide, who lets writing speak and has composed the books; who gives to the skilful and to the physicians who accompany him, skill to cure' (Pap. Eb. I), the novice was admitted to his august office. All Egyptian physicians were employees of the state. 'On military expeditions,' Diodoros of Sicily explained (I, 92), 'and on voyages, everyone is treated without fee, the physicians being paid by the state.' Since every state department was organized on hierarchic lines, Egyptian medicine had its Head Physicians, Physicians-in-

Chief, Medical Supervisors, and even Head Physicians of the South and the North. The highest of all were attached to the court, led by the 'Dean of Court Physicians', the 'Inspector of Medicine to the Court', and the 'Physician-in-Chief of the King'. If we are to believe Herodotos (II, 84), 'every court physician was in charge of a single illness'. This could not have been true of Iri, whom we mentioned earlier, since he was not only a court physician but also a specialist on diseases of the eye, the bowels, the stomach, and the anus—a general practitioner, in short. Still, we have clear evidence that Egypt always had her dentists, ophthalmologists, and surgeons who practised only their specialty. According to Clement of Alexandria, a very early medical text consisted of six chapters, the fifth dealing with diseases of the eyes and the sixth with diseases of women. It seems likely that the first two chapters dealt with general medicine, that the third (corresponding vaguely with the Smith Papyrus) was devoted to bone surgery, and the fourth to anatomy.

ANATOMY AND PHYSIOLOGY: THE HEART

What did the Egyptians know of the structure of the human body? Despite the fact that their exceptional embalming skills ought to have given them every chance of examining the internal organs, Egyptian physiology never made great headway. Apparently, the Egyptians knew nothing of the existence of kidneys, and while we cannot blame them for having failed to anticipate Harvey's discovery of the circulation, we cannot but be astonished at their explanation of the role of the cardiac muscles and the so-called 'vessels'. The Papyrus Ebers contains a treatise on the heart, accompanied by an explanation of some of the technical terms employed. This is how it is introduced:

The beginning of the physician's secret knowledge of the heart's movement (physiology) and knowledge of the heart (anatomy). There are vessels from it to every limb. As to this, when any physician, any Sekhmet-priest (surgeon?) or any exorcist applies the hands or his fingers to the head, to the back of the head, to the hands, to the place of the stomach, to the arms or to the feet, then he examines the heart, because all its limbs possess its vessels; that is, it (the heart) speaks out of the vessels of every limb. (Pap. Eb. XCIX.)

While the Egyptians deserve great credit for having observed that the heart 'speaks', they never thought of counting the pulse. It was not until the third century B.C. that Herophilos of Alexandria began to count pulse-beats by means of a small clepsydra. As for the vessels, they were said to be forty-six in number (another 'authority' put their number at twenty-two), and to be tubes filled with liquid, air and waste. One of these liquids was blood, found, for instance, in the vessels of the nostrils and the temples. 'There are four vessels in his nostrils, two give mucus, and two give blood; there are four vessels in the interior of his temples which give blood (to) the eyes; all diseases of the eyes arise through them, because there is an opening to the eyes' (Pap. Eb. CXIX). These 'vessels' must have been the arteries, since it was by placing his fingers on them that the physician felt the heart-beat.

But the vessels contained other liquids as well—for example, tears, urine and sperm—which they carried to various parts of the body. 'There are two vessels to the bladder; it is they which give urine . . . There are two vessels to the testicles; it is they which give sperm . . . There are four vessels to the liver; it is they which give to it humour and air; likewise those to the lungs and the spleen' (Pap. Eb. C). The air in the vessels was obtained from outside, for 'the air enters the nose, and thence proceeds to the heart and the lungs, which carry it quickly to the entire body'. How odd to have thought that the heart carries air from the nostrils to the lungs!

Other vessels carried waste products from various parts of the body to the anus: 'There are four vessels that open to the anus; it is they which cause humour and air to be produced for it. Now, the anus opens to every vessel to the right side and the left side and in arms and legs when (it) is overfilled with excrement' (Pap. Eb. C).

Apart from constituting the vascular system, the vessels also acted as lachrymal duct, ureter, vas deferens, *etc*. Though all these tubes have, in reality, different terminations, the ureters, for instance, joining the kidney to the bladder, the Egyptians believed that all vessels started from the heart: 'There are vessels from it (the heart) to every limb.' Clearly they looked upon the heart as the central motor of the body which, by means of its vessels, controlled all physiological functions.

INTERNAL DISEASES; RESPIRATORY PASSAGES

Because of their deficient anatomical knowledge, particularly concerning the heart and the role of the vessels, the Egyptians had to grope in the dark when it came to treating internal diseases. Thus the term *sema*—which is commonly translated as lungs—stood for all the respiratory organs: larynx, bronchi, bronchioles, and the lobes of the lung. Most of the vague respiratory complaints which Egyptian texts mention must therefore have been laryngitic and bronchitic rather than lung diseases proper. All of them had one thing in common—coughing, 'which causes a rupture to break out and take form', according to the keen observation of the Papyrus Ebers (CVI).

The Papyrus Ebers mentions twenty-one cough mixtures—three

5 Sculptor weighing gold

6 Surveyor holding coiled rope

more than the Berlin Papyrus. It accords pride of place to honey (mentioned twelve times), then to cream (mentioned nine times) and milk (mentioned seven times). For instance, 'Remedy to expel cough: honey and cream are mixed together and swallowed with beer for four days' (Pap. Eb. LIII). Or: 'Cow's milk and manna are placed in a vessel which is put over the fire as (when) cooking beans. After it has been boiled, the patient shall chew this manna and swallow (it) with the milk for four days' (LIV).

Apart from such potions, the physicians also prescribed what were doubtless more efficient remedies. For example:

Another (remedy): orpiment, bitumen, bran are ground together. Thou shalt fetch 7 stones and heat them by the fire; thou shalt take one thereof and place (a little) of these remedies on it and cover it with a new vessel whose bottom is perforated, and place a stalk of a reed in this hole, thou shalt put thy mouth to this hole so that thou inhalest the smoke of it. Likewise with all stones. Thereafter thou shalt eat something fat, of fat meat, or oil. (Pap. Eb. LV.)

Obviously the Egyptians assumed that there was a connection between coughing and the stomach, and, in fact, the fatty diet enjoined by the papyrus was also prescribed by Dioscorides (first century), and is still recommended today.

As for such diseases of the lungs as abscesses, congestion, pneumonia and tuberculosis, the Egyptians, we repeat, did not even suspect their existence. Still, they treated them, inasmuch as coughs might have been the clinical indications of many pulmonary conditions for which fatty foods would, in fact, have acted as effective remedies.

DIGESTIVE TRACT

1 The Papyrus Ebers contains a very ancient and rather obscure section called 'Instructions concerning affections of the stomach'. These instructions are twenty in number and obviously served as rules of thumb to medical practitioners. Only five of the cases discussed deal with real stomach complaints, *viz.* indigestion, dilation, cancer, haemorrhage (possibly the result of an ulcer), and acute gastritis accompanied by vomiting. The others deal with such varied complaints as coryza, coughing, angina pectoris, diabetes, *etc.*, which the Egyptians must have associated with the stomach in some inexplicable way.

The instructions for treating acute gastritis contain one of the few clinical hints found in the entire section:

If thou examinest a man for an obstacle in his stomach, and he is too oppressed to eat, his belly is narrow, and he walks miserably, like a man suffering from burning in the anus, then thou shalt examine him lying on the back. If thou findest his belly warm and a resistance in his stomach, thou shalt say to him: it is a liver-case. Thou shalt prepare the secret herbal remedy which is made by the physician: (the plant) *pakh-seret* and date kernels are mixed, strained, and drunk by the patient every morning for 4 days, so that thou emptiest his belly. If, after having done that thou findest the two sides of his belly: the right one warm and the left one cool, then thou shalt say about that: it shows that the disease is consumed (*i.e.*, it decreases?). Thou shalt examine him again, if thou findest his entire body cool, thou shalt say: his liver is opened and has been cleaned, he has received the medicine. (Pap. Eb. XXXVI.)

2 The Papyrus Ebers also mentions the lower part of the digestive tract, *i.e.* the intestines, on some twelve occasions, mainly in connection with constipation which Egyptian physicians apparently treated with success. They prescribed medicines compounded of such simple ingredients as powdered cypress, powdered ricinus seeds, honey, oil, and beer. 'Remedy to empty the belly and to expel putrefaction (?) in the belly of a man: seeds of ricinus are chewed and swallowed with beer until all that is in the belly comes out' (Pap. Eb. VIII). Oddly enough diarrhoea and dysentery, which are so frequent in Egypt, were not deemed worthy of mention by the compilers of the papyrus. On the other hand, many passages of the Papyrus Ebers are devoted to intestinal worms, and particularly to roundworms and tape-worms. The vermifuges prescribed were usually taken in beer or oil, though some were eaten dry, or applied externally to the stomach by means of poultices.

3 The anus eventually became the special province of physicians with the resounding title of 'Guardians of the Anus'. Thirty-three paragraphs of the Papyrus Ebers, some passages of the Berlin Papyrus, and an entire treatise in the Chester Beatty Collection are devoted to affections of the rectum, among which only haemorrhoids and rectal prolapses can be identified with certainty. Other references in these papyri are to symptoms rather than conditions, *e.g.* irritation of the anus, congestion, heat, pains, *etc.*

The medicines were administered in various ways—by mouth (usually mixed with beer to make them more palatable), or anally by means of lint plugs. Lotions and ointments were also prescribed. One suppository mentioned in the Papyrus Ebers contained frankincense, pignon, fruit of juniper, yellow ochre, cuttle bone, cumin, honey, myrrh, and cinnamon. Another 'remedy to expel burning in the anus and in the bladder that is accompanied by many flatuses without his perceiving it' was made up of '*ibu*-plants, salt, watermelon and honey, ground together and made into a suppository and put in the hinder part' (Pap. Eb. XXXI).

4 The liver was largely ignored by the scribes, who, moreover, knew nothing about its structure or functions. It was, however, considered the vague cause of one stomach ailment. To deal with what was undoubtedly jaundice, Egyptian physicians prescribed remedies consisting mainly of figs.

URINARY SYSTEM

Egyptian physicians, we saw, also ignored the kidneys. According to them, two vessels starting from the heart carried the urine straight to the bladder. The Papyrus Ebers mentions a disease called 'accumulation of urine in the belly', *i.e.* retention, but its causes (urethritis or prostatitis) were passed over in complete silence. The treatment generally consisted of administering vegetable substances dissolved in water. In some cases, ointments were applied to the penis.

Incontinence on the other hand (including nocturnal enuresis) is discussed by the Papyrus Ebers at some length. The medicaments, again, were largely made up of vegetable matter. Other bladder ailments are also mentioned, together with appropriate treatment. 'Remedy to expel a heat-obstacle in the bladder (probably acute cystitis), when (the patient) has pain in the urine: northern salt, cream, balanites-oil, honey and sweet beer are injected into the anus' (Pap. Eb. LXIX). Another remedy to 'put right a violent pain in the urine' might well have been a cure for blenorrhagia.

The Papyrus Ebers repeatedly mentions blood in the urine, due no doubt chiefly to bilharziasis, a disease so common in the Nile valley that it was often called 'Egyptian hematuria'. The Papyrus Ebers gives some twenty remedies, consisting mainly of potions and electuaries 'to expel hematuria in the belly and in the heart' (Pap. Eb. XLIV). This reference to the heart need not surprise us, since we know that the Egyptians assumed a close connection between it and the bladder. The Berlin Papyrus had a great liking for fumigations in the treatment of bladder complaints, and also prescribed the urine of an impuberal boy (Berl. Pap. 6o). The fact that the Egyptians used such obviously ineffective cures, borrowed no doubt from the magicians, shows clearly how impotent they felt in face of a disease which the Papyrus Ebers claimed was 'placed by a god or a dead man in the belly'.

THE HEAD

The Egyptians knew more about the external parts of the body than about the internal organs. Thus, the head (the face and the skull) was studied in great detail. Still, they also knew something about the brain and the spinal cord. They treated encephalitis with ointments, friction, and compresses rather than with drugs. They had special remedies against migraine, called 'pains in one side of the head'. According to one of these prescriptions (Pap. Eb. XLVII) the head of a patient was to be rubbed with the head of a silurus fish so that the headache might pass into the animal.

The Papyrus Ebers also dwells at length on scalp disorders. Castor oil was prescribed for keeping the hair of women thick. Baldness, which, judging from mummies, was very common in Egypt, particularly among the Pharaohs (Amenophis III, Rameses II and Queen Nefertiti were all bald), was treated with 'fat of lion, fat of hippopotamus, fat of crocodile, fat of cat, fat of serpent and fat of ibex'. Another remedy, the formula of which is alleged to go back to the reign of Tety (6th dynasty), was made up of 'leg of hound, date kernels and hoof of ass, boiled thoroughly with oil'. All of these remedies obviously must have been quite ineffectual.

Another common complaint, alopecia areata of the scalp, was treated in various ways, generally by combinations of magic and pharmacology—an indication of how little faith the Egyptians had in medicine as such. Similarly, a number of remedies to expel 'grizzling of the hair' were also based on magic; for instance, the remedy to 'expel grizzling effectively (*sic!*) and treat the hair', which consisted of 'blood of a black ox put in oil and (the head) is anointed therewith' (Pap. Eb. XLV).

Compared with their medical colleagues, Egyptian surgeons were real masters of their craft. The first of the forty-eight cases discussed in the Edwin Smith surgical Papyrus was a head wound penetrating to the bone but which left the bone itself uninjured—'an ailment which I shall treat', the surgeon pronounced confidently (Smith Pap., Case 1). The treatment consisted of binding the wound with fresh meat and then applying grease, honey and lint every day until the patient recovered. A more serious case such as a 'gaping wound in the head', the surgeon again refers to as 'an ailment with which I will contend' (Smith Pap., Case 4). He would 'moor the patient at his mooring-stakes until the period of his injury passes by. His treatment is sitting. Make for him two supports of brick until thou knowest he has reached a decisive point. Thou shouldst apply grease to his head, (and) soften his neck therewith and both his shoulders.'

Head injuries must have been very frequent indeed, if only because of incessant warfare and the kinds of weapons that were used. Thus King Sekenenre, who fell in battle against the Hyksos, had five wounds in his head, each of which could have killed him.

THE FACE
The face contains 'the seven holes of the head'; the nostrils, the ears, the mouth, and the eyes.

1 The Papyrus Ebers devotes no more than three passages to the nose, two dealing with a fetid nose (ozena) and one with sneezing. One of its remedies is semi-magical, semi-pharmaceutical, and starts with a colourful incantation:

Flow out, fetid nose! Flow out son of a fetid nose! Flow out thou who breakest bones, destroyest the skull, diggest in the bone-marrow and makest the 7 holes in the head ill. Rē's servants, praise Thoth! Behold I have brought thy remedy against thee: the milk of (a woman) who has borne a male (child) and fragrant gum . . . (Pap. Eb. XC.)

By contrast, see the treatment prescribed by the Smith Papyrus for a 'break in the column of the nose':

Thou shouldst cleanse (the nose) for him with two plugs of linen. Thou shouldst place two (other) plugs of linen saturated with grease in the inside of his two nostrils. Thou shouldst put him at his mooring stakes until this swelling is reduced. Thou shouldst apply for him stiff rolls of linen by which his nose is held fast. Thou shouldst treat him afterwards (with) grease, honey, (and) lint, every day until he recovers. (Smith Pap. 11.)

2 One might have expected the papyri to mention ear ailments at length since the Egyptians believed that the 'breath of life enters into the two vessels at the right ear and the breath of death enters into the two vessels at the left ear' (Pap. Eb. CIII). However, the papyri restrict their comments to fetid discharges (Papyrus Ebers) and to stabbing pains, symptoms of acute otitis (Berlin Papyrus). Deafness is not even mentioned by the Berlin Papyrus, and the Papyrus Ebers simply prescribes an infusion of balanites-oil as a pain-killer for one having a 'bewitched' (deaf) ear. Without doubt the Egyptians looked upon deafness, like baldness, as being incurable.

3 Dentistry was a specialty from the time of the Old Kingdom, a fact noted by Herodotos, who spoke of Egyptian 'tooth-doctors'. Judging by mummies, dentists must have been kept very busy indeed —gumboils, pyorrhoea, and caries seemed to have been extremely widespread at least among the upper classes, who are known to have dined well. Teeth affected by caries were polished with a compound of crushed stones, red ochre and chrysocoll, spelt, turpentine, honey and water. Apart from 'filling' teeth, dental surgeons carried out other delicate operations. Thus two teeth joined by a gold thread were discovered at Giza; the surgeon must have thought that he could keep the loose tooth in place by tying it to its firm neighbour. Another skeleton had two holes drilled into the lower jaw-bone to drain an abscess in the root of the first molar.

We do not know if Old Kingdom dentists pulled teeth but we do know that their Coptic successors commonly practised tooth extraction 'by the iron' after first applying an analgesic containing hellebore to the patient's cheek, or a balm containing *malabathron* (wild fennel?) and cantharides to the root of his tooth.

Many of the remedies in the Papyrus Ebers dealing with the gums (which have no special name in Egyptian and are therefore described as 'teeth') are prescribed with a view to 'strengthening' the tissues and 'expelling the ulcer' (Pap. Eb. LXXXIX)—no doubt a reference to stomatitis ulcerosa. In other words, Egyptian dentists were stomatologists-cum-odontologists.

THE EYES

Eye diseases have forever been one of the greatest scourges of Egypt —the heat, dust and flies all help to spread them. No wonder that Egyptian oculists thrived under the Pharaohs and that their fame spread far across the frontiers. The section of the Papyrus Ebers called 'Diseases of the Eye' contains more than a hundred remedies, most of which, while without great inherent interest, nevertheless enable us to assess what Egyptian physicians knew about the subject.

It appears that they were practically ignorant of the internal structure of the eye, never even suspecting the existence of the conjunctiva, the cornea, the crystalline and vitreous humours, the retina, and the optic nerve. Even so, they managed to identify a certain number of eye diseases.

The affections of the eyelids and eyelashes mentioned in the Papyrus Ebers were undoubtedly ciliary blepharitis, trichiasis, and ectropion. Blepharitis was treated with ointments or liquids containing mainly olibanum, chrysocoll, powdered colocynth, and acacia leaves. This is how the remedy was administered: '(The mixture) is put into water; it remains during the night in the dew, is strained and herewith (the eye) is bandaged for four days. Another lection: thou shalt instil it by means of a vulture's feather' (Pap. Eb. LVI). In the case of trichiasis, the application of the ointment was followed by the removal of the lashes, a method used to this day. Another remedy: 'Gall of *ujat*-bird, a straw is moistened therewith and applied to the place of the hair, after it has been pulled out' (Pap. Eb. LXIV). Ectropion, called 'eversion of the flesh', a frequent complaint in Egypt, was treated correctly with astringents, *e.g.* chrysocoll, frankincense, and red ochre (Pap. Eb. LXIII).

2 The main disease affecting the conjunctiva was trachoma, also known as Egyptian ophthalmia. This rather widespread complaint was generally treated with natural and appropriate substances. For example, 'Remedy to expel trachoma in the eyes: stibium, red

ochre, yellow ochre, red natron, are applied to the eyelids' (Pap. Eb. LXVII). It was also treated with gall of tortoise and laudanum. Pterygium, a triangular patch of mucous membrane growing on the conjunctiva, was treated in various ways, including the application to the eye of a compound of pelican's dung, northern salt and frankincense (Pap. Eb. LXIX). Another eye disease treated by physicians was called 'grain in the eye', and might well have been pinguicula, a small yellowish-white patch situated on the conjunctiva between the cornea and the canthus of the eye. Finally, injuries affecting the conjunctiva, together with the sclerotic and the choroid, were bandaged with balms or ointments for a few days.

The iris, though known, was given no special name. We know that Egyptian physicians treated what could only have been iritis, and another ailment very much like mydriasis, *i.e.* the permanent dilatation of the pupil. Hence they prescribed a 'remedy to contract the pupil of the eye', namely, chip of ebony, sulphide of arsenic from Upper Egypt, pounded with water and applied very often to the eyes' (Pap. Eb. LVII).

3 Of the diseases of the cornea and the crystalline humour, both leucoma corneae and cataract are mentioned. 'White spots' on the cornea were treated with gall of tortoise and magic; magic was also one of the chief cures for what the Papyrus Ebers (LX) calls 'water-suffusion of the eye' (cataract). It was the Greeks who first used surgical methods for dealing with cataract.

4 Although they never identified the retina, the Egyptians treated hemeralopia (night-blindness), a symptom of its pigmentary degeneration. The London Medical Papyrus (35) suggests the following remedy: 'Ox-liver placed over a fire of grain or barley stems and suffused with the vapours they emit, the resulting liquid to be pressed on the eyes.' A remarkable remedy, when we consider that raw liver and liver extracts, which are rich in vitamin A, have remained the orthodox treatment for hemeralopia.

Degeneration of the retina and of the optic nerve were the causes of many cases of complete blindness. All the suggested remedies smack of magic, a clear sign of the failure of more mundane methods. Thus the Egyptians believed that by pouring the humour of a pig's eye into the ear of a blind man (Pap. Eb. LVII) they could replace a sick organ by a healthy one. The ear was chosen since it communicated to the eye through a 'vessel'. Blindness was deemed a divine chastisement; hence an inscription discovered on a stele: 'I am a man who has sworn falsely by Ptah, the Father of Truth; he made me to see darkness in the light of day.' Clearly therefore, only the gods could restore sight, and only their forgiveness, obtained through prayer, could work a cure for blindness.

GYNAECOLOGY

All the medical papyri refer to diseases of women, an important branch of medicine in any country, but particularly in one like ancient Egypt, where child marriages, frequent pregnancies, bad hygienic conditions and pre-natal neglect exposed women to inordinate risks.

1 Diseases of the uterus seem to have been particularly common. Prolapses were sometimes treated by means of pessaries, but more often with poultices applied to the hypogastric region, and with strange fumigations: 'dry excrement of men is placed on frankincense, and the woman is fumigated therewith' (Pap. Eb. XCIV). Another remedy: 'An ibis of wax is placed on charcoal, and let the fumes thereof enter her vulva.' The main symptom of metritis is described correctly as a burning sensation, and treated by an injection into the vulva of ammi and rush nut ground with oil (Pap. Eb. XCVI). 'Contractions of the womb' were treated by injections with frankincense and celery ground with oil, or with hemp ground in honey, or again with obscure fruit or plant juices. Cancer of the uterus, accompanied by a smell which the Kahun Papyrus likens to that of roast meat, was treated 'homoeopathically': 'What smell dost thou emanate? (the physician asked the patient). If she tell you: I smell of burnt meat . . ., thou shalt fumigate her with all kinds of burnt meat each having the same nature as her smell' (Pap. K. 2). Needless to say, the remedy could not have proved very effective.

The Egyptians knew nothing about the functions of the ovaries— not surprisingly when we consider how little even Hippocrates knew about them. Even so, they did mention visual complaints caused by menstrual troubles, *e.g.* sclerokeratitis, gonococcal iritis, and cephalea. The common treatment was fumigation and injections, and the Smith Papyrus adds the application of ointments.

2 The Papyrus Ebers alludes vaguely to diseases of the breast, and suggests two remedies, one of which is an incantation. The Berlin Papyrus mentions a swelling of the breast but does not state whether it was due to retention of milk, mastitis, or a tumour. The suggested cures are poultices containing various ingredients.

3 Contraception is mentioned in the Berlin Papyrus (192), which suggests a method of fumigation to prevent pregnancy. The Papyrus Ebers suggests measures 'to make a woman cease to become pregnant for one year, two years, or three years'. Such measures could not have been called for very often, since the Egyptians were very anxious to have large families. Barren women would frequently implore the dead to intervene on their behalf, and such prayers are depicted on many engravings. Egyptian women were also much interested in sex-determination, and suitable methods are suggested

by the medical papyri. Some of these methods found their way into Greek medicine and into modern superstitions. Urinoscopy was the best-known of these prophetic 'techniques':

Method to discover whether a woman will bear children or not: (Thou shalt place) barley and wheat (into two linen bags) which the woman shall water with her urine every day; likewise thou shalt place dates and sand into the two bags. (If) the barley and the wheat alike will sprout, she will bear children; if the barley will sprout (first) the child will be a boy, if the wheat will sprout (first) the child will be a girl. If (neither) will sprout she will bear no children. (Berl. Pap. 199.)

Another method for determining fertility rather than sex was the following:

Other means of settling (the same question): Let the woman keep within the frame of a door, if thou shouldst find that one of her eyes resembles that of an Asian and the other that of a Nubian, she will not bear children; if both are of the same colour, she will bear children. (Berl. Pap. 198.)

Yet another method (Carlsberg Papyrus No 4) was also mentioned by Hippocrates in his Treatise on Sterile Women: 'Method to distinguish a woman who will give birth to children from one who will not: Thou shalt cause a moistened clove of garlic to remain in her vulva throughout the night, if the smell of the garlic passes into her mouth, she will bear children, if it does not, she will never bear children.'

4 Parturition is not described by any of the medical papyri. However, the Papyrus Ebers mentions the subject in passing, as follows: The woman should squat naked on a mat, and inject warm potsherd ground in oil into her vulva, or else imbibe a drink of date-wine, northern salt, and oil 'at finger warmth' to speed the delivery. Other remedies were ointments and bandages, compresses, poultices, and vaginal suppositories. In particularly difficult deliveries, force had to be used. Thus a mummy of a young woman with an abnormally narrow pelvis shows a tear caused by violent outside intervention during birth.

A Ptolemaic bas-relief on a temple wall in Armant (no longer extant) represented a birth-scene. The woman, called the 'Mother of Rē', was shown squatting naked on the ground, like any mortal. Birth is also mentioned in the Westcar Papyrus which describes the various stages of the birth of triplets. Goddesses, acting as midwives, are shown assisting in the birth of the future founders of the 5th dynasty: 'Then Isis placed herself before (the woman), Nephthys behind her, and Heket speeded the birth. . . . The child then slid into her hands . . . they washed it having cut its cord and placed it into a cot made of bricks. . . .' The birth of the other two is described in the same terms, and we are told that, after her confinements, the mother purified herself for fourteen days.

Pre-natal prognoses went hand in hand with post-natal determinations of a child's viability. 'Cognizance of a child on the day of his birth: if he says *ny* this indicates that he will live, if he says *am̃by* this indicates that he will die. Another cognizance: if his voice of moaning is heard this indicates he will die; if he turns his face downwards this also indicates he will die.' (Pap. Eb. XCVII.) The Egyptians were greatly concerned with child welfare, tested the mother's milk, and dealt with early bladder complaints, children's coughs, abnormal crying, and teething. Teething troubles were treated with cooked mice, a 'remedy' prescribed also by Greek, Roman, Arab, and even sixteenth-century English physicians.

Egyptian, unlike Israelite boys, were not circumcised eight days after they were born. Odd texts, the bas-reliefs in Sakkara and in Karnak, and inscriptions from Beni Hasan and Naga-ed-Dir suggest that circumcision was deferred until the age of puberty, and that even then it was not universally practised. According to Dr Jonckheere, the Egyptians freed the glans by splitting the prepuce and did not perform full peritomies.

SURGERY

The Smith Papyrus is unique in that, far from being a mere collection of remedies, it is a very careful, near-scientific treatise on bone surgery and surgical pathology. It discusses forty-eight cases of wounds, including superficial injuries, perforations, and fractures.

The papyrus begins with an examination of wounds in the head, and then goes on to discuss compound fractures of the skull and the nose, a perforation of the temple, a slit in the outer ear, a fracture of the mandible, wounds and bruises of a cervical vertebra, fractures of a clavicle and a humerus, tumours and wounds in the breast, sprains of the sterno-costal articulations, fractured ribs, a gaping wound in the shoulder, *etc.*

We have seen how head wounds were treated; let us now examine how the Egyptian surgeons dealt with dislocations:

(Title). Instructions concerning a dislocation in his mandible. If thou examinest a man having a dislocation in his mandible, shouldst thou find his mouth open (and) his mouth cannot close for him, thou shouldst put thy thumbs(s) upon the ends of the two rami of the mandible in the inside of his mouth (and) thy two claws (meaning the remaining fingers of both hands) under his chin, (and) thou shouldst cause them to fall back so that they rest in their places.

(Diagnosis). Thou shouldst say concerning him: one having a dislocation in his mandible. An ailment which I will treat. (Treatment). Thou shouldst bind him with *ymrw* (and) honey every day until he recovers.

(Smith Pap. 25.)

The mineral substance called *ymrw* was possibly a disinfectant. Naturally the 'binding' was applied only after the dislocation had been reduced by a method that was also that of Hippocrates and that continues to be common surgical practice.

An extremely grave case, the dislocation of a cervical vertebra, was diagnosed as follows:

(Title). Instructions concerning a dislocation of a vertebra of (his) neck. (Examination). If thou examinest a man having a dislocation of a vertebra of his neck, shouldst thou find him unconscious of his two arms (and) his two legs because of it, while his phallus is erected because of it, (and) urine drops from his member without his knowing it; his flesh has received wind [abdominal tympanism]; his two eyes are bloodshot [subconjunctival haemorrhage]; it is a dislocation of a vertebra of his neck extending to his backbone which causes him to be unconscious of his two arms (and) his two legs. If, however, the middle vertebra of his neck is dislocated, it is an *emissio seminis* which befalls his phallus. (Diagnosis). Thou shouldst say concerning him: One having a dislocation in a vertebra of his neck while he is unconscious of his two legs and his two arms, and his urine dribbles. An ailment not to be treated.

(Smith Pap. 31.)

The dislocation was clearly incurable, and hence no treatment was prescribed. The observation that paralysis of the arms, the legs, of the vesical sphincters on the one hand, and *emissio seminis* on the other, are produced by dislocations of characteristic cervical vertebrae, speaks very highly of the Egyptian surgeon's acuity.

Chest wounds were diagnosed and treated in the following way:

(Title). Instructions concerning a wound in his breast. (Examination). If thou examinest a man having a wound in his breast, penetrating to the bone, perforating the *manubrium* of his *sternum*, thou shouldst press the *manubrium* with thy fingers (*although*) he shudders exceedingly. (Diagnosis). Thou shouldst say concerning him: 'One having a wound in his breast penetrating to the bone, perforating the *manubrium* of his *sternum*. An ailment which I will treat.' (Treatment.) Thou shouldst bind it with fresh meat the first day, thou shouldst treat it afterwards (with) grease, honey and lint every day, until he recovers. (Smith Pap. 40.)

These case histories are not only remarkable because they were based on shrewd examinations, diagnoses and prognoses, but above all because they show us that Egyptian surgeons used procedures many of which have stood the test of time, including the use of lint and of bindings resembling adhesive plaster. Moreover, the Egyptians were the first to have tied the lips of wounds with sutures, and to have supported fractured limbs with wooden splints covered with linen.

Other Egyptian inventions were the use of brick supports (see above) for holding cases with head injuries in a vertical position, of wooden tubes to allow tetanus cases to take in nourishment, and finally the fire-stick, which was rotated rapidly in a block of wood until it caught fire, to be used as a kind of cautery. The Papyrus Ebers mentions the heating of a lancet for cutting out tumours, and which might have served as haemostatic forceps.

Egyptian surgeons never prescribed medicaments, and on two occasions the Smith Papyrus makes a special recommendation that the patient be left to his normal diet.

PHARMACOLOGY

Most critics of Egyptian pharmacology have been unnecessarily harsh, dismissing that branch of Egyptian medicine as purely demoniacal or excremental. In fact, we must distinguish two categories of prescriptions: those based on magic alone, and those compounded by practising physicians.

Only a magician could have prescribed 'laundry water' against pains in the back of the neck or in the eyes. Magic, too, was responsible for the entire range of excremental medicaments, such as pelican droppings or crocodile dirt (Pliny's *crocodilea*) against pterygium, or cataract. *Crocodilea* were also used for determining the fertility of women. Hippocrates followed in the footsteps of his Egyptian forerunners when, adapting the method to the needs of his more refined compatriots, he substituted scents for the various excrements but kept essentially to the method. Dried human excrement was used for treating prolapse of the uterus, and flyspecks scraped from walls for combating alopecia, trichiasis, for 'curing' ailments of the breast, for compounding vaginal suppositories and for stilling the cries of children. Urine, too, played its part, and we saw that the urine of an impuberal boy was thought to cure parasitic haematuria.

Other magical procedures were based on transference, *e.g.*, rubbing migraine into the head of a catfish, or pouring the 'humour' of a pig's eye into the ear of a blind man. The last cure had to be accompanied by an incantation: 'I have brought this which was applied to the seat of yonder and replaces the horrible suffering' (Pap. Eb. LVII).

How was it possible for physicians living at the same time as the accomplished surgeons who compiled the Smith Papyrus, to have prescribed primitive remedies which smack of rank barbarism? The answer must be sought in their innate conservatism and respect for old traditions. However, we must remember that they frequently combined magical with more effective remedies. Thus the remedy for stilling the cries of children was not flyspecks alone, but poppy seeds as well.

Natural remedies consisted largely of plants, and involved all the trees and bushes of Egypt, and many from abroad, *e.g.* acacia, sycamore, palm, carob tree, juniper, pomegranate, persea, fig, ricinus; all the edible and aromatic plants and herbs, such as cucumber, melon, colocynth, celery, garlic, onion, pea, poppy, cypress, wheat, spelt, corn, barley, millet—their leaves, seeds, fruits, resin and juice, as well as grape and date wines.

Other remedies were derived from the animal kingdom: grease, fresh meat (particularly in surgery), gall of ox, tortoise, goat and pig; ox and cat liver; fat of lion, crocodile, hippopotamus, cat, serpent, ibex, ox, oriole and goose; blood of ass, ox, pig, dog, goat, lizard and bat; human, cow's and sheep's milk; honey (mentioned on almost every page of the Papyrus Ebers) and beeswax. Fish and reptiles were also used.

Minerals, too, loomed large on the Egyptian medical horizon, including arsenic, copper, alabaster, malachite, natron, mineral oil, silica, flint, chrysocoll, hydrated copper silicate (green eyewash), and galena (black eyewash). In this connection, we might mention that galena (native lead sulphide), rather than antimony, was the basis of Egyptian eye-shadow.

In inscriptions, the ingredients of the various remedies—potions, electuaries, ointments, bandages, poultices, enemas, fumigations— were generally marked with a vertical stroke, showing that they were to be used in equal parts. Other dosages were given in fractions of the *hekat*, the smallest being the *ro*, which was equal to $\frac{1}{320}$ of a *hekat* (15 cc.). All prescriptions were therefore measured rather than weighed, and it was the Greeks who substituted weights for measures and thus gave pharmacology an immense impetus.

What was the therapeutic value of Egyptian remedies? Clearly some were far superior to magical pills—so much so that many of them are used to this day, such as castor oil for treating and stimulating the scalp, and as a purgative. Thousands of years ago, Pharaonic physicians were already prescribing aromatic inhalations and fatty diets against respiratory ailments. However, Egyptian remedies were more or less ineffective; at best, many of them had purely analgesic properties. Moreover, some of the prescriptions which proved their value did so by the presence of an unsuspected ingredient which, nowadays, we should use by itself. Thus, if modern physicians prescribe liver extract against hemeralopia, they do so because they know that hemeralopia is caused by avitaminosis and that liver is rich in vitamin A; the Egyptians simply hit on liver empirically. The same is true of the treatment of eye diseases with the bile of birds, pigs, and tortoises, which we now know to be a source of cholic acid, the basis of cortisone. Again, the blood of bats went into the making of an ointment applied to the eyelids of people suffering from trichiasis. (The Copts subsequently substituted bat urine, and the Chinese used bat excrement for the treatment of all kinds of eye diseases.) It is now known that the excrement and probably the blood of bats contains a much larger quantity of vitamin A than, for instance, does cod liver. Since the ancients had no means of synthesizing pure vitamins they had to obtain them in the natural state, often combined with toxic substances. In fairness, therefore, we cannot simply dismiss out of hand those Egyptian remedies that strike us as preposterous. For, among the many prescriptions based on magic, superstition, custom and ignorance, there were some with markedly curative properties.

'In pharmacology and in medicine alike, we must give the Egyptians credit for having made what real discoveries they did, some thirty centuries before our time.' What we have learned since Maspero wrote this sentence in 1876, shortly after the publication of the Papyrus Ebers, has only caused our respect for Egyptian physicians and particularly for their surgeons to grow. Egyptian bone surgeons deserve our fullest admiration for their good sense, their methodical approach, and their ingenuity; like Egyptian sculptors, they attained a peak of skill during the Memphitic period. As for the physicians, if, like Molière's doctors, they adhered too closely to the opinion of their elders, and if they showed a lack of courage and of curiosity, they nevertheless paved the way for Greek medicine, and hence for Western medicine as a whole.

BIBLIOGRAPHY

General Works

A. ERMAN and H. RANKE, *La civilisation égyptienne*, Paris, 1952.
S. R. K. GLANVILLE, ed., *The Legacy of Egypt*, Oxford, 1942.
A. REY, *La science orientale avant les Grecs*, 2nd ed., Paris, 1942.
G. SARTON, *A History of Science*, I, Cambridge (U.S.A.), 1952.

Exact Sciences

An excellent bibliography of books and papers devoted to the exact sciences in Egypt will be found in IDA PRATT, *Ancient Egypt, Sources of Information in the New York Public Library*, New York, 1925 and 1942. Vol. I (1925) discusses the calendar (pp. 162–167), astronomy (pp. 220–222), mathematics (pp. 229–230) and metrology (pp. 233–236). Vol. II (1942) deals with publications from 1925 to 1941 (calendar, pp. 121–122; astronomy, p. 168; mathematics, pp. 174–175; metrology, pp. 178–179).

Hence we shall mention only the most important sources:

T. E. PEET, *The Rhind Mathematical Papyrus*, Liverpool, 1293; *Mathematics in Ancient Egypt*, Manchester, 1931.

A. B. CHACE, H. P. MANNING, R. C. ARCHIBALD and L. S. BULL, *The Rhind Mathematical Papyrus*, Oberlin, Ohio, 2 vols., 1927–29.

O. GILLAIN, *L'arithmétique au Moyen-Empire*, Brussels, 1927.

K. VOGEL, *Die Grundlagen der ägyptischen Arithmetik*, Munich, 1929.

W. W. STRUVE and B. A. TURAJEFF, Mathematischer Papyrus des staatlichen Museums der schönen Künste, *Quellen und Studien zur Geschichte der Mathematik*, Part A. I, 1930.

O. NEUGEBAUER, *Die Grundlagen der ägyptischen Bruchrechnung*, Berlin, 1934; *Vorgriechische Mathematik*, Berlin, 1934; *The Exact Sciences in Antiquity*, Providence, R.I., 1957.

R. A. PARKER, *Calendars of Egypt*, Chicago, 1950.

O. NEUGEBAUER and R. A. PARKER, *Egyptian Astronomical Texts*, I: The early decans, London, 1961.

J. R. NEWMAN, *World of Mathematics*, 4 vols., London, 1960.

J. F. SCOTT, *A History of Mathematics from Antiquity to the Beginning of the 19th Century*, London, 1958.

B. L. VAN DER WAERDEN, *Science Awakening*, Groningen, 1954.

See also the recent articles by J. J. CLÈRE in Kêmi, *Revue de philologie et d'archéologie égyptiennes et coptes* X, 1949, pp. 4 ff., and in *Journal of Near Eastern Studies* IX, 1950, pp. 143 ff.

Medicine

J. H. BREASTED, *The Edwin Smith Surgical Papyrus*, Chicago, 1930

E. CHASSINAT, *Le Papyrus médical copte*, Cairo, 1921.

W. R. DAWSON, *Magician and Leech*, London, 1929.

B. EBBELL, *The Papyrus Ebers* (translated), Copenhagen–London, 1937.

G. ELLIOT-SMITH, *The Royal Mummies*, Cairo, 1912.

H. GRAPOW, *Untersuchungen uber die altägyptischen medizinischen Papyri*,

Leipzig, 1936; *Grundrisse der Medizin der alten Ägypter*, Berlin, I, 1954, II, 1955.

F. LL. GRIFFITH, *Hieratic Papyri from Kahun and Gurob*, London, 1898.

DR F. JONCKHEERE, *Une maladie égyptienne: l'hématurie parasitaire*, Brussels, 1944; *Le papyrus médical Chester Beatty*, Brussels, 1947.

G. LEFEBVRE, *Tableau des parties du corps humain mentionnées par les Egyptiens*, Cairo, 1952; *Essai sur la médecine égyptienne de la période pharaonique*, Paris, 1956.

A. PECKER and H. ROULLAND, *L'accouchement au cours des siècles*, Paris, 1958.

W. WRESZINSKI, *Der Papyrus Ebers* (Umschrift), Leipzig, 1913; *Der grosse medizinische Papyrus des Berliner Museums*, Leipzig, 1909.

R. O. STEUER and J. B. DE C. M. SAUNDERS, *Ancient Egyptian and Cnidian Medicine*, Berkeley, Calif., 1958.

7 The goddess Nūt supporting the sun

8 Circumcision

CHAPTER 2

Mesopotamia

HISTORICAL INTRODUCTION

OUR FIRST RECORDS from Mesopotamia are clay tablets dating back to about 3500 B.C. They were engraved by means of pointed reeds, and the resulting script is called cuneiform, *i.e.*, wedge-shaped. Once engraved, the tablets were left to bake in the sun. Hundreds of thousands of such clay tablets have been recovered, many in an excellent state of preservation.

The first people to have used cuneiform symbols, the Sumerians, were a small nation of unknown origin who inhabited a small region of the lower valley of the rivers Tigris and Euphrates. They were not the first inhabitants of that country, for when they settled there (at an unknown date) they found a highly developed agricultural civilization already in possession. Other Western Semitic nomads were also mixing with the original population, but it is to the Sumerians that we must attribute Mesopotamia's first creative upsurge, and it is due to their intellectual contributions that Mesopotamia saw the rise of a civilization that was to continue right up to the Christian era and to make its influence felt throughout the Near East. The history of that civilization, affected as it was by constantly changing ethnic influences and almost incessant invasions, is extremely complex.

After a predominantly Sumerian period, the Semitic people managed to gain political supremacy towards 2400 B.C. and to retain it for almost two centuries under the Akkadian dynasty founded by Sargon of Agade. That dynasty extended its empire along the great trade routes right up to the Mediterranean, the Upper Euphrates and the Persian province of Elam. Meanwhile the Sumerian inhabitants had lost none of their dynamic vitality. When the Akkadians were vanquished by barbarian tribes it was the Sumerians who eventually liberated the country, in about 2000 B.C. They attained to their fullest material and intellectual heights at that time, and because of their great achievements we are inclined to forget that the Sumerian stock was continually being mixed with Semitic elements. In fact, the settlement in Sumeria of yet another nomadic tribe culminated

65

virtually in the supremacy of the newcomers. Thus, by about the nineteenth century B.C. the Sumerians had completely lost their ethnic identity, though their culture continued to flourish for a long time.

The Semitic tribes reached their Babylonian apogee under King Hammurabi, the great legislator (about 1780 B.C.). Simultaneously, they extended their influence as far as Mari, the central Euphrates, Assyria (then ruled by Shamshi-Adat I), and Susiana. This was doubtless the golden age of the Semitic genius, for, rooted in ancient Sumerian and Akkadian traditions and leavened by new influences, it produced a creative spirit and a spontaneity of expression never quite to be repeated.

However, towards 1650 B.C., the Near East was once again invaded, this time by the first wave heralding the great Indo-Aryan migrations. New races emerged from historical obscurity: Hittites, Hurrians, and Kassites. The Hittites seized Babylon after a brief raid from their empire in Cappadocia, while the Hurrians subjugated Assyria and founded the Kingdom of Mitanni. As for the Kassites, they overran the whole of Babylonia and settled there permanently. There ensued a long period of obscurity from which it took Babylonia a long time, and Assyria a somewhat shorter time, to emerge.

From then on, the history of Mesopotamia was the history of political rivalry between Babylon and Assyria. The vicissitudes of that struggle were often exploited by the Aramaeans in their westward drive towards the Euphrates and by the Elamites in their constant attempts to gain a foothold in the plains. Meanwhile, Assyria pursued a policy of military expansion and made a series of increasingly powerful thrusts, mainly under her great leaders Tukulti-Ninip I (1255–18), Tiglath-Pileser I (*c.* 1100) and Assurnasirpal II (883–59). Assyria reached the height of her power in the seventh century B.C. under the dynasty of Agade, founded by King Sargon, ruling over Nineveh and Babylon alike and thus becoming the most powerful nation of the East.

Then a new Indo-Aryan wave threatened the Western frontiers. Under the combined forces of the Medes, the Babylonians, and the Scythians, Assyria, her strength sapped further by internal strife, finally collapsed in 615 B.C. Rid of its great rival, Babylon enjoyed a relatively short period of renewed greatness, until her capture and subjugation by Cyrus in 538. Under Persian (Achaemenid) rule, the Aramaean language began to supplant the Akkadian in every walk of life, though ancient cuneiform texts were still copied under the Persians (539–330), the Seleucids (312–104) and the Parthians (until *c.* 60 B.C.). Sumero-Babylonian culture had become a relic of the past.

* * *

Before we can make a detailed study of the various aspects of Mesopotamian civilization, we must first solve a preliminary problem. In what way did each of the peoples involved contribute to the development of the community?

Now, the Assyrians never played more than the subsidiary role of recording, compiling and transmitting what the Sumerians had created. Their contribution was, however, very important, inasmuch as the encyclopaedic libraries set up by some kings of Assur and Nineveh (Tukulti-Ninip I, Tiglath-Pileser III and—above all—Assurbanipal) made possible the co-ordination and preservation of the literary and scientific works of previous centuries.

The Kassites played a similar role inside Sumeria, treasuring their hosts' heritage and adapting it with lasting effects.

As for the Hittites and Hurrians, they, too, are known to have borrowed from, rather than contributed to, Mesopotamian thought. The only extant scientific texts in the Hittite language are translations of simple medical writings and elementary mathematical problems. The mathematical translations are full of errors—clear evidence that, far from having contributed to the culture of their time, the Hittites could not even digest the knowledge of their neighbours.

Elam, and especially Susiana, were receptive to Babylonian influences from the earliest times. In particular, some of the mathematical texts compiled by local scribes roughly at the time of King Hammurabi are equal in worth to many clay tablets from Mesopotamia proper. We may even take it that the Susianians had an original way of presenting mathematical arguments, since some only of their methods are expressly said to be of Akkadian origin. By and large, however, Susianian science was merely a reflection of the Babylonian.

Hence, the scientific climate not only of Mesopotamia but of the entire Near East, before the triumphs of Hellenism, may be called Sumero-Akkadian[1] or Sumero-Babylonian. The individual elements which went into this cultural complex are difficult to distinguish, though the study of Mesopotamian systems of notation throws some light on the respective contributions of the Sumerians and the Semitic peoples in that sphere. Apart from the 'lists' which we shall discuss later, all our documentation is too recent to establish exclusive Sumerian primacy in the cultural field. Language alone cannot be used as a criterion, since the earliest quasi-scientific Sumerian texts stem from a period in which the fusion of the two main ethnic groups had become so intimate that it was bound to have repercussions on their means of communication.

[1] The term 'Akkadian' may be used in two ways: 1, to refer to Agade alone, or 2, to refer to all the Semitic elements (Babylonian and Assyrian).

Nor is it any easier to define the purely Semitic contribution, even in the post-Sumerian era. The Semitic elements continued to extend the Sumero-Akkadian horizon all the while, and kept its great influence alive. However, the details of this development are difficult to define.

Except for occasional documents, Sumero-Akkadian texts are anonymous and undated. Most of the tablets found in royal and private libraries are mere copies or collections of earlier works, the dates and authors of which are never acknowledged. Babylonian sources are commonly grouped into three main periods: the Old-Babylonian (eighteenth century B.C.), the Assyrian (seventh century), and the Neo-Babylonian (Seleucid) (fifth and third centuries). But this classification, however authenticated, never implies that the contents of a given text were not based on older material or on oral traditions.

This question of oral traditions brings us face to face with an important historical problem, namely the fact that Mesopotamian scientific texts consisted exclusively of practical hints, lists of references, and worked examples. None of them dealt with theories, doctrines or principles. Does this mean that—as has been suggested so often—the Sumerians and Akkadians were averse to abstraction and that their knowledge was purely empirical? To assume that would show a basic misunderstanding of the real significance of the texts. Clearly, a great deal of abstraction must have gone even into the representation of concrete phenomena by pictograms, let alone by syllabic ideograms, or into the adaptation of the ancient Sumerian syllabary to the radically different requirements of Akkadian phonetics, making it more accurate, and fitting it to the needs of successive periods.

The same is true of the mathematical texts, for while they present solutions without explanations, proofs, or arguments based on any theoretical principles, their very notation implies great powers of abstraction.

Similar considerations apply to most other spheres of recorded Mesopotamian knowledge, all of which were primarily concerned with studying problems, developing skills, and with practical applications. Theoretical texts dealing with principles or methodology were never written down, probably because they were transmitted by the kind of oral teaching we know to have existed and to have played an important part in all Babylonian schools.

The fact that knowledge is transmitted orally is not necessarily a sign of esoteric practices on the part of a chosen few, jealously guarding their secrets from the profane masses. True, some branches of Babylonian science were of that type, but we have no right to generalize from these. All we can say with certainty about Mesopotamia is that an oral tradition went hand in hand with a recorded tradition, and that we are unlikely ever to obtain any direct evidence of the former. Even so, we must try, from what knowledge we have of Babylonian lists and calculations, to reconstruct the unwritten principles of which they were the concrete applications.

MAGIC AND DIVINATION

To restrict our study of Mesopotamian science to a study of the exact sciences would mean ignoring the basis of their civilization. By recognizing the superstitions so inherent in their thought we not only take the wider view, but also gain a better appreciation of the Herculean task the Babylonians had to perform in order to throw off the shackles with which their minds were originally bound.

MAGIC
It has been said that magical thought is tantamount to primitive thought, and that it played a major role in the everyday affairs of all ancient societies. When it comes to Mesopotamia, that claim is no more than a half-truth.

Sumero-Akkadian thought as we know it was at no time the expression of a primitive mentality. By the time the first extant records were made, the Mesopotamians could look back on a long intellectual past and on a great many technical advances.

Moreover, what we know of Mesopotamian magic shows it to be quite unlike the secret and malevolent witchcraft practised by modern primitive races. No doubt the Mesopotamians, too, had their witch-doctors, for we know that they would attribute many diseases, misfortunes and accidents to evil spells and to sorcery. But it is significant that the sorcerers whom they blamed for their ills were generally foreigners—*e.g.* Scythians and Elamites—and that sorcery was systematically stamped out and punished by law. Official Mesopotamian magic was state-controlled in its constitution, religious in its inspiration and benevolent in its objects. Magic was the prerogative of priests, exorcists and incantators, who derived their powers from the holy city of Eridu and who worked on behalf of the gods, Ea and Marduk, by interpretations, incantations, purifications and magical rites, for good but never for evil.

Incantations were the most important of all their rites, for devils were exorcized by the very conjuring up of their names. Next in importance were magical rites, which had to be specific and were therefore almost innumerable. They were all based on elements common to most forms of magic: colour, the constraining force of knots, the virtue of the circle, attraction or repulsion by specifics, the purifying action of water, the dissolving power of fire, the power of occult forces, and transference.

It would, however, be wrong to take Mesopotamian descriptions of the world of devils too literally. To read them, one might easily believe every demon was thought to have a clearly defined personality and characteristic spells. In fact, a closer comparison of the texts shows a surprising confusion, not only between literary descriptions and pictorial representations of devils but also among the pictures themselves.

In fact, the priests had probably gone beyond popular superstitions and popular pictorial ideas to arrive at a spiritual vision of the world, all the elements of which, animate and inanimate alike, were endowed with consciousness and volition. The universe was built on forces tending either towards divine harmony or towards chaos. The temporary success of the latter was the cause of all misfortunes, and affected even the gods themselves.

The Semitic people, on the other hand, rejected the notion of blind fate, and looked upon all diseases as divine punishments. For them, the problem of evil introduced factors largely ignored by the Sumerians, namely, direct human responsibility and divine retribution.

The Sumerians held that their priests alone, protected as they were by the gods, could brave the mysterious and often evil forces pervading the universe. Their main task was to predict the presence of these forces from omens and to tame them in good time, or even to use them to advantage.

By observing these omens carefully, Babylonian priests were thus unwittingly blazing the path for science. There is no need to mention the many pertinent comments on the role of magic in the development of scientific thought,[1] but what must be stressed is that Mesopotamian magic was an independent scientific and sacerdotal discipline, precise in its principles, its applications and its methods, and not a universal system governing all branches of knowledge.

A history of science is not the place to discuss religious problems in detail. Undoubtedly the Sumerians and Babylonians could not conceive a godless universe, but they never looked upon their religion as an all-embracing scientific doctrine. All they required of it was that it provided them with a cosmogony, the main principle of which was that the world had been created out of water. Before that time, the gods had been born out of chaos and had gradually assumed their individuality. Then, after a long struggle, order was established by the 'young gods', one of whom, the demiurge, created the earth and the men upon it, placed the stars in the heavens, and set them into

[1] See, for instance, A. Rey: *La science orientale avant les Grecs*, pp. 40–47.

motion. Other religious myths told of man's original increase, of his almost total destruction by the Flood, of his new start in life and his gradual development from savagery to civilization, through the awakening of his intelligence.

The many claims that religion or magic also played a privileged role in Mesopotamian attempts to understand and explain the phenomenal world must be rejected. They believed in divination, it is true, but this was quite independent of their activity in listing and classifying the data of experience.

DIVINATION

The Babylonians considered that the field of divination was almost illimitable, and that everything in the whole universe might well represent a premonitory sign. Man's fate was governed inexorably by the total destiny of the cosmos, and all divination was based on the belief that phenomena recurred in cycles and that human actions must be made to fit them. Thus the art of divination was to record as fully as possible the associated elements that went into the making of any given situation, so that the detection of one element would become evidence for the presence of the others. Hence the emphasis on unusual or strange phenomena: they were the most easily discernible of all.

Divinatory literature was divided into various classes according to whether it dealt with oneiromancy, astrology, haruspicy, hepatoscopy, lecanomancy, physiognomy, or any of the other related disciplines.

Most of these need not concern us, except to note the accurate observations that went into them. There is no doubt that the study of the normal and abnormal behaviour of domestic or wild animals, of normal and abnormal plant phenomena, of peculiar minerals, strange stellar constellations, and even of the relationship between the physical appearance and the character of men, was bound to develop a sense for accurate detail.

ASTROLOGY

It is generally held that astrology was the most typical form of Babylonian divination. After all, Chaldean magi were renowned throughout the ancient world as great casters of horoscopes and as unequalled fortune-tellers. In reality astrology as such, and the casting of horoscopes in particular, came to Mesopotamia fairly late in her history, even though the twelve signs of the Greek Zodiac were modifications of earlier Babylonian symbols. The earliest known Babylonian horoscope dates from 410 B.C., when the country was already under Persian domination.

Classical Akkadian astrology is described in a book called *When
Anu, Enlil. . . .* Its four sections are devoted to the respective astral
activities of the gods Sin (Moon), Shamash (Sun), Ishtar (Venus),
and Adat (the god of storms). The book discusses the 'meaning' of
the motion of the stars, of their juxtapositions, and of atmospheric
disturbances. Unlike all other forms of divination, astrology affected
the community as a whole, since its omens heralded famines, epidemics, floods and war, or else good harvests, peace, prosperity, *etc*.
Astrological omens applied particularly to the King, whom the gods
treated as the personification of his people; there were special omens
for victorious campaigns, changes of dynasty, revolutions, sudden
deaths, and peaceful reigns.

Astrology, though based on methods common to all forms of
divination, had a number of specific notions by which it was distinguished as an independent discipline. According to these notions,
the sky contained the 'stations' of the three main gods who governed
the 'celestial roads', which were three belts running, respectively,
along the celestial equator (Anu), the Tropic of Cancer (Enlil), and
the Tropic of Capricorn (Ea). These 'roads' formed the framework
for describing all stellar motions.

Beyond that, Babylonian astrologers assumed that all places on
earth had their counterparts in the sky, and that the two were intimately related. Thus the familiar quadrangle of Pegasus represented
the temple of Babylon, Cancer the town of Sippar, and the Great
Bear the town of Nippur. The surface of the moon was thought to be
divided into four sectors each representing one of the four great
countries, and hence the cardinal points, of the Babylonian world:
Elam, Akkad, Amuru, and Subartu.

The planets had special virtues. Jupiter was held to be the star of
the kings of Akkad, or Assyria; Mars the star of the enemy, *i.e.*
Amuru or Elam. Saturn, the 'sun of the night sky', represented
order, justice and peace, while Venus was either good or bad according to its position in the sky. Mercury was quite particularly the star
of the heir-apparent.

Babylonian astrologers attributed greater importance to the brightness of a planet than to its mere presence. If it was pale, it was under a
'minor influence' and hence boded ill for the King whom it symbolized; if, on the other hand, it shone particularly brightly, the King
and his people could look forward to great fortune.

If Mars drew close to Jupiter, Amuru was about to exert pressure
on the country of Akkad; Jupiter in Sagittarius, or moving towards
Taurus, forbode the death of the king of Akkad, while its presence in
Cancer presaged a peaceful reign and good fortune for the King's
subjects.

Though all these omens applied in all circumstances, they derived their full effects from the moon, the major sign, and particularly from its eclipses.

For the general interpretation of astrological signs, the time of the observation was also of great importance, since months, days, and hours of night were so spread over the four 'countries' that particular 'moments' were all favourable or unfavourable to the Babylonians.

Other 'signs' had to be taken into account as well, including atmospheric disturbances, haloes around the moon, clouds, and thunder. A complex discipline with multifarious elements, Babylonian astrology displayed great strictness of method in all its procedures. Still, we must stress again that, notwithstanding its powerful influence in the court at Nineveh, Babylonian astrology did not come into its own until the decline of the Mesopotamian civilization. Hence i cannot be considered the most characteristic expression of the Babylonian genius.

HARUSPICY

Not so haruspicy, or divination by inspection of the entrails of sacrificial animals. Haruspicy was the prerogative of the *bârûs*, an aristocratic group of priests who had to be of perfect physique and of excellent lineage. The *bârûs* traced their descent and their special skills to a legendary king of Sippar, who had reigned there long before the Flood. Hence, haruspicy must be considered to have its roots in ancient Mesopotamian history, a claim that is borne out by early Sumerian and Akkadian references to it.[1]

Any attempt to define the nature and developments of Babylonian thought must therefore be based on an examination of this form of divination.

Now, we find that Babylonian haruspicy was developed like a true science, for it applied reason to what were thought to be the indisputable facts. Among its accomplishments was a detailed knowledge of the internal organs of sheep, and hence of other animals and man. Haruspicy was based on over ten thousand observations, and the *bârû* may therefore be said to have shown an attitude of mind foreshadowing the exact scientific approach. Not only did he note the appearance of the various organs, their positions, inter-relationship, dimensions, similarities, *etc.*, but he often set the experimental conditions and, in doubtful cases, even fell back on counterproofs. It is thus not unreasonable to see in the systematic observations and interpretations of the Babylonian diviners the birth of the scientific spirit.

[1] Haruspicy was also practised in Etruria. On the possible relationships between Babylonian and Etruscan haruspicy, *see page* 267.

The haruspicers established a technical vocabulary which owed little to the normal language and which, moreover, had a distinctive quality. The various parts of the liver, for instance, were described in a 'functional' way, but this was ominous rather than biological. The examinations, again, were based on special principles which recall the Platonic 'forms'. Stress was laid on such oppositions as 'right and left', 'high and low', 'clear and obscure'. The resulting 'empirical tables' bore positive and negative signs, indicating the presence or absence of significant elements. The *bârûs* were essentially 'combiners' or 'confronters' (as they described themselves), inspecting entrails by a two-fold method: the observation of abnormal signs, and the 'consultation' of all the combined signs as a means of obtaining divine answers to given questions and of establishing the particular 'aura' of an examination. They did not simply gather omens but rather combined them according to fixed rules. Thus, certain ambiguous signs, or the simultaneous appearance of contradictory signs on the right side (*pars nostra*) and on the left side (*pars hostilis*) might completely reverse the results.

While other Babylonian scholars wrote commentaries on all branches of esoteric knowledge, the haruspicers recast all teaching in the light of their own special subject. They collected the written and oral omina of all the various 'disciplines' and grouped them into 'lessons' of given signs with their various interpretations, thus setting up what we might call a critical apparatus. They then tried to reconcile the differences and to explain the contradictions. Thus some paradoxical findings were presented by way of 'Questions and Answers': 'Thou sayest the sign A is good, though if it be found in B thou wilt declare it bad. Answer: In the living sheep, the position of B is reversed, and it is according to that reversed position of B that thou must pronounce judgment: thou must reverse the sign thou hast found in the sacrifice.' It is in the nature of divination to stress traditional rather than observed signs, hence the facts must be made to fit the theories.

When haruspicy of the type we have been discussing first appeared, towards 2000 B.C., it already possessed all its principles, all its methods, and most of its observations. Nevertheless it grew more and more complex with time, not only because it became increasingly the province of specialists jealous of their secrets, but also because it was constantly *controlled* by experiment and often revised accordingly. But the diviner, faced with the errors of his method, would not (as we should do) admit the falsity of his traditional premises, for these were to him sacrosanct. Experimental refutations were taken as evidence that the observation was inadequate or the interpretation erroneous. Hence, observations were necessarily continued until they became 'perfect', *i.e.* until they were found to support the foregone conclusions.

If the haruspicers persevered in their errors, they also held fast to the pursuit of what they considered the truth. Their constant attempts to perfect their observations and interpretations are illustrated by all the extant texts. Babylonian haruspicy remained an 'open science' in the Bergsonian sense of the word, so much so that its body of knowledge grew from century to century. The *barūtu* (divination) series of texts was not definitely completed until the Seleucid period, when the *bârûs* had lost their power—not through popular scepticism of their methods but through the growth of faith in astrology.

THE 'SCIENCE OF LISTS'

Another fundamental aspect of Mesopotamian thought was the so-called 'science of lists'. The invention of writing, and hence the advent of philology, forced the scribes to compile *lists of signs* which we may regard as the first dictionaries. They cannot be said to have done so for practical reasons alone, for the Egyptians, despite the complexity of their own script, felt no need to catalogue their own hieroglyphics until Roman times. Rather, the Sumerian lists reflect a natural inclination to classify all experimental data. Now, these lists were not at first complete dictionaries, for they generally concentrated on nouns and ignored verbs and adjectives. Nouns were chosen in preference because the Sumerians and Akkadians considered nouns, *i.e.* names, synonymous with 'existence'. To name a thing was to create it, and a list of nouns was not merely a list of words but also a symbolic collection of the things they stood for. In short, a good vocabulary provided knowledge of the external world as well as knowledge of writing.

Although these catalogues were never considered to be exhaustive they extended to all branches of knowledge: biology, botany, mineralogy, technology, *etc.* There were lists of utensils, of garments, of buildings, of food and drink; of gods, stars, countries, rivers, and mountains; of human organs, human types, trades, and social classes.

The principles of classification often elude us and, in fact, some of the lists are known to have been mere enumerations. Generally, the names—and consequently the things or beings the lists represented—were grouped in families or species, each represented by a distinctive ideographic symbol.

When the Akkadians took over the art of compilation from the Sumerians, they applied it chiefly to the classification of the vocabulary and to the grammar of the Sumerian language, and hence changed its entire direction. Names which, for the Sumerians, represented external reality became mere words to be translated into the Akkadian language.

While Mesopotamia was still bi-lingual, knowledge of Sumerian was pursued by Akkadian scholars for its practical and cultural value, but Sumerian continued to flourish even subsequently as the religious and scientific language of Mesopotamia.

The simplest Sumero-Akkadian dictionaries gave straight translations from one language into the other, but there were also dictionaries with further columns giving the pronunciation and name of the sign, an Akkadian synonym and explanatory comments.

The Babylonians were also interested in the study of dialects and of foreign languages. Thus they compiled translations of Sumerian words into the Emesal and Emeku dialects, and made comparative lists of Babylonian and Assyrian terms. There were also many Kassito-Babylonian and Hittito-Akkadian dictionaries, and even Sumero-Akkado-Hittite tri-lingual tablets, not to mention the Aramaic glossaries or the Greek transliterations of Akkadian syllabaries.

In lexicography and its related disciplines, the Sumerian 'science of lists' can therefore be said to have laid the foundations not only of philology but also of a great many other subjects of study. Without it there could never have been such branches of knowledge as Mesopotamian historiography, which is based on the dynastic lists. Some of these purport to go back to antediluvian times and the creation of the world, but they mix history and myth together. The rise and fall of the various dynasties is seen as the reflection on earth of corresponding runs of fortune and misfortune of the gods, and the lists also speculated on such topics as the decline of prehistoric epochs and, to a lesser extent, on the periodic repetitions which make up the 'great cosmic year'.

These dynastic lists of the Sumerians were extended and clarified by the Akkadians, who turned them into reliable historical documents. Moreover, by including the history of neighbouring countries the Akkadians laid the bases of general, as opposed to local, history.

A similar development took place in geography. While the Sumerians dealt exclusively with the local topography of their own parishes, provinces, mountains, rivers, canals, lakes and seas, the Akkadians extended their predecessors' geographic horizon. Unfortunately the resulting Akkadian lists lack scientific cohesion, for those that were more than mere catalogues simply reflected their authors' administrative, religious, or commercial preoccupations. Far too rarely they introduced what ought to have been the very fruitful notions of distances and routes.

The Babylonian view of the Universe was a primitive cosmology, in which the earth was a flat disc floating on the ocean. Its centre was Babylon. This conception was the basis of the only map of the world dating from the Neo-Babylonian period (see *fig. 10*). Other maps were purely local, and gave the plans of towns, town quarters, canals, or buildings.

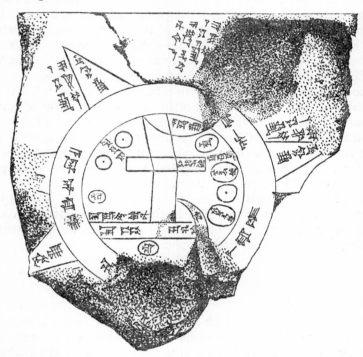

fig. 10 Babylonian map of the World (Cuneiform Texts . . ., *London, XXII, 48*). *On its interpretation, see B. Meissner:* Babylonien und Assyrien, *II, p. 379.*

The only Sumerian, and later Akkadian, lists relating to the exact sciences were the zoological, botanical, geological, and allied compendia. Since they were all compiled on the same principles, we shall look at the zoological lists alone.

Animals were grouped into a given family, for example the 'dog' family, which included dogs, lions, jackals, cheetahs, badgers, otters and others simply because their names were derived from the Sumerian ideogram for 'dog'. Similarly, horses, mules, wild asses, dromedaries, and camels were said to belong to the ass family. A special sign distinguished all fishes; orthopterous insects (grasshopper, cricket, and mantis) were lumped together with birds; eels were classified among the snakes, and tortoises among the fishes.

While these lists were therefore linguistic rather than scientific, they nevertheless show that the Sumerians had the tendency to classify nature by common elements.

The Akkadians took over these lists, modifying and adding to them as they went along. However, their lists, like the Sumerians', can at best give us a glimpse of their linguistic prowess and very little information about their knowledge of the animal kingdom, which must have been fairly wide. We know that the kings of Assur and Nineveh maintained large zoological gardens in the royal parks, and that diviners always made a careful study of the behaviour of savage and domestic animals, the better to interpret their 'omens'. Babylonian fables display a shrewd and often ironical knowledge of animal psychology. Moreover, the mastery with which Babylonian artists depicted the muscles of horses and deer on bas-reliefs is clear evidence that they were well-acquainted with external anatomy, while the profound studies of the haruspicers must have provided a great deal of information about the internal organs.

All in all, there can be no doubt that the 'science of lists' with its catalogues of all perceptible and intellectual phenomena played a fundamental role in the formation and in the development of scientific thought in ancient Mesopotamia.

MEDICINE

The role of medicine in the life of the Mesopotamians has been misunderstood since the days of antiquity. Thus Herodotos claimed that physicians were quite unknown in Babylonia, and modern scholars tend to describe what medicine the Babylonians practised as pure magic.

This traditional view is not altogether surprising, since the texts on which it is based are very confusing. They come mainly from the Royal Library of Assurbanipal or from temple archives, and most of the scribes responsible for their publication were compilers rather than specialists on medical questions. Hence they composed hotchpotches of ancient writings on diseases.

Exorcists and Physicians
When we look at these texts more closely, however, we find that, quite apart from the magical component attributable to the exorcists (*âshipû*), Mesopotamian medicine also had a distinct clinical aspect which was under the control of trained physicians (*âsû*).

Exorcists were consulted only when the disease was thought to have supernatural causes, and there was never any confusion in the minds of the Babylonians about the specific spheres of medicine (*âsûtu*) and magic (*âshipûtu*).

We need not dwell on the magical aspects of Babylonian medicine, since we have already discussed magical principles in general. We shall therefore concentrate on the role of the physicians proper.

The Code of Hammurabi tells us a great deal about their social position and personal qualifications. It gives a list of legitimate fees and also of penal sanctions in cases of transgressions against professional ethics. The permissible fees were such as to leave no doubt about the high regard in which physicians were held, a fact borne out also by the renown which they enjoyed abroad. At the time of El-Amarna (fourteenth century B.C.), for instance, Babylonian physicians travelled throughout the Near East, where, like their Egyptian colleagues, they were paid princely retainers by foreign rulers.

Letters written by or about Babylonian physicians tell us much of their journeys, their private lives and, particularly, their outlook on life, as well as their methods of treatment. They always looked upon medicine as a purely empirical and humane discipline, and their references to clinical examinations, the use of bandages, poultices, lotions, ointments, potions, and massages, are devoid of any magical overtones. Though they sometimes claimed that the gods could speed or retard the cure, they were nevertheless convinced that the cure itself was based on pharmacological remedies.

These letters are interesting from another point of view as well. Their chronological sequence explains much that the mere perusal of professional documents would otherwise leave obscure. Thus, while it is generally held that magic was the most ancient form of medicine, and that rational notions were gradually superimposed upon magic, the oldest of these letters show quite clearly that Babylonian medicine proper had always been quite independent of magic and possessed characteristic methods of its own.

An additional proof of this contention has only just been discovered, namely a medical tablet from Nippur which shows that at the height of the Sumerian period, at about 2000 B.C., physicians were already prescribing remedies which were not in any way connected with rituals, incantations, or appeals to gods and demons. Moreover, the authors were so sure of their treatment that they must obviously have relied on an even earlier tradition.

PHARMACOPOEIA

Compared with exorcists, physicians published a very small number of documents. Hence we must attach particularly great importance to a lengthy Assyrian tablet signed by the physician Nabū-le'ū. The tablet is divided into three columns giving respectively the names of plants, the diseases against which they were prescribed and the method of administering them.

The first column, which enumerates more than 150 medical essences, describes, wherever necessary, the part of the plant to be used (seed, root, shoot, juice, *etc.*), and shows what steps must be taken to gather it properly. The third column explains at what temperature, with what frequency, or at what time of day the substance must be administered, and whether the patient must be put on a fast beforehand.

But though this tablet is by no means an isolated instance of Akkadian medical literature, there is no doubt that it—and similar fragments from various periods—were not nearly as common as the scribes' unsystematic compilations of assorted bits of medical knowledge, which they divided into two groups: diagnostic and therapeutic.

Diagnostic and Prognostic Texts

Mesopotamian diagnostic and prognostic texts, at least from Kassite times onward, are peculiar in that they have been lumped together into one single collection, whose components we have no means of disentangling.

This collection consists of forty tablets or chapters, carefully numbered and grouped into five parts, each with its own title. Despite this care for technical detail, the whole work was obviously put together by a compiler. Exorcists and physicians are treated together, and some paragraphs are obviously of distinct professional origins.

Pure exorcism is discussed first in two tablets giving a list of 'diagnostic' omens. The second part, consisting of twelve tablets, is a kind of medical-cum-magical treatise on symptomatology, based on the condition, colour, and temperature of different organs or parts of the body (numbered from the head to the feet). The diagnosis is made either from isolated symptoms or even from very arbitrarily chosen elements of symptoms, or else from combined symptoms characterizing a given syndrome.

The next two parts consist of ten tablets each, some of which have been lost. Though these tablets are less homogeneous than the preceding ones, they have the advantage of first discussing diseases chronologically, by successive stages, instead of topographically, and then ontologically (as morbid entities).

The fifth and last part of the entire work, consisting of six tablets some of which are also missing, was probably devoted to the diseases of women, particularly those arising out of pregnancy and malnutrition.

The trend of the whole work tells us a great deal about the basic theoretical approach of Babylonian medicine. Medicine was already

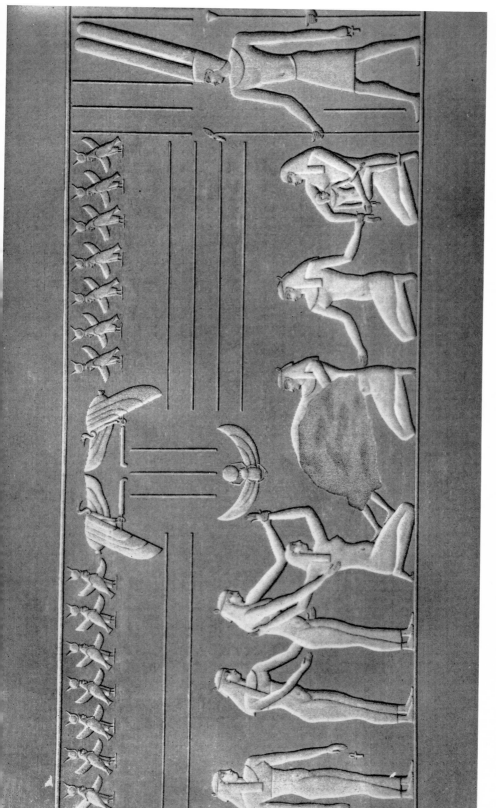

9 The birth of a child

10 Prince Gudea, holding plan and graduated ruler

divided into the four branches of symptomatology, etiology, diagnosis, and prognosis. In essence, all its pronouncements were of the following type: 'If a man be covered with red spots and if his body be black, he has come by it through a woman. It is the hand of *Sin*, and he will recover.' 'If his face be black, he will suffer long and then he will succumb.' Or, 'If his mouth be red he will recover, if it be black he will die.'

The great concision of the last two sentences is a challenge rather than a revelation to us. The prognostic value of such symptoms taken in isolation is nil—to us, as it must have been to the Akkadians. However, the documents show that the Akkadians generally used these indications in conjunction with other clinical signs. Thus we shall find a clinical description of icterus gravis (jaundice), if we care to piece it together from chapters on the eyes, the face, the tongue, the intestines, *etc*. The same method of scattering the description of symptoms is known to have been followed by Greek physicians as well.[1] Had Babylonian medical texts been preserved in their entirety, we should most probably have found that the individual symptoms of any condition were always described out of context.

This very dissection of associated symptoms is but another example of the traditional 'science of lists' and of the influence of divination, which tended, as we saw, to break down and to analyse all the complex data of experience as carefully as possible. This method had the one advantage that it enabled the physician to look up particular references very quickly.

THERAPEUTIC DOCUMENTS

Akkadian therapeutic texts were far more numerous, much more involved, and no less dismembered. For the most part they were compendia of medical and magical prescriptions against given ailments.

Their formulation differs appreciably from that of the prognostic texts. A description of the symptoms is sometimes followed by a diagnosis and more rarely by an etiological account of the ailment, and then by the essential part—the treatment, or rather the various treatments, since icterus, for instance, could be treated in thirty-two different ways. Each treatment is marked off by a dash to stress its perfect independence of all the others, thus enabling us to isolate medical from magical cures, though the two are, of course, never so designated.

Then comes the prognosis which, for most conditions, was favourable, provided, of course, that the patient did as he was told. In the relatively few fatal prognoses, no treatment at all is prescribed; in fact medical intervention in such cases was often formally prohibited:

---

[1] J. Filliozat: *Journal asiatique 1952*, pp. 305–6.

6

'If a man suffer from icterus gravis (*aḫḫâzu*), and if his head, his face, his entire body, and the root of his tongue be black, thou shalt not reach out thy hand to him. For he will surely die, and cannot be healed.'

Although they jumbled together magical and medical texts quite indiscriminately, Akkadian compilers must be given credit for having tried to introduce some logical order into the considerable mass of therapeutic tablets, many of which they arranged into distinct and fairly specialized groups, according either to anatomical regions or, more rarely, to pathological indications.

Of these tablets, the initial series is devoted to the skull and the face, and discusses especially headaches, migraine, and stabbing pains in the temple. A good many of the proposed remedies are of magical character, for the Akkadians blamed a demon, the Spectre, for all these conditions. But side by side with magical applications and incantations they also mention poultices and sedative lotions. The same twin approach is found also in the last chapter of this series, which is concerned with such scalp conditions as tinea, pediculosis, and loss or premature greying of the hair.

Another series dealt with the ears. Though humming or whistling noises were again ascribed to the actions of the Spectre, and hence belonged to the province of the exorcist, some conditions, including otitis, pains in the inner ear and suppurations, were treated by means of oil plugs, instillations, or insufflations:

(If his ears cause him to suffer), thou shalt take water of a pomegranate or an apopanax and thou shalt moisten a tuft of feathers (therewith) to introduce into his ears. Thou shalt do so for three days. On the fourth day, thou shalt remove the tuft from inside his ears which thou shalt then wash carefully. When the pus no longer flows except drop by drop, thou shalt grind alum, and by means of a reed, blow it into his ears.

Ophthalmology was the subject of a relatively large number of Akkadian tablets. Here, too, the 'hand of the Spectre' accounts for some of the symptoms, though the majority of conditions is said to be due to winds, to dryness, to dust, or to pollen. The symptoms are either vague ('If he have sick eyes') or detailed as bloodshot, streaming, inflamed, yellow or copper-coloured. Also noted were impaired vision (temporary blindness, blurring, flashes, *etc.*), pustules on the eyeball or eyelids, and styes.

Leaving aside incantations and magical bindings, we find that physicians generally prescribed ointments, instillations, and eye-baths made of vegetable matter (particularly styrax), of animal fats, used either by themselves or as excipients, and of mineral substances such as salt, copper compounds, antimony, arsenic, and the oxides of

zinc and iron. Sometimes the patients were advised to keep out of the
wind while under treatment, or to avoid the glare of the sun by
boarding up their rooms and staying within.

Among further groups of fairly cohesive texts there is an important
series on respiratory ailments, ranging from simple colds to pulmonary haemorrhage, and including congestion, pleurisy, and
pneumonia. What strikes us at once about this series is the fact that
all the remedies prescribed are pharmaceutical and that there is no
mention whatever of magic. The most common prescriptions were
sedative potions, soothing poultices, emetics, and tracheal infusions.
Here, for instance, is a remedy against coughing: 'Thou shalt boil
the green parts of shepherd's purse and mix them with sugared milk
and purified oil. The patient will fast and then drink (the mixture)
and he will be cured.'

Many remedies are prescribed against 'sick lungs' or 'congested
lungs', consisting mainly of poultices and anti-irritants (linseed,
mustard, frankincense, *etc.*). Coughs were generally treated with
gargles, fumigations, or nasal instillations.

A number of tablets are devoted to hepatic ailments, called 'ailments of the bile'. Patients suffering from such conditions were said to
eat and drink normally but to have choking fits and facial convulsions, or to feel pains in the head, in the nape of the neck, in the
digestive system, and in the feet.

Apart from such general descriptions, the tables give specific
indications of hepatic conditions, including fits of biliousness and skin
disorders accompanied with profuse sweating. There are frequent
references to headaches and giddiness.

Most of the remedies prescribed were purgatives or emetics
administered by way of potions, washes, or suppositories, and consisting chiefly of common salt, aloe, cumin, frankincense and lemon-
grass oil.

The Akkadians called jaundice the 'yellow disease', which they
sometimes diagnosed from the colour of the eyes. Jaundice was normally treated with purgative potions, sometimes in conjunction with
local insufflations of ground tamarisk leaves. Acute or malignant
icterus was called *ahházu*, after the demon of that name, and
generally pronounced incurable and fatal.

Another important series of tables dealt with ailments of the genital
organs, considered as purely local phenomena. Blennorrhagia was
frequently diagnosed from the appearance or consistency of the urine
alone (whitish, thin, resembling beer or wine yeast, varnish, or the
urine of asses). Sometimes these symptoms were said to be accompanied with 'pains in the penis, and in the ribs, retention of urine, and
the appearance of blood after urination', or else with 'local tingling

sensations, spermatorrhea, impotence, and constant suppuration'.

A great many texts deal with urethral constriction, which the Akkadians called 'strangling of the tube'. They must have known that there was a possible connection between such conditions and prostatic hypertrophy (prostatomegaly), since one paragraph suggests that a rectal examination be made. The general symptoms accompanying 'stranglings of the tube' were thought to include pains in the loins, general debility, lapses of memory, nightmares, palpitations, and insomnia.

The same series of texts also discusses rectal prolapses and stones, or gravel (*tittu* = clay) in the bladder.

The remedies, which varied according to the patient's condition, were generally potions, repeated irrigations, massages, and urethral injections by means of a bronze blow-pipe. The various pharmaceutical ingredients included asafoetida, myrrh, galbanum, shepherd's purse, styrax, saltpetre, alum, and eggshell ground in oil; the irrigations were generally based on rosewater, which, with suitable ingredients, was thought to dissolve stones.

A number of tablets deal with gastric conditions, but we must pass over them in silence since far too many of the symptoms listed have not yet been identified. For instance, the Akkadian *libbu* referred equally to the heart, the stomach, and all the inner parts of the body. All we can say with certainty is that the conditions discussed included enteritis, intestinal obstructions, colic, diarrhoea, and probably dysentery. The remedies were a mixture of magic and pharmacology.

We come next to the very important series of tablets dealing with anal conditions (rectal haemorrhages, haemorrhoids, fistulae, recto-stenosis, constipation, *etc.*). Every one of these tablets contains religious and medical allusions, and each condition is described purely topographically. The treatment, which was invariably pharmaceutical, included poultices, soothing ointments, douches and, above all, suppositories. For example:

If a man have pains in his buttocks, if the upper part thereof be injured, if he rise up continuously during the night and suffer throughout the day, thou shalt boil one third of a *qa* of saltwort in beer, add as much strong vinegar again, together with five shekels of salt and five shekels of ammi; thou shalt grind (everything) into oil and pour (this preparation) into his buttocks.

Another passage mentions the treatment of haemorrhoids:

Thou shalt wrap thy finger with a lint steeped in honey, thou shalt then rub (the part) vigorously until blood appears. Once the blood has ceased to flow, thou shalt mix saltwort juice and crushed nigella, to prepare a suppository which thou shalt pass into his buttocks.

The final series of tablets is devoted to the lower extremities. The symptoms discussed include stabbing pains, swellings, ulcers, and numbness. In only a single case is the cause said to be of supernatural origin, pains and weakness in the legs and trembling in all the limbs being ascribed to a fouling of the path of the demon *râbiṣu*. The most important ailments discussed in this section were what the Akkadians called 'thickening' (*kabartu*), and 'muscle-swell' (*sagallu*). *Kabartu* is thought to have referred to œdema or mycetoma, though the term probably applied to conditions affecting legs and feet alike. The disease, the texts point out, may advance as far as the bone, when the latter must be scraped. If 'decay' ensues, the prognosis is invariably fatal. In some cases *kabartu* may be caused by the violation of a taboo: the patient may have unwittingly walked over holy waters or sacred places.

Sagallu was probably gout and podagra in particular, though its symptoms affected the entire leg up to the thigh. Like *kabartu* it could result from the unwitting violation of taboos, and the remedies were therefore a mixture of natural prescriptions (frictions, massages, baths) and of magic incantations.

In all the series of tablets we have so far been discussing, diseases were classified topographically. Other Akkadian series also follow a system of symptomatological or etiological classification. They are, however, far less systematic than the topographical series, and divide diseases into four large groups: demoniac (in particular, those caused by 'the hand of the Spectre'); paralytic; cutaneous; and feverish (particularly the 'dry fevers'). All in all, this series of texts is really no more than a rearrangement of the tablets we have been discussing.

SURGERY

Akkadian surgery is completely undocumented, though we know from the Code of Hammurabi that surgeons were greatly skilled in setting broken bones and that they often performed critical operations. What knowledge of anatomy Akkadian surgeons had could not therefore have been learned from books but must have been acquired by practical training. From isolated references to bronze knives and lancets, and from the fact that the Code of Hammurabi mentions a delicate surgical operation in the ocular region, we can piece together a few corners of the jig-saw puzzle. Thus a simultaneous reference to a bistoury and to an opaque lens seems to prove that cataracts were being treated by surgical means. Medical tablets refer to surgical interventions in cases of severe necrosis, while the lancing of an hepatic abscess and the puncturing of a purulent pleura through the eighth or ninth intercostal space is mentioned in a passage devoted to recuperation. Though there is no direct evidence, we have reason to believe that trepanning was a common practice, since the skulls of three Assyrian soldiers discovered at Lakish had clearly been trepanned. Moreover, one of these skulls showed that its owner had survived the operation for some time.

MEDICAL THEORY

Though it is relatively easy to give a descriptive account of Mesopotamian medical practices, it is much more difficult to define the theory on which they were based.

One thing is certain from the texts: Akkadian symptomatology was an exact science based on observation and the fullest possible detailed description. Moreover, though the physicians were much more interested in symptoms than in general pathological notions, they recognized the need for interpretation or going beyond experimental data in order to formulate criteria by which the correct significance of a given symptom could be evaluated.

The first of these criteria was topographical—the right side (favourable) was distinguished from the left (unfavourable)—in accordance with a basic law of divination. It seemed to fit the case excellently well since many of our organs are duplicated and since some of the resulting prognoses proved correct. Hence the *Book of Prognoses* tells us that physicians would investigate first the right organ, then the left, and finally compare the two. Even unpaired organs were often divided, quite arbitrarily, into right and left parts.

However, it must be stressed that the physician's conclusions from this topographical method were by no means as automatic as the diviner's. Thus the distinction between right and left was often elaborated, or else expressly ignored. The same is true of another diagnostic principle, the criterion of colour so important in magic and divination. Though medicine acknowledged its value in theory, it ignored it increasingly in practice, preferring to speak of jaundice rather than yellowness, and of feverishness rather than redness.

More often clinical criteria were of quite another kind, being based on the association of different symptoms and the time of day or night when they were first observed. Various letters show that physicians usually gave two reports on their feverish patients' progress, one at dawn and one at dusk, which suggests that they realized that many fevers abate in the mornings but run up in the evenings.

Some physicians even held that symptoms were only secondary and vague indications, and that it was far more important to discover the actual point in time when a disease had started.

This concern led them to investigate the characteristic courses of diseases. At least two tablets of the *Book of Prognoses* give an account of diseases from the first to the sixth day, during the first and second months, and for some days thereafter. They show what symptoms may be diagnosed at the beginning of the disease, in the course of its development, and towards its final stages. The tablets mention what improvements or relapses may be expected at what times of day, and what malignant factors may arise in given circumstances.

Akkadian physicians therefore worked with a curious set of criteria: times of day, critical periods, successive phases, and terminal symptoms. Phases are described in a passage dealing with the four kinds of fever:

If a man feel continually hot and cold with equal intensity, from the onset of his illness to its termination, and if, after the heat and sweat have first gone, his members turn hot (once again) and he feels as hot as before, if that heat disappears to give way to cold and perspiration, he suffers from one of the four fevers.

One of these fevers, called *ṭi'u*, had characteristic phases of its own, *viz.* intense headaches, and brief gastro-intestinal attacks. Together with its other listed symptoms, this disease must have been malaria, and there is no doubt that Babylonian physicians had a very accurate idea of its successive phases.

The notion of terminal symptoms is best illustrated by the following passage:

If a man who has lain ill for five days, gives forth blood from his mouth on the sixth day, the disease is coming to an end. (He suffers from) a fever of dryness.

Their interest in symptoms often led Babylonian physicians into making differential diagnoses of apparently similar diseases, for instance:

If the neck of the patient keeps turning to the right, if his hands and feet are clenched (?) if his eyes are closed and turned upwards, if spittle runs from his mouth, and if he snores—he has an epileptic crisis. If he retains consciousness during this crisis, this (diagnosis) is certain, but if he loses consciousness this (diagnosis) is not certain.

Clearly, therefore, by their careful symptomatological observations and by their attempts to interpret clinical signs objectively the Akkadian physicians had taken the first steps towards scientific medicine.

The value of their etiological and diagnostic approach, on the other hand, is much more difficult to assess. The names of many diseases have not been interpreted and Akkadian morbid conditions do not fully correspond with modern nosological descriptions. Thus some Akkadian accounts of epilepsy introduce irrelevant observations, while others show a confusion between epileptic and hysterical symptoms. Similarly, what they called 'dry fevers' were obviously quite distinct pathological conditions.

Again, while Akkadian physicians connected some symptoms with certain supernatural phenomena, such as divine anger, the actions of devils, the spells of a sorcerer, violations of taboos, *etc.*, this connection was not always causal and frequently expressed no more than the idea of predisposing influences. Often that idea was added for mere rhetorical effect, particularly in the many references to 'the hand of a god' or 'the hand of a goddess' with which the *Book of Prognoses* is studded. Thus the 'Hand of Ishtar' was simply thought to affect the actual location, colour, and 'aspect' of a symptom, once it had already appeared.

Similarly with devils, for though they 'struck down', 'seized', and 'touched' all who chanced to cross their path, accounts of their actual effects are often confused and contradictory. Their intervention was rarely considered causal, and was never made the basis of a complete medical theory. We might say that devils were generally blamed for persistent migraine, pains in the neck, buzzings in the ear, nervous tics, and general paralysis, while sorcery was held responsible for intestinal ailments, speech impediments, anorrexia, impotence, excessive salivation, insomnia, and anxiety.

But by far the greatest number of pathological conditions was never attributed to supernatural agents in any way. Most diseases were expressly attributed to such natural causes as cold weather, dryness, dust, wind, putrescence, *etc.*, or to malnutrition, liver upsets, lithiasis, venereal infections, gangrene, and so forth.

While half the *Book of Prognoses* consists of supernatural references, it must be remembered that the names of some demons or gods had become part of the clinical language, much as modern physicians speak of 'saturnine' encephalopathy, *etc.* In fact, even when the physician assumed that his patient was a victim of sorcery or of a devil, his remedies were invariably pharmacological. He apparently left it to the exorcist to worry about the supernatural causes and restricted his own activities to treating the natural effects.

This brings us to the subject of Babylonian pharmacology, which has been described as primarily magical and as based mainly on excremental and other revolting substances designed to expel devils. Recent research, and notably R. C. Thompson's work on Assyrian botany, chemistry and geology, have led to a far better and fairer evaluation. There is no longer any doubt that most of the plants and mineral substances prescribed by Babylonian physicians, particularly their emetics, astringents, laxatives, revulsives, and sudorifics, were administered for their very real medical properties. While most of the remedies contained a host of ingredients whose purpose eludes us, they generally included a number of effective substances, such as fir and pine turpentine, oleander, opoponax, mustard, and hellebore. The favourite 'triplet' was apparently *Artemisia judaica*, balm of Gilead, and Persian fennel.

However, it is quite true that the medical texts also prescribe excremental and allied remedies. In certain magical rather than medical passages, bitter potions, foetid fumigations, or nauseating poultices were undoubtedly intended to expel devils from the patient's body. But again we must not generalize. Certain of these substances (urine, shells, fresh blood of birds, *etc.*) might very well have been chosen for their therapeutic properties. Others again, based on old traditions, were subsequently adopted by the Greeks, from whom they passed into our own folklore.

In this connection we must also mention the considerable role of mystical or symbolic names. From the lexicographic lists we learn that 'human skull' is another name for the tamarisk, 'human bone' for the asafoetida, 'human sperm' for gum-dragon, 'lion fat' for opium, and 'human excrement' for an unidentified plant. Further knowledge of the Babylonian pharmacological vocabulary will doubtless enable us to extend this list and hence gain a clearer understanding of the use of many mysterious Babylonian remedies.

In any case, we must remember that the number of all unusual or excremental ingredients was relatively small compared with the host of vegetable or mineral substances which we now know the Akkadians to have prescribed for their medicinal properties alone. Hence they were rightly renowned throughout the Near East for their herbal knowledge, both as pharmacists and also as compounders of perfumes and ointments. Medicinal essences were the objects of a particularly flourishing trade, and, according to some texts, their manufacture was the task of specialists, possibly under official control. No wonder then that the term 'Akkadian' prefixes the names of many medicinal plants both in antiquity and, to a lesser extent, in modern pharmacology.

MATHEMATICS[1]

All our knowledge of Mesopotamian mathematics is of relatively recent date—it is based on the work of O. Neugebauer (1935) and of F. R. Thureau-Dangin (1920–38).

In the main, Babylonian mathematical texts can be divided into two groups: numerical tables and problem texts. The numerical

[1] M. Roger Caratini, who has written a comprehensive work on Babylonian mathematics, was kind enough to take charge of the sections devoted to Mesopotamian mathematics and astronomy.

tables are much like our own, and consist of columns of numbers in increasing or decreasing order. The problem texts are collections of exercises much like those found in modern school books, though often without full explanation of the steps involved, which were no doubt taught orally. Frequently, successive problems are separated by a single or double stroke, as in one tablet containing 247 problems of the same type, all of which were solved by the same method. (These are problems with one unknown, but with different coefficients.)

Problems of a geometrical type were often accompanied with illustrative diagrams with simple numerical legends, but they were not 'constructions'. These diagrams were never introduced into the actual solutions, and their proportions were often wrong. The Babylonians could obviously make 'correct' calculations from badly constructed models.

Arithmetic

NOTATION

The Babylonians used a system of sexagesimal place-value notation which was unlike any other system used in antiquity. For while all other systems involved repetitions of individual symbols (as in Roman numerals), the Babylonian, like our own Hindu-Arabic system, used positions to express different values of the same symbols. Thus when we write 3,333 we use one and the same symbol to stand for 3, 30, 300, and 3,000. Their system, like ours, has the immense advantage of simplifying the basic operations by turning them into mere routine, and of providing expressions for any number, no matter how big or small.

In addition to this system of notation, the Babylonians also used a cumulative decimal system, though never in mathematical and astrological texts, all of which are based on sexagesimal place-value notation. In that notation, the last space represented the numbers 1–60, the penultimate space multiples of 60, preceded by multiples of 60^2, *etc.* Hence, the Babylonian 327, which we shall write 3,2,7, would be equal to $3 \times 60^2 + 2 \times 60 + 7 = 10,927$, and not to $3 \times 10^2 + 2 \times 10 + 7$ as it is in our decimal system.[1]

The Babylonian system had two shortcomings. First, the symbolism was clumsy, since there were only two signs: one representing 1 and the other 10. Second, it was only in astronomical texts of the Seleucid period that the zero symbol was used, and even here never at the end of a number. The Babylonian astronomers wrote 0,25 but

[1] In what follows, we shall render sexagesimal figures by separating them with a comma. Hence 3,0,21,11 stands for $11 + (21 \times 60) + (3 \times 216,000)$. Fractions are separated from integers by a semicolon, *e.g.*, $0;15 = \frac{15}{60}$; $0;0;15 = \frac{15}{3,600}$; *etc.* Unit fractions are therefore expressed as 0;30, 0;20, 0;15, 0;12, 0;10, *etc.*

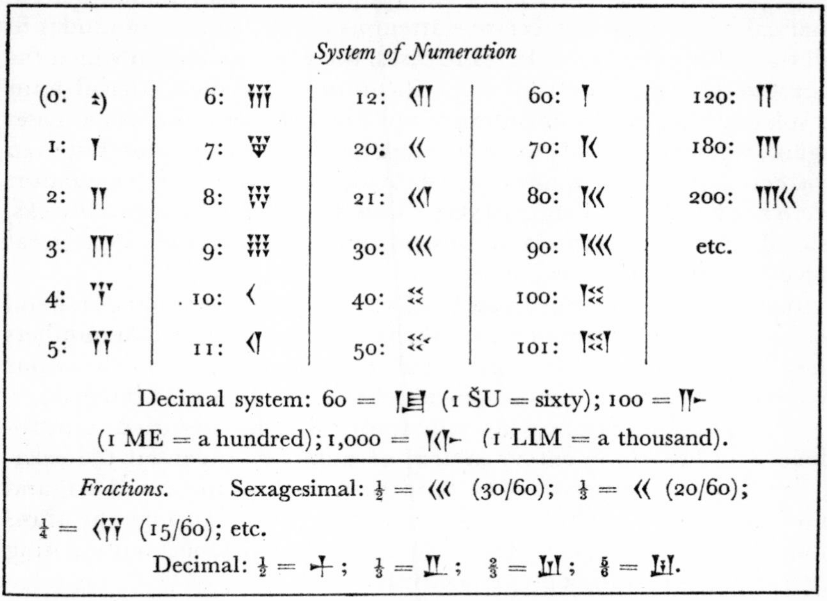

System of Numeration

(0: ᵕ)	6: 𒐚	12: 𒌋𒐖	60: 𒁹	120: 𒌋𒌋
1: 𒁹	7: 𒐛	20: 𒌋𒌋	70: 𒌍	180: 𒌍
2: 𒐖	8: 𒐜	21: 𒌋𒁹	80: 𒐏	200: 𒐏𒌋𒌋
3: 𒐗	9: 𒐜	30: 𒌍	90: 𒐐	etc.
4: 𒐘	. 10: 𒌋	40: 𒐏	100: 𒐕	
5: 𒐙	11: 𒌋𒁹	50: 𒐐	101: 𒐕𒁹	

Decimal system: 60 = 𒋗 (1 ŠU = sixty); 100 = 𒈨 (1 ME = a hundred); 1,000 = �5𒈨 (1 LIM = a thousand).

Fractions.   Sexagesimal: $\frac{1}{2}$ = 𒌍 (30/60); $\frac{1}{3}$ = 𒌋𒌋 (20/60); $\frac{1}{4}$ = 𒌋𒐙 (15/60); etc.

Decimal: $\frac{1}{2}$ = ; $\frac{1}{3}$ = ; $\frac{2}{3}$ = ; $\frac{5}{6}$ = .

fig. 11 Babylonian numerals.

never 25,0, and it would therefore be wrong to consider their zero as having been functionally identical with ours. Still, there is no doubt that the lack of a zero was felt by Babylonian mathematicians even in the Old Babylonian period, for some early tablets left blanks where their successors would have put the special symbol.

The lack of a zero in their earlier texts might have led to a great deal of confusion, since the unit symbol could equally well have stood for 1, for 1,0 (60), for 1,0,0 (3,600), *etc.* However, the resulting ambiguity probably did not bother Babylonian mathematicians overmuch, because they presumably remembered what magnitudes were involved in particular calculations. On the other hand it makes our own task of deciphering their mathematical texts extremely difficult. Thus 12011 might equally well have stood for:

$$1,20,1,1, \ i.e., \ 1 \times 60^3 + 20 \times 60^2 + 60 + 1 = 288,061;$$
$$\text{for } 1,21,1, \quad i.e., \ 1 \times 60^2 + 21 \times 60 + 1 = 4,861;$$
$$\text{or for } 1,22, \quad i.e., \ 1 \times 60 + 22 = 82,$$

not to mention the many other numbers resulting from possible empty spaces between successive powers of 60, or the possible introduction of fractions. Only the mathematical context of some of the problems enables us to read them correctly.

In practice, therefore, every interpretation of Babylonian mathematical texts involves successive attempts to find what magnitudes fit all the given conditions. In some cases, the very manner in which the signs were combined, or the specification of the metrological units involved, simplifies our interpretative endeavours. In other cases again, we must not only work through the entire calculation but even correct some of the figures, for Babylonian (like other) calculators were not beyond making mistakes. Notwithstanding these drawbacks, the Babylonian place-value system must be considered a great development in number theory.

In Babylonia, the use of place-values invariably went hand in hand with the sexagesimal system, so much so that all sexagesimal numbers may be said to have had place-values and *vice versa*, much as our decimal system combines place-values with the first nine integers.

It was the Sumerians who, apparently after having tried to introduce a rather rudimentary system of notation, invented the sexagesimal system, using first the Sumerian symbols for 1 and 10, and later additional symbols for 60, 300, and 3,600. During the third millennium B.C. they added a further two symbols, representing 36,000 and 60^3 (216,000), respectively.

While it is easy to understand how the decimal system developed from counting on the fingers, it is much more difficult to see why Babylonia should have adopted a sexagesimal notation. Various hypotheses have been put forward[1] none of which seems to us to be very plausible.

To complete our account of Babylonian notations, we must add that fractions like $\frac{1}{2}$, $\frac{1}{3}$, $\frac{2}{3}$ and $\frac{5}{6}$ were known in fairly early times. The last two fractions were an original contribution to pre-classical mathematics which had previously relied on unit fractions alone. Unfortunately our documents tell us nothing about the manipulation of these fractions, so that we must pass over this subject in silence.

WEIGHTS AND MEASURES

Babylonian metrological units were remarkable in more than one respect. First of all, their systematic character and the method of converting them into one another were clear evidence of a great concern for mathematical consistency. Thus Neo-Babylonian units were systematically based on decimal, and Old Babylonian units on sexagesimal, multiples and sub-multiples. Another striking fact was the existence of units far too large to be of any practical value (for instance a unit representing some 9,600 acres). The fundamental units of length, capacity, and weight were the *cubit*, the *qa*, and the *mina*.

[1] Cf. particularly F. Thureau-Dangin: *Esquisse d'une histoire du système sexagésimal*, Paris, 1932.

From a ruler shown lying across the knee of the Sumerian prince Gudea, and from comparisons of the base of the 'Tower of Babel' and a cuneiform tablet giving its dimensions, archaeologists have established that the cubit was equal to about 20 inches. Again, a vessel with its capacity marked on the neck showed the *qa* to have been equal to about 14¾ pints, and it was easy to establish from stamped weights that the *mina* was equivalent to about 18 ounces.

The unit of area was the *sar* (or rod), equal to a square with a side of twelve cubits (20 ft. square), but fields were measured in units of capacity, *i.e.* by the volume of seeds required for sowing them.

The complete Sumero-Akkadian metrological system formed a coherent whole, in which the various units were in simple proportions, easily converted into one another by means of simple tables. Thus the *qa* was $\frac{1}{144}$ of the cubic cubit, and the *mina* was the weight of a volume of water equal to $\frac{1}{240}$ cubic cubit.

It is not necessary here to list all the multiples and sub-multiples of each of these units, but we shall describe the units of length by way of example. The sub-multiples of the cubit were the *digit* of $\frac{1}{30}$ cubit, the *ampan* of ½ cubit, and the *foot* of ⅔ cubit; its multiples were the *rod* of six cubits, the *gar* of 12 cubits, the *cord* of 120 cubits, and the *league* of 180 cords (about 6 miles).

Coins were not used by either the Sumerians or the Akkadians, whose legal tender was barley and subsequently copper, silver and (sometimes) lead. Gold, too, was used, under the Akkadian dynasty, but very rarely indeed. In 493 B.C., an edict of Darius I introduced silver coin into the Persian Empire and hence into Babylonia.

SURVEY OF BABYLONIAN ARITHMETICAL KNOWLEDGE

Most of the extant arithmetical texts are simple multiplication and reciprocal tables, reflecting the fact that the Babylonians performed their divisions in two separate stages. To divide a number *m* by a number *n* they would first look up the reciprocal of *n* and then multiply *m* by it, *i.e.*, by $1/n$.

In this connection, we might point out that it is an easy matter to obtain the reciprocal of any number *n* so long as its factors are also factors of the notational base or of any of its powers. Thus any number of the form $2^x \times 5^y$ can be divided into 1 in the decimal, and any number of the form $2^x \times 3^y \times 5^z$ can be divided into 1 in the sexagesimal system. Neugebauer has called such numbers 'regular', and regular numbers are, in fact, the only ones given in the texts. Hence we have no idea what the scribes did when their divisions involved 'irregular' numbers.

The multiplication tables contained the products of 'regular' numbers multiplied by 1 to 20, by 30, by 40, and by 50, from which other products could be obtained by addition. We have no tables giving the products of irregular numbers (excepting 7), and it would therefore seem that by our standards at least the multiplication tables were rather primitive.

The texts also contain tables of perfect squares and of perfect square and cube roots. In addition, we know that the Babylonians had obtained very good approximations of $\sqrt{2}$ and also a method of calculating cube roots not included in the tables.

Different approximations of $\sqrt{2}$ appear on two tablets:

(1) Tablet AO 6484 gives $\sqrt{2} = 1;25$ (sexagesimal notation) $= 1.416$ (decimal notation). This approximation is identical to the one obtained by Heron (*Metrica*, XXV) by putting $\sqrt{(a^2 - b)} = a - b/2a$, where $a = 1,30$ and $b = 0,15$ (sexagesimal notation) though we do not know how the Babylonians arrived at it.

(2) The Tablet YBC 7289 contains a square with the number 30 written against the side, the number 42;25,35 written across the diagonal, and the number 1;24,51,10 to show by what number the side must be multiplied to give the diagonal, *i.e.*, $\sqrt{2}$. This approximation is more accurate than Heron's, for translated into the decimal system it gives $\sqrt{2} = 1.414213$, which is correct to five decimal places. Again, we have no idea how the scribe arrived at this result.

Tablet YBC 6295 shows how to obtain the cube root of any perfect cube n, too large to be found in the tables. The scribe takes a perfect cube p, which must be a 'regular' number (*i.e.*, a number whose reciprocal is a factor of 60), divides n by p and then uses the formula $\sqrt[3]{n} = \sqrt[3]{p} \times \sqrt[3]{(n/p)}$.

Whether such simplifications imply unsuspected mathematical skills in the scribes is a moot point, but the point strikes one forcibly whenever one is brought face to face with the methods and the answers of Sumerian and Akkadian mathematicians.

Our admiration increases further still when we learn that the table texts also contained lists of progressions and tables of logarithms. Judging from them, we are bound to conclude that the Babylonians must have used formulae which they never bothered to explain in writing. Take again Tablet AO 6484, which begins with the following problem: 'If a geometric progression has the ratio two, what is the sum of its first ten terms?' The solution is given without further explanation: 'Double the last term and subtract 1'. In fact, the calculation amounts to applying the modern formula $S = a(r^n - 1)/(r - 1)$ to the special case: $r = 2$, $a = 1$, and $n = 10$. Hence $S = 2^{10} - 1 = 2^a + (2^a - 1)$, where 2^a is the last term.

The tables and the calculations we have been discussing display a sense of order and method which stamps them with an authentic scientific character. In addition, we have the far more theoretical

Tablet Plimpton 322, which was analysed by O. Neugebauer in 1945.

The four-columned text, dating back to at least the eighteenth century B.C., deals with 'Pythagorean triangles', *i.e.* right triangles whose sides are integers. If a denotes the longer and b the shorter leg of the triangle, c being its hypotenuse, we have $a^2 + b^2 = c^2$. Column I gives the ratios of c^2 to a^2; Columns II and III the respective values of c and b; and Column IV numbers the triangles considered from 1–15. Since, in its present state, the tablet represents the right-hand part of a larger text, the original might well have contained an additional column of a-values.

The tablet makes it quite clear that the Babylonians were familiar with the 'Pythagorean' Theorem and that they solved the problems involved by theoretical methods based on number theory. Number theory also entered into their treatment of many elementary arithmetical problems, including the four basic rules and division into equal and unequal parts. For while all the problems were based on concrete examples, they were really solved by (implicit) methods of the kind that would later become classical.

Algebra

To us, algebra is the art of manipulating symbols and formulae, and we might have thought that the Babylonians' lack of such general symbols as 'x' and 'y' would have precluded them from algebraic operations. However, the symbolic aspect of algebra is a fairly late innovation designed to facilitate and widen the scope of earlier techniques. Thus, we may fairly call 'algebraic' those Babylonian tablets in which highly evolved mathematical techniques were systematically applied to problems involving equations of the first and second degree, with one or more unknowns.

Generally, the tablets concerned contain a number of propositions —of the same or of similar type—together with the relevant calculations and answers. None of them gives theoretical explanations of the formulae involved, though the consistency with which problems were treated leaves no doubt that the answers must have been obtained by means of implicit abstractions.

It would be quite wrong to look upon these texts as mere treatises on practical surveying or book-keeping. True, the problems dealt with concrete questions, but they did so only by way of exercises, much as modern school-books do. Thus it is clear that a problem like: 'Six times the area of my (square) field added to $3\frac{1}{2}$ times its side gave 906 (decimal notation); what is the side of my field?' was an intellectual exercise rather than a problem in surveying. Moreover, the fact that this problem is followed by twenty others of the same type shows its didactic character. In that respect, the very arrangement of certain tablets is most suggestive: problems of the same type are divided by double separation marks.

What picture of Babylonian algebra can we reconstruct, then, from the hundreds of relevant texts?

While we have to grant that the Babylonians must have been acquainted with those principles of which their solutions were the practical expression, it would be wrong to assume that the theory of equations was known in Hammurabi's day, simply because they solved certain problems involving equations of the third degree. Often these 'surprising' solutions were merely the results of successive trials and errors which the scribes refrained from discussing.

On the other hand, we have no reason to be hypercritical and must acknowledge that, from earliest times, the Babylonians had some sort of theoretical approach to mathematics. They made constant attempts to rationalize their findings by the systematic organization of tables, the methodological arrangement of problems, the standardization of solutions, and concern with many problems unconnected with everyday activities. The consistent solution of equations could have not been accidental, and the fact that the Babylonians solved second-degree equations much as we do is clear evidence of their mathematical reasoning powers.

In this connection we must make another general observation: unlike the Greeks, who were, above all, geometers, the Mesopotamians tended to reduce all mathematical relations to numbers, and to algebraize even purely geometrical problems. We shall find that they used the same approach in astronomy.

EQUATIONS OF THE FIRST DEGREE
A classical example of Babylonian mathematics is found in Tablet YBC 4652, which, according to its colophon, contained twenty-two examples on the determination of weights. Of these, eleven have been partly preserved and only six can be fully restored. One of them went as follows:

I found a stone but did not weigh it; after I added one seventh and added one eleventh, I weighed it: 1 *mina*. What was the original weight of the stone? The original weight of the stone was $\frac{2}{3}$ *mina*, 8 *shekels* and $22\frac{1}{2}$ *še*.

The first phrase makes it clear that the scribe was presenting a theoretical problem and not a pragmatic exercise. If we call the unknown weight of the stone x, and know that 1 *mina* = 60 *shekels*, and 1 *shekel* = 180 *še*, the problem becomes:

11 Babylonian weights

12 Babylonian astrological tablet

$$\left(x + \frac{x}{7}\right) + \frac{1}{11}\left(x + \frac{x}{7}\right) = 1 \; mina = 1,0 \; (60) \; shekel.$$

Expressed in *shekels*, the solution gives $x = 48;7,30$ (48.125 in decimal notation), which is the very answer obtained by the scribe since $\frac{2}{3}$ *mina* = 40 *shekels*, and $22\frac{1}{2}$ *še* = 0.125 *shekel*. Let us note in passing that the text did not make it clear whether

$$\frac{1}{11}\left(x + \frac{x}{7}\right) \; \text{or} \; \frac{x}{11}$$

was meant; only the answer shows which was intended. This fact is significant, for it suggests that the details of the problem must have been filled in orally.

The following problems involved equations of the same type, though of increasing difficulty. One of them, which introduces subtraction, amounted to:

$$\left(x - \frac{x}{7}\right) - \frac{1}{13}\left(x - \frac{x}{7}\right) = 1,0 \; shekel \; (\text{No. 8}).$$

while another combined addition and subtraction:

$$\left(x - \frac{x}{7}\right) + \frac{1}{11}\left(x - \frac{x}{7}\right) - \frac{1}{13}\left[\left(x - \frac{x}{7}\right) + \frac{1}{11}\left(x - \frac{x}{7}\right)\right] = 1,0 \; shekel \; (\text{No. 9}).$$

Other problems were more complicated still, for instance No. 19:

$$(6x+2) + \tfrac{1}{3}.\tfrac{1}{7}.24(6x + 2) = 1,0 \; shekel.$$

All these problems are clear evidence of the Babylonians' interest in pedagogical lucidity. The texts dealing with problems involving equations with more than one unknown are more interesting still, because they include intermediate calculations which bring out the algebraic skills of the scribes. Here is an example:

Length, breadth. What the length is, the depth is also (except for the co-efficient 12). A box is hollow. If I add its volume to its cross-section, which is 1;10 (1.16 in decimal notation) and if the length measures 0;30 (0.5 in decimal notation), what is the width?

Multiply 0;30, the length, by 12. You will obtain 6 for the depth. Add 1 to 6, you will obtain 7. The reciprocal of 7 cannot be calculated. By what figure must we multiply 7 to obtain 1;10? By 0;10. The reciprocal of 0;30 is 2, you will find it (in the tables). Multiply 0;10 by 2. You will obtain 0;20 (0.3 in decimal notation) which is the width.

(Tablet BM 85200).

The modern interpretation would be: Let x be the length, y the width, and z the depth of the box. Hence its cross-section $s = xy$ and its volume $v = xyz$. Then:

$$
\begin{array}{lrl}
(1) & z = kx & (k = 12) \\
(2) & xyz + xy = p & (p = 1;10) \\
(3) & x = a & (a = 0;30)
\end{array}
$$

Substituting (1) in (2), we obtain

$$xy(kx + 1) = p$$

and hence the scribe's intermediate calculation, $kx + 1 = 7$, obtained by factorization. There remains the problem of finding out by what number $(kx + 1)$ must be multiplied to give p,

i.e.
$$xy = \frac{p}{kx + 1} = \frac{p}{7} = 0;10$$

which gives
$$y = 0;1 \cdot \frac{1}{0;30} = 0;20.$$

This example is typical of the hundreds of others dealing with first-degree equations, none of which mention factorization explicitly, though their solution clearly involves that operation. Similarly, substitutions were never mentioned as such, yet were performed with apparent skill even in second-degree equations which we shall now discuss.

EQUATIONS OF THE SECOND DEGREE

The Babylonian method of solving second-degree equations is best illustrated by a typical example:

I have added 7 times the side of my square to 11 times its surface, to obtain 6;15 (6.25 in decimal notation). Reckon with 7 and 11.

(Tablet BM 13901, probl. 7.)

The injunction to 'reckon with 7 and 11', simply means:

$$11x^2 + 7x = 6;15$$

There follows six lines of calculations which strike the uninitiated reader as so much legerdemain. However, once he breaks them down and applies modern algebraic notation to them, he will find that the Babylonians must, in fact, have used a formula equivalent to

$$x = \frac{-b \pm \sqrt{(b^2 + 4ac')}}{2a}$$

(By putting $c' = -c$, the Babylonian formula becomes identical with the modern one used for solving equations of the second degree.)

This is what the scribe did:

Multiply 11 by 6;15 to obtain 1,8;45 (68.75 in decimal notation). Take one half of 7=3;30 (3.5 in decimal notation). Multiply 3;30 by itself =12;15 (12.25 in decimal notation). Add 12;15 to 1,8;45=1,21 (81 in decimal notation). The square root of 1,21 is 9. Subtract 3;30 from 9=5;30. The reciprocal of 11 is not found in the tables. By what must I multiply 11 to obtain 5;30? By 3;30 (0.5 in decimal notation). 0;30 is the side of my square.

Putting $a = 11$, $b = 7$, and $c = 6;15$, we find that in this calculation

$$11 \times 6;15 = 1,8;45 \quad \text{corresponds to} \quad ac'$$
$$\tfrac{7}{2} = 3;30 \qquad ,, \qquad ,, \quad b/2$$
$$\tfrac{7}{2} \times \tfrac{7}{2} = 12;15 \qquad ,, \qquad ,, \quad (b/2)^2$$

$$12;15 + 1,8;45 = 1,21 \qquad ,, \qquad ,, \quad \frac{b^2 + 4ac'}{4}$$

$$\sqrt{(1,21)} = 9 \qquad ,, \qquad ,, \quad \sqrt{\left(\frac{b^2 + 4ac'}{2}\right)}$$

$$9 - 3;30 = 5;30 \qquad ,, \qquad ,, \quad \sqrt{\left(\frac{b^2 + 4ac'}{2}\right)} - \frac{b}{2}$$

The final step is to divide the last line by a and so obtain the classical formula, except that the negative root is not retained.

The method is equivalent to that used by al-Khwārizmi and is known as the completion of the square. It consists of dividing the expression $ax^2 + bx + c = 0$ by the coefficient of the square term, then adding to both sides of the equation a number sufficient to make the left-hand side a perfect trinomial square.

An examination of Mesopotamian problems involving second-degree equations shows that they all had three characteristics:

1. The solutions were almost invariably rational, which is only to be expected, since all the problems were constructed from known answers.

2. Whenever possible the scribe tried to change the form of the problem, either by considering the sum and products of the roots, or by introducing an additional unknown.

3. Negative quantities were systematically discarded or ignored.

The first characteristic was the direct result of the didactic nature of the problems considered. Nevertheless there are some exceptions which bear witness to their author's interest in the logic of the argument. Thus Thureau-Dangin has drawn attention to a problem with an irrational solution, in which the equation $x^2 = y^2 + 22;30$ ($x = 5$) occurred.

Since square root tables were restricted to perfect squares, one might have expected the scribe here to use Heron's method of approximation; in fact, he proceeded to solve an indeterminate equation in which x fulfilled the conditions of the problem as closely as possible, *viz.*, $x = 5.15$ and $y = 2.15$ (decimal notation).

The second characteristic is best illustrated by the problems found in Tablet AO 6484, where two unknown reciprocal numbers are found from their sum. In other words, the problem was to find x' and x" from their product 1 and their sum a. An analysis of the scribe's procedure shows that he used the formula:

$$x = \frac{a}{2} \pm \sqrt{[(a/2)^2 - 1]}$$

which is in fact the method modern textbooks would use.

The Tablet AO 8862 gives a number of instances of the use of additional unknowns. Thus in problems with two unknowns involving fourth-degree equations in x or y, the introduction of the additional unknown $z = x - y$ enabled the scribes to reduce the problem to a second-degree equation in z. Other problems were solved by introducing $z = (x - y)/2$. Finally, we know that the Babylonians were familiar with factorization, so that they could break down equations of degree higher than 2.

THE CONCEPT OF FUNCTIONS

Functions crop up in Seleucid astronomical tablets as the consequence of the observation that many astronomical events had obvious mathematical interrelations (for instance, a planet's visibility period and its angular distance from the sun). But long before that, Old Babylonian scholars had considered obscure functional relations for reasons which elude us, but which nevertheless do credit to the scribes' mathematical curiosity.

Thus, the Tablet VAT 8492 contains a list of numbers n ranging from 26–48, together with a list of corresponding values of $n^2 + n^3$. Other tablets list 'variables' against their exponential functions. The Tablet MLC 2078, finally, lists the powers to which a given number must be raised to equal another number, *i.e.* the logarithms to a given base a.

It would be extremely foolish to generalize from these few tablets, which are all we have to go by. All we can say is that this early mathematical curiosity of the Ancient Babylonians is a sign of their general intellectual precocity.

The Babylonians were calculators in the strict sense of the word, who used their extremely subtle notation to achieve a very high degree of arithmetical virtuosity. They were the real inventors of algebra, and it is quite possible that Diophantos' methods were based on theirs. However, they were not really at home once they ventured beyond their special field, for their geometry is no more than a pretext for considering further algebraic problems—so much so that they enunciated even the Theorem of Pythagoras in numerical, not 'spatial', terms.

Geometry

It was formerly believed that geometry was a much older branch of mathematics than arithmetic or algebra, if only because of its concrete subject-matter and its immediate usefulness in practical affairs. Moreover, in classical antiquity the advent of Pythagorean arithmetico-geometry had clearly been the off-shoot of the science of shapes and sizes. However, no such development ever took place in Mesopotamia, where spatial relations were investigated for their arithmetical interest alone. Thus, the Theorem of Pythagoras never induced the Babylonians to investigate the shape of triangles with sides in the ratio 3:4:5; rather were they concerned with finding a general algebraic formula giving the 'diagonal numbers' of all squares.

Geometry can be divided into 'positional' propositions, such as that the diameter divides the circle into two equal parts, or that the perpendiculars drawn from the vertices of a triangle to the opposite sides are concurrent, and into 'analytical' propositions, such as the Theorem of Thales, theorems on similarity, areas, volumes, *etc.* The first group corresponds to geometrical knowledge in the Greek sense of the word, and forms the basis of the second. Now Babylonian geometrical texts belong exclusively to the second group, and were kept 'geometrical' only in so far as they were found essential for establishing numerical relations.

Geometrical problems usually involved constructions with one or two unknowns, which the scribe would translate into equations involving unspecified geometrical properties and then solve by purely algebraic methods. It would, however, be wrong to assume that correct solutions implied knowledge of correct proof-procedures.

PURE GEOMETRY
We have no Babylonian texts on the geometrical properties of the straight line, the triangle, or the circle, other than a brief reference to the inscription of the right triangle in a semicircle:

1,0 (*i.e.*, 60) is the circumference, 2 the straight line which I have dropped (perpendicularly on the chord). What is the length of that chord?   (Tablet BM 85194.)

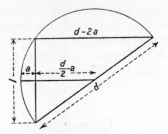

fig. 12 Evaluation of the length of a chord from the known length of the sagitta
(BM *85194*).

The solution is given without any further explanation:

You will square 2, =4. Subtract 4 from 20, the diameter, =16. Square 20, the diameter, =6,40 (400 in the decimal system). Square 16=4,16. Subtract 4,16 from 6,40, =2,24 (144 in the decimal system). The square root of 2,24 is 12. That is the length of the chord. This is the procedure.

This text, which is accompanied by a figure (*fig. 12*), contains the sum total of what we know of Mesopotamian pure geometry, namely that a right triangle can be inscribed in a semicircle, that the two lines perpendicular to a given line are parallel, and that the diameter is an axis of symmetry.

The problem really amounted to finding the length of a chord when the length of the sagitta is known. If *d* is the diameter, and *a* the sagitta, the figure shows that the length of the chord is:

$$\sqrt{[d^2 - (d-2a)^2]}$$

This is, in fact, what the scribe has done, putting $\pi = 3$ (whence $d = 20$).

The elementary notions needed in solving this problem are of the kind traditionally attributed to Euclidean geometry. We do not wish to claim that the Babylonians were the Greeks' teachers in this sphere, but merely note that they dabbled in it during the second millennium B.C., though for purely didactic reasons and without adducing any proofs.

THE THEOREM OF PYTHAGORAS

Matters were quite different when it came to 'analytical' questions, which, as we saw, were put forward simply to provide mathematical tiros with the necessary arithmetical equipment, and never to introduce them to the properties of space. As we have said earlier, this branch of geometry considered similarity, the Theorem of Pythagoras, and areas and volumes.

We have previously mentioned the existence of purely arithmetical tables of Pythagorean numbers and of Pythagorean diagonal numbers, and we shall now examine some problems in algebraic geometry based upon them. For example, Tablet AO 6484 obtains the length l, the breadth b, and the diagonal d of a rectangle from $l+b+d = 40$ and $lb = 2,0$ (120). The scribe simply put down the correct answer without mentioning the use of the formula $d^2 = l^2+b^2$.

The same tablet shows how to obtain the side of a square from its diagonal, by using the formula $a = d/\sqrt{2}$, and then derives the area of an isosceles triangle from its side 5 and base 6. The scribe begins by finding the height:

Multiply the side by itself: $5 \times 5 = 25$; multiply 3, half the length of the base, by itself $= 9$. Subtract 9 from 25 $= 16$. What is the square root of 16? 4. (That is the required height.)

These and many other texts are evidence that the Babylonians knew that the square over the hypotenuse was equal to the sum of the squares over the other two sides. They even tried to prove this theorem, though without much success. Thus, Tablet VAT 6598 contains a diagram (*fig. 13*) in which the lengths of the sides a, b of a rectangle are marked. The length of the diagonal cannot be obtained from tables, since $d = \sqrt{(a^2+b^2)}$ gives an irrational answer. To get over the difficulty, the scribe tried to obtain an approximate formula, and his efforts in this direction forced him to look more closely into the whole relation. He tried 'Heron's' formula first, but being dissatisfied he went on to another method which, by the way, was less accurate still. Since the rest of the tablet is destroyed there is little point in speculating about what other approximations he may have tried.

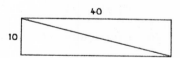

fig. 13 Figure accompanying an attempt to apply the theorem of Pythagoras (VAT 6598).

SIMILAR TRIANGLES

Tablet AO 6484 also contains two problems on similar right triangles. In the first, we are given the height H and the width e of a wall, and we are told that a pole tops the wall by length h. We are then asked to find at what distance x from the bottom of the wall an observer must be placed to see the top of the pole (see *fig. 14*).

Clearly, the solution involves the similarity of the triangles ABC and CB′A′, *i.e.*, $h/e = H/x$, and $x = eH/h$, which is, in fact, how the scribe obtained his answer.

The same formula is then used for solving the second problem, namely to calculate H, when h, e, and x are given.

The Babylonians realized that relations of similarity enabled them to solve a host of problems, and they did so with great gusto, exploiting proportionate arithmetic to the full.

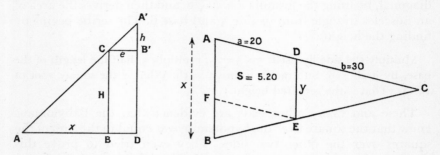

fig. 14 Reconstruction of a calculation using the properties of similarity.

fig. 15 Method of geometrical calculation (MLC 1 950).

Tablet MLC 1950 is a characteristic example of their approach to these problems. The text was accompanied by *fig. 15*, in which $a = 20$, $b = 30$, $S = 5,20$ (320) and in which x and y are unknown.

The scribe solved the problem most elegantly by expressing $\frac{1}{2}(x+y)$ and $\frac{1}{2}(x-y)$ as functions of S, a, b:

$$x = \frac{S}{a} \times \frac{S}{2b+a}; \ y = \frac{S}{a} - \frac{S}{2b+a}.$$

He arrived at these results in the following way: He made EF∥AC, whence $BF = x - y$.

From $S = \dfrac{a(x+y)}{2}$, he obtained $\frac{1}{2}(x+y) = \dfrac{S}{a}$ (1)

From the triangles he obtained $\dfrac{x}{a+b} = \dfrac{y}{b} = \dfrac{x-y}{a}$,

and then, by finding x and y in turn, and adding the expressions so obtained, member by member, and dividing by 2:

$$\frac{1}{2}(x-y) = \frac{S}{2b+a} \qquad\qquad (2)$$

Adding and subtracting (1) and (2), he then obtained the final answer.

We could cite a great many more examples of Babylonian skills in applying algebra to geometry, all of which would merely emphasize the great discrepancy between their calculating and geometrical skills. Thus, in the preceding problem the area of the trapezium ABED was not really

$$\frac{a(x+y)}{2}$$

which would have been correct only if the angle CAB had been a right-angle. Hence, the height of the trapezium should have been taken as 19·7736, and not as equal to 20, the figure used by the scribe. Had his geometry equalled his algebra, he could easily have avoided that mistake.

THE CIRCLE

Of all geometrical figures, the circle usually fascinates the beginner most. Not so in Babylonia, where circles were treated as purely ornamental structures in which perfect hexagons could be inscribed.

Nevertheless, the Babylonians took some interest in the metric properties of circles, notably in the value of π. Most existing texts give $\pi = 3$.[1] In 1938, P. Scheil published the text of a tablet giving fourteen values of the circumference against corresponding values for the area. Here the area was obtained from $\frac{1}{12}$ the square of the circumference, *i.e.*, $\pi = 3$. This is also the value which was used in the first problem we have discussed, where the diameter 20 was obtained from the circumference 1,0 without further explanation—clear evidence that $\pi = 3$ must have been taken for granted. This value of π is found again, many centuries later, in the Bible.

AREAS AND VOLUMES

We have seen that the Babylonians were none too particular when it came to calculating areas. While they used correct formulae for finding the areas of squares, rectangles and right triangles, the areas of other polygons were obtained from formulae in which the sides were looked upon as perpendiculars. Tablet YBC 8633 with its accompanying diagram (*fig. 16*) shows what calculations were involved. The required area $S = S_1 + S_2 + S_3$ was obtained by assuming

[1] A very much better approximation ($\pi = 3\frac{1}{8}$) was given by a tablet found by French archaeologists at Susa in 1936. Cf. E. M. Bruin's: Quelques textes mathématiques de la mission de Suse, *Proc. Ac. Amst.*, 1950.

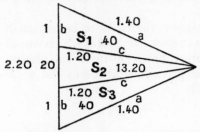

fig. 16 Evaluation of areas (YBC *8 633*).

the individual triangles to be right-angled, the height being confused with the side.

In the first triangle, $a = 1,40$ (100), $b = 1$ (60) and $c = 1,20$ (80); *i.e.* the sides are 3, 5, and 4 times 20 respectively. The figure 20, which was therefore a factor of all three lengths, was called the *makṣarum*.

The confusion of sides with heights seems a characteristic of Mesopotamian geometry, although we know of some exceptions. Thus we have seen how an isosceles triangle was divided into two right triangles to obtain its height; but in that case the height was a rational number, while in the last example we have:

$$h = \sqrt{[1,40)^2 - (1,10)^2]} = \sqrt{(1,25,0)}$$
$$(\sqrt{(5,100)} \text{ in decimal notation})$$

and 1,25,0 did not appear in the square root tables.

Babylonian problems on areas were all of a kind; they involved reductions into manageable parts, and then evaluations of the individual areas from given lengths, or *vice versa*.

The same is true of volumes. Those of cubes and parallelepipeds were determined from correct formulae (area of base × height). Generally, volumes were discussed in connection with simple arithmetical problems, such as assessing the wages of a labourer from the volume of earth he had shifted, how many bricks went into a given building, finding one edge of a prism when the others were known, *etc.* In short, they were simple arithmetical exercises.

The volumes of other polyhedra were found by approximations which must have been based on older sources, since they appear as exercises in many texts of quite different origin. Thus the volume of the frustum of a pyramid was repeatedly found by the formula:

$$V = \tfrac{1}{2}(a^2 + b^2)h$$

where a and b are the sides of the bases and h is the altitude.

Spherical figures are mentioned very rarely. The volume of the cylinder was obtained by multiplying the base by the height (with $\pi = 3$), and the frustum of the cone was found by the very poor approximation

$$V = \tfrac{1}{2}(r+r')h$$

Finally, the Babylonians had no formula for finding the volume of a sphere.

ASTRONOMY

The Greeks were the first to credit the ancient Mesopotamians with extensive astronomical knowledge. Simplicios tells us that Callisthenes, while campaigning with Alexander, sent Aristotle a complete list of eclipses, ostensibly observed by the Babylonians during the past 1,900 years, *i.e.* from the end of the third millennium B.C.! Geminos and Ptolemy also spoke highly of Babylonian astronomy. However, while these Greek scholars paid tribute to Babylonian observations, they never even suggested that the Babylonians might have propounded worthwhile astronomical *theories*. Pliny alone (*Hist. Nat.*, VII, 57) gave a fair account of the 'treasure' of Mesopotamian astronomy without traditional exaggerations or omissions.

It is largely due to the work of Epping, Kugler and Strassmaier during the past fifty years, and more recently still to Schaumberger, that we have been able to form a clearer picture of the actual knowledge of the ancient Babylonian astronomers. A methodical analysis of the tablets concerned has shown that Assyrio-Babylonian astronomy was not only based on admirable observations, but also on a theoretical foundation in which mathematics played a paramount role.

These tablets can be divided into two categories. The first, and most ancient, consisted of lists of omens, of such astronomical phenomena as the names of constellations or of planets accompanied by numbers in arithmetical progression, and of observations of the rising and setting of Venus. The provenance of the first group of tablets is as follows:

Reign of Ammisaduqa (*c.* 1650 B.C.): observations of Venus.

Kassite period: (a) Nippur text indicating a universe of eight concentric spheres, beginning with the sphere of the moon. (b) Texts describing the sky, and assigning numbers to the constellations. (c) Lists of omens of small astronomical interest.

Eighth and seventh centuries B.C.: (a) Tablets of the series 'MUL-APIN', summarizing the astronomical knowledge of the time (classification of fixed stars according to three 'paths', visibility of the moon and the planets, length of seasons, *etc.*). (b) Systematic observations of eclipses.

The second group of texts was published in later times. Most of them are Seleucid documents (written after 311 B.C.) of high scientific level. From the sixth century onwards the need of fitting the lunar calendar to the solar cycle had, in fact, forced Babylonian astronomers to develop a theory about the lunar cycle, and incidentally about the motions of the planets. Seleucid texts presenting this new found knowledge consisted mainly of ephemerides divided int-numerical reference columns. Modern scholars have had the utmost difficulty in interpreting these references which, as we shall see, concerned not only individual positions of the moon and the planets but also their mutual relations.

Babylonian astronomers pursued their observations until the Roman period—the most recent tablet is an almanac written during the reign of Vespasian.

Since the oldest texts are such that we can draw few reliable conclusions about their authors' astronomical knowledge from them, we shall base our attempts to evaluate the scientific basis of Assyrio-Babylonian astronomy on Seleucid documents alone.

The Form of Assyrio-Babylonian Astronomy

ASTROLOGY AND ARITHMETIC

Astrology is based on the belief that there is a close connection between man's life and the position of the stars at the moment of his birth. Hence, successful horoscopes depend on accurate determinations of the 'ascendant birth star', to borrow a term from Sextos Empiricos, to whom we also owe a description of two 'Chaldeans'—astrologers—one observing the sky while the other prepared to strike a cymbal at the precise moment of birth of the personage whose horoscope was to be cast. This type of astrology was clearly unencumbered with the theoretical problems so typical of Greek astronomy. The Babylonians never bothered to look for geometric explanations of stellar or planetary motions and were quite satisfied with determining the position of a given constellation at a given moment. Hence, their ephemerides.

Even so, astrology was more than irrelevant observation for it contained a germ of scientific truth. It was based on the determinist principle that there was a close nexus between celestial and human events, and though no such nexus exists in fact, astrologers were formally right to assume that given causes produce given effects. The periodicity of celestial events suggested to them quite readily that there was a necessary order in nature. Astrological prophecies were therefore the forerunners of scientific predictions.

Babylonian astrological writings are compounded of prophecy and observation in almost equal proportions. Thus we are told:

When the moon and the sun are seen together on the sixth day of the month, war will be declared on the king. The king will be besieged in his palace for one month, the enemy will invade the country and his progress will be triumphant. When on the fourteenth and fifteenth days of the month of Tammuz the moon and the sun are together invisible, the king will be besieged in his palace. If the moon is visible on the sixteenth day, there will be joy for Assyria, and unhappiness for Akkad and Amurru. . . .

We have looked for Mars twice and thrice but have failed to find him.

If the king, my master, should ask me: Is his invisibility an omen of anything, I shall reply: No.

Mars has entered into the constellation of Allul. This is no omen.

These few quotations will suffice to show that the Babylonians made other than astrologically 'significant' observations as well, though their search for omens was a considerable brake on the development of 'disinterested' astronomy. Thus astrologers were mainly concerned with the relative positions of a given planet and a given sign of the zodiac, and with the relation between eclipses and the rising of the sun. In fact, observations of eclipses were their *forte*.

At the same time, they were great calculators, and generally accompanied their records of the successive positions of a planet with sets of figures. That their mathematical interest must have been aroused by the regularity of observed phenomena is borne out most remarkably by a document from the library of King Assurbanipal, a table of the phases of the moon. In it, the face of the moon was divided into 240 parts and the number of bright parts was shown to increase from 0 to 240 within fifteen days.

The text shows that its author was not content with recording his observations, but accompanied his records with independent calculations showing that the bright parts increased in geometric progression during the first five, and in arithmetic progression during the last ten, days. He did so by extrapolation, much as modern physicists extrapolate lines or curves from fairly regularly distributed points on a graph, and hence postulate laws which isolated experiments fail to reveal.

As for Babylonian astronomers, they obtained their laws by trial and error. Having found that the geometric progression outstrips the actual course of events after five days, they looked for another law that would explain the moon's increase during the remaining ten days.

Their method was in fact doubly original. It was not empirical, since it tried to fit the phenomena to what must have been arbitrarily chosen laws. In that respect, it differs radically from all pre-Hellenic astronomical traditions. Then again, it was not Euclidean, *i.e.* purely geometrical. To Babylonian astronomers, 'explaining' invariably meant fitting the facts into familiar numerical theories.

Hence, Mesopotamian astronomy was above all arithmetical and positional, and all their observations were merely grist to their calculating mills.

OBSERVATIONAL INSTRUMENTS

The Babylonians were almost as well-equipped for astronomical observations as the Greeks, though they lacked an alidad (used for measuring the angular distance of stars). Their instruments included:

(1) *The gnomon*—the simplest instrument known in antiquity. This was a vertical rod by which the length of shadows was measured. The shortest shadow cast during the day indicated noon (the sun's transit across the meridian), and the shortest and longest shadows cast during the year indicated the summer and winter solstices, respectively.

(2) *The clepsydra*. During bad weather, and more generally at night, gnomons were of little use. Instead, time had to be told by the clepsydra, a graduated cylindrical vessel into which water was fed slowly from a reservoir. The clepsydra, like the gnomon, was also known to the Egyptians and to other oriental peoples. The Romans perfected the instrument by introducing floats which turned a wheel with a fixed pointer in front of a graduated scale. Similar instruments were still being used during the reign of Louis XIV.

(3) *The polos*. The polos was an exclusively Mesopotamian instrument, consisting of a hollow hemisphere so placed as to catch the sun's rays on its inner surface. On this surface the path of the sun was traced by means of the shadow of a bead suspended over the centre of the hemisphere. A simple inspection of the shadow would establish the time of day and year.

The polos was later improved by the Greeks. Instead of a hemisphere they used a skeleton sphere consisting of a central belt (the zodiac) and of circular hoops arranged at right angles to that belt. This instrument was the armilla ('armillary sphere') from which the relative positions of the stars could be found by direct comparisons.

Though the Babylonians had all the necessary instruments for observing the sky, none of their observations had anything like the importance of those made by, say, Hipparchos or Ptolemy. The main reason for this deficiency was their exclusive concentration on the time of the appearance and disappearance of celestial bodies above the horizon. Now, although the eastern sky is particularly bright, the horizon itself is seldom sharply defined and is confused further by frequent sandstorms. In addition, observations of the horizon made soon after sunset or before sunrise, which Babylonian astrology required, could not possibly be as accurate as an observation made in the middle of the night. Hence the Babylonians had great difficulty in solving their major astrological problem, which was to determine the exact point at which the crescent of the moon first appeared after a new moon.

On the other hand, the Babylonians excelled in making observations of eclipses, so much so that Ptolemy, who complained about the lack of reliable Mesopotamian planetary observations, was able to consult a list of eclipses going back to the reign of Nabonassar (eighth century B.C.).

The Content of Assyrio-Babylonian Astronomy

Our knowledge is such that we can say but little about the scientific value of Babylonian cosmology and even less about that of the Sumerians. Both, we saw, were dominated by myths and religion, and there was no secular cosmology of the kind found, for instance, in Ionia.

The Babylonian astronomers, even in their astrological investigations, never tried to *explain* observational facts. Their main problem was the correlation of the lunar calendar with the sun's cycle. The motion of the planets and the mapping of the sky always remained subsidiary questions.

THE LUNAR CALENDAR
The moon with its regular phases is obviously the perfect clock for all pastoral people, and the Babylonians, too, based their original calendar on the lunation—*i.e.* on the interval between two successive new moons.

Now, lunations vary in length from roughly 29 days 6 hours to 29 days 20 hours, so that the average lunar month is 29 days 12 hours 44 minutes 2 seconds, or a little more than 29½ days. Hence a year with alternate months of 29 and 30 days each can be brought into harmony with the lunar cycle if an extra day is added every 13 months.

Mesopotamian names for the months differed from town to town, especially in Old Babylonia, and so did the date of the New Year's day. The New Year generally coincided with the first lunation after the spring equinox, but, because of persistent religious traditions, the Babylonians also continued to observe New Year's day on the first day of Teshrît, an autumn month the very name of which meant 'Beginning'.

The Old Babylonian calendar, adopted by the Assyrians in about 1100 B.C., was divided into the following twelve months:

(1) Nisam (March to April)   (7) Teshrît (September to October)
(2) Ayar (April to May)   (8) Arahsamma (October to November)
(3) Siwân (May to June)   (9) Kislimu (November to December)
(4) Tammuz (June to July)   (10) Tebet (December to January)
(5) Ab (July to August)   (11) Shebat (January to February)
(6) Elul (August to September)   (12) Adar (February to March).

The Babylonians divided the day into twelve equal *bêru*, corresponding to two hours each. Because the Mesopotamian notation was sexagesimal, the *bêru* was divided into sixty 'double-minutes', and each 'double-minute' into sixty 'double-seconds'—purely theoretical units since no Babylonian clepsydra was accurate enough to measure them. We might note in passing that the Hebrews, after their Babylonian captivity, adopted this system of time-measurement, as did the Greeks and, later, the Romans.

Babylonian calendar-makers were faced with two problems, the first of which was the discrepancy between the lunar year and the solar year. Since twelve average lunar months are equivalent to 354 days, they fall 11¼ days short of the solar year. At the end of three years the discrepancy becomes more than a month, and at the end of nine years more than a season. Hence a periodic readjustment of the calendar had to be made by adding a thirteenth month to some years, much as we add an extra day to February in leap years. The addition of this extra month was originally imposed by agricultural needs but was soon afterwards put on a simple astronomical basis: each month was observed to coincide with the heliacal risings of one or a number of stars, and whenever a 'reference' star rose outside its normal period, a royal decree would declare an intercalary month, bearing the name of the last one and the word *dirig*, 'extra'. Thus Hammurabi decreed: 'This year has a gap. Let the following month be called Elul II.' And, anxious lest he encourage a delay in tax-remittances, he quickly added: 'Taxes must be paid to Babylon by the 25th of Elul II, and not by the 25th of Teshrît.'

Regular intercalary months were not introduced until the sixth century B.C., so that, previously, it was not uncommon to find years of fourteen months or even two consecutive years of thirteen months each, and so on. By the fifth century B.C., seven intercalary months every nineteen years had become the general rule, based on the simple observation that 235 lunar months are equivalent to nineteen solar years (*i.e.* to nineteen lunar years plus seven months). This was the Metonic cycle, so-called after Meton, a fifth-century Greek astronomer.

But the adoption of the lunar calendar involved yet another problem, much more difficult to resolve. The Babylonian month began with the first visibility of the new crescent moon, soon after sunset. Now, this phenomenon occurs one or two nights after new moon, depending on whether the previous month had twenty-nine or thirty days, and while practical determinations of the exact date were difficult enough when the horizon was hazy, the problem of predicting future dates, *e.g.* the length of Kisilimu (November/December), in the preceding Tebet (December/January), was graver still.

To solve this problem, or rather the more general problem of the duration of individual lunar months, Seleucid astrologers began to publish ephemerides in 311 B.C., in which various factors determining the visibility of the new crescent were taken into account.

LUNAR EPHEMERIDES

These ephemerides were tablets divided into a number of columns. While their decipherment was simple enough—they were merely columns of figures—their interpretation was not. For, unlike the algebraic texts, which can be interpreted from their context and by comparison with modern methods of solution, the astronomical tables contain no clue to their significance and may refer to any set of observations whatsoever. The problem was finally solved by Epping and Kugler.

Kugler has shown that the ephemerides fall into two categories: System A, in which the sun is assumed to move with constant velocity on two complementary arcs of the ecliptic (an arithmetical simplification which, though not in accord with observation, leads to regular series of numbers in the columns); and System B, in which successive positions of the sun are listed month by month, though these numbers do not form an arithmetic series because the velocity of the sun is not constant. For various reasons, System A is considered the older of the two though System B never superseded it, so that both were used until the dawn of the Christian era, not only in Babylon but also in Uruk.

THE LENGTH OF LUNAR MONTHS

We have said that calendrical considerations were the key to the ephemerides. Before examining the latter in greater detail, we must first state the problems involved in modern terms.

At new moon, the sun, the earth and the moon are said to be in conjunction, the bright side of the moon being turned away from the earth. Immediately after new moon, a small portion of the moon becomes visible and the moon is said to be crescent. Now, the first visible sign of the crescent moon, and hence the beginning of the month, depends on the moon's angular distance from the sun, for if the two are too close the glare of the sun will prevent observation of the crescent. Now, it would have been a simple matter to predict the distance from the sun at which the moon becomes visible if the moon and the sun moved uniformly. As it is, the moon advances on the sun by from 10 to 14 degrees every day, the amount being variable at different times of the year. Thus it became necessary to establish tables of the relative positions of the moon and the sun for each month before the different times of first visibility could be calculated. Here, a new difficulty arose: the obliquity of the ecliptic. We know that the sun, in its apparent annual motion, follows a path among the stars known as the ecliptic, which is inclined at $23° 27'$ to the terrestrial equator. This path can be described by the sun's position relative to certain given constellations, the 'signs of the zodiac', and is traditionally divided into twelve sectors of $30°$ each. At the winter and summer solstices the sun occupies extreme positions in this path, being at the full $23° 27'$ below or above the equator. As Babylon is at latitude $32°$ N., its horizon makes an angle of $58°$ with the celestial equator, and the extreme noon altitudes of the sun are $58° - 23° 27' = 34° 33'$ at the winter solstice and $58° + 23° 27' = 81° 27'$ at the summer solstice.

Moreover, the moon oscillates about the ecliptic with an amplitude of $5°$ which affects the visibility of the new crescent when the sun is near its winter solstice position.

Hence if the beginning of a lunar month is to be fixed by the first visibility of the new crescent after conjunction, the relative velocities of sun and moon, and also of the sun's height above the noon horizon, must be taken into account. Now the lunar ephemerides were set up precisely to supply all the elements from which the length of the lunar months could be established.

We shall restrict our analysis to a fragment of an ephemeris studied by Kugler (272 81–7–6 obv., lines 8–20, columns A and B), which reads as follows:

Line No	Months	A				B				Signs
8......	Elul II	29	18	40	2	23	6	44	22	Libra
9......	Teshrît	29	36	40	2	22	43	24	24	Scorpio
10......	Arahsamma	29	54	40	2	22	38	4	26	Sagittarius
11......	Kislimu	29	51	17	58	22	29	22	24	Capricornus
12......	Tebet	29	33	17	58	22	2	40	22	Aquarius
13......	Shebat	29	15	17	58	21	17	58	20	Pisces
14......	Adar	28	57	17	58	20	15	16	18	Aries
15......	Nisam	28	39	17	58	18	54	34	16	Taurus
16......	Ayar	28	21	17	56	17	15	52	14	Gemini
17......	Siwân	28	18	1	22	15	33	53	36	Cancer
18......	Tammuz	28	36	1	22	14	9	54	58	Leo
19......	Ab	28	54	1	22	13	3	56	20	Virgo
20......	Elul I	29	12	1	22	12	15	57	42	Libra

Column B gives the position of the sun in the zodiac for the first day of the month shown in column 2. Thus, during the conjunction which marks the end of Elul II and the beginning of Teshrît, the sun is at 23° 6′ 44″ 22‴ in Libra. During the next conjunction it is at 52° 43′ 24″ 24‴ in Libra, *i.e.*, at 22° 43′ 24″ 24‴ in Scorpio, *etc*. These solar longitudes are, of course, those of the moon as well, since they apply to conjunctions of the two.

When the sun has passed from position A_8 to position A_9, one lunar month will have elapsed, so that the difference of 52° 43′ 24″ 24‴ − 23° 6′ 44″ 22‴ = 29° 36′ 40″ 2‴ represents the monthly displacement of the sun, precisely the figure given in A_9. Similarly, other figures in column A represent the sun's displacement during the remaining months. Since these figures vary, the ephemeris in question clearly belongs to System B.

Column A also shows that, if we neglect the seconds and thirds, successive readings form groups, each member of which differs by ±18′ from its predecessor. Thus the first three lines (29° 18′, 29° 36′, 29° 54′) show a regular increase, and the next six lines (29° 51′, 29° 33′, 29° 15′, 28° 57′, 28° 39′, 28° 21′) a regular decrease from a maximum *M*, while the last four lines (28° 18′, 28° 36′, 28° 54′, 29° 12′) show a regular increase from a minimum *m*.

These facts can be represented graphically by plotting the figures

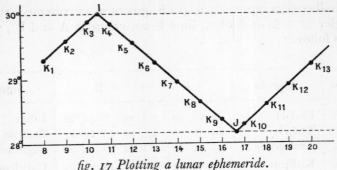

fig. 17 Plotting a lunar ephemeride.

of column A against successive months. See *fig. 17*. The points K1, K2, *etc.*, obtained in this way, fall into three groups:

  (a) Points K1, K2, K3 form a straight line D of slope +18.

  (b) Points K4, K5, ... K9 form a straight line D′ of negative slope −18.

  (c) Points K10–K14 form a straight line D″ of slope +18.

The points of intersection $I(x_i y_i)$ and $J(x_j y_j)$ of the lines D and D′, and D′ and D″ respectively are thus easily obtained. We find that $y_i = M = 30° 1′ 59″$ and $y_j = m = 28° 10′ 39″ 40‴$.

In short, the monthly motion of the sun oscillates between two limiting values M and m, with a mean value:

$$\mu = \frac{M + m}{2} = 29° 6′ 19″ 20‴.$$

If we plot the series of maxima and minima we obtain a zigzag line in which the distance T between two consecutive peaks measures the period of the function, *i.e.* the length of the solar year expressed in lunar (synodic) months.

Fig. 18 shows that $T = 2d$. Now $\tan \alpha = h/d = r$ (arithmetic difference), whence $T = 2/r$. In the given case $h = M - m = 30° 1′ 59″ - 28° 10′ 39″ 40‴ = 1° 51′ 19″ 20‴$ and $r = 18$. Whence, using sexagesimal notation, we obtain

$$T = \frac{(1,51,19,20) \times 2}{0;18,0,0} \simeq 12;22$$

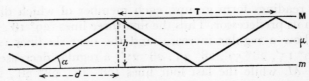

fig. 18 Method of evaluating the duration of the solar year. (Fig. 17 on a reduced scale.)

Hence, the solar year is just over $12\frac{1}{3}$ (12,20) lunar months.

Most lunar ephemerides belonging to System B had a total of eighteen columns which gave, in addition to the data we have been analysing, the respective lengths of days and nights, changes of lunar velocity, the length of synodic months, the dates of consecutive conjunctions, the inclination of the ecliptic to the horizon, latitude of the moon, and other such information.

All these data allow one to determine a parameter p measuring the time during which the new quarter will remain above the horizon. When p had attained an (unfortunately unspecified) minimum value the new month was said to have begun; if it had not, a further day was needed; if it was too large, the month was said to be in its second day.

The reader might wonder whether the meticulously compiled ephemerides were, in fact, true reflections of the observable facts. The answer is clearly that they were not, if only because the Babylonians had no means of measuring time within seconds, let alone within thirds. However, it was their mathematicians rather than their astronomers who had the urge to go beyond experiment, to turn sets of apparently unrelated figures into regular mathematical sequences, which alone were thought to stamp knowledge as 'scientific'.

ECLIPSES

Once the ephemerides were established, it was a simple matter to predict eclipses of the moon, for its conjunctions and oppositions with the sun (syzygies) could be read off from the tables without further ado.

In fact, even in Sargon's day, which was before the advent of systematic ephemerides, lunar eclipses were already being predicted from the simple observation that they occurred only at full moon (the middle of the month), and only when the path of the moon cut the ecliptic, a region of the sky with which Mesopotamians were more familiar than with any other.

Eclipses of the sun were much more difficult to predict, since their visibility from any one point on the earth depends not only on the distance of the earth from the sun and from the moon, but also on the relative dimensions of these bodies, which were not known at the time.

The only prediction that the Babylonian astronomers could therefore make was whether an eclipse of the sun was theoretically possible.

Though some scholars have claimed that the Mesopotamians were familiar with the cycle of 233 lunations (a little more than eighteen years) governing the recurrence of eclipses, there is no evidence in favour of that contention.

THE ZODIAC

We have already mentioned the great interest which Babylonians took in horoscopes. Their astrological preoccupations led them to chart the path of the sun through a series of reference points, consisting originally of the brightest stars (a system used until the end of the Seleucid period) and later of well-known constellations.

Thus, it was in tablets dating from before the destruction of Nineveh that the modern signs of the zodiac first appeared (Taurus, which then governed the spring equinox; Leo, Capricorn, Scorpio, Aries, *etc.*). These constellations were spread over a 20°-wide 'belt' whose division by the Babylonians into sectors of 30° goes back at least to the reign of Cambyses (523 B.C.).[1] Macrobius' claim that the zodiac was an Egyptian invention, based on clepsydra measurements, must be dismissed if only because such measurements, could they have been made in the first place, would be significant only for the equator; the zodiacal signs do not 'ascend' uniformly on the ecliptic. Moreover, the Mesopotamian zodiac is quite independent of inundations of the Nile and the Sothic cycle, on which all Egyptian astronomy was based.

THE PLANETS

Let us first of all recall some basic facts about the apparently complex motions of the planets. We know that these bodies move in ellipses, at one of the foci of which the sun is situated. Their own motion, combined with the apparent motion of the sun about the earth, makes the planets appear to follow an irregular path among the stars. This is compounded of their own motion (from West to East) and a retrograde motion (from East to West), following upon a stationary interval. Moreover:

(a) The angular velocity of an inferior planet (Mercury or Venus) in its own orbit is greater than the angular velocity of the sun about the earth. We can divide the ecliptic into two unequal arcs, so that the motion of the planet P is added to the apparent motion of the sun along the longer arc, when the planet appears to be moving more quickly than the sun, but is contrary to the sun's motion on the smaller arc, when the planet seems to be travelling backwards.

(b) The angular velocity of a superior planet (Mars, Jupiter, and Saturn) is smaller than that of the sun, and the planet describes a retrograde motion along the longer arc.

(c) The visibility from the earth of any planet, inferior or superior, depends on its angular distance from the sun. In the case of the

[1] This division may very well go back to a tablet from the second half of the 2nd millennium B.C., in which every sign of the zodiac is accompanied with 30 vertical lines, probably corresponding to the 30 days of the month.

inferior planets, the arc of invisibility can be shown to be greater near the superior conjunction than it is near the inferior conjunction; hence, unlike the superior planets, the inferior planets cannot be observed throughout the period of their retrogression.

Greek astronomers took no more than a passing interest in these phenomena since, according to their theory of epicycles, they were only to be expected. On the other hand, the Babylonians, who lacked any theory to explain the anomalies of the planetary motions, and who were haunted by horoscopic problems, concentrated almost exclusively on the appearances, disappearances and stations of the planets in order to fit them into a regular series. This study led them to the extrapolation of the position of a planet P at any given moment *t*.

Let us look at the case of Jupiter and Mercury. Kugler has shown that the Babylonians had three different systems of extrapolating their observations of Jupiter:

In the oldest tablets, the ecliptic was divided into two zones, from 0° Sagittarius to 25° Gemini, and from 25° Gemini back to 0° Sagittarius, representing constant synodic arcs of 36° and 30° and synodic revolutions of 366 and 402 days, respectively. Hence, the mean synodic arc of Jupiter was 33° 50'. The heliacal risings and stationary points of Jupiter were then evaluated according to one or other of these arcs. The Babylonian calculations gave sixty-five synodic revolutions in seventy-one years—a very good approximation indeed.

In later texts the synodic arc was evaluated even more strictly. Here, the ecliptic was divided into four zones:

From 9° Cancer to 9° Virgo	Synodic arc: 30°	
„ 9° Virgo to 2° Capricorn	„ „ 33° 45'	
„ 2° Capricorn to 17° Taurus	„ „ 36°	
„ 17° Taurus to 9° Cancer	„ „ 33° 45'	

This gives a mean synodic arc of 33° 20' 37'', from which the motion of the planet and its stations can be calculated more simply and correctly than from the older system. In a still later system, the synodic arc was assumed to decrease uniformly from 38° 8' to 28° 50' 30'' by 1° 48', which gave a mean synodic revolution of 398.89 days. (The actual value is 398.92 days.)

As for Mercury, the results of Babylonian astronomers are of 'surprising accuracy and superior to those obtained by Hipparchos' (Bigourdan). Babylonian astronomers argued as follows: if both the sun and Mercury moved with constant velocity, successive appearances of Mercury as the morning star at a given point and moment would be represented by a uniform set of points a', a'', *etc.* As it is, these points are not uniform because the velocities concerned are not constant. The problem is therefore to divide the ecliptic into zones of constant velocity for each of the two bodies concerned, and hence to evaluate the points *a′ a″*, *etc.*, by successive approximations. To that purpose, they set up their System A ephemerides which gave the required solutions.

Generally speaking, Babylonian astronomy may be said to have been primarily analytical. While the study of planets with regular motions, such as Venus, was made without dividing the ecliptic into zones, the study of planets like Mars involved the division of the apparent path of the sun into six parts, within each of which the planet's motion was assumed to be constant. The results obtained by this method are very near to modern values, and often more accurate than the results obtained by the Greeks. Thus the Babylonians obtained:

Mercury	145	synodic revolutions in	46	years
Venus	5	,,	,,	,,	8	,,
Mars	15	,,	,,	,,	32	,,
Jupiter	65	,,	,,	,,	71	,,
Saturn	57	,,	,,	,,	59	,,

We have seen that the Babylonians followed much the same procedure in astronomy as they did in mathematics, collecting data and then arranging them into systems according to traditional methods. Though they made no attempt to give theoretical descriptions of the universe, the Babylonian astronomers were not entirely devoid of a scientific outlook, albeit one based on a rather naïve form of determinism.

By observing phenomena quantitatively and by establishing constant arithmetical relations between them, rather than by trying to explain them by metaphysical or theological speculations, the Babylonian astronomers showed an almost Comtian approach to the world around them, which we are therefore fully entitled to call scientific.

BIBLIOGRAPHY

All the works mentioned below contain additional bibliographies to which the reader is referred.

B. MEISSNER, *Babylonien und Assyrien*, II (Heidelberg 1925). Chaps. xv, XVII–XXI.

W. VON SODEN, *Leistung und Grenze Sumerischer und Babylonischer Wissenschaft, Die Welt als Geschichte*, II (1936), pp. 411–464, 509–557.

B. LANDSBERGER, *Die Fauna des alten Mesopotamiens . . .*, Leipzig, 1934.

R. C. THOMPSON, *A Dictionary of Assyrian Chemistry and Geology*, Oxford, 1936; *A Dictionary of Assyrian Botany*, London, 1949.

F. KUCHLER, *Beitrage zur Kenntnis der assyrisch-babylonischen Medizin*, Leipzig, 1904.

H. HOLMA, *Die Namen der Körperteile im Assyrisch-babylonischen*, Leipzig, 1911.

E. EBELING, Keilschrifttexten medizinischen Inhalts, *Arch. f. Gesch. d. Med.*, XIII (1921), XIV (1923).

G. CONTENAU, *La Médecine en Assyrie et en Babylonie*, Paris, 1938.

H. E. SIGERIST, *A History of Medicine*, Oxford, 1951, pp. 377–497.

A. PECKER and H. ROULLAND, *L'accouchement au cours des siècles*, Paris, 1958.

R. LABAT, *Traité akkadien de diagnostics et pronostics médicaux*, Leyden, 1951.

A. HOOPER, *Makers of Mathematics*, New York, 1948.

H. V. HILPRECHT, *Mathematical, Metrological and Chronological Tablets*, Philadelphia, 1906.

FR. THUREAU-DANGIN, *Esquisse d'une histoire du système sexagésimal*, Paris, 1932.

O. NEUGEBAUER, *Mathematische Keilschrifttexte*, 3 vols., Berlin, 1935–37.

FR. THUREAU-DANGIN, *Textes mathématiques babyloniens*, Leyden, 1938.

O. NEUGEBAUER and A. SACHS, *Mathematical Cuneiform Texts*, New Haven, 1945.

H. LEWY, Studies in Assyro-Babylonian Mathematics and Metrology, *Orientalia*, XVIII (1949).

O. NEUGEBAUER, *The Exact Sciences in Antiquity*, Providence, R.I., 1957.

E. M. BRUINS, *Hoofpunten vant het praegrieske en grieske wiskuding denken*, Leyden, 1953.

F. X. KUGLER, *Sternkunde und Sterndienst in Babel*, I–II, 1907–10.

E. WEIDNER, *Handbuch der babylonischen Astronomie*, 1915.

J. SCHAUMBERGER, *Sternkunde und Sterndienst*, Ergänzungsheft, 1935.

O. NEUGEBAUER, *Astronomical Cuneiform Texts*, 3 vols., London, 1955.

A. PANNEKOEK, *History of Astronomy*, London, 1958.

CHAPTER 3

Phoenicia and Israel

IN THE THIRD MILLENNIUM B.C., the region between Upper Mesopotamia and Egypt, and particularly the Phoenician coast and Palestine, witnessed the rise of a relatively homogeneous and fairly original civilization which modern archaeologists have called the Canaanite. This name is taken from the Bible, which calls the original population of Palestine by that name, though the Bible and other sources also used 'Canaan' to refer to the whole of Phoenicia and some parts at least of Syria. In the course of its development over some 3,000 years, the Canaanite civilization became influenced by Egyptian, Mesopotamian, Aegean and Hittite elements, and hence differed from region to region.

It was in Phoenicia that the Canaanite civilization existed in its purest state. The Phoenicians generally wrote on papyrus and very little of their literature has survived. We should therefore know little of their history were it not that the inhabitants of Ugarit (now Ras-Shamra) in Northern Canaan had discarded papyrus in favour of clay tablets. It is on examination of these that our brief account of Phoenician science has been based.

This chapter also deals with ancient Hebrew science, for when the children of Israel settled in Palestine they absorbed much of their neighbours' culture. For instance, it was to the king of Tyre that David and Solomon applied for architects, masons, joiners and artists when they built the Temple and restored Jerusalem. In many other respects, too, Hebrew civilization might be called a variant of the Canaanite, so that there is good reason for treating the two together.

PHOENICIAN SCIENCE:
THE UGARIT TABLETS

During the fifteenth, sixteenth, and eighteenth centuries B.C., the coast of Syria facing Cyprus saw the rise of a town called Ugarit. Its ruins were discovered in 1928 and first explored in 1929 by an expedition led by Claude Schaeffer.

Among the many objects dug up were a great number of clay tablets, some written in Assyrio-Babylonian, and some in proto-Phoenician, a script using an alphabet of thirty letters that looked like a radical simplification of the cuneiform syllabary. By 1929 it was well-established that our own alphabet can be traced to the Phoenicians, who transmitted it to the Greeks and thence to the rest of the world, with the exception of China.

NOTATION AND WEIGHTS

Many of the Ugarit tablets are simple 'delivery notes' for a variety of goods, and particularly for wine and oil. While most of the numbers are spelled out in full, some are in Babylonian numerals or fractions. The notation was decimal, though it showed faint traces of the Sumerian sexagesimal system, notably in the use of 'three and three' for 6, and of 'six and six' for 12. While additions abound in these documents, there is no trace of any of the other three simple rules.

Phoenician weights were based on the *shekel* (about ⅓ oz.) and the *talent* (3,000 *shekels*). The intermediate weight, the *mina*, is not mentioned in any of the texts but was found on stone weights by the side of bronze balance-trays. These weights were in the shape of olives or reclining cows, one of which represented a *mina* equal to 16 oz., *i.e.* a *mina* greater than the Egyptian but smaller than the Babylonian.

CALENDAR AND COSMOLOGY

The Phoenician year was divided into twelve lunar months of uncertain order and having names which, with one or two exceptions, were quite unlike the Babylonian or Assyrian.

It seems reasonable to assume that the inhabitants of Ugarit borrowed Mesopotamian notions of astrology, though all we have to go by is a short reference to a daughter of the legendary King Danel, who was said to be a repository of knowledge about the paths of the stars.

HIPPIATRY

The finds included a small treatise of ten chapters listing remedies to be administered to horses suffering from short wind, retention of urine and such-like complaints. Amongst these remedies were lettuce, gruel, and *chndrs*, which was clearly *chondros*, the Greek for spelt. All these remedies were administered for their veterinary properties alone and there is no mention of associated magical rites.

ANCIENT HEBREW SCIENCE

Our knowledge of ancient Hebrew science, as indeed of most other aspects of Hebrew civilization, is based almost exclusively on the Bible. While the Bible is essentially a religious book, it nevertheless enables us to assess some of the scientific conceptions which held sway in ancient Israel. It appears that the children of Israel, who played so important a role in the religious history of mankind, contributed little to scientific advance. Here, as in many other spheres, this small and originally nomadic people was bound to be greatly influenced by such ancient and powerful civilizations as the Canaanite, the Mesopotamian and the Egyptian. Thus the science of ancient Israel was almost entirely that of her neighbours. It must be remembered that the Israelite tribes did not join into one monarchy until the end of the eleventh century B.C., that the political power of the Hebrew kings was relatively short-lived and never very great, and that, starting from the eighth century B.C., Israel passed successively under the domination of the Assyrians, the Chaldeans, the Persians, the Ptolemies, the Seleucids and the Romans. In other words, Israel had little chance to develop an original civilization and hence to make great scientific contributions of her own. In what follows, we shall restrict our remarks to a discussion of ancient Israel up to 70 B.C., when Titus's capture of Jerusalem put an end to her independence.

MATHEMATICS

Ancient Israel employed two notational systems, the decimal and the sexagesimal, of which the first was the more common. In Hebrew the tens, from 30 to 90, are designated by the plurals of the numbers 3 to 9. The people whom Moses led across the desert were counted in tens and multiples thereof (fifties, hundreds and thousands). Their standard of capacity was the *homer*, equal to 10 *baths* or 10 *ephahs* (Ezekiel 45:11), and their religious and moral code was a decalogue.

But traces of the Babylonian sexagesimal system were also kept alive. Thus there were twelve tribes of Israel, twelve loaves of showbread, twelve gates to the Jerusalem of Ezekiel's dreams, and so on. Again, weights had sexagesimal subdivisions; as in Babylonia, one *talent* was equal to sixty *minas* (*manehs*) and one *mina* to sixty *shekels*

(Ezekiel 45: 12). However, in Exodus (38: 25–26), we are told that a hundred *talents* are equal to 300,000 *shekels*—a system clearly based on the one used in Ugarit, where 1 *talent* = 3,000 *shekels*, and 1 *mina* = 50 *shekels*. Hence the Bible may be said to have combined two systems in a rather arbitrary way.

Hebrew geometry was extremely rudimentary, and was applied exclusively to technical problems, though with considerable skill. This is borne out, for instance, by the subterranean channels whereby Hezekiah conveyed the waters of the fountain of Gihon to Jerusalem, and which must have involved much accurate planning (II Chron. 32: 30). Ancient Israel knew nothing about pure mathematics or the abstract science of numbers, but contented itself with purely empirical procedures.

COSMOLOGY

The Hebrew held extremely naïve views about natural phenomena. Rain, for instance, was thought to be poured down by God from gigantic celestial vessels either through celestial aqueducts or else through the windows of heaven (*râquîya*), a kind of roof which spanned the sky like a canopy. Heaven was so close to the earth that birds could easily fly up to it—hence, the 'birds of the heavens' (Jer. 4: 25). As God looked down upon men from his heavenly throne, he beheld them the size of locusts. Not only rain, but also dew, snow, hail and storms had their own dwelling-places in the heavens from which they came forth at God's bidding. So vast was the content of the firmament and of its many chambers that one heaven alone was thought unable to contain them all.

Light was thought to exist independently of the sun, and was, in fact, created first. It, too, dwelled in Heaven, as did all shadows. The sun, the moon and the stars meekly followed a course set by God. While Genesis 1 simply calls the stars 'lights in the firmament' other Biblical passages endow them with personality. Thus, the sun is compared to a 'bridegroom coming out of his chamber rejoicing as a strong man to run a race' (Ps. 19: 5), and the morning stars are said to have sung together at the spectacle of the Creation (Job 38: 7). The stars are the army of Heaven, commanded by God who 'telleth their numbers and calleth them all by their names' (Ps. 147: 4). The book of Job mentions a number of constellations, amongst which the following have been identified fairly conclusively: the Great Bear (*aǎ*), Orion (*kesîl*), and the Pleiades (*kîmah*). Of course, such simple observations are in no way comparable with the astronomical achievements of the Babylonians.

Thunder, too, had a divine significance. It was the voice of Jehovah, the God of Israel, whose arrows were as lightning, and whose (rain)bow was hidden by the clouds. When it shone forth it was a clear sign that Jehovah's wrath had abated.

The firmament was supported by mountains, the pillars of heaven, whose unshakable foundations went down to the very bottom of the great void. In effect, this void was a kind of cosmic ocean in which the world swam and which fed its springs and hence its rivers. The earth itself was a flat disc and would have been in constant danger of being engulfed by the void from which it had sprung, were it not for God's covenant with Noah, that never again would there be a flood to destroy the earth. In the first chapter of Genesis, the void or primordial ocean is called *tehôm*—a word with a root similar to the Babylonian *Tiamat*, a formidable monster personifying the void in the Babylonian poem about the Creation. Moreover, we are told that God separated the waters which were under the firmament from those which were above it (Gen. 1: 6) by 'binding them up' (Job 26: 8) much as the Babylonian god Marduk tamed the monster Tiamat.

Thus the Hebrews, like the Babylonians, considered the universe to be divided by the earth into an upper firmament, heaven, and a lower, watery firmament, the void. Lower still was a region called *sheôl*, the subterranean retreat of the dead, though according to an earlier and probably commoner belief *sheôl* lay within the earth itself. Thus the earth simply opened its mouth to swallow erring Levites like Kora, Dathan and Abiram straight into *sheôl*, and when the witch of En-dor conjured up the spirit of Samuel, it rose up straight from the earth.

The first chapter of Genesis is the only one in the entire Bible to give a fairly coherent cosmogonic account. That chapter was, in fact, the beginning of a much larger work, the *Priestly Document*, parts of which have found their way into the first six books of the Bible. It is generally believed that the Document itself was written in about the fifth century B.C. by priests anxious to give an historical justification of basic Hebrew observances. It begins with an account of God's creation of the world in six days, and of His resting on the seventh—the basis of Sabbath observance. It tells how God successively created light, the heavens, the sea, the earth and its vegetation, the stars, the birds, the fishes and land animals (including man). It is remarkable for its system of classification. The vegetable kingdom, for instance, was divided into two groups: 'plants yielding seeds and fruit trees bearing fruit in which is their seed'. As for man, 'God created him in His image and after His own likeness', for the authors had no doubt that the human form was divine.

GEOGRAPHY

The ancient Israelites knew but a small corner of the earth, which to them was its navel. Thus their cardinal points were based on Palestine: the west was called the sea (*i.e.* the Mediterranean), and the south was called *Negev* after the desert between Palestine and Egypt.

Chapter 10 of Genesis tells us a little about their restricted geographical horizon, and about what ethnic and historical ideas the Hebrews held about their neighbours. This chapter is, in fact, made up of two distinct texts, the *Jahvist Document* (ninth to eighth century B.C.) and the *Priestly Document* which we have already mentioned. Because of the difference between their dates, the *Priestly Document* had rather more advanced geographical notions than the *Jahvist*. Thus, though both trace all nations back to Noah and his sons—Shem, Ham, Japheth—they do so in distinct ways. While the *Jahvist Document* relates all nomadic tribes (including Israel) to Shem, all established civilizations (the Egyptian, the Assyrio-Babylonian, and the Canaanite) to Ham, and the barbaric Northern tribes to Japhet, the *Priestly Document*, more concerned with geographical niceties than its predecessor, relates the nations of Mesopotamia and Syria to Shem, the Arabs and Egyptians to Ham, and the Anatolians and Europeans to Japhet. Again, while Assur is said to be a descendant of Ham in the *Jahvist Document*, the *Priestly Document* calls him a son of Shem.

CALENDAR

Strict observance of religious festivals requires an exact calendar. The Israelite calendar was essentially founded on the lunar month, beginning with first visibility of the crescent moon. The year consisted of twelve successive months, but since the solar year is $365\frac{1}{4}$ days and twelve lunations only 354 days, the months gradually fell outside their due seasons and harvest festivals, for instance, would presently coincide with sowing times. To adapt the lunar cycle to the solar year, which was also the agricultural year, an intercalary month was added every two or three years, when the month of *Adar* (in late winter) was doubled, and the year in question became an embolismic year. This practice has remained part and parcel of the Jewish calendar, so that, for example, the Jewish year 5705 (September 1954 to September 1955) consisted of 355 days while the three subsequent years lasted 383, 354 and 385 days, respectively.

It was probably from the Canaanites, who were the earlier inhabitants of Palestine, that the Israelites borrowed their calendar and also the names of their months, all of which appear to have had agricultural connotations. Thus, the first month of Spring (March to April) was called *Abib*, an ear of grain. Later these Canaanite names were replaced with ordinal numbers, begining with Spring. *Abib* then became 'the first month'. Then, after the Babylonian exile, the Jews adopted the names of the Nippur calendar, commonly used throughout Mesopotamia since the reign of Hammurabi. In it, the first month was called *Nisan*, followed by *Iyar, Sivan, Tammuz, Ab, Elul, Tishri, Marcheshvan, Kislev, Tebeth, Sebat* and *Adar*—the names used in the synagogue to this day.

In ancient times the year apparently began with the autumn equinox; autumn, in effect, marked the transition from one agricultural cycle to the next. In accordance with this ancient usage, the Jewish New Year's Day (*Rosh-hashanah*) became the first of *Tishri* (September–October), after the exile. But we have seen that there used to be yet another New Year's Day, according to which the month of *Abib* (March–April) was called the first month. Passover, the first of the series of annual religious festivals, always fell on the fifteenth day of this month.

The week, with its six working days and the Sabbath, played an important role in the Hebrew calendar. As a quarter of a month, it may well have been related originally to the four phases of the moon, though we cannot be certain. The weekdays had no special names— Sunday was simply the 'first' day, Monday the 'second', and so on. The sixth day of the week, *i.e.*, Sabbath Eve, was called *arubtâ* ('vigil') in Aramaic, and παρασκήνη (preparation) in Greek. The religious day always began at dusk—as it does in the synagogue to this day.

Towards the end of the second century B.C. two apocalyptic books, the Book of Jubilees and the Book of Enoch, introduced an entirely new calendar based mainly on the division of the year into four seasons (*t'kufoth*) of three months each. In each season, the first month counted 29, the second 30, and the third 31 days, making a total of 91 days, *i.e.*, exactly 13 weeks. Hence, the year consisted of 364 days or 52 weeks. In that system there was a perfect if artificially produced harmony between the solar cycle (the four annual seasons), the cycle of months (three months to the season, twelve months to the year), and the cycle of weeks (thirteen weeks per season, fifty-two weeks per year). Now, since twelve lunations really take 354 days, and since the year was fixed at 364 days, the New Moon Celebrations were often held when the moon was anything but new. Moreover, since the solar year is 365¼ days and not 364, there was a further discrepancy of 1¼ days annually between the official and the real solar year. We have no idea how the calendar was reconciled with the astronomical events, but the attempt to bring years, months and weeks into some sort of harmony was remarkable in itself. A scroll discovered at Qumran, near the Dead Sea, shows that this kind of calendar was being used by the Essenes, a Jewish sect, in the first century B.C. Since it was not introduced before the Hellenistic period, the division of the year into four seasons was probably borrowed from the Greeks. Ancient Israel knew only two seasons, a dry and torrid summer and a wet and cold winter.

CHRONOLOGY

The ancient Hebrews had no era like ours and counted their years from unusual events; for example 'two years after the earthquake', 'the year that Tartan came unto Ashdod', *etc.* In official writings, years were counted from the beginning of the ruling king's reign. Later, in the Hellenistic period, the Jews adopted the Seleucid era, beginning on the first of *Nisan*, 311 B.C.

The Bible also used eras of 480 years each, one of which was said to separate the building of Solomon's Temple from the exodus from Egypt, and another counting from the end of the exile. The figure 480 was chosen simply because it represents twelve generations.

Since the Middle Ages, the synagogue has counted its era from the Creation, in accordance with Biblical and traditional chronologies. It appears that 3,761 years separated Adam from Christ; hence, the year 1960, for example, corresponds with the Jewish year 5721 (=1960+3761).

WRITING

When the Israelites first settled in Palestine they adopted Hebrew, a Canaanite dialect, as their common language. While most of the Bible is therefore written in Hebrew it nevertheless contains Aramaic passages, for Aramaic, another Semitic dialect used throughout the Near East from the time of the Persian conquest, gradually supplanted Hebrew, particularly after the exile.

The ancient Hebrew script was taken directly from Phoenicia. Phoenician writing was alphabetical and unlike any of the ideographic or syllabic scripts. By the middle of the 2nd millennium, the Phoenicians (or proto-Phoenicians) of Ugarit had perfected an alphabet of thirty letters, consisting almost exclusively of consonants. Towards the end of the second century B.C. (inscription on the coffin-lid of Ahiram, King of Byblos, and on other monuments) there appeared another script with only twenty-two consonants, which was quickly adopted by Phoenicia's neighbours—the Aramaeans, the Hebrews, and the Moabites—and hence by the Greeks and most of the classical world. Most modern scripts are therefore derived, directly or indirectly, from the Phoenician.

The ancient Hebrew script is known from an inscription on the Farming Calendar of Gezer (*c.* 900 B.C.), from an inscription on the

9

aqueduct of Siloam (*c.* 700 B.C.) and also from a number of seals, intaglios, and ostraca. This script shows a number of differences from the Phoenician, and also introduces vocal consonants, the so-called *matres lectionis*, which were used as long vowels and thus facilitated reading. *Matres lectionis* have also been found on ancient Aramaic inscriptions (ninth to eighth century), and on the Moabite Stele of King Mesha (ninth century), but never on Phoenician inscriptions.

The Aramaic script subsequently underwent marked changes of its own, and it was that script in its final stages which, at about 200 B.C., the Jews turned into the 'Square Hebrew' alphabet which they have been using ever since. Among the earliest documents written partly in Square Hebrew are the Dead Sea Scrolls (200 B.C. –A.D. 100). Since some of these scrolls were also written in the Palaeo-Hebrew cursive script, they, together with the writing on Jewish coins from the Maccabean age to Bar-Kochba's revolt (135 B.C. to A.D. 132–35), are clear evidence that the ancient script had survived into even the Roman period, though only side by side with what had by then become the more common Square script.

MEDICINE

Though we have no Hebrew medical texts comparable with, for instance, those of Egypt and Babylonia, Biblical references nevertheless enable us to form some picture of Hebrew medicine. This science was still completely steeped in religion and magic, but some of its therapeutic measures were rational enough. Pathology remained rudimentary, since the law forbade post-mortems as involving pollution by contact with the dead. Hence, only superficial wounds and fractures could be examined with any degree of certainty. Leviticus 13–14 mentions leprosy and some cutaneous infections, but simply for the guidance of priests whose task it was to pronounce certain cases as 'unclean', and not for any medical purposes. Thus the word *sara'at* referred both to lepers and also to unclean garments and dwellings.

The Bible mentions pestilence on a number of occasions, and even associated it with a 'plague of rats'. Since sexual impurities were thought to be accompanied by involuntary seminal emissions (Leviticus 15), venereal diseases were confused with normal physiological phenomena. Eye diseases were apparently frequent and so were sunstrokes. Sunstroke is described in II Kings 4: 18–20, which tells how the son of a Shunammite woman went out to find his father in the fields. 'And he said unto his father, My head, my head. And he (the father) said to a lad, Carry him to his mother . . . and he sat on her knees till noon, and then died.' Apoplexy is mentioned in the story of Nabal who, having gorged himself at table, became 'as a stone' (paralysed) after 'his heart had died within him' (*i.e.* after he had lost consciousness). Ten days later he died.

Diseases were generally believed to be of divine or demoniac origin. In cases of wounds or other injuries, the obvious causes were of course taken into account. For instance, Tobit became blind because bird-droppings had fallen on his eyes. But these were exceptions and not the rule. Thus, when pestilence devastated Ashod it was said that 'the hand of the Lord was heavy upon them' (I Samuel 5: 6); Job, too, was said to have suffered for the same reason. But though Jahveh was the real author of all these afflictions, it was Satan acting as His agent who, for example, 'smote Job with sore boils from the sole of his foot unto his crown' (Job 2: 7), and who struck Jerusalem with pestilence (II Samuel 24: 15–18). Mental diseases, in particular, were the work of Satan, or Belial, and of his minions, who took possession of men either at God's behest or out of sheer malice.

Clearly, such conditions could only be cured by prayer or magic, according to whether they were due to God or Satan. Thus a number of the psalms were originally prayers to God for recovery. Possession, on the other hand, could not be cured by prayer alone but called for the services of healers with supernatural contacts: holy men, magicians and priests. Leviticus 14: 1–8 gives a purely magical prescription against leprosy, and the prophets Elijah and Elisha even resuscitated the dead by lying down upon them (I Kings 17: 17–22; II Kings 4: 32–35).

The Hebrew pharmacopoeia, too, was largely magical. Thus Hezekiah was cured of his boils covering them with a 'lump of figs' (II Kings 20: 7), and the angel Raphael prescribed fish-liver against Tobit's cataract. According to Josephus Flavus, the Essenes were healers *par excellence* who had made a special study of the medical properties of roots and stones.

Wounds were generally treated by surgeons who washed the scar and then bandaged and soothed it with oil. According to an ancient law, anyone who inflicted a wound had to make good his victim's loss of time and also pay for the healer's services (Exodus 21: 18–19).

Rational methods of therapy were not introduced into Hebrew medicine until the Hellenistic period, when Hippocratic physicians began to exert some influence over their Jewish colleagues. The new trend was not welcomed by all Jews, since many of them considered it irreligious. They may have cited the case of King Asa who died not so long after he had sought the advice of the physicians, and not of Jahveh, when he was 'diseased in his feet' (II Chronicles 16: 12). But at about the same period, the author of Ecclesiasticus spoke most highly of physicians and showed that piety was not necessarily opposed to common sense. He wisely enjoined the sufferers to regain God's favour by admitting the error of their ways, and to leave the rest of the cure in the hands of the physician:

Honour a physician with the honour due unto him for the uses which ye may have of him: for the Lord hath created him. For of the Most High cometh healing, and he shall receive honour of the king. The skill of the physician shall lift up his head: and in the sight of great men he shall be in admiration. For the Lord hath created medicines out of the earth; and he that is wise will not abhor them. Was not the water made sweet with wood, that the virtue thereof might be known? And he hath given men skill, that he might be honoured in his marvellous works. With such doth he heal (men) and taketh away their pains. Of such doth the apothecary make a confection; and of his works there is no end; and from him is peace over all the earth. My son, in thy sickness be not negligent: but pray unto the Lord, and he will make thee whole. Leave off from sin, and order thine hand aright and fence thy heart from all wickedness. Give a sweet savour and a memorial of fine flour, and make a fat offering, as not being. Then give place to the physician for the Lord hath created him. Let him not go from thee, for thou hast need of him. . . .

(Ecclesiasticus 38: 1–15.)

BIBLIOGRAPHY

I. BENZINGER, *Hebräische Archäologie*, Tübingen, 1907, pp. 159–188.

A. BERTHOLET, *Histoire de la civilisation d'Israël*, Paris, Payot, 1929, pp. 316–339.

A.-G. BARROIS, *Manuel d'archéologie biblique*, II, Paris, 1953, pp. 118–193.

W. EBSTEIN, *Die Medizin im Alten Testament*, Stuttgart, 1901.

J. PREUSS, *Biblisch-talmudische Medizin*, Berlin, 1911.

A. GEMAYEL, *L'hygiène et la médecine à travers la Bible*, Paris, 1932 (perhaps too uncritical).

CHAPTER IV

Ancient Indian Science

THE HISTORY OF INDIAN SCIENCE is one of the longest of all and one of the most amply documented. It begins in about 2500 B.C., and India continues to make original scientific contributions to this day. Though science was at first mentioned only incidentally, over the centuries it became the subject of an immense number of specialized works, many of which are unfortunately lost. Most were written in Sanskrit, which was the 'Latin' of India, her cultural and diplomatic language and, in its refined form, the means whereby India extended her literary influence over her neighbours from Afghanistan to Japan and from Indo-China to Indonesia. Later, when the vernaculars (*Prakrits*) were developed into an (artificial) literary language in about the second century A.D., Sanskrit remained the polished expression and the guarantor of India's scientific heritage. However, other languages, too, have helped to perpetuate India's achievements. Scientific works were also written in Tamil (Southern India), in Pali, the sacred language of the Hīnayāna Buddhist scriptures (Ceylon and Indo-China), in Ardha-māgadhī, the sacred language of the Jains of India. All in all, Indian languages, and particularly Sanskrit, influenced the ancient scientific literature of Upper Asia, of Tibet and Mongolia, and of the Cambodian peninsula—Burma, Thailand, Laos, Cambodia, and Indonesia—much as Greek literature, imitated, copied, or translated into Latin, Syriac or Arabic, influenced the thought of all Western countries.

Moreover, Indian and Greek thought also had a direct effect on each other. Finally, while, through Greece, India was moulded by various Near-Eastern influences, she was also affected directly by Chinese traditions. Because of these several factors, the history of Indian, like that of Western science can be divided into periods. More precisely, Indian scientific history had (*a*) a proto-historical period, (*b*) a period in which it established contact with Babylonian and Greek science (from the time of the Achaemenid emperors onward), and (*c*) a classical period marked by cultural interchanges with the Roman Empire and by a considerable cultural expansion both towards the interior of Asia, and also towards the South. This period was closed when Islamic culture penetrated into India without, however, diminishing India's external influence.

PROTO-HISTORICAL ANTECEDENTS

Our knowledge of the proto-historical period is based on two groups of documents: archaeological texts describing the ancient civilization of the Indus basin, and philological texts containing common technical terms and ideas from which we can reconstruct the original language and culture of those ancient Aryan tribes who later split up to lay the foundations of the civilizations of India and Iran.

Excavations in the Indus basins, and particularly at the archaeological sites of Harappā and Mohenjo Daro, have brought to light the remnants of an ancient civilization unsurpassed in such feats of civil engineering as (particularly) drainage and bathing-pools. While these ruins tell us a great deal about ancient hygienic measures, they tell us little about the scientific knowledge on which they were based, particularly since none of the seals has so far been deciphered. All we can say with certainty is that hartshorn, cuttlebone, and bitumen (*śilāyatu*) were being used for their medicinal properties.

Towards 1500 B.C. the Indus valley was invaded by Vedic Aryans, related to the Iranians, whose sacred songs and rituals were soon afterwards to become the material of the *Veda* ('Knowledge'), a canonical text in archaic Sanskrit which was related to the ancient tongues of Iran. The *Veda*'s hymns recall the destruction of ancient towns of the kind that excavations have, in fact, brought to light at Harappā. The *Veda* also alludes to many scientific notions, some of which are given in ancient Iranian text. Apart from detailed information about diseases, drugs and stars, the most remarkable ideas common to the *Veda* and to ancient Iranian documents bore on the order of the world, which was conceived as governed by a cyclical law, the *rta*, meaning both 'normal' and 'true'. In Iranian, that law was called *asha* (in the *Avesta*), or *arta* (in ancient Achaemenid texts). The similarity between these names indicates a common origin in prehistoric times, while the agreement between the corresponding notions may have resulted from interchanges subsequent to the division of the prehistoric Indo-Iranians into Iranians and Vedic Indians. In fact, the Iranians and the Vedic Indians remained in continuous historical contact, so much so that the Iranian *arta*, corresponding with the Brahmanic *rta*, first appeared on inscriptions from the period of Persian domination of the Indus basin.

In any case, the notion of *rta* is very important, since, referring as it does not only to the natural but also to the moral order, it represents an overall determinism. It differs from strict scientific determinism in that it rejects all apparent irregularities out of hand, simply because they are irregular. It is less concerned with physical laws than with norms, less with order, as such, than with 'good' order.

SOURCES OF VEDIC AND BRAHMANIC SCIENCE

The Vedic and Brahmanic periods, which overlap to a large extent, correspond to different literary, rather than historical, periods. While the *Vedas* are a collection of sacred texts, the *Brāhmaṇas* are ritual commentaries on the subject-matter of the *Veda*. Their language is less archaic and they are therefore the more recent of the two. However, they do not differ in doctrine, and the *Brāhmaṇas* introduce no novel concepts. There are four *Vedas*: the *Ṛg Veda*, a collection of sacrificial hymns; the *Sāma Veda* in which some of these hymns are arranged as liturgical chants; the *Yajur Veda*, a collection of sacrificial formulae; and finally the *Atharva Veda*, a collection of more recent hymns, used mainly for magical spells and incantations.

The basic Vedic texts were first given their final form in about 1500–1000 B.C., and the various *Brāhmaṇas* from about that time until the beginning of Buddhism, in the fifth century B.C. In fact, Buddhism may be called the culmination of Brahmanism, though the latter continued to flourish by its side. Thus Brahmanism rather than Buddhism was the basis of the many technical and particularly phonetical studies which coincided with the beginning of the Buddhist period. These texts, based on keen observation, analysed and classified all linguistic sounds according to the parts of the vocal organs involved: vocal cords, palate, lips, teeth, tongue, *etc*. Brahmanism was also responsible for compiling the *Jyotishavedānga* (Astronomical Element of Knowledge) which describes the principles of the calendar, and of Vedic cosmology. This text is generally thought to have been written between 300 B.C. and A.D. 300.

What medical and physiological phenomena are described in Vedic literature are mainly found in the *Ṛg Veda*, and also in the *Atharva Veda*. Many of these descriptions were developed further in in the *Brāhmaṇas*, and in the *Āraṇyakas* and *Upanishads*, special appendices to the latter. The *Āraṇyakas*—'Books of the Jungle-Men'— were compiled by sages who had renounced all worldly activity and had gone to meditate in the forests. The *Upanishads*, again, gave the key to the mysterious relations existing among the things of this world. According to their very name—'Sitting Aside'—their main purpose was to look at the world objectively. They tried to establish the relations of similarity, identity, dependence, or number, which govern world order and all its transformations. The *Upanishads* tried to explain the multiplicity and diversity of phenomena by simple natural laws, often mistaking the superficial and false for basic connections. Even so, they took a step in the right direction, for they no longer taught passive submission to inscrutable fate. Hence, they are evidence of an authentic scientific wish to make all phenomena intelligible, to subject nature to reason.

Other Vedic texts include the *Sutras*, listing Vedic rites and rules of Brahmanic conduct. Special treatises give the correct method of reciting Vedic hymns and all add to our knowledge of ancient Indian science. In particular, the method of reciting hymns is based on a scientific analysis of phonetics.

ASTRONOMY

Vedic Astronomy

The *Ṛg Veda* lists a number of stars, and divides the year of 360 days into twelve months. It may also have contained an allusion to an intercalary thirteenth month of thirty days (I, 25, 8). This month is certainly referred to in the *Atharva Veda* (XII, 3, 8), which mentions efforts to bridge the gap between the civil and the tropical year, so as to cause periodic events to fall in their proper seasons. Two passages in the *Yajur Veda* give a list of twenty-seven constellations, a third passage, and also one in the *Atharva Veda*, mention twenty-eight constellations, the so-called *nakshatras*, which have remained the 'guiding' stars of Indian astronomy.

For a long time, historians looked upon the *nakshatras* as lunar mansions, or houses successively occupied by the moon in its monthly revolution. They did so because one lunation—27 or 28 solar days—corresponds to the 27 or 28 *nakshatras*. Hence, historians have spoken of an Indian lunar 'zodiac', distinct from the solar zodiac of classical antiquity.[1]

In reality, the *nakshatras* were used to follow the motions of the sun, as well as that of the moon and the planets. The calendars of the Vedic and Brahmanic epochs were neither purely lunar nor purely solar, but luni-solar. Indian astronomers have always considered astronomical phenomena as indivisible.

The moon can be seen in the sky whenever it is not too close to the sun, and the position of the sun can be fixed against that of a constellation a little before sunrise or after sunset when the sun's

[1] There is partial agreement between the Indian *nakshatra* and the Chinese *hsui* (*see p.* 170).

light is too weak to blot out that of the other stars. Now, Vedic and Brahmanic, unlike Western, astronomy mapped the sky by the phases of the moon rather than by the heliacal risings or settings of certain stars. At full moon, when sun and moon are in opposition, the position of the sun is automatically given by that of the moon.

Even during the other phases and the intervals between them, the position of the sun can generally, though less easily, be deduced from the observed position of the moon. The motions of the moon and the sun can therefore be correlated for each day, or rather night, of the civil year by means of the 27 or 28 *nakshatras*.

This concern for treating lunar and solar motions together goes back at least to the Brahmanic period with its intercalary month of thirty days, and the subsequent intercalation of a 25 or 26 day month, mentioned in the *Śatapatha Brāhmaṇa*. Intercalary months were added every five years, the so-called *Yuga* periods, at the end of which the sun and the moon were each thought to have completed a round of complete revolutions. The length of five 'normal' years of 1,800 days was thus brought up to 1,830, and later to 1,825 or 1,826 days, which is closer to the correct 1,826¼ days.

Astronomical periods played an important role in Vedic-Brahmanic thought, which considered them to be successive parts of the ever-returning cosmic cycle. The temporal aspect of that cycle was but one facet of the creative cosmic power, of the 'word' of Prajāpati, the World-Spirit, with whose wisdom the *Vedas* were suffused. The year was the unit of time of Prajāpati's actions, and the *Veda* contains as many metrical divisions as there are 'moments' in the year. The *Śatapatha Brāhmaṇa* states that the World Spirit's year embraces 10,800 moments, whence the *Ṛg Veda* has 10,800 metrical divisions, the so-called *pankti* of forty syllables each, giving a total of 432,000 syllables. The 10,800 moments were obtained from the division of the year into twelve months, of the month into thirty nychthemera, and of each nychthemeron into fifteen moments of day and fifteen moments of night. The 'moment' was therefore the thirtieth part of the day.

The fractions $\frac{1}{15}$ and $\frac{1}{30}$ were applied directly to the lunar month of twenty-seven or twenty-eight days. First the lunar month was divided into two parts (*paksha*) of fifteen lunar days (*tithi*) each, but the thirty *tithi* so obtained were found to exceed the days of the actual lunar month. They were probably introduced merely to establish some sort of harmony between the revolutions of the sun and the moon, and to help trace the path of the moon through the *nakshatras*. But since the apparent velocity of the moon (and hence the lunar day) is not uniform, the *tithi* were purely spatial abstractions.

The numbers 10,800 and 432,000 were also the bases of the cosmic cycles of later Indian and even foreign astronomers. Thus, according to Censorinus, the Great Year of Heraclitos was 10,800 years, and the Babylonian astronomer Berossos mentions a cosmic cycle of 432,000 years. These figures first appeared outside India long after the *Śatapatha Brāhmaṇa* was written, and although Greek and Babylonian astronomers were not otherwise greatly influenced by Indian ideas, they must have been in this respect. In effect, Heraclitos wrote at a time when Parthian domination extended over Greek and Indian lands alike, and when there was an intensified exchange of ideas between the two. Again, Berossos lived towards the end of that period, marked by the destruction of the Persian empire by Alexander, and the subsequent rise of the Seleucid Kings.

The *Jyotishavedānga*

The most important of the short texts on the principles of the calendar, comprising the 'Astronomical Element of Knowledge' of the *Rg Veda*, are contained in the *Jyotishavedānga*. Their main purpose was to fix the dates of Brahmanic ceremonies, so that they could coincide with given moments in the cosmic cycle, and thus ensure its regularity.

The principles listed are unfortunately so condensed as to be partly obscure. Moreover, they contain no direct information about Indian astronomy, which must therefore be reconstructed from recalculations and inferences. The year of 366 days was apparently divided into three seasons of four months each, and one *Yuga* was equal to 1,830 days (*i.e.* to sixty months *plus* one intercalary month, all of thirty days each). Twenty-seven *nakshatras* marked the twenty-seven ideal divisions of the ecliptic, each equal to 13° 20'.

These purely ideal figures were used in the third century B.C. by the Emperor Asoka to calculate the precise duration of his intended Buddhist pilgrimage. This fact shows clearly that Vedic astronomy was by then in common use. We also know that the basic teaching of the *Jyotishavedānga* was incorporated in writings of the Jain religion which arose at about the same time as Buddhism, *i.e.* in the sixth century B.C. Jaina texts help us to elucidate certain obscure passages in the *Jyotishavedānga*.

The *Sūriya-Canda-pannatti*

These texts are called *Sūriya-pannatti* ('Understanding of the Sun') and *Canda-pannatti* ('Understanding of the Moon'). Though they have many elements in common with the *Jyotishavedānga*, the Jaina versions contain an original cosmography which greatly influenced subsequent astronomical thought. Thus, they state that the centre of the universe is a mountain called *Meru*, running from North to South and surrounded with seven concentric zones. The central zone had four divisions, one of which was *Bharatavarsha*, the Indian sub-continent. The Jaina texts were alone in assuming the existence of two suns, two moons, and two systems of stars. Hindu cosmography, developed in the learned treatises known as the *Purānas* ('the Ancient') written during the classical period (from the beginning of the Christian era to the Middle Ages), is very much closer to Western notions about these matters.

THE BEGINNINGS OF ASTROLOGY

No astrological considerations can be found in any Vedic, Buddhist or Jaina texts before the Christian era. It is, however, true that during the centuries immediately preceding the Christian era people were apparently named after some stars, and hence were probably placed under their special protection. Names like Pushyamitra, Brhaspatimitra, Budhamitra, *etc.*, meant 'Friend of the Flower' (a star in Cancer), 'Friend of Jupiter', 'Friend of Mercury', *etc.* But it was only under the influence of the Greeks that horoscopic astrology made its debut in India, thereafter to achieve quick popularity.

Classical Ancient Astronomy

After the Vedic and Brahmanic periods, there was a great upsurge of astronomical literature, particularly during the first few centuries of the Christian era, after a long period of historical contacts with Babylonia and Achaemenid Greece. Many Greeks had settled in India or were trading with her, and the new-found knowledge was recorded in a great number of books, side by side with the old.

From the conquest of the Indus basin by Darius I, *c.* 519, until the defeat of Darius III by Alexander, India was thrown wide open to Babylonian influences. Most Persian officials were Babylonians who spoke and wrote in Aramaic. Their Aramaic script was subsequently modified to accord with the Indian and became the Arameo-Indian script, later known as *Kharosthī*. It was greatly superior to the original Aramaic, which lacked a precise vowel notation. The Persians also brought India contacts with Greece, and these were greatly intensified during Alexander's campaigns and again when the Greco-Bactrian kingdoms were established in India, and when maritime and overland commerce with the West began to flourish. It was after a long period of such contacts that *Siddhānta* astronomy, filled with notions of Greek astrology, first made its appearance.

THE FIVE *Siddhāntas*

There were five *Siddhāntas* or 'solutions', of which only one, the *Surya Siddhānta* ('Solution by the Sun') is extant. The others are known from the critical appraisal at the beginning of the six century A.D. by the astronomer Varāhamihira in his *Panca Siddhāntika* ('On the Five Solutions').

The remaining texts, named after their reputed authors, were the *Païtamaha Siddhānta*, the *Vāsishtha Siddhānta*, the *Pauliśa Siddhānta*, and the *Romaka Siddhānta*.

The *Païtamaha Siddhānta* ('the Ancestral Solution') was revealed by the god Brahman, often called the 'Ancestor', who is considered to have been the first teacher of science from sheer compassion for humanity and for man's limited powers of understanding. The astronomical doctrine of this text is still very much that of the *Jyotishavedānga*, and probably dates back to just after the *Śakha* period, begun in A.D. 78.

The *Vāsishtha Siddhānta* was considered very unreliable by Varā-hamihira, who therefore did not describe it in detail. What little we know of it we owe to the description of the eleventh-century Persian scholar Al-Bīrunī, who tells us that the work mentions a method of locating moving celestial bodies by fixed points of reference, and of expressing angular distances in degrees and minutes. Moreover, the *Vāsishtha Siddhānta* used the signs of the zodiac (*rāsí*) instead of *nakshatras*, and therefore introduced the Babylonian and Greek systems. The use of twelve signs dividing the sky into twelve parts of 30° each involved a more precise determination of angular distances than the old division into twenty-seven segments of 13° 20'.

The *Pauliśa Siddhānta* seems to have propounded the teachings of Paul of Alexandria, whose original work is lost. Similar to the *Vāsishtha Siddhānta*, though of a higher standard, it gave a method of determining the exact length of the day and a rough means of predicting eclipses. The *Pauliśa Siddhānta* did not stick to the letter of Paul of Alexandria's doctrine, for authors from different epochs tell us that its text was modified in the course of time.

The *Romaka*, i.e., the Roman, *Siddhānta*, was apparently written by the Indian Śrīsena, who based his work on Roman, or rather Alexandrian, sources. The 'Roman Solution' gave a luni-solar cycle of 2,850 years, 150 times as long as the Metonic cycle of 19 years, and an evaluation of the length of the year in agreement with Hipparchos and Ptolemy, and hence more accurate than that of the *Jyotisha-vedānga*. It also gave 150 tables of equations of anomaly, similar to those of Ptolemy, and a method of calculating for the meridian of Alexandria the number of days elapsed since the beginning of a given cycle. This method became known as *ahargana*—'group of days'. The *Romaka Siddhānta* is clearly post-Ptolemaic and possibly very much so, since the year A.D. 505 is apparently the beginning of one of its cycles. It would therefore have been written shortly before Varāhamihira reviewed it. However, since there is no direct evidence about the original date of its publication in the text itself, we can say no more than that it must have been written between the second and sixth centuries. The *Romaka Siddhānta* did not merely expound Greek views; it adapted them to the needs of Indian astronomy, so that some of its calculations have an original Indian flavour.

THE *Sūrya Siddhānta*

According to Varāhamihira, the 'Solution of the Sun' is by far the best of the five solutions. Small wonder then that the *Sūrya Siddhānta* is the only one to have survived. According to the real date of the astronomical events described, it was first published in the sixth century B.C. The original version was subsequently re-edited, for there are references which coincide with events in the fifth century and possibly even later. Al-Bīrunī has attributed the work to one Lāta, who claimed to have recorded the revelation of a solar divinity to the *asura*, Maya. The *asuras* were lesser gods often charged with expounding the teachings of the gods themselves. The term was also applied to the Iranians, who worshipped *Ahura* (the Iranian for *asura*). In a verse which was probably added later, as it is not found in all the manuscripts, we are told that the Sun invited Maya to go to Romaka, there to be taught astronomy—clear evidence of the high regard in which the 'Roman' school of Alexandria was held. It has even been suggested that the term '*asura* Maya' was a corruption of Turamaya, the Sanskrit for Ptolemy. (The Ptolemies of Egypt were called Turamayas in third-century India.)

In reality, the *Sūrya Siddhānta* is no more than indirectly related to the Alexandrian school. Specifically Indian notions, like the *nakshatras*, played a major role in it and what Alexandrian concepts it included were radically altered. Its *Romaka* was in fact a purely fictitious place situated on the equator, and 90° from the 'Indian' meridian which is assumed to have passed through Ujjayinī in Central India and Lanka (Ceylon). The fact that the teaching of astronomy was ascribed to a solar deity is explained by the great vogue of solar cults at the time of the first edition of the *Romaka Siddhānta, viz.*, under the Guptas, who were solar kings according to their title.

As is common in Indian textbooks, all of which are written summaries of oral teachings, the text was condensed into 500 couplets, divided into fourteen chapters. The first chapter discussed the measurement of time, the second gave the oldest known sine-tables.

While these may have been based on the chords of Hipparchos and Ptolemy, the original substitution of semi-chords, *i.e.* sines, for chords, led to great progress in trigonometry. Apart from discussing 'semi-chords' (*jyārdha* or *ardhajyā*), the *Sūrya Siddhānta* also considered the cosine (*kotijyā*) and the versed sine (*utkramajyā*). The third chapter dealt with meridians, cardinal points, equinoxes and solstices. Chapters 4 and 5 covered eclipses of the moon and sun, Chapter 6 graphical projection of eclipses, Chapter 7 planetary motions, Chapter 8 the inclination of the *nakshatras* to the ecliptic, Chapter 9 what seem to be Greek notions about the heliacal risings and settings of stars, and Chapter 10 the relative motions of the moon and the sun. Chapter 11 introduced astrological ideas of 'evil' conjunctions, Chapter 12 presented a cosmography, Chapter 13 discussed elementary astronomical instruments of the kind used by the Greeks, and the last chapter dealt with calendar computations. The whole work was extremely condensed and, moreover, listed numerical tables in symbolic terms. Since every number could be represented by a host of words of different metrical lengths, even very large numbers could be interpreted so as to conform to the very strict rules of Indian prosody. The style is elliptic but is luckily illuminated by commentaries, for it presupposes a full understanding of the subject-matter and the technical terms. In short, the *Sūrya Siddhānta* is a pocket-book for accomplished scholars rather than a textbook for students.

The Cosmology of the *Sūrya Siddhānta*

The stars revolve about Meru, the cosmic mountain which is the polar axis of the world, and whose summit is the dwelling-place of the gods ruling the northern hemisphere. The opposite, southern, hemisphere is haunted by the god's antagonists, the *Pretas*. The earth is a sphere (*bhūgola*) divided into four continents whose centres are four equatorial towns at equal distances from one another. The continent of India is called Bharatavarsha, with Lanka as its capital (Lanka was also the name of Ceylon, though the mythological Lanka was nowhere near that island). Going westward, one comes first to Ketumālavarsha, with Romaka as its capital, then to Kuruvarsha with the capital Siddhapura, and finally to Bhadrāśvavarsha with Yamakoṭī. 'Sunrise at Lanka is sunset at Siddhapura, midday at Yamakoṭī, and midnight at Romaka.' The summit of Meru marks the North for all these continents, and over it the sun never sets but shines constantly on its gods. Even so, during the spring equinox, the sun crosses the equator to shine even more brightly on the gods, and is directly overhead at the summer solstice. At the winter solstice it is directly above the seat of the *Pretas*. The interval between the spring and autumn equinoxes is one divine day, its complement one divine night. The human year is therefore one divine nychthe-meron. The motion of the sun between the winter and summer solstices was called the 'course towards the North' (*uttarāyana*), the complementary motion the 'course towards the South' (*dakshināyana*). The *Sūrya Siddhānta* also mentions five planets (*graha*): Mercury (Buddha—or Jna—'the Wise'), Venus (Śukra—the 'White'), Mars (Angāraka—the 'Firebrand'), Jupiter (Brhaspati—the 'Lord of Prayer'), and Saturn (Sani—the 'Slow'). It also names their ascend-ing and descending nodes, *Rāhu* and *Ketu*. The motions of the planets are said to be caused by a cosmic wind, in accordance with an ancient Vedic conception which attributes all motions in nature (the macrocosm) and the human body (the microcosm) to such a wind. The fact that the planets do not describe perfect circles was noted, and ascribed to the action of 'Weather-forms' which had their seat in the zodiac. They were called *śighrocca* ('maximum speed') and *mandocca* ('maximum slowness') and *pāta* (nodes). They were more or less personifications and were effective because their hands were bound to the planets by 'cords of wind'. In more mathematical terms, the planets were thought to move in epicycles, a notion that could not have been part of the original text.

COSMIC TIME

One divine year was thought to consist of 360 divine days or 360 human years, and the Great Cosmic Year, at the end of which all the stars were thought to return to their original position, after having completed a whole number of revolutions, to represent 12,000 divine years. That figure was calculated not only from rough esti-mates of planetary and stellar cycles, but also from the great Brah-manic numbers 10,800 and 432,000. Thus 12,000 divine years, or one full 'cosmic cycle', were equal to $10 \times 432,000$ solar years. The solar year itself is shown by J. B. Biot to have been 365 days 6 hours 12 minutes 35.556 seconds, so that the smallest number of solar years containing a round number of days was 1,080,000, *i.e.* one quarter of 4,320,000 and a multiple of 10,800.

Moreover, 108 is the product of 4 (the phases of the moon) and 27 (the *nakshatras*); and 432 the product of 16 (the theoretical parts of the lunar disc) and 27; while 4,320,000 is the number of 'lunar' years representing 12,000 divine years, each of 360 human years of 12×30 days each.

The peculiar properties of these numbers convinced Indian astronomers that they had solved the mysteries of the stars once and for all, so much so that Indian astronomy became completely para-lysed or diverted into the wrong channels.

The Great Year (*nahayuga*) was divided into four *yugas* which, according to non-astronomical considerations about the decline of morals and order, were thought to be unequal in perfection and duration. The four *yugas* were therefore 'calculated' to be in the ratio 4:3:2:1, whence the fourth, the *kaliyuga*, was $\frac{1}{10}$ of the *nahayuga*, or 432,000 years. Its beginning was traditionally fixed to coincide with a theoretical starting-point of the celestial revolutions at a junction of the *nakshatras* Revatī and Krttikā, corresponding to midnight on February 18th, 3102 B.C. in Lanka.

THE MOTION OF THE EQUINOXES

Fairly accurate determinations of the sun's position by means of their *nakshatra* system enabled the Indian astronomers to notice very early that the equinoctial and solstitial points do not remain stationary. However, this fact was not mentioned in any text earlier than the *Sūrya Siddhānta*, which speaks of a libratory motion rather than a rotatory precession. It has been assumed that this notion was borrowed from Greek astronomy which does, in fact, have a theory of that kind, though there is no reason why the Indians could not have arrived at it independently. Thus, many first-century Indian and other astronomers believed that the first *nakshatra* was that belonging to the vernal equinox, though various early Vedic and Brahmanic texts used other systems. While ancient Vedic lists began the first *nakshatra* with the Pleiades (Krttikā), the *Jyotishavedānga*, which is alleged to be an appendix to the *Veda*, started with Aries (Aśvinī) or with the Indian Fly (Bharanī), and the more recent *Brāhmaṇa* once more with the Pleiades. Then again, during the first centuries of our era, the vernal equinox was observed to coincide with Aries. From comparisons between ancient texts and the observed facts, Indian astronomers came to the conclusion that the equinoctial points 'librated' between the Pleiades and Aries.

The velocity of the motion was estimated at 54 seconds per year, a remarkable approximation if one considers that Hipparchos' figure of 36 seconds was much farther removed from reality. However the number '54' was adopted for mystical rather than scientific reasons, for 54 is one-half of the ever-recurring 108. In fact, the total amplitude of the libration was assumed to be 108°, *viz.* 20° on either side of Revatī (Pisces) and again on either side of Aśvinī (Aries).

From the position of the original junction, the amplitude and velocity of the precession, and from traditional ideas of the original chanting of the Vedic hymns, the date of the beginning of the Kaliyuga has been calculated restrospectively, and the date so obtained was made the starting-point of the current era. However, the calendar based on it was incompatible with the ancient dynastic chronology of the Purānas. Subsequent attempts to revise that chronology scientifically have failed, because all of them were based on the mistaken notion of the libration of the equinoxes.

FUNDAMENTAL NUMBERS

All the results of the *Sūrya Siddhānta* are thus based on the following fundamental numbers, by which traditional myths were welded to astronomical theories:

27 (nakshatras) ×4 (phases)   = 108 = degrees of libration of the equinoxes.

27 (nakshatras) ×16 (lunar parts) = 432.

30 (days)   ×12 (months)   = 360 (days).

30 (moments) ×360 (days)   = 10,800.

360 (days)   ×12,000 (divine years) = 4,320,000 = the Great Year.

4,320,000 ÷ 4 = 1,080,000 = number of years containing an integral number of mean solar days.

4,320,000 ÷ 10 = Kaliyuga.

ASTRONOMICAL INSTRUMENTS

The *Surya Siddhānta* mentions only two astronomical instruments: the simple gnomon and the armillary sphere, which has always played an important role in Indian astronomy.

ĀRYABHATA

The period during which the *Sūrya Siddhānta* was written and later re-edited into the basic handbook of Indian astronomy also witnessed the birth of Āryabhaṭa, the great astronomer, who tells us that he had completed the first 23 years of his life at the end of the year 3600 of the Kaliyuga, *i.e.* about A.D. 499. There is no good reason for assuming, as so many have done, that his great work, the *Āryabhaṭiya*, was also *written* in that year, for Āryabhaṭa simply mentioned the date because of its remarkable numerical properties. In any case, the work was completed by about the beginning of the sixth century. As was the custom, its four sections and 121 couplets were written in terse style. The first section is an introduction to the special method of expressing numbers by syllables. The remaining 108 couplets, whose very number is a key to astronomy, are devoted to mathematics, and to the study of the earth and the positions of the moon and the sun. The *Āryabhaṭiya*, while mainly in agreement with the

Sūrya Siddhānta, introduces special notions of its own. Thus it mentions the rotation of the earth and develops the theory of epicycles. (P. C. Sen Gupta has suggested that the *Sūrya Siddhānta* was subsequently amended to fall in with Āryabhaṭa's views.) It divides the Great Year of the *Sūrya Siddhānta* into four equal epochs of 1,080,000 years each, whence the Kaliyuga represents 1,080,000 years, and not 432,000 as it does in the *Sūrya Siddhānta*.

Āryabhaṭa was one of the most original scientific authors India has produced, but though his school continued to flourish, particularly in Southern India, it was the *Sūrya Siddhānta* which exerted the greater influence on those of India's neighbours who, in Indo-China and Indonesia, adopted Indian cultural ideas from the beginning of the Christian era onward.

VARĀHAMIHIRA

In the middle of the sixth century, Varāhamihira wrote his *Panca-siddhantikā,* in which he summarized the astronomy of the five *Siddhāntas.* It may be called a critique of the earlier work and belongs to the astronomical treatises called *karanas.* Unfortunately the work is in a very poor state of preservation. Varāhamihira also wrote treatises on astrology, on divination and on practical knowledge. The most important of these is the *Brhatsamhitā,* the 'Great Compendium', which describes the motions and conjunctions of celestial bodies and their ominous significance. It also deals with meteorological phenomena, and with the divinatory significance of human behaviour, animals, precious stones, *etc.* In addition, Varāhamihira wrote two books on purely horoscopic astrology, the *Brhatjātaka* ('Great Horoscopy') and the *Laghujātaka* ('Short Horoscopy'), in which he used a great many Greek astrological terms beginning with the *hora,* the hour of birth.

BRAHMAGUPTA

Brahmagupta, born in 598, flourished in Ujjain, wrote his *Brāh-masphuṭa Siddhānta* in 628 and his *karana* on astronomical calculations, the *Khandakhādyaka,* in 664. Though Al-Bīrunī considers him the most accomplished of Indian astronomers he was an opponent of Āryabhaṭa's doctrine that the earth rotated. His influence was greatest in Western India.

With Brahmagupta, the classical period of ancient Indian astronomy must be considered closed. There followed the Moslem invasion and increasing contacts with Arab science, and then the medieval period of Indian astronomy, with such authors as Bhāskara in the twelfth century.

CHRONOLOGY: THE DIVISION OF TIME

Ancient astronomical works had established the beginnings of a great number of eras, and also methods of dividing time for chronological and astrological purposes.

Each lunar month, *i.e.* the interval between two full moons, was called by the name of the *nakshatra* in which the full moon occurred. The lunar month was divided into thirty 'lunar' days or *tithis* and also into two fortnights—a 'clear' one beginning at new moon, and a 'dark' one beginning at full moon. Each *tithi* had a special name and was divided into two *karanas*. Calendars related lunar to solar days.

Solar months were called by the names of the corresponding lunar months, or, after the introduction of the signs of the zodiac, by the zodiacal sign in which the sun appeared. Since lunar months and days are of uneven lengths, Indian astronomers were forced to add to, or subtract from, them from time to time. On the other hand, the precession of the equinoxes upset the original correspondence between the months and the signs of the zodiac, much as it did in Western astrology. As a consequence, Indian astrologers used two systems: the *sāyana* ('with the displacement') and the *nirayana* ('without the displacement').

The week of seven days, named after the planets in the Greek order, made its debut in the *Siddhānta* period, together with the signs of the zodiac and other manifestations of Greek astrology. The three Vedic seasons gave way to six seasons of two months each, namely:

SEASONS	
vasanta (Spring)	caitra (March–April)
	vaiśakha (April–May)
grīshma (Hot Season)	jyaishṭha (May–June)
	āshādha (June–July)
varsha (Rainy Season)	śrāvana (July–August)
	bhādrapada (August–September)
śarad (Autumn)	āśvina (September–October)
	kārttika (October–November)
hemanta (Winter)	margaśirsha (November–December)
	pausha (December–January)
śiśira (Frosty Season)	māgha (January–February)
	phālguna (February–March).

The revolution of Jupiter served as the basis of two cycles, one of twelve years, and another of sixty (5 × 12) years which was in more general use, and each of whose years had a special name. The twelve-year cycle was either taken as the interval between a heliacal rising of Jupiter and its next setting, or else its individual years were obtained by dividing the sidereal period of Jupiter by twelve. In both cycles, Jovian years were shorter than solar years, since the period of Jupiter is less than twelve full solar years. Hence a Jovian year had to be omitted from time to time. This practice was stopped in A.D. 907, when the names of the years of the sixty-year Jovian cycle were simply transferred to series of sixty solar years.

MATHEMATICS

Brahmanic Mathematics

While there are no special Vedic or Brahmanic mathematical texts, the Vedic language itself is evidence that large numbers were in fairly common use, for it contains special terms for the powers of ten, up to 10^8. The Classical Sanskrit language went further still, for it continued the Vedic series as far as 10^{23}. (The Greeks stopped at 10^4.)

Since the ancient Vedic and Brahmanic scripts are quite unknown there is no means of telling whether they had a written notation, or on what system it might have been based. However, we do know something about Vedic geometry since Vedic altars were constructed according to strict geometrical principles. In fact, Vedic rituals were designed to reproduce in form and expression the behaviour of those forces of the universe which they were meant to aid or control.

THE *Śulva Sūtra*

The *Kalpa Sūtra*, a series of texts on ritual observances, contains the *Śulva Sūtra* ('Rules of the Thread' or 'Measuring Line'), devoted quite particularly to the correct rules of altar construction. Its principles go back to the so-called Baudhāyana, Āpastamba, and Kātyāyana schools, and though no precise date can be assigned to the work, many scholars have claimed that its geometrical information is a relatively late addition to ritualist texts. However, since one of the basic Vedic texts, the *Taittirīya Samhita*, already mentions various altar shapes described in the *Śulva Sūtra*, there are no grounds for holding that its geometry was an innovation.

Sacrificial fires (*vedi*) had to be stacked into simple geometrical forms with sides in fixed proportions, and brick altars (*citi*) had to combine fixed dimensions with a fixed number of bricks. Moreover, their surface areas had to be such that the altars could be increased without change of shape, and this is where geometrical skills came in. The theorem of Pythagoras was propounded in the following

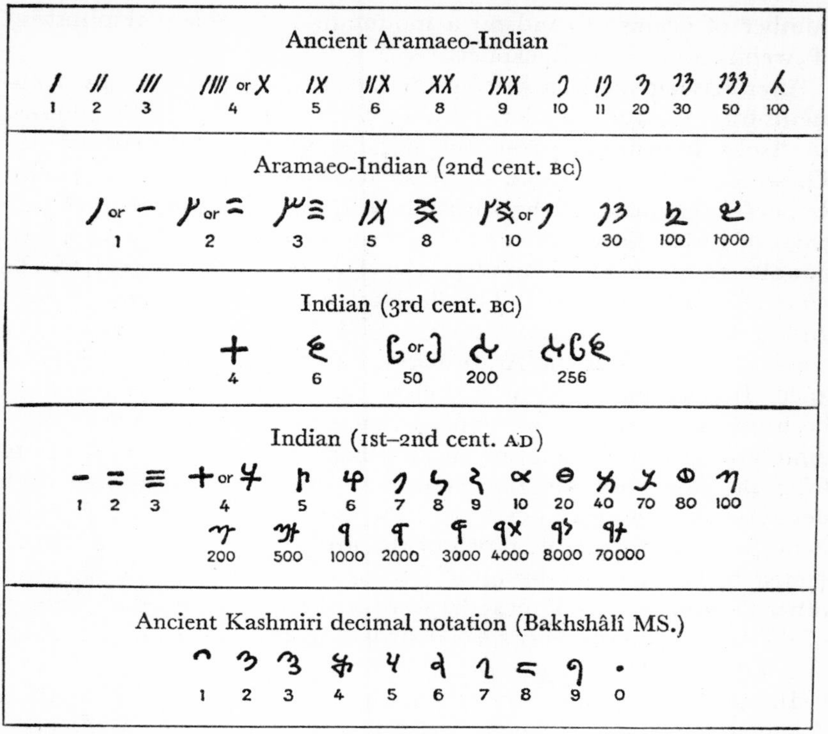

Ancient Aramaeo-Indian													

fig. 19 Indian numerals.

form: 'The transverse chord of a rectangle produces (by the construction of a square on itself) what the length and the breadth produce separately'.

By its very nature, the text, which was meant to provide rules of thumb, failed to give any proofs of its procedures. Hence, while we know the mathematical results we are ignorant of the methods or arguments on which they were based.

Early Classical Mathematics

Apart from geometrical information, the Brahmanic ritual texts also give us incidental hints about other mathematical concerns. Thus we have mentioned astronomical speculations about the 'remarkable' numbers 27, 10,800 and 432,000. A Buddhist text, the *Lalitavistara*, which describes the life of the Buddha (who preached his doctrine in the fifth century B.C.) and which lists the sciences mastered by the Buddha child, alludes to a method of assessing the number of grains of sand on a mountain—a problem reminiscent of Archimedes' Sand-Reckoner.

After having made a brief proto-historical appearance in documents from the Indus valley, number symbols were officially adopted on Asoka inscriptions from the middle of the third century B.C. These symbols were found to be so satisfactory that they survived for several centuries of the Christian era, and even longer in certain parts of India. Special symbols were assigned not only to each unit but also to all tens and hundreds, so that 220, for instance, could be rendered without a zero. The decimal notation using nine figures and a special zero-sign, which would later be disseminated as 'Indian' throughout the Arab world, had not yet made its appearance. It does not necessarily follow that that system had not yet been invented since, as we shall see, once invented it was not immediately used to the exclusion of all others. In any case, inscriptions from the first post-Christian centuries (the *Nāsik* inscriptions) still describe numbers up to 70,000 in the old way, the higher numbers being formed by combinations of the lower. Thus 4,000 was represented by the thousand-symbol followed by the four-symbol, while other thousands (and hundreds) were written down by combinations of the basic symbols with special strokes to give, for example, 2,000 and 3,000 or 200 and 300, *etc.*

In north-west India, documents in the *kharosthī* script used an Aramaic notation. (*Kharosthī*, we saw, was an Aramaic modification of the ancient Indian phonetic script.) That notation was first introduced during the Persian conquest of the Indus basin, and before Alexander expelled the Parthians, and its use was widespread in Central Asia up to about the seventh century A.D., but particularly during the first centuries of our era.

Later Classical Mathematics

Mathematics played an important role in classical Indian astronomy, though the relevant texts tell us little about mathematical developments as such. The standard of mathematics seems to have been fairly high. Thus the *Sūrya Siddhānta* contains the earliest known sine-tables, and the second chapter of the *Āryabhaṭīya* (*ganita*) is devoted to arithmetic and algebra. Āryabhaṭa extracted square and cube roots by the method we use today, *i.e.* by dividing the squares or cubes into groups of two or three figures. In other words, he must either have used a decimal notation with nine figures *plus* a zero (not the ordinary system then in vogue), or else an abacus, where empty spaces would have represented the zero symbol.

ĀRYABHAṬA

We saw that Āryabhaṭa also expressed high numbers by means of syllables. He could do so since ancient Indian phoneticians had devised a phonetic alphabet including fifteen vowels, twenty-five stopped consonants (k–m) and eight other letters (y–h). Āryabhaṭa used the stopped consonants to represent the numbers 1–25, when they preceded the vowel a, and higher decimal powers of these numbers (up to 10¹⁶) when they preceded other vowels. The letters y–h were used to represent the numbers 30–100. Thus while *ṭa* represented 3, *ṭi* stood for 300 and *ṭu* for 30,000.

Āryabhaṭa also studied algebra and solved simultaneous equations of the first degree by reciprocal division.

In geometry he obtained the value of π as follows: 'The circumference is 62,832. The diameter is 20,000. By this rule the relation of circumference to diameter is given.' Its value works out at 3.1416. While this was an example and no general rule, Āryabhaṭa also formulated general laws, *e.g.* 'One should subtract the sum of the squares of two factors from the square of their sum. Half the result is the product of the two factors.' Or, as we should put it

$$ab = \frac{(a+b)^2 - (a^2+b^2)}{2}.$$

DECIMAL NOTATION

We have seen that the so-called Arab notation was known to Āryabhaṭa at the beginning of the sixth century. It made its first known appearance on inscriptions in 595 (in the year 346 of the *Cedi* era).

The actual form of the zero, which varied from region to region, is known only from ninth-century archaeological inscriptions though there are references to it going back to the sixth century. The first recorded zero was a simple point, and though it was later turned into a circle, Kashmir retained the original form until long afterwards.

A decimal notation without a zero symbol is used to this day in the Tamil script of Southern India, in which there are special symbols for tens, hundreds and thousands. Units placed before these symbols are multipliers, while units placed after them are added. Hence, as we stated earlier, the mere invention of a zero sign was by no means tantamount to its adoption. While it is quite possible that the Indians borrowed their zero sign from Mesopotamia, India was the first country to have used the complete decimal system of place-value notation which has since become universal.

BRAHMAGUPTA AND MAHĀVĪRA

In the seventh century, the astronomer Brahmagupta outstripped Āryabhaṭa in algebraic, though not in astronomical, knowledge. He managed to solve indeterminate equations of the second degree, and initiated a period of constant progress in mathematics which culminated in the work of the ninth-century Jaina master, Mahāvīra of Mysore, the *Gaṇitasārasaṇgraha* ('Brief Explanation of the Compendium of Calculation'). The book is based on the work of Brahmagupta, but simplified and extended many of his concepts. It begins by defining all its mathematical terms, and then deals with fractions, the rule of three, areas, volumes and, particularly, with calculations applied to excavations and shadows. The book is studded with examples and with solutions of problems, and though it is condensed like all other rhymed Indian texts, it represents a great pedagogical advance.

MEDICINE

Vedic Medicine

Medicine is alluded to frequently in Vedic texts, primarily as a magic art. A number of hymns of the *Atharva Veda*, in particular, were thought to act as remedial incantations, and the *Kauśika Sutra* lists them as such and prescribes special rituals for reciting them. These hymns and the accompanying ritual prescriptions mention a great number of diseases and many plants with real medicinal properties. Thus magical procedures went hand in hand with fairly detailed practical knowledge. The richness of the anatomical vocabulary of Vedic Sanskrit is evidence of careful observations of the structure of the human body, and also of that of a number of animals —particularly of horses, the main victims of Vedic sacrifices. Moreover, Vedic references to diseases and their remedies did not represent the sum total of the medical knowledge or practices of the times. In fact, the texts are somewhat derogatory of physicians, and could therefore not have been written by qualified practitioners.

ANATOMY AND PHYSIOLOGY

Vedic anatomical nomenclature also included terms referring to the more obscure constituents of the human body. Among these were *ojas* (energy) and *rasa* (vital juice). *Rasa* may be compared with the 'humours' of classical Western medicine. Physiological processes were thought to have their counterparts in nature at large. Thus, the *Yajur Veda* asserts that bile acts in the human body much as fire acts on water. The idea that bile had an igneous nature was to persist even in classical Indian medicine. The most important vital element and also the prime mover of life was the breath (*prāṇa*) which was but one manifestation of the wind (*vāta* or *vāyu*), the moving force of the Universe. In other words, Vedic physiology was a highly developed pneumatic doctrine. 'Breath' not only governed respiration but all the other physiological processes as well. In fact, five different types of breath were often cited. The *Brāhmaṇas* claimed that mucus represents the element water in living bodies.

NOSOLOGY AND THERAPY

Vedic nosology described individual diseases by their major symptoms, *e.g.*, pains, emaciation, fever, *etc.* It made few attempts to examine the possible relationships between associated symptoms and contented itself with describing some as brothers or cousins of others. Etiology was largely neglected, and what causes are mentioned (mainly in the *Brāhmaṇa* legends) are usually magical or mythical rather than pathogenic. Demons, and notably the *grāhi* (who 'seized' men), played an important though not paramount role in causing illnesses. Breaches, voluntary or not, of the cosmic order (*rta*) were punished especially with dropsy, a disease commonly attributed to the 'clansmen' of Baruṇa, the guardian of the *rta*. Remedies were generally based on plants, incantations, practices of mimetic magic, and often on apparent analogies. For example, the resin which closes the scars of trees was thought to help the formation of scabs when taken orally—a primitive kind of nature cure.

Classical Medicine

TRADITIONS

Those medical texts which were held in high repute during the first centuries of the Christian era became the source books of the *Āyur Veda* ('Knowledge of Longevity') which, suitably amended in the course of time, have lost none of their authority to this day. Because of the high regard in which they have always been held, these texts were responsible for the oblivion into which all earlier medical texts have fallen. Still, the basic elements of the ancient doctrines can be isolated from a common thread running through the works of a chain of authors, the earliest of whom were mythical and the latest the authentic founders of the two main schools of medical thought: the *Ātreya* and the *Suśruta*. The *Ātreya* is known from the *Caraka Samhitā* ('Compendium of Caraka') attributed to Bhela and the apocryphal Hārīta, and from the *Suśruta Samhitā* ('Compendium of Suśruta'). Caraka was Court Physician to the Indo-Scythian king Kanishka, who lived at the end of the first or the beginning of the second century A.D. He was looked upon as the mouthpiece and reviser of Agniveśa, a disciple of Ātreya. Part of his work was modified and completed in later times, but his earlier doctrine had a great deal in common with that of Bhela, a pupil of both Ātreya and of Agniveśa. This doctrine was therefore neither Caraka's, Agniveśa's nor Bhela's but probably went back to Ātreya. Moreover, the traditional belief that Ātreya was the real founder of the doctrine is reflected in Buddhist texts, according to which Ātreya was the teacher of Jīvaka, a contemporary of the Buddha. Hence, Ātreya must have lived in the sixth century B.C. and, in any case, long before the Christian era. Also, since the notions attributed to Ātreya are really a development of Vedic physiological conceptions, there seems every reason to suppose that the two were not too distant in time, and that the more polished *Caraka Samhitā* was the later of the two compendia.

Suśruta set himself the task of presenting the doctrine of Divodāsa, King of Benares and incarnation of the god Dhanvantari, the mythical holder of the liquid of immortality. His *Samhitā* is based on traditions which apparently go back to the same Brahmanic sources as those of the *Caraka Samhitā* with which it shares its basic doctrines.

THE BASIC DOCTRINES

The *Āyur Veda* develops a theory of organic functions and disturbances. It avers that the five elementary substances constituting the universe also constitute the human body. Thus earth, water, fire, wind, and space, correspond respectively to firm tissue, humour, bile, breath and organic cavities. While earth and space are inert, the three other substances are active. The *Caraka Samhitā* still bears traces of ancient attempts to attribute a basic physiological role to only one of the three active elements, but states quite clearly that Ātreya had insisted on their mutual interactions.

Wind, fire and water act in the body in the form of breath, bile and mucus. This triplet, called *tridhātu*, appears in various guises because each organic element has five principal forms.

Breath is more than mere respiration, for it consists of *prāṇa*, breath in our sense of the word, *udāna* which causes vocal sounds to appear, *samāna* which stokes the internal fire (governs digestion), *apāna* which expels faecal matter, and *vyāna* which flows through the entire body and governs the motions of the limbs.

The bile, *pitta*, also has different functions. As *pācaka*, the igneous constituent, it helps to 'cook' the food; as *ranjaka* it gives colour to *rasa,* the vital juice resulting from digestion, in order to turn it into blood; as *sādhaka* it kindles the desires of the heart; as *ālocaka* it shines from the eyes and governs vision; and as *bhrājaka* it glistens in the skin.

Mucus, *kapha* or *śleshman,* a viscous fluid, keeps the organs together, helps to articulate the joints, and is responsible for such processes as the adhesion of food to the tongue.

Seasons, climatic changes, and hygienic conditions help to speed up or slow down the action of the three organic elements. Moreover, a particular element can predominate in one person, as a result of his particular constitution. Sudden over-excitation of a given element leads to general physiological disequilibrium and a morbid state, so that the three elements are sometimes called the *tridosha* or 'triad of troubles'.

Disequilibrium of the 'elements' usually leads to complex pathological conditions, caused by various combinations of 'troubles'. The simultaneous disorder of all three elements is called *sannipāta.* Beyond that, diseases are rarely pure or typical, varying as they do according to personal temperaments and conditions. Even if one element is the main culprit, it invariably throws the others out of gear. Most diseases are therefore associated with particular disturbances of breath, bile and mucus, combined in various ways.

Nosology was highly developed. Diseases were classified in three ways: (1) according to the main organic element responsible for them (thus *vātavyādhi*—'diseases of the breath'—were thought to cause lack of muscular co-ordination, convulsions, contractions, and paralysis); (2) according to their anatomical situation (*e.g.* diseases of the head, the skin, the eyes, *etc.*); and (3) according to the nature of the major symptoms (fevers, tumours, *etc.*). Nosological considerations were particularly used in the work of Suśruta, who devoted much space to local or surgical conditions. While Caraka's etiology (*nidāna*) was restricted to a discussion of fevers (*jvara*), haemorrhagic diseases (*raktapitta,* blood and bile), internal tumours, urinary affections, skin diseases, consumption, psychological conditions and epilepsy, Suśruta added a number of localized conditions, including piles, anal fistulas, erysipelas, various ulcers, *etc.*

This kind of nosology has striking parallels in Greek medicine. Thus the Hippocratic treatise *On Breaths* refers diseases to processes in nature, very much as did Ātreya and the ancient Vedic texts on winds and organic breaths. Like the Greeks, the Indians referred to nature rather than to demoniac possession to explain epilepsy and other convulsive disorders. Plato's pathology, developed in the *Timaeos,* is almost indistinguishable from the doctrine of the *tridosha,* both of which cite the same three elements—air, fire and water, or breath, bile and mucus. Not only is Plato's conception of bile very similar to that of the Vedic texts, but such notions as haemorrhagic diseases due to an eruption of the bile into the blood are found in both.

Plato's intermittent fevers, too, were known to Indian medicine from the *Atharva Veda*, though their causes were explained differently. In fact, many of Plato's explanations differ from the Indians', and it appears that the two schools often derived different conclusions from common principles and similar observational criteria.

The Indian classical texts were written later than the *Timaeos* but their sources were older than Plato's. Hence there can be no question of India's having borrowed her medicine (like so many other disciplines) from Greece. On the contrary, India may very well have influenced the Hippocratic Collection and the *Timaeos*, particularly since Plato failed to mention his sources and since, moreover, his doctrine is closer to the Indian than to that of any contemporary Greek school. The influence of Indian ideas on certain aspects of Greek medicine during Plato's time is further supported by the mention of Indian medicaments, including pepper, in the *Diseases of Women*, part of the Hippocratic Collection. Indian medical knowledge must have seeped through the Parthian Empire, then the overlord of parts of India and Greece alike, along the trade routes described by Strabo and Pliny. In Aristotle's time it was, moreover, generally accepted that Indian intellectuals had visited Greece even before Alexander's campaign. Thus, a disciple of Aristotle, Aristoxenes of Tarentum, reported that an Indian sage—to whom he attributed ideas in accordance with what we know about Indian thought of that time—came to call on Socrates in Athens. Hence the similarities between Indian and Greek medicine may well be explained by common contacts, from which two parallel schools later emerged.

MEDICAL METHODS

Indian medicine, based as it was on nature, generally ignored all supernatural diseases, or else discussed them outside the more rational texts. Thus all references to demons, and all prognoses based on omens and oneiromancy, are confined to special chapters, whose resemblance to an Akkadian treatise used by the Persians suggests that they were imported into India by the Parthians.

Diagnoses were made from symptoms and the circumstances of their first appearance, and from determinations of the vital elements involved. Once that was done, established precedents were used for restoring 'elemental' equilibrium, and prognoses were made accordingly. Though examinations were extremely thorough Indian knowledge about the human body remained rather primitive, as did that of all ancient schools of medicine where anatomy and physiology lagged behind clinical practice. Suśruta gave a method of dissecting organs, after they have begun to disintegrate in water, and was therefore a forerunner of Lacauchie, who introduced hydrotomy in the nineteenth century. However, that method could not have been the basis of normal diagnoses.

Methodological concepts, on the other hand, were far more highly developed. The need for submitting traditional interpretations and analogies to a strict critique was felt in fairly early times. Caraka, above all, introduced logic into the critique of clinical criteria. Logic, in fact, was a characteristic of Indian culture during the first centuries of the Christian era, when Indian scholars made a point of testing the validity of all their arguments and beliefs by strictly rational means.

THERAPY

Indian medicine could draw not only on theoretical texts but on a considerable repertoire of therapeutic and hygienic procedures. While notions of hygiene were based mainly on physiological theories, therapy was based primarily on observation.

The Indian *materia medica* consisted mainly of vegetable substances, at least until the Christian era, when minerals were also introduced.

Apart from edible plants, administered for dietetic reasons, Indian physicians also prescribed plants with purely medical properties for use as electuaries, infusions, powders, ointments and enemas, and also as errhines, which were not commonly prescribed by Western physicians. Oils (*taila*), or rather oils used as excipients combined with powders or electuaries, played a very important role in Indian medicine.

Surgeons used a variety of instruments for performing embryotomies, for removing bladder stones, cataracts, *etc.* They even introduced a special method of tying intestinal wounds which must have involved a great deal of prior research. Since normal sutures caused the intestines to become constricted, Indian surgeons hit upon an original method of joining the lips of the wound: they caused them to be bitten by large ants. They then cut off the body of the ant, leaving behind the mandibles as clamps which were tolerated by the system. The abdominal wall was closed by ordinary sutures. This method was later adopted by the Arabs, who passed it on to the West. It survives to this day, notably on the Somali coast, where it is used to good effect (when no infection sets in).

SECONDARY CLASSICAL TEXTS

From the beginning of the Christian era until the eighth century A.D. Indian medical literature was augmented with the addition of a large number of texts distinct from the traditions of Ātreya and Dhanvantari embodied in the *Caraka-*, *Belha-*, and *Suśruta-Samhitās*. The most important were the *Yogaśataka* and the *Amrtahrdaya*.

The *Yogaśataka* is a medical compendium in one hundred stanzas and was extremely popular and widespread in its time. It was translated into the Kuchean language (Central Asia) in the seventh or eighth century A.D. and later into Tibetan. To this day, it is consulted in Ceylon. It is probably the work to which the seventh-century Chinese monk, I-Ching, referred when he described a newly published volume, for his description tallies perfectly with the contents of the *Yogaśataka*. Indian tradition, on the other hand, attributes the work to the Buddhist patriarch Nāgārjuna, who lived in the second century, though we cannot entirely rely on this because some manuscripts of the *Yogaśataka* mention one Vararuci, and not Nāgārjuna, as the author.

The name Nāgārjuna is mentioned in another tradition as belonging to an alchemist, and he is referred to by the eleventh-century Arab scientist, Al-Bīruni, as living only a hundred years before his own time. But as early as the seventh century the Chinese monk, Huan Chang, confidently identified an alchemist named Nāgārjuna with the second-century Buddhist philosopher, so that there seem to have been at least two writers of this name.

In any case, the *Yogaśataka* is based on the classical *Āyur Veda* and not on alchemy. A purely alchemical treatise on mercury and its derivatives, the *Rasaratnākāra*, is also attributed to a Nāgārjuna, and probably with greater justification, though we cannot tell to which of the two scholars bearing this name. There is no doubt that the alchemical knowledge of earlier centuries was incorporated in the seventh-century writings. Though always distinct from the medical tradition, alchemy paved the way for a new medicine, by suggesting those mineral drugs which were finally incorporated into later *Āyur Vedic* texts.

The *Amrtahrdaya*, the 'Essence of Ambrosia', is a large medical treatise in four sections, of which only the Tibetan translation is extant. It must probably be placed in the late classical period for it contains such innovations as pulse-taking (*nāḍīparīkshā*) which was subsequently to become an important Indian method. Because of its four sections, its Tibetan name is *Rgyud-bzi*, 'the Four Books'. Tibetan sources attribute the work to a Buddha, Bhaishajyaguru, the 'Master of Remedies'. Despite its innovations, the work has the form and approach of the great classical texts, and quotes a number of classical authorities. The Tibetan version was later translated into Mongolian and remained the medical classic both in Tibet and Mongolia until fairly recently, though other Indian medical works were also translated into these languages.

Vāgbhaṭa

The medical works of Vāgbhaṭa probably appeared in the late classical period, as well. The three works attributed to this author are the *Ashtānga Samgraha* and the *Ashdāngahrdaya Samhitā*, which are, in fact, two different versions of one and the same book, largely in agreement with the *Suśruta-* and *Caraka-Samhitās*, and an alchemical book, the *Rasaratnasamuccaya*. Vāgbhaṭa's best-known work is the *Ashdāngahrdaya Samhitā*, and it is because of it that he has been ranged by the side of the classical authors of the *Suśruta* and the *Caraka*. The work has been translated into Tibetan.

Veterinary Medicine

Veterinary medicine is mentioned in numerous texts, mainly of the post-classical period, though all are based on a very old tradition. There are separate works on the diseases of horses and of elephants, both of which go back to Vedic or mythological sources. The effective treatment of elephants, as a separate medical discipline, is mentioned by Megasthenes in the fourth century B.C. In his account Megasthenes, Seleucos' ambassador to King Candragupta, describes the kind of treatment which was subsequently to be incorporated in such treatises as the *Hastyāyur Veda* of Pālakāpyamuni. The greatest Indian authority on horse-breeding and hippiatry was Śalihotra.

BIBLIOGRAPHY

General Science

L. RENOU and J. FILLIOZAT, *L'Inde classique. Manuel des études indiennes*, Vol. II, Paris, 1954, pp. 138–194 and 720–738.

Astronomy and Mathematics

G. THIBAULT, Astronomie, Astrologie und Mathematik, *Grundriss des Indo-Arischen Philologie*, 1899.

B. DATTA and A. N. SINGH, *History of Hindu mathematics*, Lahore, 1935–38; Vol. I, *Numeral notations and arithmetic*; Vol. II, *Algebra*.

A new edition in one volume was published by the Asia Publishing House (Bombay and London) in 1962.

H. T. COLEBROOKE, *Algebra with Arithmetic and Mensuration from the Sanskrit of Brahmagupta and Bhaskara*, London, 1817.

Culvasutra, ed., trans. G. THIBAULT, in *The Pandit*, 1875–77 (*Baudhāyana*); A. BURK in *Zeitschrift der Deutschen Morgenländischen Gesellschaft*, 1902.

G. R. KAYE, Bakhshali manuscript, *Archaeological Survey of India*, XLIII, Calcutta, 1927–33.

G. R. KAYE, Hindu astronomy, *Memoirs of the Arch. Survey of India*, No 18, Calcutta, 1924.

Jyotishavedānga: A. WEBER, Ueber den Veda-Kalendar namens Jyotisham, *Abhandlungen Akad. Berlin*, 1862; LALA CHHOTE LAL, Allahabad, 1907; R. SHAMASHASTRI, Mysore, 1936.

Pancasiddhāntika: G. THIBAULT and SUDHAKARA DVIVEDI, Benares, 1889, and re-ed. Lahore, 1930.

Sūryasiddhānta: trans. SUDHAKARA DVIVEDI, Calcutta, 1909 and 1925; E. BURGESS and W. D. WHITNEY, *Journal of American Oriental Society*, 1860, republished by PH. GANGULY, Calcutta, 1935.

ĀRYABHAṬA: W. E. CLARK, *The Āryabhaṭīya of Āryabhaṭa*, Chicago, 1930.

Brhatsamhitā: trans. H. KERN, *Journal Royal Asiatic Society*, 1870–75.

BRAHMAGUPTA: *Khandakhādyaka*: trans. P. C. SENGUPTA, Calcutta, 1934.

Medicine

J. JOLLY, Medizin, *Grundriss der Indo-arischen Phil.*, 1901; Eng. transl. by KASHIKAR, Poona, 1951.

J. FILLIOZAT, *La doctrine classique de la médecine indienne, ses origines et ses parallèles grecs*, Paris 1949; Pronostics médicaux akkadiens, grecs et indiens, *Journal asiatique*, 1952.

Suśruta: Eng. transl. K. L. BHISHAGRATNA, Calcutta, 1916–19.

Caraka: transl. *Shree Gulabkunverba Ayurvedic Society*, Jamnagar, 1949, 6 vols.

Vāgbhaṭa: Germ. transl. L. HILGENBERG and W. KIRFEL, Leyden, 1941.

13 Young girl writing

14 The Iron Pillar at Delhi

CHAPTER 5

Ancient Chinese Science

HISTORICAL BACKGROUND

The main theatre in which Chinese history was unfolded was the basin of the Hwang-Ho or Yellow River. This river descends through tremendous gorges from the high Tibetan plateau and makes a large sweep through a mountainous region covered with fertile yellow soil, deposited there by the high winds. It finally enters the maritime province of Shantung, an alluvial promontory jutting into the sea. To the south, another historical river, the Yangtze Kiang, also twists through mountain regions enclosing fertile plains, the most important of which is the 'Red Basin' in Szechuan.

The humid climate of China encouraged the growth of forests, but intensive fellings since the Neolithic period have largely destroyed them. During the third millennium B.C., the banks of the Yellow River saw the rise of a Neolithic agricultural civilization, whose contact with neighbouring cultures is inferred from similarities in their decorated pottery vessels. It is a fair deduction to say that the Chinese were a pastoral people when they first settled in the river basin and their language shows that they were related to the Central Asian mountain dwellers, of whom the Tibetans were the western-most and the Burmese the southernmost representatives. Thus, all these peoples used the same written symbols to designate 'sheep'. Soon afterwards, however, crop-growing began to supplant the earlier stock-breeding and animal husbandry was reduced to the rearing of pigs, dogs, and draught-oxen. The monsoon, and the climate with which it is associated, made a pastoral existence on the plains very precarious, hence agriculture became the economic basis of Chinese civilization.

On the other hand, China's northern and western neighbours in the valleys of the high Asiatic plateau, where the climate is too dry for trees to flourish, have maintained a pastoral way of life since the earliest times. Thus China, unlike India, Mesopotamia and Egypt, was the only fertile country to place agriculture before stock-breeding. This is one of the main reasons why she was able to preserve

her language and civilization despite frequent invasions by the
neighbouring pastoral peoples during the thousands of years of her
history.

It is to those prehistoric times that we must trace back the legends
about the mythical emperors and ancient culture-heroes of the 1st
dynasty. The first identifiable archaeological documents are bone
inscriptions found at Anyang, in Honan, one of the capitals of
the 2nd, or Shang, dynasty. By the fourteenth century B.C. the
Chinese had learned to write, and from the astronomical and
astrological events described by royal diviners we can reconstruct
the picture of a highly organized society. The bronze vases fashioned
during that period represented unexcelled craftsmanship.

Traditionally, it was in the year 1122 B.C. that the Prince of Chou,
a province somewhere in the area of the present Kansu and Shensi,
seized the Shang capital and founded the 3rd royal dynasty. After
some centuries the introduction of new techniques, such as the iron
plough, and the spread of Chinese civilization into the valley of the
Yangtze, led to the collapse of the closely-knit Chou state. Feudal
lords proclaimed themselves kings and formed independent states,
the chief of which were the dukedoms of Chhi in Shantung, of Chi
on the upper Yellow River, and of Chhin in the extreme West. The
time of this division of the Chou state is called the Warring States
period (eighth–third centuries B.C.), and the anarchic conditions
then prevailing hastened the birth of the 'hundred schools' of philosophy, whose founders tried to remedy the chaos by prescribing rules
of good government and neighbourly peace.

We must distinguish two groups among these schools, the 'activists'
whose philosophy was typical of stock-breeders and sailors and who
held that worth-while objectives could be attained only by active
effort, and the 'passivists'. One activist school meriting the attention
of historians of science was the Mohist (*mo chia*) whose doctrine was
that of universal love spread and preserved by might of arms. Another
important school was the Legalist (*fa chia*) to whom peace was much
what it was to the Romans: coercive unification under a central
government, which alone could enforce obedience to its laws.

The passivist schools stemmed from agricultural traditions. To
them, all active effort was anathema. The most important was the
Confucian (*ju chia*), which considered that all volition without knowledge was impotent, and that man could not be studied outside his
environment. Confucius idealized the patriarchal society of the Bronze
Age, and considered the essential virtues to be embodied in the rules
of proper conduct, namely rites (*li*) and equitable dealing (*i*). The
ideogram for '*i*' contains a sheep, which nobles used once to divide
among themselves at their feasts, but which had since become the

symbol of mutual aid. Confucius denounced selfishness (*ssu*), a word characterized by the symbol for wheat, no doubt reflecting the fact that the peasants were reluctant to surrender their corn to the nobles. Still, Confucianism fitted in well with the mores of a peasant civilization. The most famous of Confucius's disciples, Mencius (Meng Kho), was wont to compare men with plants, saying that if one tugs at plants to bring them to flower, one simply causes them to die. For Mencius, governments must be held as responsible for social unrest as peasants for the bad state of their fields. Clearly, Confucius and his school looked upon the art of government as a science and hence were the forerunners of modern sociology.

A related school, the Taoist, looked upon men as isolated individuals, and taught that each thing had a *tao*, or 'way', of its own. The Taoists held that men could achieve longevity, and even immortality, by discovering the *tao* of natural man—*i.e.* of man before he became moulded by society, and before he lost the secret of his real nature. The Taoists were no respecters of property or of social hierarchies, but strove for the simple life. Hence, though their studies led to some technological advances, these advances rested more often on the development of personal skills than on a general raising of the scientific level. Even so, the Taoists must be considered the first Chinese psychologists and naturalists. Their world-view was devoid of all transcendent or anthropocentric notions. Thus, we may read in the *Lieh Tzu* that the blessings of the earth were no more bestowed upon men by the heavens than man was bestowed upon fleas or tigers.

None of these various schools (or *ka*, as the Chinese called them) had official backing, but in 318 B.C. the King of Chhi founded his famous academy staffed by Taoists, Confucianists and Mohists alike. Meanwhile, a Legalist School flourished in the western provinces, and when the western King of Chhin became the first emperor of unified China in 221 B.C. that school emerged triumphant. (The word 'China' is, in fact, derived from Chhin.) However, its brutal methods, which involved the destruction of the works of poets, historians and philosophers, rendered it very unpopular. Then, in 206 B.C., three years after the death of the founder of the empire, a bandit chief founded the Han dynasty, and restored Confucianism as the official doctrine. China, with her agricultural traditions and production, and her lack of maritime or overland contacts with neighbours of a comparable degree of civilization, had no need for a highly centralized state on the Western pattern. Hence Confucianism and Taoism reflected her temper best in the long run, the former predominating during the periods of prosperity, and the latter during times of trouble and famine.

In 141 B.C., the Han government dismissed all Legalist officials, and in 124 B.C. founded an official school in the capital where future dignitaries were taught Confucian principles.

On the other hand, the most famous of the Han emperors consulted Taoist philosophers to learn particularly the secret of immortality. After the Han dynasty had spread towards Japan, Korea and Kweichow, and had annexed the Kingdom of Non Yüeh, its reign was interrupted from A.D. 9 to 23 by the so-called 'interregnum' of Wang Mang, the first and last Hsin emperor. He declared all land to be state property. While iron and salt works had been nationalized previously, Wang Mang wanted to go further and to help the peasants and the treasury alike by nationalizing the grain trade, by liberating the slaves, and by distributing the land in a more equitable fashion. But inundations of the Yellow River caused a peasant uprising led by a secret Taoist society, the Red Eyebrows, and put an end to his reign.

Han China was by far the most prosperous and advanced country of all Asia, and remained so until a second peasant uprising. This was led by the Yellow Turban society and split up the empire in A.D. 184. The period of the Three Kingdoms (*San-Kuo*), from A.D. 220–280, was one of constant wars between three dynasties, which depopulated the country. (It was during that period that the wheelbarrow was first invented and that the use of paper became more widespread.) Finally, unity was briefly restored by the Chin dynasty. The northern barbarians carried their raids farther and farther inland, and when they captured the Chin capital in A.D. 311 and 317, they put an end to that period of China's history which we have tried to sketch out very briefly. We shall now turn our attention to ancient China's main contributions in the scientific field.

MATHEMATICS

NOTATION

The Chinese language uses monosyllabic words to designate the first ten integers and also the hundreds, thousands and ten thousands. Tibeto-Burman (a group of languages related to Chinese) has similar numerals, and so has the Thai group. Since Thai languages have no other terms in common with Chinese, they may well have borrowed these names from China, in which case Chinese numerals go back to prehistoric times.

The first bone inscriptions (thirteenth century B.C.) show that numerals were written and pronounced as they are in modern

Written	Numbers		Numerals	Celestial roots			
	Pronunciation						
	Ancient	*Modern*					
一	ʔiĕt	i	|	甲	kap	chia	1
二	ñi'	erh	||	乙	ʔiĕt	i	2
三	sâm	san	|||	丙	püAng	ping	3
四	si'	ssu	||||	丁	tieng	ting	4
五	'ngo	wu	✕	戊	mŏu'	wu	5
六	liuk	liu	T	己	'ki	chi	6
七	ts'iĕt	ch'i	⫪	庚	kɛng	keng	7
八	pat	pa	⫪̄	辛	siĕn	hsin	8
九	'kiou	chiu	⫪̿	壬	'ñiĕn	jen	9
十	žiŏp	shih	—	癸	'kwi	kuei	10
百	pɛk	pai					100
千	ts'ien	ch'ien					1000
萬	müAn	wan					10,000

fig. 20 Chinese numerals and celestial stems.

Chinese. Thus 547 days was written 500, 40, 7, suns. Clearly, numbers were expressed decimally and analytically from the earliest times.

The Chinese also distinguished certain 'higher' from 'lower' numbers by ten 'celestial stems' (*fig. 20*). In astronomy, these celestial stems could be combined in certain ways with another numerical series, the twelve 'celestial branches', so as to give a total of 60 numbers.

Apart from these ideograms, the ancient Chinese also (and more generally) expressed the first ten numbers by a combination of strokes, representing counting rods, which we shall now describe.

CALCULATION

As the Romans used 'pebbles', or *calculi*, to perform simple calculations, so the Chinese used small counting rods, which they would place on a ruled table or on a tiled floor. Since spoken Chinese analyses numbers into their decimal components (*e.g.,* 14 is read as 10,4) all the calculator had to do was to set out large numbers in successive squares, corresponding to hundreds, tens, and units (from left to right). The counting board would then represent numbers by a positional notation similar to ours. To obviate errors, the Chinese would place the rods upright in odd columns (units, hundreds, ten thousands) and horizontally in even columns (tens, thousands). While we know nothing about their actual methods of calculation before the third century A.D., counting-rod numerals were found on much earlier bronze inscriptions and coins.

Addition and subtraction were performed in the normal way, carrying over as we do. To multiply two numbers, the multiplier was placed in the uppermost row of the counting board, and the multiplicand in the lowermost. The partial products were then set out in the middle row, and the products added up, step by step. Division was performed similarly, the divisor being placed in the bottom and the dividend in the middle row. The quotient, obtained by inverse multiplication, was written on top. Sun-Tzu (third century) says that if the dividend has a remainder, then the divisor must be taken as 'mother' (denominator) and the remainder as 'child' (numerator). This shows that he understood fractions.

The extraction of square roots was also known at the time. In A.D. 263, Liu Hui showed that if a remainder was left, the process could be continued by taking ten as a 'mother' (denominator). Hence he obtained square roots to at least one decimal place and, in fact, decimal fractions were in common use at that period.

GEOMETRY

Geometry is first mentioned in Mohist writings, which gave definitions of the point and the line and also of simple mechanical concepts.

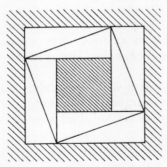

fig. 21. Chou Kung's proof of the theorem of Pythagoras.

Other Chinese texts concentrate exclusively on evaluations of areas and volumes. The earliest work of this kind, the *Arithmetical*

Classic of the Gnomon and the Circular Paths of Heaven (*Chou Pei Suan Ching*) considers a right triangle of sides 3, 4 and 5, though it was only at the end of the second century A.D. that Chou Kung added a diagram which constitutes an original proof of the 'Pythagorean' theorem. He fitted eight congruent right triangles into a square with side equal to the sum of, and leaving an inner square with side equal to the difference between, the two sides of the right-angled triangle (*fig. 21*).

Ancient texts generally give the ratio of circumference to diameter as 3, but a bronze cylinder preserved in Peking and dating from the reign of Wang Mang shows knowledge of a more accurate value. It bears an inscription to the effect that its base is a circle containing a square of side 1 foot. The distance from each corner of the square to the circle is given as 9 *li* 5 *hao* (= 0.095 inches). The area of the circle is 162 square inches, the depth 1 foot, and the volume of the whole 1,620 cubic inches. From this it is clear that the maker of this standard measure, Liu Hsin, must have used $\pi = 3.1547$.

ARITHMETIC AND ALGEBRA

An anonymous work from the Han period, the *Nine Chapters on the Mathematical Art* (*Chiu Chang Suan Shu*), gives us a summary of the mathematical knowledge of the time. The nine chapters are:

(1) *Surveying of land*, which gives correct rules for the areas of rectangles, trapezoid figures and triangles. It also gives the area of a circle, using $\pi = 3$, and the four rules.

(2) *Millet and rice*, which deals with proportions and percentages.

(3) *Distribution by progression*, which discusses partnership problems and the rule of three.

(4) *Diminishing breadth*, which deals with finding the sides of figures when areas are known, or the converse, and with square and cube roots.

(5) *Consultations on engineering works*, which deals with the mensuration and determination of volumes of solid figures (prism, cylinder, pyramid, *etc.*). It gives the area of the segment of a circle as: 1/2 sagitta × (sagitta +chord).

(6) *Impartial taxation*, which deals especially with problems on the time allowed for people to carry their grain contributions to the capital's granaries.

(7) *Excess and deficiency*, which gives methods of solving equations of the type $ax = b$ by a Chinese invention, the Rule of False Position, which involved making two fairly close guesses, one too high and one too low.[1]

[1] This method was known to Al-Khwārizmī and subsequently reached Europe under the name *Al Khaṭā'ain*, i.e., 'the Chinese' (method).

(8) *The way of calculating on the counting board*, which deals with simultaneous linear equations with *n* unknowns. On the counting board, each equation occupied a vertical column and the coefficients of all the *x*'s, all the *y*'s, *etc.*, lay in the same horizontal row. For example:

$$x+2y+3z = 36$$
$$2x+3y+ z = 34 \quad \text{was written}$$
$$3x+2y+ z = 39$$

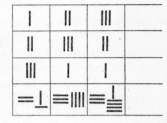

The equations were then solved by moving the appropriate rods. When negative numbers appeared, coloured rods were replaced by black. Negative numbers (*fu* = false) were thus distinguished from positive numbers (*chêng* = correct).

(9) *Right angles*, which deals with the properties of the right-angled triangle, and hence with equations of the second degree.

TWO MATHEMATICIANS

The earliest known names of mathematicians go back no further than the third century. The first was Liu Hui, who evaluated π by means of an inscribed polygon with 192 sides and then another of 3,072 sides, pointing out that this process could be continued. He gave π = 3.14159. In A.D. 263 he wrote the *Sea Island Mathematical Manual* (*Hai Tao Suan Ching*), in which he showed how to evaluate the distance of inaccessible points by means of similar right triangles.

During the following centuries there appeared *Sun Tzu's Mathematical Manual* (*Sun Tzu Suan Ching*) which considered the four rules and the mensuration of areas and volumes, and gave a method for finding the smallest number which would leave remainders of 2, 3 and 2, when divided by 3, 5 and 7, respectively.

THE MUSICAL SCALE

The Chinese also investigated the mathematical aspects of music in antiquity. Thus *Master Lin's Spring and Autumn Annals* (*Lin Shih Chhun Chhiu*), written at the end of the Warring States period, gives the rules for constructing twelve pipes emitting the twelve notes of the chromatic scale: the second pipe must be 2/3 the length of the first, and the third would have to be 2/3 of the second, were it not that it would then emit a note of another octave. To obviate this difficulty, its calculated length must be doubled. In this way, *i.e.* by doubling the length when necessary, he obtained the series: 1, 2/3, $2^3/3^2$, $2^4/3^3$, $2^6/3^4$, $2^7/3^5$, $2^9/3^6$, $2^{11}/3^7$, $2^{12}/3^8$, $2^{14}/3^9$, $2^{15}/3^{10}$, $2^{17}/3^{11}$.

Now the thirteenth note, *i.e.*, $2^{18}/3^{12}$, or 262,144/531,444 of the original length, proved just short of 1/2, the correct value for an octave, and the other lengths, too, were shown to represent unequal intervals. These problems were studied in the Middle Ages.

Another difficulty in the Han period was the actual calculation of the required lengths of the pipes. With 81 as the length of the first pipe, and 54, 72, 48, 65 for the next four, the lengths of the remaining pipes were evaluated as 42 2/3, 56 2/3, 75 2/3, 50 2/3, 67 1/3, 44 2/3, 59 2/3, by the historian Ssuma Chhien, and as 43, 57, 76, 51, 68, 45 and 60 by the Prince of Honan.

The five notes of the pentatonic scale, *kung*, *shang*, *chio*, *chih* and *yü*, corresponded to the intervals $2^3/3^2$, $2^3/3^2$, $2^5/3^3$, $2^3/3^2$ and $2^5/3^3$. From ancient times onwards the Chinese also used a 7-note scale with two flats (*pien kung* and *pien chih*), each of which divided the interval $2^5/3^3$ into $2^3/3^2$ and $2^8/3^5$, *i.e.* into a tone and a demi-semitone.

ASTRONOMY

OFFICIAL ASTRONOMY
The ancient Chinese state employed official astronomers, clock-makers, astrologers, geographers and geologists.

The first known bone inscriptions contained astronomical data of eclipses of the moon in 1361 B.C., eclipses of the sun in 1216 B.C., and a reference to a nova. Astronomical observations were made mainly to predict government fortunes.

There was also the task of fixing the calendar. For this purpose the Chinese relied on the gnomon, which pointed to the noon and solstitial shadows and also to the geographical north; on the clep-sydra, which was used to divide the interval between two successive noons into 12 equal parts; and on ritualistic jade objects in the shape of tubes or rings which no doubt symbolized ancient instruments. The Chinese also used a water-mill to turn a bronze celestial sphere, the invention of which is attributed to Chang Hêng, who also developed a seismograph in the second century A.D. In addition, the Chinese used sundials and some of the preserved specimens from that period have their circumference divided into 100 equal parts.

THE CALENDAR
In the earliest texts the year was stated to equal $365\frac{1}{4}$ days and the circle was divided into as many degrees. The civil year began in

winter and consisted of twelve or thirteen moons, which were simply known by their number and had no special names. During the Warring States period the peasants also divided the year into 24 'breaths' (*chhi*), each fortnight being known by such names as 'winter solstice', 'big rains', 'little snow', 'sleep of animals', *etc*. On bone inscriptions dates are given by means of 60 combinations of the 10 'celestial stems' and 12 'celestial branches' to which we have already referred. Thus the same date recurred every 60 days, and it was only in the Han period that the years were dated in the same manner.

The Chinese described rather than named the planets. Thus Venus was the 'Great White Star', Jupiter the 'Annular Star', *etc*. Their periods were known to within one day. The 12-year cycle of Jupiter was divided into periods, each with a name of two or three words whose meaning is obscure. The same names were occasionally used for the months and hours. An invisible counter-Jupiter, moving in the opposite direction to the planet, was called *Thai Yin* (the 'Great Dark Planet') and was thought to affect agricultural and meteorological phenomena.

The periods required for the sun and moon to return to the same relative positions were also known in ancient China. The 19-year or Metonic cycle was called *chang* and the 76-year cycle was known as *pu*. The smallest number of lunations to give a round number of days was found to be 81, which suitably combined with the lunar eclipse cycle of 135 months to give a cycle of 405 lunations or 11,960 days. It was also found that 27 *chang* were equivalent to 47 lunar eclipse periods, *i.e.*, to 513 years, and this interval was called a *hui*. Three *hui* (or 81 *chang*) constituted a round number of days (1,539 years); and 420 *pu* or 31,920 years equalled one *chi*, after which 'all things return to their original state'.

PLOTTING THE STARS

Chinese calendar science, unlike the Egyptian, was based not on the observation of heliacal risings or settings of the stars, but on their transit across the meridian (the great circle of the celestial sphere passing through the pole star and the observer's zenith). In this way the Chinese obtained a series of hour lines cutting the celestial equator, which they divided into 28 'lunar mansions' or *hsui*.[1] The *hsui* may be imagined as segments of the celestial sphere bounded by hour circles and named from constellations which provide determinative stars. Originally the system of 28 mansions was undoubtedly based on the 28 successive positions of the moon during the course of the month. Thus the *hsui* called *hsin* ('heart') was associated with

---

[1] The Chinese *hsui* are comparable with the Indian *nakshatras* (*see p.* 136).

spring, because spring full moons occur in it, though it is visited by the sun in autumn and corresponds with Scorpio in the Greek zodiac.

THE BEGINNINGS OF ASTRONOMY

The *Historical Classic* or *Shu Ching* mentioned positions of stars during solstices and equinoxes, and deduced that the year had 366 days. We have seen that thirteenth-century inscriptions gave the more correct value of 365¼ days; hence the *Historical Classic* must go back to a much earlier period. This is also borne out by its descriptions of solstitial and equinoctial points. We know that these points are not static because of the precession of the equinoxes. Since the first Chinese astronomer to have discovered and studied this phenomenon was Yü Hsi (A.D. 336), and since the *Historical Classic* fails to give the correct hours of its observations, we cannot possibly use its equinoctial points for ascertaining when the *Classic* was written.

The precession of the equinoxes is associated with a shift of the celestial pole (pivot of the diurnal motion). In Chinese cosmology, the celestial pole was the symbol of the sovereign, around whom the whole of society revolved. The polar star of the Han period was called the 'celestial pivot', and the celestial pole of 1000 B.C. the 'star of the celestial emperor'. The names the 'Great Unique' and the 'Celestial Unique' were applied to two small stars of the fifth magnitude which may well have been considered pole stars during the second millennium B.C. Finally, a constellation called the 'Purple Forbidden Enclosure' had two end stars, the 'Right Pivot' and the 'Left Pivot', between which lay the polar star of 3000 B.C. Since that date is prior to any extant documents from China, early Chinese polar astronomy may well have been based on an alien tradition.

THE CATALOGUE OF STARS

Chinese star-names are as old as they are precise. In the Warring States period, three astronomers, Shih Shen of the State of Chi, Kan Tê of the State of Wei and Wu Hsien (of unknown origin) drew up a catalogue of 1,464 stars divided into clearly defined constellations, for each of which they gave the distance from the celestial pole in degrees, *i.e.* the declination (one right angle was equal to 91 3/8 of these degrees), and the distance in degrees from the meridian of the nearest *hsui* on the right, *i.e.* the right ascension.

COSMOLOGICAL THEORIES

In ancient China three cosmological doctrines existed side by side. The oldest, reminiscent of Near-Eastern theories, was propounded in the *Arithmetical Classic of the Gnomon*. According to it, the firmament of fixed stars is a hemispherical cover revolving over a square earth.

The sun and the moon, though having a proper motion of their own, are carried along like ants by a millstone. This was the *Kai Thien* ('Heavenly Cover') theory.

The second theory, which is attributed to Lohsia Hung, who lived in the second century B.C., was developed by Chang Hêng. That theory was called *Hun Thien* ('Spherical Sky'), and according to it the heavens are like a hen's egg and 'as round as a crossbow bullet'. The earth is like the yolk, while the heavens are the shell. The total diameter of the egg is 2,032,300 *li*, and 'what is beyond no one knows'.

The third theory, attributed to Chhi Mêng, who flourished in the later Han, was only developed in medieval works. It was called *Hsüan Yeh* ('Infinite Empty Space'), and taught that there is no solid firmament, that the blue of the sky is merely an optical illusion, and that the stars, the sun and the moon float freely in empty space, borne along by a 'hard wind', *Kang Chhi*. A Taoist work attributed to Lieh Tzu states that since there is no solid firmament there is no danger of the heavens falling down.

PHYSICS AND GENERAL BIOLOGY

THE PHYSICS OF MO TI

The same fragments of the canons of Mo Ti which discuss geometry, also refer to the elements of mechanics and optics.

In them, Mo Ti defines duration (*chiu*), the 'moment without duration' (*shih*), and also contact, coincidence and continuity. The motion (*fên*) of solid objects is caused by the force (*li*); cessation of motion (*chih*) is caused by an obstacle (*chu*). When an arrow flies through the air, its continued motion is due to some sort of laziness. Weight is a force. The camera obscura was called the 'locked treasure room' (*Ku*), and the inversion of images was explained correctly. Concave mirrors (*wa chien*) were known to give small and inverted, or large and normal images according to their distance from the object, and convex mirrors (*t'uan chien*) were said to give only one kind of image.

PHYSICAL THEORIES

The natural philosophy which was later to triumph in China was first outlined in the Hung Fan chapter of the *Historical Classic* (*Shu Ching*). Its concepts were developed at greater length in the 'Tiger Pavilion', a special palace built by the King so that he could listen to the teachings of Tsou Yen.

According to Tsou Yen, all natural events were due to interactions between the feminine principle *Yin* (dark, cold, humid, and odd) and the male principle *Yang* (luminous, hot, dry, and even). Tsou Yen is also considered to have been the first scientist to propound the theory of the five elements or 'agents' (*hsing*): earth, fire, metal, water and wood. Everything in nature and society was subject to, and explained by, the two principles and the five agents. Hence early Chinese science may be said to have been qualitative and dynamic. All that was good in man, nature and society was ascribed to equilibrium between *Yin* and *Yang*; the alternation of day and night, of summer and winter, of the sun (the great *Yang*) and the moon (the great *Yin*), were all evidence of the great and beneficent interaction of the two principles. The five agents were associated with five places (the four cardinal points and the centre of the world), with five colours (jade, red, yellow, white and black), with five tastes (sour, bitter, sweet, astringent and salty), with five musical sounds (the notes of the pentatonic scale), with five groups of animals, and so on.

All Chinese scientific theories were based on these seven principles,

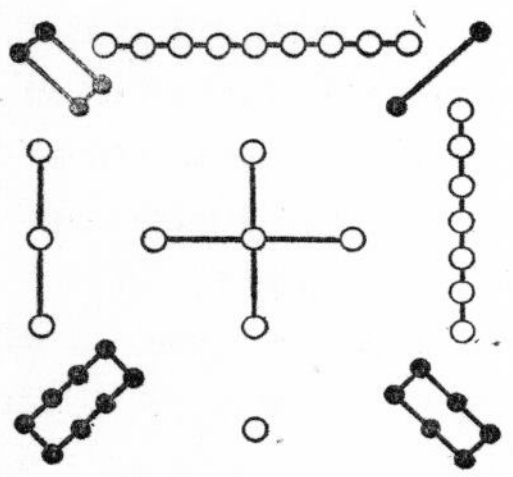

Trigrams	Names	Pronunciation	
		Ancient	*Modern*
☰	乾	giän	ch'ien
☷	坤	k'uon	k'un
☳	震	tśiĕn'	chên
☵	坎	'k'âm	k'an
☶	艮	k n'	kên
☴	巽	sẅän'	sun
☲	離	liĕ	li
☱	兌	duâi'	tui

fig. 22 (left) Chinese magic square, the oldest magic square known. According to legend, it was inscribed on the back of a tortoise which the heavens ordered to come forth from the river Lo and to appear before the Emperor Yü. Its nine numbers symbolized the Nine Chapters of the Historical Classic (Shu Ching).

fig. 23 (right) The Pa Kua, *eight trigrams revealed by the mythical ruler Fu Hsi. They have no connection with numeration and Leibniz was wrong to consider them as a system of binary notation.*

and so were the pseudo-sciences (astrology, cleromancy, geomancy, *etc.*). See *figs. 22* and *23*.

The Chinese did not distinguish between mind and matter as we do. According to Hsün Tzu (third century B.C.), a Confucian who approximated closely to the Legalists, nature exhibits a kind of gradation:

Water and fire have *chhih* (breath or energy) but not life (*sêng*). Plants and trees have *sêng* but not perception (*chih*); birds and animals have *chih*, but not a sense of justice (*i*). Man has spirit, life and perception, and in addition a sense of justice.

Another of Hsün Tzu's concepts, *li*, has often been translated as 'reason'. In reality, the term referred to the structure of precious stones and hence, by analogy, to any kind of structure, organization or order. Correct action must be based on the study of the *li* of things, *i.e.*, of their inner structure rather than of the reason of their being.

Similarly, the word, *chhing*, normally translated as 'psyche' or 'soul', really referred to the heart, the organ which the Chinese considered to be the seat of consciousness and volition.

MEDICINE AND BIOLOGY

A document from the Warring States period asserted that diseases were caused by an excess of *chhih* (breath). There were six types of *chhih*: cold and heat, wind and rain, light and darkness.

Three of the most famous names in ancient Chinese medicine were Chhin Yüeh, Hua Tho, and Chang Chung Ching. Chhin Yüeh, who was controller of the state granaries, was dismissed from his post for practising medicine without permission. In his voluminous plea for reinstatement, he listed twenty-five of his clinical cases, and showed how the five 'solid' organs, the heart, lungs, liver, spleen and kidneys, were related to the five colours, *etc.* The treatments he prescribed were mainly pharmacological and included purgatives, galactagogues (*Scopolia japonica*), vermifuges (*Daphne genkwa*), *etc.*

Hua Tho was a surgeon who prescribed physical exercise and hydrotherapy, and produced general anaesthesia by means of a special wine. Chang Chung Ching, who flourished at the end of the second century A.D., was the author of a treatise on fevers (one of which has been identified as typhoid) and of the 'Synopsis of the Golden Chamber', in which he described other diseases. He prescribed *Ephedra*, aromatic cinnamon, infusions and *gleditschia* powder. In cases of suicide by hanging he recommended artificial respiration and in cases of poisoning stomach washes.

The oldest Chinese views on physiology and pathology are found in the *Nei Ching*, which describes the dimensions of the organs. The skull is only a store of marrow, and the blood was said to circulate between the heart and the organs at the rate of six inches per breath. Apart from the five 'solid' organs, the book also describes five 'hollow' organs (alimentary canal, bladder). The 'holes' of the body are related to the five visceral organs and the five 'agents', with *Yin* and *Yang*.

The body was likened to a State, of which the heart was the king, the lungs the ministers, the liver the commander-in-chief, *etc*. The four methods of diagnosis were: observation, auscultation, questioning and pulse counting.

Since Confucianism stressed the importance of preserving the human body intact, surgery soon fell into decline. In the third century A.D. Huang Fu wrote his *Chia i ching*, a treatise on acupuncture and moxa which laid the foundations of a characteristically Chinese medical discipline. Wang Shu Ho edited Chang Chung Ching's *Treatise on Fevers* and also wrote a celebrated treatise on the pulse, *Mo Ching*, in ten books. Pulse counts became another characteristic of Chinese medicine.

PHARMACOLOGY, BOTANY AND CHEMISTRY

The ancient Chinese devoted more care to the domestication of plants than any other people. Thus, certain plants ignored as weeds by all the Chinese include the small crucifer *Capsella bursa-pastoris* Med. ('Shepherd's purse'). This weed is mentioned in the 'Classic of Poetry', *Shih Ching*, and is used in Chinese salads to this day. Trees which deforestation schemes would otherwise have eradicated were planted in orchards, including the Maiden-hair Tree, *Ginkgo biloba* L. Ancient Chinese pharmacopoeias give us a great deal of information about what plant products were thought useful, useless or poisonous in early times. The most ancient of all, the *Shen Nung Pên Tshao Ching* ('Pharmacopoeia of the Heavenly Husbandman') lists more than 300 plant substances and 36 mineral substances.

Apart from these general works, often commissioned by the kings, there were others written at the courts of princes. One such work is the *Huai Nan Tzu* ('Book of the Prince Reigning South of the River') which contains a dynamic account of the formation of mineral strata in the earth's crust: 'When the *chhi* (breath or vapour) of the central region ascends to the Dusty Heavens, they give birth after 500 years to *chüch* (an unknown mineral, perhaps realgar). This, in turn, produces after 500 years yellow mercury; yellow mercury after 500 years produces yellow metal (gold), and yellow metal in 1,000 years gives birth to a yellow dragon . . . ' The book goes on to say that if the *chhih* blows from the East it gives birth to azurite or malachite after 800 years, if it blows from the South it takes 700 years to produce red products (cinnabar, copper); if it blows from the West the products are white (arsenolite, silver) and the changes take 900 years; finally, if the *chhih* blows from the North the products are black (iron) and take 600 years to appear. These notions were not quite as fantastic as they seem. In fact, the earth of Central China is yellow, the blue sea is to the east, snow-capped mountains lie towards the west, and the sun, the symbol of fire, is in the south. All these proto-scientific notions are therefore hasty generalizations rather than idle speculations. There is no doubt that at that period material progress went hand in hand with the growth of knowledge.

CONCLUSION

After the Warring States Period, *i.e.* in the fifth century B.C., China became the most technically advanced country in the world. Her achievements, particularly under the Han and Chhin, were far ahead of those of Macedonia, Rome or India. Yet China always lagged behind Greek scientific attainments; her scientific knowledge never kept up with her technical skill.

Chinese science possessed elements which might have led to achievements comparable with the Greeks'. They were contained in the works of the Mohist school, which taught that knowledge (*chih*) was gained by hearing about something (*wên*), making an inference (*shuo*), experiencing it personally (*chhin*) and then by acting accordingly (*wei*), *i.e.* by experiment. The Mohist canon distinguished clearly between cause (*ku*) and effect (*chhêng*). The emphasis on action in politics and logistics was, in fact, one of the main distinctions between the Mohist and Taoist schools. We have seen that the Mohist school flourished during the Warring States Period. Now, the most important of these states were the pastoral provinces of Chhin and Chin in the West, and the maritime provinces of Chhi and Wu in the East. China's situation might therefore be said to have resembled that of the Mediterranean countries and of Greece in particular, where a pastoral and maritime economy have often been thought to have been the mainsprings of scientific thought. The relations shepherd—sheep, helmsman—oarsman, pirate—slave are said to have given rise to a dualistic view of the universe (gods—man, spirit—matter) and to have suggested the possibility of grasping universal laws *a priori*.

But in fact, China's geographical cohesion, her isolation from other civilized countries, and her concentration on agriculture rather than on commerce and navigation, engendered quite another mode of thinking. Confucian sociology and politics, and Taoist psychology, found it easy to eradicate all traces of Mohism, and with them to

15 Salt mining in ancient China

16 Mercury still

kill any germs of a deductive science resembling that of Greece.

As it was, Taoists or Confucians felt no need to define principles because objective reality was the only principle they recognized. Since cause and effect were reciprocal, all deliberate action (*wei*) was vain.

It is because of this outlook that Chinese scientists emphasized algebra at the expense of geometry, action at a distance (*e.g.*, magnetism or acoustic resonance) at the expense of mechanics, and acupuncture and moxa at the expense of surgery. Similarly, it was held that sages and saints must teach by precept rather than by law.

It would be wrong to aver that the Chinese lacked a scientific and rational view even during that period. They considered no phenomenon to be transcendent or inexplicable; to them man and society were objects of knowledge. If they failed to produce mathematical arguments based on *a priori* definitions, it merely shows that scientific ideas and methods are the offspring of social climate and not merely of technical achievements.

BIBLIOGRAPHY

A very full bibliography will be given in:

JOSEPH NEEDHAM, *Science and Civilization in China*, Cambridge University Press (Vols. I–IV, 1954–62), which, when completed, will consist of at least seven volumes.

See also:

P. HUARD, *La science et l'Extrême-Orient*, L'école française d'Extrême-Orient, Hanoi, 1948–49.

P. HUARD and MING WONG, *La médecine chinoise au cours des siècles*, Paris, 1959.

J.-B. BIOT, *Recherches sur l'ancienne astronomie chinoise*, 1840; *Études sur l'astronomie indienne et sur l'astronomie chinoise*, 1862.

L. DE SAUSSURE, *Les origines de l'astronomie chinoise*, Paris, 1930.

HENRI MASPERO, L'astronomie chinoise avant les Han, *T'ong pao*, XXVI (1929); Les instruments astronomique des Chinois au temps des Han, *Mélanges chinois et bouddhiques*, VI (1939).

MARCEL GRANET, *La pensée chinoise*, Paris, 1929.

G. SARTON, *Introduction to the History of Science*, 3 volumes in 5 parts, 1927–48.

PART II

Science in the Greco-Roman World

AT ABOUT 1000 B.C., while science was developing along almost
independent lines in India and China, Near Eastern science was
falling into a steep decline. Simultaneously, a new civilization,
destined to play a decisive role in history and to add new significance
to scientific methods and attainments, rose up on the islands and
shores of the Aegean Sea. This was the Greek civilization and its
science was more profound, more abstract and much more rational
than any that had preceded it.

The second part of this book is devoted to Hellenic science and its
continuation in the Roman Empire, and covers the period from the
beginning of the sixth century B.C. until the end of the sixth century
A.D. The very controversial problem of the causes of Greek scientific
pre-eminence will be examined in the light of both Greek and Roman
history. The influence of Greece and Rome on modern science will
be discussed in Part III of this volume and in Part I of Volume II.

GREEK SCIENCE

PAUL TANNERY HAS CALLED 'HELLENIC' that period of Greek science which coincided with the history of Classical Hellenism, and we shall use the term accordingly. Hellenic science covers a span of three centuries, from Thales to the first of Aristotle's disciples. While there is no doubt that, even before the sixth century, the Greeks had been acquainted with notions of mathematics, astronomy and pharmacology, the appearance of Ionian schools in the sixth century marks a turning-point that may well be called the real beginning of Greek science, for it was then that the mere accumulation of knowledge gave way to its consolidation. The end of the Hellenic period can be fixed with greater accuracy still, for it coincided with the sudden spread of Hellenism in the wake of Alexander's conquests.

The most monumental heritage of these three centuries is the Hippocratic Collection of medical writings and the Aristotelean Corpus, which lists the achievements of fourth-century physics and natural science and examines their historical antecedents. Unfortunately, the other texts we have from that period, and particularly from the sixth and fifth centuries, are few and far between and difficult to interpret. The historian of science may often be likened to the archaeologist, who must use odd fragments to reconstruct ancient buildings that have long since disappeared. This aspect of his work may be arduous but it is not in vain, since it is only by studying odd bits of information, embedded in, for instance, the great mythological poems, that he has been able to form any kind of picture of the first stirrings of positive science.

While no one would deny the debt owed by Greece to the East, we must not, as the Greeks themselves were wont to do, exaggerate its importance. Thus, when fourth-century authors from Isocrates to Porphyry claimed that Pythagoras had been taught in Egypt, Babylon or Phoenicia, they merely repeated current legends to which little credence need be given.

While the Greeks were heirs to Eastern knowledge, gathered over millennia, it was by their own efforts that they gradually fashioned science into an intellectual discipline in its own right. They separated it from religion and magic and at the same time raised it above the level of pure technology. Greek scientific thought was reflective and critical; it endeavoured not only to harness, but also to understand the facts which it described and the truths which it discovered. Simple predictions were not enough—Greek science was concerned with the ontological roots of phenomena. Even when it examined relations it always endeavoured to reduce them to common principles. Hence, science as we understand it is undoubtedly a creation of the Greek genius, with its desire to find reasons for appearances (λόγον διδόναι). The surprising rapidity of the progress of Greek science was the result of its disinterested aims and is clear evidence of its superiority over Eastern science.

Greek science covered a vast field, for the search for unity implies an exhaustive study of diverse phenomena. The first Milesian scholars admitted no bounds to the field of their investigations. Thales was physician, mathematician, astronomer and geographer, all in one. Eudoxos and Aristotle were equally versatile, and a wide scientific education was given in all the Greek schools, despite the inevitable specialization which followed in the wake of continuous scientific advances.

A detailed study of the various branches of Greek science will show that, their special interests notwithstanding, they all involved the same methodological approach, the same research into causes, the same reduction of facts to a small number of principles, and hence the same rejection of myths in favour of rational science—of τέχνη in favour of ἐπιστήμη.

In demonstrating the logical necessity and the generality of theorems, previously verified only by particular cases, Pythagoras and his disciples endowed mathematics with the dignity of a liberal discipline and incorporated it into the exact sciences. Later, Democritos, while paying lip-service to the great knowledge of the Egyptian *harpedonaptai*, had no hesitation in calling himself their equal when it came to 'combining lines with certainty of proof'.

Though related to the oldest of human skills—agriculture, hunting and fishing—botany and zoology were not made the objects of scientific studies until very much later. Even so, in the late Hellenic age there appeared the great biological syntheses of Aristotle and Theophrastos, who, by their remarkable classifications, made the first recorded attempt to bring order into a vast number of previously unrelated phenomena.

Medicine followed a similar path. It emerged from sorcery to become first the sacred art of the healer and then, in the schools of Cnidos and particularly of Cos, an original and fruitful body of theoretical knowledge.

Medicine, natural history and pure mathematics are rightly considered to have been the most striking scientific creations of Hellenism. In these three fields the Greeks, heirs to the science of the East, and following a different though parallel course, made unprecedented advances.

Their achievements in physics and astronomy pale in comparison. The greatest astronomical works were written during the Alexandrian period, and Aristotle's *Physics* is generally considered the poorest of all his writings. Though their concern to 'save the appearances' —to explain phenomena in terms of common experience—was not unfruitful, Hellenic scientists far too often produced explanations by a kind of legerdemain which forced the facts to fit their theories. Still, this criticism does not detract from the great merit of those physicists and astronomers, from Thales to Aristotle, who by their observations and discoveries, and even by their errors, but above all by their brilliant hypotheses about the structure of the universe as a whole and of its elements, paved the way for future advances.

CHAPTER 1

Physics and Cosmology from Thales to Democritos

IN THIS CHAPTER we shall examine the beginnings of Greek science from its first emergence from myths until the time when the atomists of Abdera put forward their radically new and coherent mechanistic and materialist conceptions. That period lasted for almost two centuries, in the course of which there flourished a number of schools known generically as the pre-Socratic, though the founder of one of them, Democritos, was born *c.* 460 B.C., some ten years later than Socrates. Because the biographical dates given by Greek historians do not always tally, it is difficult to establish the exact chronological order of the various schools and of their leaders. (Some of them, *e.g.* Pythagoras and Leucippos, are, in fact, said to have been legendary.) Nevertheless, modern historians are more or less agreed on the following traditional dates.

Thales of Miletos was born *c.* 624 B.C. and, according to Apollodoros and Sosicrates, flourished in 597 B.C., though modern scholars antedate both events by some ten years. He was followed by two other Milesians, Anaximander (*fl. c.* 570) and Anaximenes (*fl. c.* 546) When speaking of these three we had best avoid the term 'school', which might give the impression of an organized body of knowledge, for no traces of such an organization have, in fact, been discovered. Xenophanes of Colophon and Pythagoras of Samos, both of whom were born in about the middle of the sixth century, had to flee their home when it was threatened by the Persians and took refuge on the Greek mainland. Heraclitos of Ephesos flourished in 505 B.C., and Parmenides, the founder of the Eleatic school, is said to have been born in 540 B.C. by Diels, Zeller and Rivaud, but in 514 B.C. by Abel Rey. In any case, he flourished during the first half of the fifth century, and his disciple Zeno between 460 and 450. Empedocles of Acragas and Anaxagoras of Clazomenae were contemporaries of Zeno. Finally, the founder of atomic theory, Leucippos, is said to have been born either in Abdera in Miletos or in Elea, according to the school he is assigned to by various authors. His disciple Democritos was born in Abdera about 460 B.C. He flourished in 420 and his work must have continued for a very long time if, as some of his biographers claim, he lived to the age of 109 years.

Despite many profound differences in doctrine and assumptions, all these Greek philosophers are linked by their common endeavour to give rational explanations of material phenomena, and to suggest increasingly rational hypotheses about the structure of matter and the architecture of the universe. Their investigations embraced all the sciences, though all of them were mainly concerned with the nature and origin of matter, the form of the universe and the laws governing it.

We shall at first ignore their contributions to other fields and concentrate on problems of the kind we have just mentioned. All of these are physical (in the wider sense of the word φύσις) and involve various theories of matter and new astronomical conceptions.

THE PRIMARY ELEMENT

THALES

The first Milesian philosophers have rightly been called physicists, or 'physiologers', for none of the many problems they investigated interested them more keenly than that of the transformation of matter. The perceptible world struck them as being neither stable nor permanent; nothing in it was indestructible; bodies changed, and so did their very constituents. While many familiar phenomena (steam, fire, rain, *etc.*) had previously been explained by magic, the Greeks felt convinced that they could give a rational account of them, and it was that belief which was the mainspring of the Milesians' great intellectual effort. When Thales first posed the question of the primary element, he set subsequent Greek philosophy on its characteristic path.

According to Thales, the basic element generating all others was water. It has been suggested that his solution was based on the ancient myth of the mother-ocean, but if Thales accepted that myth he only did so after much careful thought. No life is possible without water; its condensation produces solids, its evaporation produces air, and air in turn gives rise to fire. Having once engendered the world-universe, water also supports it, for water englobes it everywhere. As Thales himself put it, 'the earth is borne on water', 'the universe is supported by water', 'the fire of the sun and of the stars, indeed, the entire world, is surrounded by exhalations of water'.

ANAXIMANDER OF MILETOS

The same problem of the ἀρχή, the primary substance, was treated by Anaximander in a way that had similarities with, and yet profound differences from, that of Thales. Like Thales, Anaximander recognized only one basic element which, spread throughout all space, generated and supported the universe. However, that element was neither water nor any other of the elements mentioned by Thales. According to Theophrastos, Anaximander held that the material cause and the first element of all things was the *apeiron*, a word difficult to translate, because it embraced two indefinable concepts: something limitless and indefinite. Hence, while Anaximander asserted 'that the first cause is eternal and surrounds the entire world', he was unable to define its exact properties. No wonder, then, that scholars have never ceased to discuss its precise significance. 'Once it was assumed that any element could be transformed into any other', Brunet and Mieli wrote, 'it became a matter of indifference which particular generative element was chosen.' But according to Theophrastos, Anaximander was quite emphatic that the primordial substance 'is neither water nor any of the other elements, but an entirely different substance'. Moreover, according to yet another school of thought, *apeiron* was simply tantamount to chaos. It contained all the elements in undifferentiated profusion and was the cause of all things, precisely because the universe was born out of the organization of that amorphous infinity. 'Anaximander', Simplicios wrote, 'did not ascribe the origin of things to a modification of matter, but claimed that opposite properties of the primordial substance . . . were separated' (*Phys.* 150, 20). This phrase (which agrees with many other accounts of Anaximander's doctrine) shows that he considered all the elements to have pre-existed in the *apeiron*, though in opposition (*i.e.*, in disorder), and the world (the material universe) to have been born from their separation.

ANAXIMENES

Anaximenes gave another answer to the problem of the first principle. According to him, the primordial substance surrounded the entire universe and generated all material bodies. Though, like Anaximander, he would sometimes call this infinite and amorphous substance *apeiron*, his *apeiron* was closer to Thales' than to Anaximander's primordial element.

'Anaximenes', wrote the pseudo-Plutarch, 'held that air was the universal principle, for air, though indeterminate in itself, is determined by the qualities which it assumes.' But while Anaximenes may therefore be said to have retreated from the advance made by Anaximander and to have reverted to the earlier notions of Thales, he undoubtedly went much further than both in methodology and explicitness. He asserted that all matter was One and described material transformations accordingly and most precisely. Everything was due to rarefaction and condensation, which, in their turn, were associated with changes in temperature. 'Expansion and condensation cause air to assume its diverse forms . . . When air expands sufficiently, it produces fire . . . when it condenses it produces first water, then earth and, at the highest degree of condensation, it produces stones.' In the fifth century, Diogenes of Apollonia was to adopt Anaximenes' first principle without adding greatly to his doctrine.

XENOPHANES

One of Xenophanes' achievements was to apply the doctrines of his Milesian predecessors to religious problems. While we have not discussed purely religious problems in this book, we must make an exception in the case of Xenophanes since his stand against polytheism may be considered a direct contribution to natural philosophy. His profound meditations on the primordial substance led him to the conception of an abstract and absolute principle that went beyond matter and was reached by reason alone. Supporting his speculations with previously unequalled logical power, Xenophanes showed that this unifying principle filled the universe, or rather that it was at one with it, and hence with God. The 'One' contains the manifold and transcends its oppositions, and hence explains both the immutability of being and the fleeting nature of its appearances—the eternity of the world and its future. A decisive turning-point in the history of philosophy, Xenophanes' doctrine paved the way for the Pythagorean school (and for all other schools of cosmology based on the manifold and its oppositions), and also for the Eleatic school. For, in so far as his 'One' was also that of Parmenides, Plato and Aristotle were right to consider Xenophanes the founder of the Eleatic school, and thus to call his school, like all the other great scientific schools, Ionian. The main difference between the cosmic view of Xenophanes and that of the first Milesians was his refusal to accept the *apeiron*, that all-embracing infinity in which the cosmos was engendered and nourished—in which it 'breathed', as the Pythagoreans put it. According to him, nothing existed beyond the perfect cosmic sphere— 'the universe does not breathe'. That expression, which gave rise to so many controversies, is the key to Xenophanes' cosmology.

THE PYTHAGOREANS

Aristotle never spoke of Pythagoras; he knew only the Pythagoreans. If we follow his example it is for convenience, and not that we subscribe to the theory that Pythagoras was a purely legendary figure. Further, there is conclusive evidence that all the members of his school submitted their work and their discoveries to him. In the scientific field with which we are concerned, the Pythagoreans were noted mainly for their contributions to mathematics. In physics, their great originality was their emphasis on the fundamental importance of *oppositions*. We have had occasion to use this word in connection with Xenophanes, but for Xenophanes the oppositions were transcended by the immutable 'One'. The Pythagoreans, on the other hand, repudiated all monistic solutions, abandoning the Milesian notion of an original substance, and they were the first to propound an explicitly dualistic philosophy. They recognized ten oppositions, of which five were of a mathematical kind (limited— unlimited; odd—even; one—multiple; straight—curved; square— polygonal), and used these to introduce plurality into existence and to construct a physics in which number became the ἀρχή, the model of all things. Hence—as Aristotle pointed out—the Pythagoreans looked upon numbers as the real constituent elements of matter.

This approach, together with the Pythagorean liking for discrete numbers and discontinuous quantities, suggests that their mathematical 'atomism' went hand in hand with the kind of physical atomism which Democritos and his school were later to develop with so much rigour. It would appear that the Pythagoreans looked upon matter as constituted of basic elements distributed in a void; they said that matter reached up into the sky, inasmuch as the latter breathed the infinite breath, and that the void enclosed all things. Though conjectural, this interpretation (Aristotle's) of the Pythagorean approach is in full agreement with the spirit of their school. However, the 'void' of the Pythagoreans was not yet the absolute void of Democritos; it was a kind of air, surrounding all matter and enabling the world to breathe, a continuous substance bridging the discontinuity of all other substances. Hence, the denial of Xenophanes, 'the Universe does not breathe', must have been directed at the Pythagoreans.

HERACLITOS
Heraclitos of Ephesos, also called the Obscure, is remarkable above all for the fervour with which he attacked the theories of his predecessors and contemporaries alike. This singular man, to whom war (*polemos*) was the key to the universe, was himself a great polemic and his jibes at Hesiod, Pythagoras and Xenophanes are well-known. (His attacks on Pythagoras confirm the existence of the great Samian, for Heraclitos would not have poked fun at a fictitious person.)

Despite his contempt for all other doctrines, Heraclitos was, in fact, their direct heir. He belongs to the Milesian line, not only by his origins, but also by his choice of fire as the primordial element. Thus he claimed that 'Fire governs the universe' (Frg. 64), and that 'All

things are changed by fire and fire by all things' (Frg. 90). It is
significant that his first element was also the most volatile. Heraclitos
not only asserted that elements could be transformed into one another,
but also stressed the great importance of transformations as expressions of the universal law of instability. Everything in the world is
transformed incessantly; nothing persists except change itself. Hence
he said, 'Death of fire—birth of air', 'We plunge and do not plunge
into the same river', 'The upward path and the downward path are
one', *etc*. His physics, that is, his description and explanation of these
perpetual changes, was a physics of contraries, apparently related
to the oppositions of the Pythagoreans though conceived in an
entirely different spirit. His opposites were hostile rather than
complementary; war was a condition of becoming, even though
the enemies were equally without rational existence: 'The straight
and the winding paths are the same', 'Good and evil are but one'
(a pointed barb at the Pythagoreans). In this vast and incessant war
of the elements, fire plays a paramount role simply because everything, however diverse, ends in it. The triumph of fire marks the end
of the 'war'. Concord and peace can only exist in a general conflagration. Then the cycle is begun anew: fire engenders air, water and
the earth, the conflict between which leads to the next great conflagration. This eternal cycle is the only known law of the universe.

THE ELEATIC SCHOOL
This school, which, like the Pythagorean, arose in Italy, was linked
to Ionia, both by its early beginnings (Xenophanes) and by the
last of its known representatives (Melissos of Samos, second half
of the fifth century). It was dominated by two illustrious names:
Parmenides and Zeno.

Parmenides developed Xenophanes' monistic philosophy to the
full, and posed the problem of the ἀρχή in a novel way. Instead of a
primordial element which engendered all substances by transmutation, transformation or division, he postulated an all-pervading and
persisting reality behind all phenomena—Being, as opposed to Non-
being. Parmenides did not deny that phenomena followed laws
which could be studied by science, and in that respect his physics
and cosmology are remarkably like those of the Pythagoreans. But
he differed from them in that, while they believed in multiplicity
and considered numbers as the models of the universe, he equated
all being with the One. All other doctrines were illusory. Parmenides
was therefore a metaphysicist first and foremost, whose main
scientific contribution was the clear distinction he made between
discernible and intelligible phenomena. That distinction concerns
the history of science not only because of its methodological conse-

quences, but mainly because it is related to the problem of the primary element.

Zeno, following in his path, developed Parmenides' concepts with a zest bordering on intoxication. 'Becoming' and 'Being' were the corner-stones of his natural philosophy. His famous paradoxes are too well-known to be discussed in great detail here, but all of them (the Achilles, the Arrow, and the Stadium) were designed to prove the logical impossibility of motion and change. In the Achilles, he argued that if time and distance were divided into infinitesimally small points, a fast runner would never manage to catch up with a slow runner who had started from a point ahead of him. To do so, he would first have to reach the point from which the slower runner had started, by which time the slower would have moved to a point farther on. When the fast runner arrived at that point, the slower runner would have advanced a little farther still, and so *ad infinitum*. The Stadium paradox, on the other hand, assumes that the divisibility of time and space cannot be limited, and hence number, space, time, and matter cannot be logically considered either as indivisible or as infinitely divisible, for both views lead to an *impasse*. When we speak of motion, change, or plurality, we refer to familiar though misleading phenomena which our minds can neither conceive nor express. They are therefore no more than deceptive appearances. The influence of the Eleatic School on the subsequent development of scientific thought was immense, both in mathematics and in physics. Henceforth, it would be impossible to avoid distinguishing between perception and reason, and to ignore the fact that any science of being and of nature (*i.e.* all physics in the wider sense of the word) must reconcile the study of phenomena with the laws of logic.

EMPEDOCLES

The philosophy of Empedocles combined traces of the Pythagorean teaching with that of Heraclitos. It wedded the belief that plurality was the principle of being to the view that the future of the world was part of an ever-recurring drama. Empedocles admitted four primordial elements: water, air, fire and earth, which he called the four 'roots' of all things (ῥιζώματα). His choice of the number four is attributed by some to his acceptance of the Pythagorean tetrad, while others claim that it reflected the wish to associate each of the elements with one of the regular solids then known (tetrahedron, cube, octahedron, icosahedron). At any rate, all scholars are agreed that Empedocles was the founder of the theory that all phenomena could be explained by combinations of the four elements. Some of the extant fragments of his works even mention the forces and laws governing these combinations. Combinations were said to take place under the action of two opposite forces, love and hate (φιλότης and νεῖχος), whose alternate victories governed the four periods of the cosmic cycle. During the reign of hate the elements are separated; during the transformation of hate into love the elements draw together and begin to combine; during the rule of love, harmony is established to produce a perfect world—and a subsequent return to hate through repulsion, decomposition. Love and hate, combination and decomposition, are the causes of every change and fully explain all becoming. The four 'roots' are indivisible, immutable and eternal. This aspect of Empedocles' doctrine foreshadows the atomic hypothesis, hence it is not surprising that Lucretius was a great admirer of Empedocles, whose name he associated with that of Epicuros.

ANAXAGORAS

Anaxagoras contributed an original solution to the problem of substances, opposed both to Empedocles' notion of simple elements and also to Pythagorean number mysticism. He was closest to Anaximander, like whom he postulated the existence of an *apeiron*, a primitive chaos from which all cosmic motion originally sprang. His physics was based on two main principles: the infinite divisibility of matter and its indestructibility. 'There is no last degree of smallness, for there is always something smaller' (Frg. 3). 'Nothing is born or dies, but existing things combine and separate' (Frg. 17). The first of his principles is clearly incompatible with any kind of atomistic physics, and the second denies the possibility of absolute creation. Anaxagoras also rejected the Milesian notion of a primordial element and the Empedoclean belief in a limited number of simple substances. For him all the substances in nature had existed from all eternity, and no transformations could possibly change their characteristic qualities. A bone reduced to powder or to tiny heaps was still nothing but bone.

Aristotle called such small 'heaps' of identical matter *homeomeres*, a term probably unknown to Anaxagoras and, in any case, associated with the atomic hypothesis which is quite incompatible with Anaxagoras' doctrine. While *homeomeres* must be imagined as aggregates of like particles which combine in the original void by their mutual attraction, Anaxagoras' particles could be subdivided *ad infinitum* and were of infinite diversity. No material substance is ever composed of identical elements: it contains every possible element, though it is the predominance of one which accounts for its apparent qualities. Thus all are contained in all, both within the material world as we know it and also within the original void. But while the latter is all chaos and confusion in which no qualities are discernible ('they are devoid of colour'), the material world has a tendency to combine

like substances into bodies with specific properties. In this fruitful
and original view, the primitive chaos is no longer the vague *apeiron*
of Anaximander, but can be grasped by the mind. The organized
universe, on the other hand, results from the action of the *nous*
(mind or breath) which first upset the chaos like a whirlwind. This
aspect is the hylozoistic (or dynamistic) part of Anaxagoras' system.

THE ATOMISTS

Like all other 'physiologers', the Atomists postulated the indestructibility of matter; like most of them they affirmed its substantial unity.
But beyond that, and this is the characteristic point of their doctrine,
they proclaimed the indivisibility of its basic elements. The subdi-
vision of any substance could only be continued up to a point, after
which one reached discrete and indivisible particles: the atoms.
Even though the Pythagoreans might have subscribed to this view,
they never stated it with any clarity. The Atomists, on the other
hand, not only propounded it but also developed it into the fundamental principle of a theory of matter. We know the singular history
of this system, which has been considered by some as the only path
leading to a true natural philosophy, but by many more as a vain
metaphysical flight of fancy. This adverse opinion is due to the fact
that the Atomists neglected observation and experiment, holding,
as they did, that atoms could not be perceived by the senses.

The atomic doctrine is associated with two names, that of Leucippos, a semi-legendary figure, and that of his disciple Democritos,
whose life is better known and many fragments of whose work have
been preserved.

Democritos' universe consisted of atoms and the void, a view suggested to him by the Pythagorean notion of figured numbers, according to which every point (number) was surrounded by an empty
space. (The reader will remember that numbers were the models or
types of things.) But while the void of the Pythagoreans was material
(it was the *pneuma* in which all things were immersed), the Atomists
propounded the notion of an absolute void purged of all material
content and gave it the name by which all later natural philosophers
were to refer to it: τὸ κενόν. The atoms in this void were said to be
infinite in number, existing from all eternity, indestructible, immutable, imperceptible, solid, impenetrable, and indivisible by virtue
of their extreme smallness (according to Leucippos), or their extreme
hardness (Democritos).

Atoms were of infinite variety. Though all of one substance, they
differed in form, dimensions (Democritos assumed the existence of
gigantic atoms), position and mutual arrangements. Aristotle compared atoms with the letters of the alphabet, each of which has its

own shape but which can be arranged in various positions or orders (A and N, H and Ⅱ, AB and BA). Finally, atoms are in motion 'within the infinite void, where there is neither high nor low, neither centre nor edge' (*De finibus*, I, 17). Motion is, in fact, an essential attribute of the basic elements of matter. Coeval with atoms, motion brings them into that incessant flux which produces all possible forms; every kind of fortuitous encounter, all the innumerable and constantly changing combinations—these are responsible for making all the many substances constituting the universe of our sense perceptions. 'We say hot, we say cold, we say sweet, we say bitter, we say colour, but nothing exists save only atoms and the void' (Sextos Empiricos, *Adv. Math.* VII, 135).

According to Abel Rey, Democritos' atoms had an infinite variety of forms simply because the Principle of Sufficient Reason showed that there was no necessity for an atom to have one form rather than another. The same was true of atomic dimensions, combinations, and directions of motion—none was privileged, since none tended towards a goal. 'Democritos', Aristotle said, 'omitted to speak of a final cause' (*De gen. anim.*, 789b). His was the most coherent and also the most abstract of all the great systems propounded before the fourth century: it contained no pre-established paths, no predestined cycles. For Democritos, it was the very structure of eternal matter which engendered nature in all its diversity, owning no law but that of chance and its causal consequences. Causality reigned supreme among the atoms, and a conception in which matter is more isolated from spirit can hardly be imagined.

COSMOLOGIES

To the ancient Greek physiologers, physics and cosmology were only two different aspects of natural philosophy. Their purpose in both was to describe phenomena, to give a coherent account of the universe based on sense data. To do so they investigated, on the one hand, the basic elements of matter and the causes of their transformation, and on the other hand, the cosmos as a whole. We have seen what solutions they offered for the former, and must now examine their views on the latter.

In early Greek astronomy we must carefully distinguish observation and observational inferences from bold and often far-fetched cosmic hypotheses.

According to Aëtios, Thales 'was the first man to state that the moon was illuminated by the sun'. That was also the opinion of Anaxagoras, who declared (Frg. 18) that 'the sun lends its brightness

17 The seven sages (mosaic)

18 Fourth-century vase (Vase of Darius)

to the moon', and of Empedocles, who wrote that 'the moon's borrowed light circles the earth' (Frg. 45). Thales also achieved fame by predicting an eclipse of the sun, probably that of May 28th, 585. His prediction must have been based on the study of the Babylonian *Saros*, which showed at what periods eclipses *might* occur, and it was only by chance that an eclipse was visible in Asia Minor at the appointed date.

In cosmology, Thales' views were naturally based on his theory of a primordial element. Surrounded and supported by water, the universe is a hemispherical ball of air, swimming in an infinite mass of water. The concave surface of this ball is our sky, and the plane surface is our earth, which is therefore a circular disc. The stars float in the upper waters, which feed the celestial fires with their exhalations. Their motions, though mysterious, are yet governed by laws, since they are regular and predictable. The earth floats on the lower waters (as it did with the Egyptians), which cause all such terrestrial and atmospheric disturbances as earthquakes, volcanic eruptions, winds, *etc*.

According to Anaximander, the earth is encircled by a series of vast wheels made of mist (opaque air), the rims of which are hollow and filled with fire. The sun, moon and stars are glimpses of the fire seen through holes in the mist, the most distant wheel being that of the sun and the nearest those of the stars. Anaximander was aware of the inclination of the solar and lunar 'rings' to the ecliptic, but cannot be called its discoverer since it was known in Asia long before him. He was, however, the first to propound that the earth was curved rather than flat, and may be called the father of cartography since he prepared the first map for navigators. In contradistinction to Thales, he also taught that the earth had no support but was suspended in air. Finally he held that our universe was not the only one, but that the *apeiron* surrounding the cosmos contained a host of other universes as well. This opinion was later adopted by the Atomists and possibly by some Pythagoreans before them.

It has often been said that science progresses by fits and starts. Anaximenes' contribution is a case in point, for though he came after Anaximander, he returned to the earlier view that the earth was a flat disc. According to him the earth sloped upwards towards the north, and this fact explained why the stars apparently disappeared as they revolved about the earth. Unlike Thales, he believed that the moon shone with its own light, and unlike Anaximander, he failed to distinguish the equatorial from the ecliptic plane. On the other hand, he was the first Greek philosopher to have distinguished between planets and stars. The sun, the moon, and planets were 'of an igneous nature' (made of fire) and were supported by air, while the fixed stars were attached like 'nails' to the celestial sphere, which was of crystalline material. Finally, he substituted spheres for Anaximander's wheels. All in all, Anaximenes may be said to have consolidated the popular cosmography of his day, which would explain the success and persistence of some of his ideas.

This return to older notions was continued by Xenophanes, some of whose archaic ideas are reminiscent of Egyptian myths. According to him the stars, far from revolving, moved along a straight line above an unbounded earth. A new sun and new stars were born every day or night.

Heraclitos' cosmology, related as it was to his 'physics', was no less naïve than that of Xenophanes. This attitude may well have been deliberate on his part, for Heraclitos was the head of what was later to become an influential philosophical school despising all cosmologies. He followed the Chaldeans in placing the moon nearest to the earth, the sun, the planets and the fixed stars following in that order. His stars were hollow bowls whose open mouths, directed towards us, collected the dry exhalations which burned in them (Tannery). The stars were lit up whenever they rose and extinguished whenever they set. 'The sun is the size of a human foot' (Frg. 3); it is 'renewed every day' (Frg. 6), and quenched each night by humid air. The only remarkable facts about Heraclitos' mythical cosmology were its emphasis on rhythm (by which Heraclitos is related to the Pythagoreans) and, above all, its sense of necessity. The only reality was an eternal 'Becoming', the return of phenomena being subject to fixed laws: 'The sun does not exceed its bounds; if it did, the Eumenides, the handmaidens of justice, would quickly discover it' (Frg. 94).

Clearly, Ionian cosmology, however original and sometimes brilliant, was rather primitive (Abel Rey even called it 'puerile') in comparison with that of the Eleatic School, and particularly with that of the Pythagoreans, who made a determined effort to relate astronomy to arithmetic, geometry and music. The century separating Pythagoras from Philolaos saw the rise of successive generations of Pythagoreans, and, their tradition being what it was, it is difficult to define the precise contribution of any one member. All we can say is that the idea of a spherical earth was first propounded by one of their founders. True, Theophrastos attributed it to Parmenides, but then Parmenides' physics was freely based on that of the Pythagoreans. Again, Anaximander, though he spoke of a curved earth, never suggested that it was spherical. (He based his hypothesis on observation, while the Pythagoreans seem to have postulated sphericity for purely aesthetic reasons—the sphere alone was a perfect solid.) In any case, the early Pythagoreans were the first to turn the sphericity of the earth into a dogma, which the school was never to abandon. On it Philolaos constructed a remarkable astronomical system, known from the writings of Aristotle and Theophrastos, according to which the centre of the cosmos was not the earth but a central fire (*hestia*) around which revolved ten celestial bodies. The nearest to the central fire was the counter-earth, which was invisible to us because it was on the opposite side of the central fire. The central fire itself was invisible because the inhabited half of the earth was always turned away from it. Beyond the earth came the moon, Mercury, Venus, the sun, Mars, Jupiter, Saturn and the sphere of the fixed stars. The relative distances of these bodies were in simple arithmetic and musical proportions. Two cosmic regions could be distinguished: one below and another above the moon. The sublunary world was degenerate and corrupt, the upper world was incorruptible. Many of Philolaos' notions were incorporated into later astronomical traditions, though others were rejected.

The Eleatic School, which propounded a monistic philosophy, was not particularly interested in describing celestial phenomena, which were considered to be so many illusions. Its astronomy, like its physics, was partly and rather disdainfully purloined from the Pythagoreans. The Eleatics admitted that the earth was spherical, and held that it remained in equilibrium in the centre of the universe 'because it has no reason to go here rather than there' (Aëtios III, 15). About it revolved 'crowns of light and darkness'. 'The sun and the moon have broken free from the circle of the Milky Way, the sun from the subtlest mixture which is heat, the moon from the densest mixture which is cold' (Aëtios, II, 20). Being imposed by 'divine government', the celestial movements were 'necessary' (as they were to Heraclitos).

The cosmos of Empedocles was egg-shaped and was governed by alternating reigns of love and hate. The revolution of the heavens was due to disequilibrium resulting from the great pressure exerted by a mass of fire on the hard shell of the atmospheric envelope. The reign of hate caused a gradual acceleration of the revolution and hence a more rapid alternation of day and night. When man first appeared on the earth, one day was as long as ten months. The increasing speed of the celestial motion was responsible for fixing the earth in the centre of the universe and for keeping it there. Like Heraclitos, and for the same reasons, Empedocles was rather contemptuous of cosmology. He was less concerned with actual observations than with the contemplation of Becoming, and adopted Heraclitos' belief in the eternal cycle in which cosmic processes are reconciled with the eternity of matter. Empedocles gave poetic expression to the great drama of this cycle, at the end of which everything starts anew.

It is difficult to reconstruct Anaxagoras' cosmology from what sparse fragments of his work are extant and from the rather contradictory accounts of his doctrine, a discussion of which would take us too far afield. It is, however, generally agreed that Anaxagoras' cosmology was related to that of the Ionian school. He believed that the earth was a flat disc and that it rested on nothing (or on air). The moon, lit up by the sun, was inhabited like the earth. More concerned with the history than with the actual nature of the cosmos, he described its genesis. Our world developed from a crust of mud over the primordial chaos, under the impulse of the *nous*—mind or, more physically, breath—which initiated the rotation of the universe and hence its orderly arrangement about the earth at its centre. The moon, the sun, and the other celestial bodies were driven away from the centre by a rotatory force. Anaxagoras preceded the Atomists in assuming that the boundless chaos contained an infinite number of universes. Vortices similar to ours could arise at any number of points. Finally these vortices could dissolve and return to chaos, while others emerged to take their place. 'The Ionians were wrong to speak of birth and death . . . things are assembled at the beginning and disintegrate at the end' (Frg. 17).

For Leucippos, as for Democritos, the primitive chaos consisted of atoms and the void, but while Leucippos divided the void into two distinct regions, one of concentrated atoms and one of empty space which the atoms invaded, Democritos considered that atoms had always existed throughout the infinite void, though without any order. Both philosophers held that an infinite number of universes was born from the initial and random organization of atoms. Atoms combined because their random motions eventually led them into vortices in which they became organized by virtue of a law according to which like attracted like. Cosmogenesis was therefore purely mechanical: atoms spread out in all directions, to collide, rebound and eventually to congregate together. The death of the universe (or the return to chaos) resulted from no less fortuitous disintegrations.

Diogenes Laërtios and Theophrastos, to whom we owe the above account, also described the two Atomist views on the structure of the universe. According to Leucippos the planets and stars revolved about the earth, their common centre. The moon was closest to us, and the sun the most distant. Because of their rapid motions, the celestial bodies were set afire. (This view is clearly a step back from the Pythagorean view, with which Leucippos may not have been familiar.) Democritos' astronomy was no less naïve and, according to Seneca, he did not even hazard a guess about the number of existing planets. Thus, while the Atomists propounded a grandiose and suggestive mechanical hypothesis, they produced a very poor cosmology. This surprising outcome has been explained as one of the main reasons why Atomism fell into disfavour, and why Aristotelean astronomy replaced it so completely. It was only very much later that Atomism was to emerge from obscurity once again.

* * *

Though particularly marked in the case of the Atomists, this discrepancy between theories concerning the structure of matter and those concerning the structure of the universe was a general characteristic of early Greek 'physics'.

To sum up, the various answers to the problem of the ἀρχή can be divided into five groups:

(1) An infinite multiplicity of substances from the beginning of time (Anaximander, Anaxagoras).

(2) A limited number of elementary substances which combined to produce all known substances in nature (Empedocles).

(3) A single primordial substance (water, air or fire) capable of transformation into all other substances by condensation, rarefaction, *etc.* (Thales, Anaximenes, Heraclitos).

(4) A single substance, without qualities but divided into discrete particles, the basic elements, which combined to form all other substances (Leucippos, Democritos).

(5) All things are the products of whole numbers. This doctrine, which came before the atomic hypotheses, was its forerunner, inasmuch as it implied that matter was discontinuous and that substances combined according to whole numbers (Pythagoras).

Of all these theories, that of the four elements of Empedocles was undoubtedly the one which exercised the greatest influence on the subsequent development of science. Thus Abel Rey was right to say that 'Empedocles is the founder of one of the most gigantic theoretical syntheses in the history of science. It remained the leading working hypothesis until the sixteenth century and even until the beginning of the seventeenth.' But Abel Rey recognized that if Empedocles won the first round, the Atomists won the second.

In cosmogenesis, all pre-Socratic schools held the common view that the universe had emerged from infinite chaos, variously imagined as water, air, *apeiron*, or mud.

Compared with such daring cosmogenetic hypotheses, Greek observational astronomy was extremely poor, and so it remained until the fifth century. Of all the pre-Socratic models of the universe, the only one to combine a measure of coherence with originality was that developed by the Pythagorean school, and perfected by Philo-laos (end of fifth century). In it, all celestial bodies were spherical, the stars revolved in concentric spheres, the cosmos was divided into a sub-lunar world and a celestial zone. Philolaos thus laid the foundations of the Aristotelean doctrine, to which astronomers were to keep adding corrections and improvements during the next twenty centuries.

CHAPTER 2

Mathematics

IN THE *Summary* of Proclos, also called the *Eudemian Summary*, the contribution of Pythagoras to the progress of mathematical science is described as follows:

After these (Thales and Mamercos, a sixth-century mathematician), Pythagoras transformed the study (of geometry) into a liberal education, examining the principles of the science from the beginning and probing the theorems in an immaterial (abstract) and intellectual manner. He it was who discovered the theory of irrationals, and the construction of the cosmic figures (regular polyhedra).

Modern reservations about these assertions notwithstanding, they contain an important grain of truth. For though the Ionians were not without scientific merit, it was the Italian school which first produced a body of truly scientific knowledge, *viz.* mathematics, by which this school understood not only arithmetic and geometry but also astronomy and music.

ARITHMETIC AND GEOMETRY

In the course of only two centuries, from Pythagoras to Euclid, Greek mathematics developed apace to produce unrivalled results. We shall study it under three sub-headings:

(1) Pythagorean arithmo-geometry, an archaic kind of mathematics that was to be taught by the neo-Pythagoreans until the end of classical times, and which was transmitted by Boëtius to medieval Europe.

(2) The preparation of Euclid's *Elements*.

(3) The beginnings of higher mathematics.

Pythagorean Mathematics

Pythagorean mathematics were originally based on speculations about numbers as the models of 'things'. This belief gave rise to Pythagorean number mysticism, the *arithmos*, which attributed secret virtues to the first ten numbers. We do not need to dwell on this part of their doctrine, which is unconnected with positive science, and we mention it only because it explains the Pythagoreans' choice of certain problems. Even after they had discovered irrational numbers, which is one of their greatest claims to fame, they continued to consider arithmetic as the science of whole numbers. Since irrational quantities were incompatible with their theory of figured numbers, they neglected them systematically in their studies of arithmetical problems.

fig. 24 Four and nine as figured numbers.

FIGURED NUMBERS

This theory, which is only of historical interest, emphasizes the close connection which early mathematicians saw between number and size. It resulted from early attempts to imagine number as a function of space, and *vice versa*.

The Pythagoreans represented numbers by points arranged to form geometrical figures. Thus the numbers 4 and 9 were called squares (*fig. 24*). Every point was a mathematical atom, surrounded by an empty field (χώρα) and indivisible. Unit points were combined according to strict rules, governing the generation of numbers. In this way there arose the geometry based on integral numbers which we have called arithmo-geometry. In it, numbers could be linear, plane, or solid, and while a given number could be arranged in more than one form, only one of these forms was considered characteristic. Thus 7 was prime (πρῶτος) and linear (γραμμικός); 4 was plane (square); 8 was solid (cubic), *etc.* Problems connected with solid numbers, *e.g.*, the generation of cubes by summation, were not treated by the early Pythagoreans, and we shall therefore restrict our remarks to plane numbers. Plane numbers were generated, not by multiplication, but by successive additions of unequal terms—that is, by the *summations of series.*

The simplest of all plane numbers were triangular and square. These are of particular importance—square numbers because they have survived arithmo-geometry, and triangular numbers because, being the simplest of all, they were the models of all polygonal numbers.

Triangular numbers, the discovery of which is traditionally attributed to Pythagoras, are obtained by summing the successive terms of the series of natural numbers 1, 2, 3, . . . (Nicomachos: *Introd. Arithm.*, II, 8, 20). The series of triangular numbers is therefore the

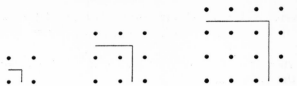

fig. 25 Gnomic growth of squares.

series 1, 3, 6, 10, 15, . . . The number 1 is a 'potential triangle', a 'potential square', and a 'potential cube'. Square numbers are obtained by summing successive terms of the series of odd numbers: 1, 1 + 3 = 4, 4 + 5 = 9, 9 + 7 = 16, 16 + 9 = 25, *etc*. The odd numbers successively added were called *gnomons, i.e.*, elements of similar shapes. Thus the gnomons of triangular numbers were increasingly long lines made up of points along the base, and those of square numbers were increasingly long pairs of sides forming right-angles (*fig. 25*). It follows that pentagonal numbers are obtained by summing successive terms of the series 1, 4, 7 (common difference = 3): 1, 1 + 4, 5 + 7, 12 + 10, *etc*. In general, numbers of a polygon of *n* sides are formed by summing successive terms of an arithmetical series with 1 as its first term and with the common difference $n - 2$.

Pythagorean arithmo-geometry also described many other kinds of figured numbers. They included such plane numbers as the oblongs (ἑτερομήκης) which had the form $n(n + 1)$ and were obtained by summing the terms of a series of even numbers beginning with 2: 2, 6, 12, 20, *etc*.; they also included such solid numbers as the various pyramids obtained by summing different series of plane numbers. Following in the footsteps of the Pythagoreans, Nicomachos of Gerasa later showed that cubes were obtained from the series of odd numbers, 1, 3, 5, 7, 9, 11, . . ., by taking the first, the sum of the next two, the sum of the next three, and so on: 1, 3 + 5, 7 + 9 + 11, *etc*.

PROPORTIONS AND MEANS

We speak of a mean (μεσότης) when, in a series of three terms, there is some equal relation between the first two and the second two terms. Eleven kinds of means are possible but though the early Greek mathematicians knew them all they studied only the three simplest: the arithmetic, the geometric, and the musical or harmonic.

The arithmetic mean is described by the formula:

$$\frac{a - b}{b - c} = \frac{a}{a},$$

and Archytas defined it as that series of three terms in which the third exceeds the second by as much as the second exceeds the first (*e.g.*

the series 2, 4, 6). Archytas also showed that the ratio of the third term to the second is smaller than that of the second to the first (*i.e.* $\frac{6}{4} < \frac{4}{2}$).

In the geometric mean, 'the first term is to the second as the second is to the third', namely

$$\frac{b}{a} = \frac{c}{b}.$$

The three terms are thus in continuous proportion, and this is why Theon of Smyrna could say that the geometric mean *is* proportion (ἀναλογία). Its fundamental property is that the product of the first and third terms is equal to the square of the middle term, *i.e. ac* = b^2. Nevertheless, in Pythagorean arithmo-geometry that mean, though called geometric, was in fact obtained arithmetically from the formula

$$\frac{a-b}{b-c} = \frac{a}{b}.$$

The harmonic mean was defined by

$$\frac{a-b}{b-c} = \frac{a}{c}.$$

While the arithmetic and geometric means have remained familiar concepts, the harmonic mean has largely fallen into oblivion. But from their definition of means, it was only natural that the ancient mathematicians should have considered it a necessary complement of the other two. This becomes clear from an inspection of the three formulae, which are:

$$\frac{a-b}{b-c} = \frac{a}{a}; \ \frac{a-b}{b-c} = \frac{a}{b}; \ \frac{a-b}{b-c} = \frac{a}{c}.$$

Different definitions of the harmonic mean were given by Archytas, Plato, Nicomachos, and Theon of Smyrna, though all led to the same result. Plato's definition, identical in substance with that of Archytas, can be found in the *Timaios* (36A): 'The mean greater than the smaller extreme by a fraction of this extreme equal to the fraction of the larger extreme by which it is itself exceeded by this extreme.' This statement can be translated as follows: In a harmonic progression, the difference between the mean and the smallest term, expressed as a fraction of the smallest term, must be equal to the difference between the greatest term and the mean, expressed as a fraction of the greatest term. Thus the series 6, 4, 3 is in harmonic progression since 4 exceeds 3 by one-third of 3, and 6 exceeds 4 by one-third of 6; or, as we should put it, since

$$a = b + \frac{a}{n} \text{ and } b = c + \frac{c}{n} \text{ } (n \text{ being greater than } 1).$$

Clearly this result is in accordance with the formulae we have given, since

$$a = b + \frac{a}{n} \text{ and } b = c + \frac{c}{n} \text{ are equivalent to } \frac{n(a-b)}{n(b-c)} = \frac{a}{c}$$

Why was this mean called 'harmonic'? It is generally agreed that the theory of means was originally based on the theory of music and, in fact, every harmonic progression whose extremes are in the ratio 2:1 (which is the commonest case), *i.e.*, the series 1, $\frac{2}{3}$, $\frac{1}{2}$ corresponds to the musical fifth, fourth, and octave. Archytas also called the harmonic mean the sub-contrary (ὑπεναντία), because the reciprocals of the harmonic series are in arithmetic progression. Thus, the reciprocals of the series 1, $\frac{2}{3}$, $\frac{1}{2}$ are 1, $\frac{3}{2}$, 2, and they have the common difference $\frac{1}{2}$. This can be expressed quite generally, since

$$\frac{a-b}{b-c} = \frac{a}{c} \text{ is equivalent to } \frac{1}{c} + \frac{1}{a} = \frac{2}{b} \text{ and hence to } \frac{1}{c} - \frac{1}{b} = \frac{1}{b} - \frac{1}{a}.$$

We have not exhausted the questions examined by the Pythagoreans, but the examples we have given are enough to show to what extent this school concentrated on problems leading to numerical solutions. Even when a figure (sum of unit points) could be broken down into proportional elements, they never considered its geometric properties: space remained the container of points and was fully described by discrete magnitudes. The great advance of expressing numbers by line segments had to await the coming of Plato.

This brings us to an important historical problem. Was not this numerical approach bound to lead to the stultification of geometry? Yet why do even the most careful critics claim that the first four (purely geometrical) books of Euclid are based on Pythagorean teachings? The apparent contradiction disappears when we consider that the Pythagoreans themselves were the first to express doubts about the possibility of breaking down every kind of problem into discrete numbers. Their discovery of irrational numbers (or, to keep to what is established beyond doubt, of the irrational $\sqrt{2}$) illustrates this point, for that discovery was considered a scandal undermining all the school's principles. Now this very inability to accept irrational quantities led them to pave the way for a geometry independent of figured numbers, even though they always remained faithful to integral numbers and their search for solutions 'according to numbers' (κατ'ἀριθμούς).

The Origins of the 'Elements'

The question of Euclid's sources raises different problems for each of the thirteen books of his *Elements*. Since we cannot treat them all in detail, we shall content ourselves with a few historical remarks about the successive schools involved.

THE SUCCESSION OF SCHOOLS

From the sixth century to about the middle of the fifth, Greek mathematics flourished under the leadership of the Milesian, Pythagorean, and Eleatic schools. The Milesians, in their search for a universal principle, assumed that all nature was the object of rational inquiry. Thales, who was a physician, an astronomer and a geometer, is traditionally considered the author of five theorems in the First Book of Euclid. The Pythagoreans not only turned geometry into 'a liberal education', but also, by considering numbers as the principle of all things, bestowed on mathematics the attributes of natural philosophy. According to Philolaos, all known things had a number without which nothing could be understood (Frg. 4). The Eleatics, again, were the first to submit scientific thought to critical examination. During the second half of the fifth and the beginning of the fourth centuries, new schools rose up in profusion. The most active centres were Chios (Hippocrates), Cyrene (Theodoros), Megara and Athens, where there were two groups: the Sophists round Protagoras, and the others round Socrates. Subsequently Athens became the intellectual centre of the Hellenic world and remained so until she was supplanted by Alexandria. Mathematics was developed particularly at the beginning of the fourth century in the first Academy, and then at Cyzicos under the leadership of Eudoxos of Cnidos, who is said to have been related to the Athenian school as a 'disciple of the friends of Plato'. The second half of the fourth century, which saw the end of the Hellenic and the beginning of the Alexandrian period (and which may have coincided with the publication of Euclid's *Elements*, possibly in 340 B.C.) was dominated by Aristotle and his immediate successors. Though Aristotle's Peripatetic School was not a seat of mathematical learning like the Academy, it nevertheless ensured the continuity of mathematical teaching. It was to one of the members of that school, Eudemos of Rhodes (*fl.* 320) that we owe the first *Historia Geometrica*, extant fragments of which are of great historical and mathematical interest.

THE CONSTRUCTION OF THE ELEMENTS

More than sixty pre-Euclidean mathematicians are known, and we shall here consider only those whose direct influence on the *Elements* is beyond doubt. The earliest of these was Hippocrates of Chios, or rather he was the first of whom we have any direct knowledge, for Paul Tannery has pointed out that his contribution was based on that of earlier Pythagoreans. After Hippocrates, *i.e.*, from the end of the fifth century, mathematicians redoubled their efforts to combine geometrical theorems into a single great work. It is worthy of note that the word στοιχεῖον—which has been translated as 'element' or first principle—originally referred to any member of a set or series, any point of a line or any link of a chain, and later to the letters of the alphabet. The title Στοιχεῖα (*Elements*) therefore stresses the orderly arrangement of the propositions and the fact that they follow from one another. Though Eudemos mentions no authors of the *Elements* other than Leon and Theudios of Magnesia, there is every reason for believing that other contributors were also involved. Thus Eudoxos is generally credited with having contributed at least the essential parts of Books V, VI, XI and XII. Theudios, too, was a contributor to the *Elements*, and it is from him that Aristotle probably borrowed his mathematical ideas.

THE THEOREM OF PYTHAGORAS

'In right-angled triangles, the square on the side subtending the right angle is equal to the squares (*i.e.* to the sum of the squares) on the sides containing the right angle' (Euclid, I, 47). Whether or not this was first propounded by Pythagoras himself, as Plutarch, Diogenes, Laërtios, Athenaeos and Proclos all asserted, this theorem was undoubtedly part of the original fund of Pythagorean knowledge. Moreover, it expresses what had long before been known to the Egyptians and the Babylonians, who had even verified it to some extent. However, the theorem still had to be proved geometrically and without recourse to number. This decisive advance was probably made simultaneously with the discovery of irrational numbers in connection with a problem without a numerical solution. This was the construction of a square equal to the sum of two given squares ('duplication of the square'). The problem showed that the diagonal of a square could never be a rational multiple of its side.

Pythagoras' theorem has been said to lack generality, for in fact the equality it affirms is true of all figures erected on the sides of a right-angled triangle, and not only of squares. A particular case of this theorem known since the time of Thales is that the perpendicular drawn from the right angle to the base divides a right-angled triangle into two triangles similar both to the whole and to one another (Euclid, IV, 8). Here, the polygon constructed on the hypotenuse is itself a triangle. It may seem odd that the Greeks failed to see a connection between these two theorems, but that connection was necessarily hidden from the early arithmo-geometers, who could not duplicate any but square figures by their method of applying polygonal numbers to them.

IRRATIONAL NUMBERS

Enunciated by the Pythagoreans, developed by Theodoros of Cyrene and completed by Theaetetos, the theory of irrational numbers is rightly considered one of the most important mathematical discoveries of Hellenic science.

The first irrational to have been studied and, in fact, the only one then known, was $\sqrt{2}$. Many hypotheses have been made about its origins, but most historians are agreed that it first arose in connection with the geometrical problem of duplicating the square, or, which amounts to the same thing, with the application of the Theorem of Pythagoras to right isosceles triangles. In both cases it proved impossible to assign a rational number to the diagonal or the hypotenuse. However, the problem of halving the octave or, to stick to arithmetic, of finding a fraction which multiplied by itself would equal 2, might have led to the same stalemate and hence have led to the same discovery.

Irrationals were first called 'inexpressibles' (ἄρρητα). Their discovery struck the early Pythagoreans as a thorn in the flesh of their theory of figured numbers, which lacked appropriate symbols to express them. It was their great merit to have recognized this fact, to have accepted it, and moreover to have *proved* that their methods could not possibly remove the difficulty.

Ancient mathematicians knew at least two methods of proving that $\sqrt{2}$ was irrational: a purely logical (apagogic) method and a geometric method, *viz.*, the method of continued fractions. The first, based on a theorem of Pythagoras, is undoubtedly very old indeed and may be summarized as follows:

In a square of side a and diagonal b, $b^2 = 2a^2$; if $a = 1$, $b^2 = 2$. Hence b must be bigger than 1 and smaller than 2. Let it be m/n, and let us express that fraction in its simplest terms, *i.e.*, in prime numbers, one of which must necessarily be odd. Since $m/n = \sqrt{2}$, $m = n\sqrt{2}$, and $m^2 = 2n^2$. Hence m^2 must be even, and so is m, in which case n must be odd. Now every square (of an even number) is divisible by 4; hence m^2 is divisible by 4, and so is $2n^2$ $(m^2 = 2n^2)$. But if $2n^2$ is divisible by 4, n^2 must be divisible by 2; hence n must be even. Since no number can be both even and odd, no 'expressible' fraction can correspond to $\sqrt{2}$.

This proof is found in Euclid (X, 117), but a reference in Aristotle makes it clear that it was known much earlier. Unfortunately, we know little about the various steps that led from this first discovery to the theory of irrationals as it is described in the *Elements*. All we can state with certainty is that according to Plato (*Theaetetos*, 147D–148B), Theodoros of Cyrene had shown, by examining the case of the numbers 3–17, that the roots of whole numbers other than squares are not commensurable. Other references by Plato, Aristotle, Pappos, and Proclos, and also the Scholia in Euclid, Book X (Prop. 9 of which is attributed to Theaetetos) make it clear that, at least from Plato's time, two types of irrationals were distinguished: those of the first degree (the roots of non-square integers) and those of the second degree (roots of other irrationals, which, according to Theaetetos' description of the Euclidean classification, were further subdivided into medial, binomial, and apotome). Irrationals of the first degree came to be known as *arreta*, in contradistinction to *aloga*, *i.e.* irrationals of the second degree.

The Beginnings of Higher Mathematics

Faithful to Platonic principles, Euclid restricted his *Elements* to problems that could be solved by ruler and compass. But from the second half of the fifth century, and particularly during the sixth century, mathematicians had begun to consider three problems of a different kind—namely, the squaring of the circle, the duplication of the cube, and the trisection of the angle. Moreover, Euclid's immediate predecessors also made a start in considering conic sections.

SQUARING THE CIRCLE
Now while the problems of duplicating the cube and trisecting the angle could be solved by algebraic means, that of squaring the circle could not. The Greeks failed to recognize the transcendental nature of this problem, as did later mathematicians until Huygens's day. Anaxagoras is traditionally called the father of this exercise, but his method is unknown. Then came Antiphon the Sophist, who in 430 B.C. proceeded to 'solve' the problem by inscribing a regular polygon, say a square, inside a circle. On each side of the square, as base, he then described an isosceles triangle with its vertex on the arc of the smaller segment of the circle, thus obtaining a regular polygon with double the number of sides. By repeating this process the circle could be almost, though never completely, filled. Bryson (end of fifth century) went a step further by considering both inscribed and circumscribed polygons. He made the mistake of supposing that the area of the circle was intermediate between them. Dinostratos (sixth century) tried to solve the problem by means of the curve of Hippias (later known as the quadratrix and originally introduced for the trisection of angles), but that curve, which was plotted from points, also failed

to give an exact solution. Archimedes and Apollonios also attempted to solve this problem.

To round off this list, we need only mention that, in the fifth century, Hippocrates of Chios discovered three quadratures of lunes (areas contained by two arcs of a circle). His discovery was, in fact, quite unrelated to the problem of squaring the circle, but until the Renaissance the misconception persisted that, if a lune could be squared, then the rest of the circle could be.

THE DUPLICATION OF THE CUBE

According to a legend told by Eratosthenes and recorded by Eutocios, the oracle of Delos once ordered the inhabitants of that town to construct an altar twice the size of the existing one, and the Delians, unable to comply, turned to Plato for help. Hence the problem of duplicating the cube came to be known as the *Delian problem*. In fact, the problem had been investigated long before Plato's day, for we know from Eratosthenes that Hippocrates of Chios had been concerned with its solution.

Hippocrates is considered the inventor of the so-called 'apagogic' method, by which a problem is reduced to a simpler problem, the solution of which simultaneously solves the main problem. Applying this method to the duplication of the cube, he showed that the problem was equivalent to finding two means in continued proportion between two straight lines, and not, as in the duplication of the square, to finding only one such mean proportional. In modern terms, the equation

$$\frac{a}{x} = \frac{x}{b} \text{ is reduced to } \frac{a}{x} = \frac{x}{y} = \frac{y}{b},$$

which can be transformed into

$$\frac{a^3}{x^3} = \frac{a}{b} \text{ or } ax^3 = ba^3,$$

or if $a = 1$ and $b = 2$, into $x^3 = 2a^3$. Hence x is the side of a cube double that of a cube with side $= 1$.

According to the Delian legend, three geometers tackled the problem of the altar, namely Archytas, Eudoxos, and Menaechmos. The two first gave theoretical solutions; Menaechmos alone produced a practical answer.

THE TRISECTION OF ANY ANGLE

Since right angles could be divided into three parts by the construction of equilateral triangles, and since obtuse angles could be broken

19 Atlas supporting the world

20 Achilles tending Patroclos

down into right angles and acute angles, the problem of trisecting angles was in fact that of trisecting acute angles. It was probably posed first in connection with the construction of the regular nonagon, and solved by the *curve of Hippias*. That curve or *quadratrix* is the locus of the points of intersection of the radius of a circle moving uniformly from a point A through 90° with a line which is a tangent at A but moves along uniformly, and always parallel to itself, until it coincides with the final position of the radius. The curve of Hippias has the historical interest of having been the oldest of all 'mechanical' curves, *i.e.*, curves representing loci. By means of it, any angle could be divided into three, or any other number of equal parts, though the practical results constituted no 'proof' in terms of Greek geometric principles. It was only in the third century that the problem of the trisection (or more generally of the multisection) of angles was solved by geometrical constructions which satisfied the demands of mathematical rigour, that is, by the conchoids of Nicomedes, which were truly geometrical and no longer 'mechanical'.

CONIC SECTIONS

Conic sections, like the trisection of angles, were not fully developed until the Alexandrian period, though their beginnings go back to Hellenic times. This brings us to the question of terminology. Before Apollonios, the words *parabola*, *hyperbola*, and *ellipse* did not refer to conics at all but to the application of areas, those familiar problems of ancient geometry. These problems involved 'applying given areas to straight lines' (*i.e.* constructing rectangles of known side and area). According to Proclos, the ancients held that, when you have a straight line set out and lay the given area exactly alongside the whole of its length, you 'apply' the said area (*parabola*, παραβολή παρά = application to); when, however, you make the length of the area greater than the straight line it is said to *exceed* (*hyperbola*), and when you make it less, it is said to fall short (*ellipse*). Euclid still used these terms in this sense, and it was not until Apollonios that they were applied to conics (Proclos, *In Eucl.*, Friedlein edition, 419–421). This semantic development was based on the fact that the equation of the parabola, $y^2 = 2px$, corresponds to the simple application (*parabola*) of the area y^2 to the straight line $2p$. Similarly, the equation of the ellipse:

$$\frac{x^2}{a^2} + \frac{y^2}{b^2} = 1, \text{ or } \frac{x^2}{a^2} = 1 - \frac{y^2}{b^2}$$

corresponds to the 'application with falling short' (*ellipse*); and the equation of the hyperbola:

14

$$\frac{x^2}{a^2} - \frac{y^2}{b^2} = 1, \text{ or } \frac{x^2}{a^2} = 1 + \frac{y^2}{b^2}$$

to the 'application with exceeding' (*hyperbola*).

The first references to conic sections (though not yet by name) were made by Menaechmos and Aristaeos, two mathematicians whose writings are unfortunately lost, but who knew that if a cone is intersected by a plane perpendicular to its generatrix, a curve is obtained which differs in form according to whether the vertex of the cone is acute, right, or obtuse.

From Proclos and Eratosthenes we know that Menaechmos was born at Proconnesos in the fourth century, that he was 'a pupil of Eudoxos and Plato', and that he was interested in mathematical terminology, in the Delian problem and in conics. His discovery of conic sections seems to have resulted from attempts to duplicate the cube, for which purpose Menaechmos produced two constructions, one obtained from the intersection of a parabola and a hyperbola, and the other from the intersection of two parabolas. Both constructions were given by Eutocios in his commentary on Archimedes. From Menaechmos to Apollonios, conics were known as 'Menaechmean triads'.

Aristaeos (second half of fourth century) exerted a direct influence on Euclid. He was the author of the *Solid Loci* which contained a study of conic sections in which he developed the work of Menaechmos. Its very title suggests strongly that the theory of conics was originally associated with the duplication of the cube. Our entire knowledge of the work of Aristaeos is based on a passage by Pappos (Introduction to Book VII of the *Mathematical Collection*). Since Euclid's *Conics* as well as Aristaeos' *Solid Loci* are lost, Apollonios' writings on conics are the oldest extant texts on the subject.

General Characteristics of Hellenic Mathematics

From our brief review of some of the most common problems treated during the two centuries separating the beginnings of the Pythagorean school from the first appearance of Euclid's *Elements*, we can now draw some general conclusions about the objects and methods of early Greek mathematics.

PROOF

When Eudemos said of Pythagoras that he formed the study of geometry into a liberal education because he 'examined the principles of the science from the beginning and tested his theorems in an abstract and intellectual manner', he implied that Pythagoras was the first of a long line of mathematicians to accept the necessity of proof procedures. What had previously been considered as self-evident was now subjected to critical examination. We often fail to appreciate this point, for, as heirs to the Greeks, we take the demon-strative character of mathematics for granted, even though it is not inherent in it and might well have remained a historic peculiarity of the Greeks. Being the founders of dialectics, the Greeks appreciated the value of persuasive arguments to the full. Not satisfied with self-evident and practical calculations or constructions, the first Greek mathematicians—probably long before Pythagoras—insisted that mathematical conclusions must follow rationally from their premises. While this approach could not have been entirely alien to the East, it must nevertheless be considered a typically Greek contribution to mathematics. However remarkable the other scientific discoveries, from Thales to Euclid, they pale in comparison with the development of logical procedures: the examination of evidence, the sifting of axioms, the critique of postulates, and the combination of originally independent theorems into the vast body of Euclid's *Elements*.

VALUE OF INTUITION

Another essential characteristic of the entire history of Greek mathe-matics, which might at first strike one as being diametrically opposed to logic, was its stress on intuitive faculties, or 'vision'. Geometric figures had to 'look' convincing—to *appear* to be proclaiming a truth. At first such figures, no matter whether they consisted of lines or Pythagorean points, were considered as proofs in themselves. But the philosophers' objections gradually forced mathematicians to become more circumspect and to adduce ratiocinative demonstrations instead. Even so, they never abandoned their demands for confirmation by visual evidence. Euclid, in particular, made a point of satisfying the intellect and the eye alike. Only figures constructed with ruler and compass were considered to be beyond reproach. Now while such requirements proved extremely useful and fruitful in the beginning, they gradually became a brake on further progress. More complex problems do not yield readily under such limitations.

INTUITIVE ARITHMETIC AND ARITHMETIC ALGEBRA

What we know of Pythagorean arithmo-geometry makes it clear that Greek arithmetic (as well as geometry) had intuitive and visionary origins. Figured numbers were thought to fill space, and ignoring or scorning any other notations, the Pythagoreans insisted on represent-ing 1 by one point, 2 by two points, *etc*. Clearly it was not practicable to express very large numbers in this way, but that was no handicap at first because large numbers were systematically excluded from the field of pure science. (For a long time pure calculation, as a minor art, was the preserve of specialists: the logisticians.) As we saw during the discussion of polygonal numbers, the science of numbers was above all the science of generating point-figures and of studying their 'gnomonic' growth. Moreover, the 'fundamental' numbers—*pythmenes* or *numeri fundamentales*—were said to be endowed with special properties and were studied for that reason. The next-highest numbers were derived from the *pythmenes* by special gnomonic applications, and once the laws governing the latter had been established, there was no point in carrying the exercise further. All arithmetic was governed by simple gnomonic laws.

'GEOMETRISM' AND GEOMETRIC ALGEBRA

Despite their predilection for discrete numbers, the Greeks also held that the notion of number invariably implied a vision of space. Hence it is not surprising that, at a later stage, geometry was to lead them to arithmetic, and to give rise to the kind of 'geometrism' which, following upon the discovery of irrational numbers in the fifth century, was to exercise an ever-growing influence upon Greek science at large. Good geometric constructions were not only proofs in themselves; they were visible proofs, satisfying the mind and the eye at once. Moreover, they overcame the handicap of the Greek method of counting by figured numbers. By means of a simple example, we shall now show how geometry could be used as a substitute for algebra.

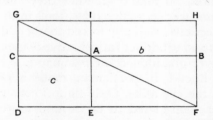

fig. 26 Geometric solution of the equation bx=c.

In modern equations of the form $bx = c$, b and c are constants and x is unknown. The problem is therefore to find x. The Greeks would solve it by constructing a rectangle of known side b and known area c, thus applying (*parabola*) a given area to a given line. Let AB = b, the given side; and let the rectangle ACDE = c, the given area (*fig. 26*). Construct ACDE on AB produced, and produce DE to meet the perpendicular to AB, BF, in F. Then produce the diagonal FA of the rectangle ABFE to meet DC produced in G. Complete the figure by joining G and H, B and H, and A and I. Clearly CG = AI = BH is the required length x, and the rectangle ABHI or bx is equal to the given area ACDE since the two rectangles ABHI (or bx) and ACDE (or c) are equal (Euclid, IX, 43), as may be seen by subtracting equal small triangles from the large equal triangles FDG and FGH.

If we now express $bx = c$ as $c/b = x$, we see at once that the geometric solution gives the same result. Hence the Greeks could perform any division by geometric means. A dividend c can always be considered as a product of two factors (if it is prime one of its factors is 1) and therefore may be represented by a rectangle. To obtain c/b, all that need be done is to represent the number c by a rectangle, and the number b by a prolongation of one of the sides of the rectangle.

ASTRONOMY

Following in the Pythagorean tradition, Philolaos (end of fifth century) developed a cosmology unlike any of the mythical systems of the earlier schools. According to him, the earth was spherical and revolved about the central fire (see above). In the fourth century Greek astronomers were divided into two groups: the respective forerunners of the heliocentric doctrine of Aristarchos of Samos and the geocentric doctrines of Hipparchos and Ptolemy.

HERACLIDES OF PONTOS (*c.* 388–312)
Though no purely heliocentric system was propounded during the Hellenic period, Philolaos' daring denial of the immobility of the earth and its central place in the universe was a step in that direction, and so was Heraclides' assertion that the apparent motion of the sphere of fixed stars was due to the rotation of the earth about its own axis. Even so, Heraclides had no doubt that the earth was the centre of the universe, and that the sun and most planets revolved directly about it, though Mercury and Venus revolved round the sun. His system may therefore be called semi-heliocentric.

In spite of these novel suggestions, geocentrism was triumphantly and vigorously affirmed. Plato and Aristotle raised it into a dogma, while Eudoxos of Cnidos built a coherent astronomical theory on it.

PLATO
We shall deal with Plato's cosmology at greater length in the next chapter; here we merely note in passing that, faithful to Pythagorean principles, Plato held that all astronomical phenomena could be expressed in mathematical terms. According to Sosigenes (quoted by Eudemos), Plato's problem was to find the regular motions whereby the movements of the planets could be fully explained. In the Platonic scheme, Anaximander's wheels and discs were replaced by spheres.

Every planet was a globe pulled along by the motion of vast diaphanous spheres which were its 'heaven'. These spheres were concentric shells, the most distant being that of the fixed stars. Plato's ideas were to prevail for two millennia; even Copernicus held them, though, unlike Plato, he placed the sun at the centre of the spheres.

EUDOXOS OF CNIDOS (*fl.* 368)

Plato's ideas became the basis of the homocentric spheres of Eudoxos, which may be called the real starting-point of traditional astronomy. With his theory, Eudoxos tried to explain the apparent motion of the heavens about an immobile earth. The largest of his spheres was that of the fixed stars, which revolved uniformly about the cosmic axis from east to west. The moon and the planets, on the other hand, though revolving uniformly as well, did not pursue the same path among the stars from month to month and from year to year. Hence, to account for their apparent irregularities Eudoxos had to associate their motions with that of more than one sphere. In his system, every celestial body was supposed to be situated on the equator of a sphere which revolved with uniform speed about its two poles. To explain the positions and retrogressions of the planets, Eudoxos assumed that the poles of a given planetary sphere were not immobile but were carried by a larger concentric sphere rotating at a different speed. The motions of the sun and the moon could be explained by three spheres each, and those of the five planets by four. With the sphere of the fixed stars there were thus twenty-seven spheres in all. Every system of spheres was entirely independent of all the others; there was no contact between the outer sphere of one planet and inner sphere of the next one. On the other hand, the spheres associated with one and the same planet were connected in such a way that the axis of rotation of the outer was fixed to the two poles of the inner. As it rotated, the inner sphere would then be carried along by the rotation, about a different axis, of the outer sphere. The planet being attached to the inner sphere, its motion was thus the resultant of a number (two or three) of motions. In this way appearances could be 'saved', and the apparent irregularities accounted for. Needless to say, all the spheres were transparent to allow the rest of the sky to be seen. In every system of spheres, the outermost described the same motion as the sphere of the fixed stars, while the second revolved about an axis normal to the ecliptic, *i.e.* it made an angle of about 24° with the plane of the equator. The different inclinations of the remaining spheres explained the observed anomalies of the planetary motions. Thus, in the lunar system, the outermost sphere revolved from east to west in 24 hours; the middle sphere moved from west to east during 223 lunations, and the innermost, to which the moon was attached, moved from the east to west like the first, but in 27 days. The combination of these three motions explained, more or less, the motion of the moon and the points (nodes) where its orbit intersects that of the sun. Hence eclipses could be predicted fairly accurately. Unfortunately, the system did not work nearly as well when it came to predictions of the orbits of other planets.

At the end of the fourth century, many corrections were made to Eudoxos' system, notably by Callippos (*c.* 335).

A theory of the true and apparent risings and settings of the fixed stars was formulated by Autolycos of Pitane (end of fourth century), the author of two treatises on mathematical astronomy: *On the Moving Sphere* and *On the Risings and Settings of the Stars*. They are the only pre-Alexandrian astronomical texts that have been preserved in their entirety.

MUSIC

Pythagorean research on acoustical phenomena bore mainly on the nature of sound and the mathematical theory of the scale. The theory of sound will be discussed at greater length when we examine the Aristotelean contribution to science; we shall here consider the purely mathematical properties of the scale.

THE PYTHAGOREAN SCALE

Music was an art long before it became a science, and the first scale was sung before it was calculated. The original Pythagorean scale was improved by Aristoxenes (*c.* 360–300) for practical as well as euphonic reasons, and his contribution may well have been based on prior attempts going back as far as the beginning of the fifth century.

On the principle that numbers are the 'models of all things', the Pythagoreans quite naturally likened sounds to numbers, and turned the musical scale into a purely mathematical construction, probably based on the length of vibrating strings. Now, strings of the same material and the same tension but of different lengths will produce harmonious sounds if the lengths are in simple numerical proportions. For instance, if their lengths are in the ratio 1:2, the strings will produce sounds one octave apart. The longer the string the lower the note.

Having once ascertained these facts, the Pythagoreans constructed their scale using the smallest integral numbers, *i.e.* 1, 2, and 3, their ratios 1/2, 2/3, 3/2, and their powers. This method struck them as being endowed with perfect beauty and elegance.

The complete scale was obtained by a series of fifths in the following manner: if the note emitted by a given string of unit length is taken as the fundamental note (do), the note emitted by two other strings of lengths $3/2$ and $2/3$, respectively, will be lower fa (fa_0) and higher sol (sol_1). Again, a string $2/3$ the length of sol_1 will give re_2. Hence re_2 is $(2/3)^2$ of do_1. Strings of length $(2/3)^3$, $(2/3)^4$ and $(2/3)^5$ give respectively la_2, mi_3, and si_3. Since the lower octave of any note whatever is produced by a string twice the length of that producing the higher note, all that remains to be done to construct the complete scale is to double the length of the strings producing re_2 and la_2, to multiply by four the lengths of the strings producing mi_3 and si_3, and to halve the string producing fa_0. In this way all the notes from do to do are obtained, corresponding respectively to strings of lengths: 1, $4/9 \times 2$, $16/81 \times 4$, $3/2 \times 1/2$, $2/3$, $8/27 \times 2$, $32/243 \times 4$, $1/2$, or 1, $2^3/3^2$, $2^6/3^4$, $3/2^2$, $2/3$, $2^4/3^3$, $2^7/3^5$, $1/2$. Again, if all these fractions are expressed with the same denominator $(viz.\ 2^2 \times 3^5)$, their relations are given by the whole-number numerators: 972, 864, 768, 729, 648, 576, 512, 486.

CHROMATIC SCALE
If now we continue the series of fifths beyond si_3, we obtain a note which, instead of giving fa_4, gives a slightly higher note. If we keep doubling the length of the string emitting it until we come back to our original octave, we shall find that this note corresponds to fa sharp. The other sharps can be obtained similarly. Again, by descending from fa_0 by successive fifths, we obtain all the flat notes. We observe that even the construction of the chromatic scale involves none but ratios of the first three integers, and that the series of flats is quite distinct from the series of sharps. In the Pythagorean scale re sharp and mi flat are two distinct notes.

Though simple from the purely mathematical point of view, the Pythagorean scale was ill-suited to musicians or to the construction of musical instruments. Subsequent generations of philosophers and musicians, beginning with Aristoxenes, have therefore added improvements which, while leading to better practical results, complicated the mathematical simplicity of the original theory.

The Pythagorean scale was also applied to astronomy, and musical intervals were likened to the respective distances of the planets from the earth.

CHAPTER 3

The Sophists, Socrates, Plato

THE SOPHISTS AND SOCRATES

NO HISTORIAN OF SCIENCE has ever felt easy about giving an objective account of the Sophists and the Socratic School, both of whom looked down upon the teaching of pure science and even attacked it on occasion. But our discussion of the Eleatic School has made it clear that a philosophically critical attitude to science can be very fruitful, if only because it forces the scientists to look to their principles and to define the objects of their investigation more carefully. Hence, the schools we are about to examine may be said to have made important contributions to the methods of science.

THE SOPHISTS

Before Plato's day, the word *Sophist* did not have the pejorative significance which it has held ever since, mainly because of the influence of Plato, on whom most of our knowledge of the Sophists is based. From the middle of the fifth until the early fourth century these philosophers, these 'masters of wisdom'—for such is the title which they applied to themselves—went from town to town to broadcast their views in the market-places.

The most ancient of the Sophists, Protagoras of Abdera (*c.* 480–410), taught first in his native town, then in Sicily, in Southern Italy, and above all in Athens. He owed his fame to his extensive knowledge and his rare oratorical gifts. His doctrine of humanistic 'relativism' is best summarized in his well-known dictum that 'man is the measure of all things' (Frg. 1). His moral doctrine was opposed to all sciences concerned with existence and particularly to mathematics. Things were what they appeared to be to men. No man had ever seen, for example, a tangent touching a sphere in only a single point; therefore 'the tangent touches the sphere in more than one point' (Frg. A7). His critique, far from destroying mathematics, forced geometers to take cognizance of the fact that their arguments applied to ideal figures and that their science was built up on abstract elements.

While discussing the trisection of angles and the squaring of the circle in the previous chapter, we mentioned the work of two Sophists, Hippias of Elis and Antiphon. According to Plato, Hippias taught arithmetic, geometry, astronomy and music (*Protagoras*, 318 D–E), and cannot therefore have held mathematics in great contempt. Antiphon, on the other hand, must have been closer in that respect to Protagoras, for in his attempts to square the circle by filling it with polygons he stopped when the circle *appeared* to be filled, and failed to realize that the process must be continued *ad infinitum*. Aristotle attacked him for it, perhaps unfairly, since according to his own lights, Antiphon was bound to consider the circle a visual rather than an abstract phenomenon.

Gorgias of Leontium, who lived in Athens in 427, was another illustrious Sophist. He carried contempt for science and for all knowledge further than all other philosophers of his school. Gorgias held that *nothing* exists. Even if some things did exist, we could not know the fact, or if, by chance, we did know, we still could not express it in words. He thus attacked not only science as such but also the very objects of its inquiry.

SOCRATES

In Plato's dialogues, Socrates (born in Athens in 470, died in 399) appears as the arch-opponent of the Sophists. Nevertheless, despite marked differences his views, particularly on the value of science, were not entirely opposed to those of his adversaries.

According to Xenophon (*Mem.* IV, 7), Socrates held that geometry should be taught in so far as it dealt with the buying, selling, dividing and ploughing of fields. But he disapproved of geometry as an exercise for its own sake, not because it eluded his grasp, but because such studies wasted men's time and diverted them from more useful occupations.

In his emphasis on practical and human problems Socrates resembles Protagoras. The same is true of his strictures on the study of astronomy and physics. Socrates was an enemy of pure science, and his denial of the possibility that science might lead to true knowledge even brings him close to the position of Gorgias. His ironic evaluation of all knowledge acquired through the senses is best summed up in his famous assertion: 'One thing I know—it is that I know nothing.'

Since nature was thus removed from the field of possible knowledge, what then were those 'more useful occupations'? They may be expressed as all that is involved in the Oracle's charge, 'Know thyself!' It is here that Socrates parted company with the Sophists, for to him all self-knowledge was fruitful. It transcended the self and led towards the higher verities. Moreover, it was communicable. By knowing oneself, one could persuade others to know themselves also and teach them the method whereby they might be borne towards the absolute (Platonic) truths from which the pessimism of the Sophists had precluded them. Socrates was surrounded by disciples until his death, all of whom set themselves the task of developing the metaphysic he had propounded in the course of his familiar discourses. There slowly emerged the commonly held view that the perceptible world was not the entire universe but, as Albert Rivaud puts it, that 'there exists another world containing in all their purity the objects of which we perceive nothing but the changing shadow'.

For the sake of completeness we must mention the other schools traditionally associated with the Socratic: the Cynics, the Cyrenaics and the Magarics, whose contribution to the progress of science was insignificant. Even so, the factor common to them all, their stress on human values, human conduct and the inward life, marked a turning-point in the history of philosophy which has been characterized by the saying that Socrates 'brought philosophy down from the heavens to earth', albeit to an earth of fleeting shadows. While pre-Socratic philosophers refused to make man the object of their study, Protagoras and Socrates taught that man was the only worthwhile object of philosophy. These enemies of science were the first to perceive that observations depended upon the existence of an observer—who tended to forget his own existence.

PLATO

Plato (428 or 427–348 B.C.), unlike the Sophists and Socrates, far from being adverse to scientific thought, considered natural philosophy one of the foremost intellectual activities. Plato was interested in scientific principles and methods, in the newest advances of mathematics, in the structure of the primary elements of the universe, and in the laws governing the cosmos as a whole, for all of which he put forward bold hypotheses of his own.

Plato and Mathematics

We cannot give a full list of all the mathematical passages written by Plato. Suffice it to say that no problem which interested the mathematicians of his day was foreign to him. He was conversant with the discoveries of Theodoros, with the contributions of Theaetetos, with the theory of irrational numbers and that of the regular solids, and with the works of Eudoxos, which dominated all mathematical thought during the fourth century. What concerns us above

all is how Plato applied his scientific criteria to observable phenomena and why he attached so much importance to mathematics
that he asked for the words 'Let none but geometers enter here' to
be inscribed over the portals of the Academy.

THE SCIENCE OF STABLE RELATIONS

We know that Plato made a distinction (foreshadowed by Socrates)
between imperfect and changeable phenomena and their eternal
models, the perfect and immutable ideas. He considered that
mathematical existents occupied an intermediate place between the
two. Take a circle traced in the sand. Such a circle is necessarily
imperfect, since the tangent to it is bound to touch it in more than
one point. Only an ideal tangent will touch an ideal circle in one
point, and one point only. Now, the ideal circle is what corresponds
to the *definition* of the circle, *i.e.* of that circle with which mathematicians are concerned. Hence, the true circle is a concept rather than
a fact. It cannot be obtained by the generalization of a series of real
objects, as there is no single object in nature corresponding absolutely to the definition of the circle. Hence the concept must have
arisen intuitively and not through reasoning. The correct approach
to the true objects of geometry was *recollection*. We shall not enter into
the methods and exercises prescribed to develop this faculty, since
all that concerns us here is to explain the occurrence of mathematical
existents that cannot be derived by reflection upon the 'real' world.
Plato first dealt with this subject in the *Meno*, where he shows us
Socrates using maieutic procedures to help a young slave 'remember'
the method of duplicating the square. According to the original
theory, recollection is nothing but the calling to mind of knowledge
acquired in previous lives. Since all such knowledge is latent and
partial it must be prodded and brought into full consciousness.
While the *Phaedo* contained no substantial changes of these earlier
notions, the *Timaeos* did. According to C. Mugler, Plato gradually
replaced his belief in the progressive restoration of past memories
(which failed to solve the problem of its original acquisition) by the
'intuitive anticipation of a reality independent of the temporal world'.
   These views about the sources of knowledge explain why Plato
placed mathematics above all the sciences dealing with perceptible
'existents'. They also explain why he, and hence Euclid, Archimedes and all subsequent Greek mathematicians, attached so much
importance to *definitions*. In the absence of a material foundation,
for there are no perfect figures in nature, science was obliged to rest
upon concepts. Mathematical definitions endowed mathematical
objects with their *static* and eternal form, opposing reality to fleeting
appearances. Being the common starting-point of mathematics and

of dialectics, definitions did more than designate objects and indicate their presence—they expressed their nature and proclaimed their essential characteristics. We have placed the word *static* in italics because it illustrates Plato's view of mathematics so admirably. It was his aim to express the stable relations between objects which were not subject to change themselves. This brings us back to the problem of irrationals, and to the important contributions of Eudoxos.

IRRATIONAL NUMBERS AND THE DEFINITION OF THE *logos*
The Pythagoreans must have looked upon their discovery of irrational numbers as either a scandal or a mere illusion. The discovery that easily constructed magnitudes expressing clear spatial relations could not be formulated (*arreton*) and were non-logical (*alogon*) was tantamount to renouncing the great dream of a universal arithmetic. But were such qualities not also and *a fortiori* the very antithesis of the Platonic demand that science be completely founded on intelligibility rather than on material constructions? In fact, they were not, for to avoid the difficulty all that was needed was to enlarge the concept of an 'existent' to include (for example) the diagonal, which then had no need to be defined by the discrete number governing the length of the side. Its logical existence was dependent only on its correct definition. Now, it was at this point that Theodoros' discoveries seemed to upset everything. Theodoros of Cyrene, Plato tells us in the *Theaetetos*, had proved that the square roots of all non-square integers from 3–17 were irrational. Since all these magnitudes could be constructed geometrically, it was not so much their existence (which he knew in any case) as its proof by Theodoros which disquieted Plato. Plato does not mention that proof, but in all probability Theodoros, using continuous fractions, had shown that irrational magnitudes were numbers that, however far pursued, could never be reached. Hence, Plato saw mathematics being thrown into the domain of motion, of the unstable, of the indefinite—the *apeiron*. However, when Theaetetos proposed a more general definition of the irrational by which Theodoros' views were brought closer to Pythagorean statism, Plato's anxieties were somewhat allayed, though it was still possible to entertain doubt. All difficulties were finally solved when Eudoxos, by his new conception of the mathematical *logos*, turned irrationals into stable notions.

Previously, no two magnitudes were considered to have a mutual 'ratio' (*logos*) unless they were in numerical proportion. To appreciate how Eudoxos enlarged the scope of the *logos* we must consider the lemma propounded by Archimedes in his preface to the *Quadrature of the Parabola*: that the excess by which the greater of two unequal lines, areas or solids exceeds the less can, by being added to itself indefinitely, be made to exceed either given quantity. Archimedes added that this lemma was also used by earlier geometers, notably to establish theorems relating to the volumes of pyramids and cones. By 'earlier geometers', he clearly referred to Eudoxos. Archimedes' lemma is, moreover, similar to Definition IV in Euclid Book V, sometimes called the 'postulate of Eudoxos', namely: 'Magnitudes are said to have a ratio to one another if they are capable, when multiplied, of exceeding one another.' It is also related to the definition in Book VI, another statement of the same principle. This is not the place to discuss the importance of all the many Eudoxian propositions about ratios. Suffice it to say, that, through them, irrationals were incorporated into the method of treating geometrical problems by arithmetic, and that Plato fully appreciated this fact (see the *Parmenides* 140B–D). Moreover, the number of occasions on which he refers to irrationals (*Hippias Major* 306B, *Laws* VII, 819D–820B, *Epinomis* 990C–991A, *etc.*) is clear evidence of his constant attempts to surmount what was previously considered an insurmountable obstacle and to place all mathematical truths on an unassailable footing.

THE MATHEMATICAL HYPOTHESIS

The great value attached by Plato to mathematics (as against natural sciences) must not lead us to suppose that he considered it a short-cut to the absolute verities. This point emerges clearly from what he had to say about hypotheses, particularly in the *Republic*, from which we quote the following significant lines:

I fancy that you know that those who study geometry and calculation and similar subjects take as *hypotheses* the odd and the even, and figures, and three kinds of angles, and other similar things in each different inquiry. They make them into hypotheses as though they knew them, and will give no further account of them either to themselves or to others, on the ground that they are plain to every one. Starting from these, they go on until they arrive by agreement at the original object of their inquiry.

(*Republic* VI, 510C.)

This passage calls for two comments, the first concerning the use of the word 'hypothesis'. Clearly it must not be taken to stand for 'conjecture', since we do not conjecture about geometric figures. It must be considered in its original etymological sense, *viz.*, the basis of argument. As for the claim that hypotheses are formed in our minds, and not founded on objective facts, Plato develops this point in the very next passage:

Then you know that they use the visible squares and figures and make their arguments about them, though they are not thinking about them, but about those things of which the visible are images. Their arguments concern the real square and a real diagonal, not the diagonal which they draw, and so with everything. The actual things which they model and draw . . . these they now use as images in their turn, seeking to see those very realities which cannot be seen except by the understanding.

Hence mathematics contains presuppositions, the rational basis of all research; but as Abel Rey pointed out, these are the first principles of science, not the absolute first principles themselves (*i.e.* the dialectical principles).

In mathematics, as in dialectics, hypotheses are taken as the starting-points of a synthesis—or as the end-points of an analysis whenever we go back from a fact to the basic principle. If A implies B, then either can be inferred from the other. But in mathematics we can never state with certainty that A exists. Hence mathematics is related to dialectics as the shadow is to the body. Its truths are irrefutable once its principles are accepted, but they remain conditional truths because the principles themselves are hypotheses. ‘Plato considered mathematical facts as mental facts which constrain the intellect while not being fully part of it’ (Abel Rey). Plato was a humanist and as such he remained faithful to the Socratic spirit. Science is man-made. True, the scientist tries to look at the eternal truths outside him, but since the means with which alone he can reach them are inseparable from himself, he can never attain more than the shadow of transcendent reality. Thus Plato, while recognizing the grandeur of mathematics, the Queen of Science, also appreciated that it has its limits like all other human knowledge. Hence, he may rightly be called both the greatest stimulator and also the greatest critic of the mathematicians of his day.

Platonic Physics and Astronomy

The Elements of Matter

According to Plato, matter is the field or receptacle (χώρα ὑποδοχή) in which the generation, the corruption and, more generally, all the changes of the sensible world occur. That world can become the object of rational knowledge because it is governed by laws, as the ancient Ionian physiologers believed. But Plato gave the term ‘law’ a new significance; physical laws became the expression of a creative intelligence which strove towards a final purpose. In this teleological view, the universe results from the seminal effects upon matter of ideas, which, in their turn, are organized by divine thought.

The basic elements of matter are the regular polyhedra (often called the *Platonic bodies*). The mathematical theory of these bodies goes back to the earliest Pythagoreans, but it is difficult to decide whether Eudemos was right in claiming that they knew the five regular figures or whether we must agree with Euclid's scholia that they were familiar with only three (tetrahedron, cube and dodecahedron). What alone is certain is that Theaetetos was the first to formulate the theory of polyhedra found in Euclid, Book XIII, and to show that no other such regular bodies could exist. In any case, even if we grant that the Pythagoreans knew all five, Plato gave the theory a new lease of life.

Plato was concerned with only their outer surfaces, *i.e.* their *faces*, leaving us to guess whether he considered their contents identical or qualitatively different. In any case, he attached much greater importance to their form than to their content. The areas bounding the regular solids—squares in the case of the cube, equilateral triangles in the case of the tetrahedron, the octahedron, and the icosahedron, and pentagons in the case of the dodecahedron— could all be broken down into isosceles or scalene triangles, and it was these triangles which Plato took as the basic elements of the universe. Four of the five polyhedra corresponded to the four elements of Empedocles. The tetrahedron (triangular pyramid) represented the element of fire, which was the most subtle, the lightest, and the most striking of all the bodies; the octahedron represented air; the icosahedron water, and the cube the earth. Some modern Platonic scholars hold that the polyhedra did not so much represent matter itself as states of matter (igneous, gaseous, liquid or solid), explaining physical changes—*e.g.* the fact that an octahedron of air may be split into two tetraheda of fire (*Timaeos* 56D)—not by simple division, which would have produced two square pyramids, but by division accompanied by a complete change of form. In any case, the essential point about Platonic physics was the belief that form alone determined the nature of the elements and the different states of matter. Democritos' atomic doctrine, which also equated qualities with forms, must therefore be related to the views of Plato, though the two philosophers differed profoundly in a number of respects. While Democritos' atoms were said to have existed *ab eterno*, to be quite independent of any organizing mind, to represent potential matter, and to be unlimited in number or size, Plato's elements were the products of thought and existed in only two or, at most, five forms if one considers the solids rather than their constituent triangles. As for their size, Plato held that they can be infinitely small since triangles are infinitely divisible, but not infinitely varied since they cannot combine in more than the five ways.

We have so far restricted our remarks to the four polyhedra corresponding with the four traditional elements, but there was a fifth, the dodecahedron, to which Plato referred in somewhat mysterious terms: 'And seeing that there still remained one other compound figure, the fifth, God used it in his final design for the universe as a whole' (*Timaeos* 55C). In fact, the dodecahedron has remarkable 'symbolic' properties: bounded by twelve pentagonal faces, each capable of being broken down into thirty triangles, it contains 360 basic elements—the number of days in a sidereal year or the degrees in the circumference of a circle. Above all, the dodecahedron is, together with the icosahedron, one of the solids whose volume is closest to that of the sphere, that perfect form which, according to the Pythagoreans, represented the universe. Plato may well have asked himself if it were not possible to bridge the small gap between the form of the dodecahedron and that of the sphere by mathematical procedures. After all, Eudoxos had used his method of exhaustion to just that purpose.

Leaving conjectures aside, we may say that Plato's physics had two distinct characteristics:

(1) A purposive view of the structure of the universe, and
(2) the mathematization of the physical elements.

COSMOLOGY

Like his physics, Plato's astronomy was based on the assumption that the universe was the creation of an organizing mind. Hence the universe was comprehensible, and it behoved astronomers to express the apparently irregular celestial motions by regular mathematical laws. With this purpose in view, Plato came back time and again to the problem of the structure of the cosmos and offered a number of different solutions (in the *Republic*, the *Timaeos*, the *Laws* and the *Epinomis*). Nevertheless, all his proposed systems had certain factors in common: the sphericity of the universe, the sphericity of all celestial bodies including the earth, the central position and immobility of the earth, and the circular motion of celestial bodies at various distances from the earth, the sphere of the fixed stars being the most distant.

To these general views the *Republic* added the following considerations: the moon (which has no light of its own but reflects the light of the sun) is the celestial body closest to the earth, with Venus, Mercury, Mars, Jupiter and Saturn following in that order. The sun, Venus and Mercury revolve at equal speeds and are almost equidistant from the earth. Other planets, and particularly the stars, travel more quickly since they are farther from the earth. The stars and planets all revolve in the same direction with the exception of Mars which apparently follows a retrograde orbit. This phenomenon must be explained and fitted into the general picture.

The *Timaeos* brought further modifications and additions. The planets in order of distance from the earth were given as: Moon, Sun, Mercury and Venus (not Venus and Mercury); and the relative distances of the planets nearest to the earth (up to Mars) were listed. Finally, four concentric celestial spheres were distinguished, corresponding to the four elements. Their sizes relative to that of the earth (radius $=1$) were: water 2, air 5, and fire 10, the nearest round cube roots of 1, 10, 100, and 1,000. The three first layers constituted the sublunary world, while the fourth, fire, contained the stars. The distance of the moon from the earth was equal to 8 $(1+2+5)$; thta of Saturn, the most distant of the Platonic planets, to 13 $(8+5)$; that of the sphere of the fixed stars to 18 $(8+10)$. The last figure also described the dimensions of the Platonic universe, which was considerably smaller than that of Anaximander.

In the *Laws*, Plato, while adding no new astronomical facts, stressed the difficulties of astronomy and the importance of explaining the apparent irregularities of the celestial revolutions. He also reiterated a point made in the *Timaeos*: that the stars were living bodies and that their motions did not differ from that of the organizing intelligence.

The *Epinomis* presents so radically different a cosmology that many scholars have claimed that it was written by Philip of Opus, one of Plato's pupils, and not by Plato himself. It would take us too far afield to give all the *pros* and *cons* of this matter, but we must point out that equally eminent scholars (including particularly P. Des Places) have made out an excellent case for the authenticity of a work which critics have in any case questioned not because of the book's contents but only because of its form. Be that as it may, the cosmology of the *Epinomis* differs in more than one respect from that of Plato's earlier writings. Thus it introduces into the cosmos a fifth element, the 'aether', whose elementary form is the dodecahedron, that figure which, according to the *Timaeos*, God had introduced for purely ornamental purposes. In other words, the *Epinomis* marks the transition between the theory of the *Timaeos* and the Aristotelian theory of five substances. Moreover because of the introduction of the sphere of the aether, the dimensions of the world have been increased, as have the distances of the planets from the earth. While no exact distances are mentioned, we are told in the *Epinomis* (983A) that the stars are immense, and that the sun, in particular, is much larger than the earth. Now, as C. Mugler has rightly observed, according to the *Timaeos* the sun could at most have a diameter one-eighth that of the earth.

CHAPTER 4

The Aristotelian School

BIOGRAPHY

Aristotle was born in 384–83 B.C. in Stagira (the present Stavro), a Greek colony in Thrace. At the age of eighteen years (*c.* 366) he came to Athens, where he became Plato's pupil and remained at the Academy until his master's death (348–47). He then lived first at Assos and later at Mitylene, whence Philip, King of Macedonia, summoned him to become tutor to his son Alexander, then thirteen years old (343–42). Six years later, after the death of Philip and the accession of Alexander, Aristotle returned to Athens to found a school in a gymnasium consecrated to Apollo Lycaeos (whence the name Lyceum). Meanwhile in 339 Speusippos, Plato's immediate heir, had died, and the Academy had fallen into a decline under Xenocrates. All but the letter of Plato's teaching, which had been turned into a dogma, was ignored. Aristotle, on the other hand, was constantly introducing new methods and enlarging the field of study, particularly in the direction of natural history, thus becoming a dangerous rival of the official Platonists. Lectures at the Lyceum were often continued by informal discussion during walks in the precincts of the gymnasium—whence Aristotle's pupils came to be known as *Peripatetics*. On the death of Alexander (323) Aristotle judged it prudent to leave Athens, since his Macedonian connections rendered him suspect. He retreated to Chalcis, where he died soon afterwards (beginning of 322) at the age of sixty-two years. His school was taken over first by Theophrastos (327–287), then by Straton (287–270) and finally by Lycon (270–228).

THE ARISTOTELIAN CORPUS

It is very difficult to settle the actual authorship of the works of Aristotle, since according to custom the writings of his pupils were commonly attributed to their teacher (*cf.* the Pythagoreans). Moreover the actual texts—even those whose authenticity seems most certain—are a jumble of careful passages and brief notes that require oral elucidation and were most probably jotted down by students. Of all the immense body of Aristotelian writing covering politics, poetry and philosophy, we shall here consider none but the scientific texts. These can be classified as:

1. The logical treatises (*Categories, Analytics, Topics, Refutation of the Sophists*), combined into the *Organon*, which are of scientific interest only in so far as they discuss the possibilities and methods of acquiring knowledge.

2. The physical writings, *i.e.* all the treatises on matter and on the form and laws of the sensible universe: the *Physics*, in eight books; the *De generatione et corruptione*, in two books; the *De Cælo*, in four books; and the *Meteorologica*, in four books. The *Physics* deals mainly with motion; *De generatione*, and Books III and IV of *De Cælo*, with the theory of the elements; *De Cælo* I and II deal with astronomical theories; and the *Meteorologica* deals with sublunary phenomena, *i.e.* phenomena associated with air, water and the earth.

3. Writings on natural history. Aristotle probably wrote a treatise on plants and possibly one on stones. Neither is extant. On the other hand, we have records of his three great works on zoology, comprising one of the most impressive contributions to Greek science, namely: the *Historia animalium*, in ten books, a vast compendium of descriptions and observation; the *De animalium partibus*, in four books; and the *De animalium generatione*, in five books. This group of texts also includes the *De anima* and the collection of minor texts known as the *Parva naturalia*.

ARISTOTLE AND SCIENCE

The best way of explaining Aristotle's views on science and the role of the scientist is to compare and contrast them with Plato's. We shall take the similarities first. Aristotle's science was one of universals and not of particulars—the study of Man and not the study of the individual called Callias. Science is based on definition and proof; no other methods are appropriate to it. The *Analytica posteriora*, the *Physics* and the *De anima* say, and repeat, that knowledge acquired through the senses is clearly distinct from rational (scientific) knowledge. For while the former is based on facts contingent in time and space, the latter has no such restrictions. 'Aristotle considered scientific thought as thought at rest, fixed and immovable' (Leon Robin). Though all these ideas were compatible with Platonism, Aristotle's methodology differed profoundly from that of Plato because the universals on which he based his definitions were not, according to him, obtained by recollection or by the direct grasp of ideas. They are grasped by the senses, which, though no part of science, are nevertheless its point of departure. Our minds, quite spontaneously and constantly, generalize from particular cases. Concepts are therefore not latent in our minds but are formed from experience by discrimination, perception and memory. Observed facts are stored, objects are classified, fleeting images are stabilized and the facts consolidated, because the human intellect has the ability to derive concepts from sensations; this is the very foundation of science.

Hence the leading place accorded by Aristotle to observation, which was so despised in the Academy. The Platonists believed that science is constructed on hypotheses grasped by the intellect and descends from these ideas towards the reality for whose appearance it is necessary to account. On the other hand, the Aristotelians held that we start with sensible objects and rise, little by little, by means of classification and generalization to truly scientific concepts. We might say that the Aristotelians followed a deductive where the Platonists followed an inductive path; that they began at the very bottom of the scale whereas the Platonists descended from the heights of heaven. In his fresco of the *Athenian School* in the Vatican, Raphael shows Plato and Aristotle in the midst of the greatest philosophers and scientists of ancient Greece and engaged in keen discussion. While Plato points towards the sky, Aristotle points towards the earth. In his painting, Raphael personifies the two equally fruitful methods which together sum up the two paths towards scientific progress. While observation is, of course, an essential scientific tool, much scientific knowledge is based on hypotheses which could not have been obtained from perception, since no model of them exists in nature (*e.g.* inertial motion, perfect geometrical figures).

We must not be misled into thinking that either Plato or Aristotle chose one conception of science to the utter exclusion of the other. But their preferences were clear, which explains why Plato looked upon mathematics as the 'queen', whereas Aristotle considered her the 'handmaiden', of science. 'Philosophy', he wrote, 'has become mathematics for modern thinkers, although they hold that mathematics is to be studied only as a means to some other end' (*Metaphysics* 992A). No wonder that the body of work attributed to the Peripatetic School contains only three in mathematics: the *Mechanics*, *On Indivisible Lines* and the *Problemata*. All three appear, in fact, to be spurious; if the first two did indeed originate in this school, the third, certainly, is a later compilation.

On the other hand, the physical texts, including the works on astronomy and meteorology, account for much of the corpus. Though not devoid of *a priori* constructions, they give evidence of a new approach and a much greater concern for reality, particularly in the theories of the elements and of motion.

But the real innovation of the school was its emphasis on the natural sciences (in the modern sense of the phrase), for though these sciences had been studied long before Aristotle, it was he who gave them the greatest impetus. Works on biology and zoology constitute one quarter of all his authentic and extant writings, and that proportion would be greater still if we included the lost works which we know to have existed and the writings of his disciples. In natural science the views of Plato and Aristotle were utterly opposed, because of their different attitudes to the concept of *corruption*. For both, the universe was divided into two regions: the sublunary world, governed by generation and corruption, and the celestial world, which was eternal and immutable. But while Plato inferred from this division that the sublunary world, subject as it was to perpetual change, was not the proper object of science (*i.e.* of certain and stable knowledge), Aristotle held that scientific certainty, which he valued as much as Plato did, must spring chiefly from the study of observable (*i.e.* sublunary) phenomena. He made clear distinction between two concepts which Plato tended to confuse, namely between corruption (or change in general) and accident. In this respect, *Metaphysics*, 1059A, which is obviously aimed at the Platonic conception of accident (as opposed to universal principle), states Aristotle's position with perfect clarity.

'Nothing', Aristotle says, 'is accidentally perishable, for that which is accidental may or may not happen; but perishability is a necessary attribute of corruptible things. Otherwise, the same thing might be sometimes corruptible and at other times incorruptible.... Thus corruptibility must be either the substance or in the substance of every perishable thing.'

Aristotle left it at that, for in this passage he was not concerned with defining the sphere of scientific knowledge. Still, the conclusions are obvious: there is no science of *accident* (of that which may or may not be); but, in the corruptible world, corruption is by no means accidental; it is both necessary and—to use Aristotle's term—'substantial'. It can therefore be the object of certain knowledge. Hence the investigation of sublunary, and particularly biological, phenomena is raised to the status of a true science.

Another aspect of the Aristotelian approach, based on the same attitude, was its stress on the history of problems. Aristotle rarely tackled any scientific or philosophical question without first making a critical examination of previous opinions. These examinations, in which his works abound, are of extreme interest to the historian of science, since much of what little knowledge we have of Greek science is based on them. Plato's contribution in this respect was considerably smaller, for while he, too, often referred to earlier doctrines, he did so in the course of imaginary dialogues in which it is often difficult to distinguish historical fact from pure fiction. Finally, it is to the Aristotelian school that we owe the earliest writings on the history of science as such: Theophrastos was the first historian of Greek natural philosophy and Eudemos the first historian of Greek mathematics.

PHYSICS AND COSMOLOGY

When Aristotle came to examine the age-old problems of Greek science—the basic constituents of matter, their transformation, and cosmology—he offered original solutions to each one.

THE ELEMENTS

While remaining faithful to the Empedoclean elements of earth, water, air, and fire (though subsequently adding a fifth not found in the sublunary world), Aristotle threw fresh light on the way in which they affected the world of perception. For him, the elements were not original bodies but different aspects of a unique substance— 'primary matter' or 'protyle' ($\pi\rho\dot\omega\tau\eta$ $\ddot\upsilon\lambda\eta$), each displaying different qualities. This matter was governed by a principle which, although extraneous to it, could not be separated from it except by intellectual abstraction. All the different forms in which matter can reveal itself are potentially contained in it. This view is the crux of Aristotelian physics and its original contribution. The potential forms contained in the protyle are expressed in the effects of the four fundamental qualities: cold, heat, dryness, and humidity. These qualities are never met by themselves for they exist in pairs, and it is the presence of one of these pairs which characterizes each one of the four elements. In theory, the four qualities ought to combine into six pairs, but two do not exist in nature, namely cold-hot and dry-humid, since contradictory qualities do not combine. The remaining four pairs were therefore: cold-dry, cold-humid, hot-dry and hot-humid. When original matter is affected by the pair cold-dry it becomes the element earth; similarly water is formed by the pair cold-wet, air by the pair hot-humid, fire by the pair hot-dry. These four elements then combine to form all the many natural substances. They can also engender one another, though only in a 'circular' way (*De generatione et corruptione*, 331B), since hot-dry, for instance, can turn into cold-humid only *via* hot-humid or cold-dry. With this restriction, all transformations are possible so that the unity of matter is preserved. Indirect transformations, such as water-air-fire, differ from direct transformations only by requiring a longer *time* to be completed (*ibid.*). The formation of all substances from only four simple elements was called *alloiosis*.

The transformation of compound substances into other compound substances had previously been explained by different combinations of their elements. Aristotle developed this theory by distinguishing between three kinds of combinations—*synthesis* (simple mechanical mixture), *mixis*, and *krasis*, the last two corresponding more or less to what we call chemical compounds and solutions. In short, all substances in the sublunary world were produced by *alloiosis*, through *synthesis*, *mixis*, or *krasis*.

We saw that the introduction of a fifth element, which goes back to Philolaos, was originally associated with the fifth regular solid, the dodecahedron. Plato, we remember, first considered it an afterthought of the Deity when he decided to adorn the world, but in the *Epinomis* it had become an elementary substance constituting the sphere of the aether, which divided the spheres of air and fire from each other. Aristotle (who, as we shall see, did not hold that there was any correspondence between elements and polyhedra) took over the aether from Plato and placed it beyond the sphere of fire to constitute the celestial world, which is immutable and imperishable.

COSMOLOGY

In the main, Aristotle's universe was very much like that of the Pythagoreans and of Plato. The central earth was surrounded by layers of water, air and fire; every element had its 'proper' place. Together, they constituted the sublunary world which was beneath the incorruptible aether and the celestial spheres, the nearest of which to the earth was that of the moon, and the farthest away that of the fixed stars. All followed a circular path about the spherical and immobile earth. Aristotle produced a number of weighty arguments against those who denied that the world was fixed (Philolaos, Heraclides). Thus he pointed out that a body thrown up vertically into the air returns to the same spot from which it was launched. If the earth revolved or moved, the body could not possibly return to that spot since, while it was going up and down, the spot would have moved away. This argument was to give rise to keen controversies right up to the Renaissance.

Aristotle's universe was unique and finite. Beyond it there was nothing, not even a surrounding void. The highest heaven was an absolute boundary beyond which no 'places' existed. This assertion was called absurd by the champions of infinite space. What path, they asked, would an arrow follow if it were shot out from the extreme edge of the universe? Aristotle countered this objection by pointing out that their void would have to be a place where there could be no bodies and which yet could contain bodies—a clear contradiction in terms. Beyond the highest heaven there were no bodies simply because there were no 'places'. Space was finite, so much so that no right line could be longer than the dimensions of the universe, whose diameter was the longest of all possible straight lines.

COMPENSATING SPHERES

Let us now consider the structure of this cosmos. Aristotle adopted Callipos' revised version of Eudoxos' homocentric spheres and endowed this purely mathematical system with physical meaning. Like Plato and Eudoxos, he was concerned with explaining the actual phenomena; but unlike them he was not content with merely postulating that the motions of the spheres were 'orderly and regular'. It struck him as important to explain why the effects of the motions of the successive layers of the sublunary spheres did not interfere with the planetary perturbations already accounted for by Eudoxos. This problem did not arise for Eudoxos because his spheres were not in contact, but Aristotle could not agree to separate them by empty space and so postulated the existence of 'compensatory' spheres whose movements cancelled out any untoward effects. These spheres 'unroll in reverse' (ἀνελιττούσαι σφαίραι) between the successive sytems of the planetary spheres, maintaining contact with them but ensuring their independence by compensating the effects of the rotation of the higher spheres on the lower. By his addition of compensating spheres Aristotle increased the number of celestial spheres to fifty-six.

MOTION

Before entering into the details of Aristotle's views on celestial mechanics, we must briefly discuss his views on mechanics in general. Motion (κίνησις) expresses the simultaneous co-existence of potency and action, *i.e.*, the transformation of one thing into another which it contains in itself. As Aristotle himself put it: Motion is the realization of a potentiality, *qua* potentiality (*actus existentis in potentia in quantum est in potentia*). All Peripatetic physics was based on three principles: matter, form, and non-existence. Matter is simply potential; form is the actualization of the potential (*entelechy*); non-existence is neither. Potential matter can assume various forms, but is actualized in only one and non-existent in the others. Actualized existence, non-existence, and potential existence are the principles of the *ens mobile*, *i.e.* of everything subject to change.

The term *kinesis* is therefore very wide and includes many distinct concepts. It is far better translated by 'alteration' or 'change' than by motion, and may refer to any of the following four processes.

1, Alteration of the substance of a body or, in scholastic terms, alteration *secundum quid*; it is produced by mixture or combination and leads to the destruction or corruption (φθορά) of the original substance and the generation (γένεσις) of another. 2, Alteration of the size of a body, which is purely quantitative—*secundum quantum*—and is caused by expansion (αὔξησις) or contraction (φθίσις). 3, Alteration of the quality—*secundum quale*; this is the *alloiosis* mentioned above. 4, Alteration or change of position—*secundum ubi*, caused by translational motion (φορά). The four types of *kinesis* therefore represent changes in quiddity, quantity, quality, and position. All can be, and are in fact, constantly produced in the sublunary world, but the aetheric bodies of the celestial world are subject only to positional changes along circular paths, for movement in a straight line would carry them beyond the limits of the universe. Rectilinear motion can thus occur only in the sublunary world, where we distinguish between vertical and other motions. Vertical motion is said to be 'natural' since all the elements tend to rise or fall to their 'natural' level. Thus, if a substance is transformed into fire by combustion, the flame rises because it tends to rejoin the sphere of fire; similarly every solid tends to fall down towards the earth from which it has sprung. Air and water find their natural levels in the same way. All other motions, *i.e.*, all non-vertical motions, and also those vertical motions which remove a body from its natural level, are 'forced'. Without an external force, all bodies would always remain at rest. External forces originate in the outermost sphere of the heavens, and are communicated by the successive layers of spheres to the sublunary world. This process is discussed mainly in the *Meteorology*.

THE PRIME MOVER—THE CYCLES

Since the outermost sphere consists of matter, it cannot cause its own motion. The problem of the original source of its motion is closely connected with two central problems of ancient Ionian philosophy, the ἀρχή and Becoming. It was on the ἀρχή that Aristotle based his theory of the 'mover itself motionless'. Since he assumed that bodies tended to remain at rest, and since he was ignorant of the concept of inertial motion, he could explain the external motion of the celestial spheres only by assuming the existence of a 'mover' which acted continuously on the outermost sphere. This mover was an immaterial substance, pure action devoid of power and hence itself motionless. The motion which it impressed was due to some sort of attraction, such as 'desire' or 'love'.

The problem of Becoming was treated by Aristotle in much the same way as by Plato and by more than one pre-Socratic cosmologist (notably Heraclitos and Empedocles). The world was eternal, and its history followed great cycles, simply because the celestial spheres revolved in such a way that, at the end of a given period, they returned to their original positions, to begin their cycles anew. As the motions of the heavens affected those of the sublunary world, the sublunary world was subject to a cyclical rhythm as well. Hence its processes of generation and corruption had been and would continue to be repeated time and again.

THE VOID AND SPACE

In the celestial, as in the sublunary, world, motion could take place only under certain conditions. Since, because of their initial inertia, material bodies did not move unless they were forced to do so, all motion required a mover which must continue to act on the moving bodies throughout their motion: *cessante causa, cessat effectus*. While all motion involved the action of the mover, it also depended on the resistance of the medium in which it took place. Resistance tended to brake the progress of the moving object and, if the resistance was equal and opposite to the moving force the body would remain at, or come to, rest. This was one of Aristotle's strongest arguments against the existence of a void. In the sublunary world bodies moved more quickly through rare than through dense media, *e.g.* faster through air than through water. If there were a void, resistance would cease to act and any body would acquire an infinite velocity, which was absurd. (Aristotle assumed that resistance and speed were in inverse proportion, so that zero resistance was equal to infinite speed.) Hence the existence of the void, far from being a prerequisite of all motion, as the Atomists held, made motion incomprehensible and impossible. Another equally important consequence of his theory was that it excluded all atomistic solutions of the problem of matter based on the existence of voids between the indivisible elements of matter. By denying the existence of any void—extra-celestial or inter-atomic—Aristotle made all matter continuous and infinitely divisible. We have previously alluded to Aristotle's rejection of the correspondence between the elements and the regular polyhedra. His reasons can now be understood, for to assume with Plato that the elements were regular solids would be tantamount to assuming the existence of a void. As Aristotle himself put it, 'The attempt to assign geometrical figures to the simple bodies is on all counts irrational . . . *the whole of space will not be filled up*' (*De Cælo* 306B). In effect, while space could be filled completely with cubes and tetrahedra, the other regular solids would leave spaces or voids between them. Hence the hypothesis of elementary polyhedra, and all physics of the atomistic type, had to be rejected.

Aristotelian cosmological considerations also bore on the problems

of infinitely large and infinitely small phenomena. While the existence of the former was denied, on the ground that the universe was
finite and that nothing could exist beyond it, the existence of the
latter was affirmed, since every body could be subdivided *ad
infinitum*. 'If one should take a definite piece away from a limited
magnitude, and then go on to take away the same proportion of
what is left, and so on, one will never come to the end' (*Physics*, III,
6). However, such divisibility was potential only, since there were no
corresponding infinitely small actions. In other words, while the
infinitely small existed, albeit only potentially, the infinitely large
did not exist in any sense at all.

NATURAL SCIENCE

Though Aristotle drew on the work of earlier naturalists, including
the first Milesian physiologers, he may be called the 'Father of
General Biology', much as the Pythagoreans are called the 'Founders
of Geometry'. Pythagoras (or the Pythagoreans), Hippocrates, and
Aristotle are therefore rightly considered to be the most eminent
figures in Hellenic mathematics, medicine, and biology, respectively.
It was undoubtedly to oppose certain trends in the Academy that
Aristotle concentrated on biology, particularly since it fell in with
his general philosophy and extended his studies of real phenomena.
Moreover, his biological classification fitted in admirably with his
logic, in which the traditional inelastic dichotomy had been modified
by the introduction of subtle subdivisions.

It is possible, though doubtful, that Aristotle himself wrote the
treatises on plants and on stones which have been attributed to him.
In any case they are lost, and it is only from his works on zoology
that we have learnt to appreciate the value of his method and the
extent of his biological knowledge.

The *Historia animalium*, the *De partibus animalium* and the *De
generatione animalium* are so closely linked with one another that they
cannot be discussed separately. True, each deals with a chosen
subject—the first with general descriptions, the second with morphology and the third with reproduction—but all three encroach upon
one another and all three are needed to reconstruct Aristotle's system
of classifying the animal kingdom.

Like Euclidean geometry, Aristotelian zoology could not possibly
have been the work of a single man; its sources must rather be sought
in early medical and veterinary writings. Nevertheless it was Aristotle himself who turned zoology into a scientific discipline. No
matter what sources he used, he submitted all their findings to
personal and critical investigations, unexcelled by any other scientist

of antiquity. Aristotle used comparative methods, argued by analogy, verified his conclusions, and brought his intellect to bear on all aspects of animal life, including behaviour, ecology, and pathology. He personally dissected at least fifty species of animals.

A table compiled by August Steier (*Aristoteles und Plinius*, p. 113) shows that there was not much difference between the number of animal species described by Aristotle (495) and by Pliny the Elder (494). But the differences are considerable if we take each genus separately. Pliny mentions 98 mammals, Aristotle only 60; Aristotle describes 160 birds, and Pliny only 120; 156 species known to Aristotle were unknown to Pliny. Moreover, Aristotle was greatly superior when it came to checking his sources. Thus, while Pliny repeated hearsay evidence and strange descriptions of a kind found only in medieval bestiaries, Aristotle mentioned only those animals that he had himself observed. For this reason he had to dismiss as fabulous, or semi-fabulous, such animals as the elephant, the camel and the hippopotamus. Finally, as Mieli has pointed out, Aristotle's superiority over Pliny becomes clearer still when one considers the widening of geographical horizons during the four centuries which separate the two men.

CLASSIFICATION

Though Book I of the *Parts of Animals* gives an account of the correct method of classification, it does not give any actual examples. Hence modern commentators have had to reconstruct Aristotle's classes of animals from data interspersed throughout the texts.

Aristotle's basis of classification was the presence or absence of red blood. Two great classes of animals were thus distinguished: the *ennaima* (sanguineous) and the *anaima* (bloodless) animals. The *ennaima* were subdivided into:

(1) Viviparous quadrupeds containing all mammals (including cetacea, seals and bats). The group was subdivided further according to the nature of their skeletons and extremities.

(2) Oviparous quadrupeds (lizards, tortoises, batrachians).

(3) Birds, subdivided into eight species according both to their feet (with or without talons, with or without webs) and their food (granivores, insectivores, *etc.*).

(4) Fishes, subdivided according to whether their skeletons are cartilaginous or osseous.

The *anaima* were divided into:

(1) Soft-bodied invertebrates.

(2) Soft-bodied invertebrates covered with scales.

(3) Soft-bodied invertebrates covered with a hard shell.

(4) Insects—subdivided into nine species.

Aristotle called these eight groups γένη μέγιστα (large genera);
and their subdivisions γένη and εἴδη (genera and species).

REPRODUCTION

The *Generation of Animals* is one of the most remarkable works of the
Aristotelian corpus and the model of a great number of subsequent
texts admired to this day, despite their inevitable errors, some of
which were not detected until the nineteenth century. The work
deals with the sexes, copulation, fertilization, embryology, birth and
protection of the young.

From what Aristotle said on many occasions about the introduction of life into inert matter, we may infer that he believed in
spontaneous generation (*Gen. Anim.* III, 10). Now, to him spontaneous
generation was not the equivalent of generation *ex nihilo*, since his
doctrine implied the pre-existence, before the appearance of any
manifestations of life, of an all-pervading soul, an omnipresent
psyche. In favourable conditions, this psyche could vitalize any
fragment of matter into the lower forms of life: non-flowering plants,
some fishes, insects and ostracoderms. With these exceptions, all
animals were born from living animals of the same species. According
to their various modes of reproduction animals were divided into
four groups: 1, viviparous animals; 2, oviparous animals; 3, scissi-
parous animals (born by fission like certain plants); 4, animals born
from the metamorphosis of other animals (larvae).

Aristotle's views on spermatogenesis were quite clear. He opposed
the *preformationists* (who based their doctrine on Hippocrates) with
his own *epigenetic* views. The preformationists held that the sperm
contained the full parent body in miniature. This meant, as Aristotle
objected, that a mutilated man was bound to engender mutilated
children, which was refuted by experience. According to Aristotle's
own epigenetic views, the transmission of acquired characters,
though not denied, was explained in quite a different way: the sperm,
far from containing the several separate parts of the body, contained
all the potential forms of the embryo and hence of the developed
organism.

It is not so much for his theoretical edifice, which the subsequent
development of science was to topple over, as for the scope of
his knowledge, the wisdom of his approach, and the accuracy of
his observations that Aristotle merits our admiration. Many of his
descriptions, which were adopted by many generations of scholars
without verification, were subsequently dismissed as so many fables,
only to be proved true by later investigations. We shall mention
only one of many known instances: his claim that the male of the
Achelous river catfish guards the eggs laid by its mate. This claim

was ridiculed as pure fantasy from the Renaissance until 1906, when its truth was established beyond doubt, and when the fish became known officially as *Parasilurus aristotelis*.

Aristotle's biological opinions may also be gathered from two of his other works: the *De anima* and the *Parva naturalia*. In the *De anima* he develops, *inter alia*, the theory of various faculties of the soul and establishes their hierarchy. The vegetative (or nutritive) faculty is found in all living organisms (animals and plants), the sensitive faculty only in animals, and the intellective faculty in man alone. In the *Parva naturalia* Aristotle considers many associated problems in greater detail, for instance, the theory of colours and of tastes (*De sensu* III and IV), on which recent studies by Paul Kucharski have thrown a great deal of fresh light.

Even if P. Zürcher is right in saying that the *De sensu* was written by Theophrastos, it is still part of the Aristotelian heritage. Its trend strikes us as being partly a late development of the *De anima* and partly, though to a much less probable extent, of the later thought of Theophrastos, *viz.* of his return to Pythagorean doctrines and their application to new fields. We saw that the Pythagoreans constructed their musical scale by assuming that the different notes correspond to numbers in simple arithmetical ratios. Now the author of the *De sensu* applies the same law to colours and tastes: only those corresponding to simple numbers and their ratios (ἐν ἀριθμοῖς) are said to produce agreeable sensations. 'The work is therefore clear evidence of a very bold attempt to combine quantitatively heterogeneous phenomena belonging to different classes into a common explanatory framework' (P. Kucharski). In this respect, the *De sensu* is a perfect example of attempts to explain reality by a non-verified and almost unverifiable hypothesis. If, as we believe, the book was written by Aristotle himself, it shows Aristotle in his most Platonic mood.

THE PERIPATETIC SCHOOL AT THE END OF THE SIXTH CENTURY

THEOPHRASTOS

Among the first Peripatetics, Theophrastos of Eresos and Eudemos of Rhodes were the two most highly esteemed by their teacher. According to Aulus Gellius' *Attic Nights*, Aristotle hesitated between the two when the time came to appoint his successor. In the end, Theophrastos carried the day and headed the school from the death of Aristotle (322) until his own death (288–87).

Theophrastos wrote an immense number of texts, many of which are lost. Only two of his books need concern us here: the *History of Plants* (in nine books) and the *Causes of Plants*—περὶ φύτων αἰτίων—(in six books). Many modern historians have attacked these works for repeating travellers' tales and traditional notions without bothering to check up on them. According to C. Singer, a part of the *Historia plantarum* is simply a compendium of popular opinions, a kind of botanical folk-lore. Even so, Theophrastos was by no means entirely without merit. Thus Abel Rey (who otherwise endorses Singer's general view) stressed that Theophrastos was a keen opponent of anthropomorphic interpretations. 'The fleshy part of the apple', Theophrastos wrote 'is not designed to be eaten by man, but to protect the fruit.' He also established a clear distinction between the vegetable and animal kingdoms, which had previously been treated as one (for instance, by Aristotle in the *Parts of Animals*, IV, 10). Finally, and above all, despite his alleged repetitions of suspect hearsay evidence, Theophrastos also made a host of valuable and exact personal observations. In fact, as an observer he was more discerning and more demanding even than Aristotle: more discerning, inasmuch as he kept strictly to the experimental data as such and did not use them to confirm particular hypotheses; more demanding, because he made it a strict rule never to consider the study of any phenomenon complete until all its concomitant qualities (τὰ συμβαίνοντα) had been fully investigated (*cf.* his description of the fall of leaves in the *Historia plantarum*, I, 9).

The *Historia plantarum* begins with a typically Aristotelian classification. In fact, Theophrastos, going further than Aristotle, raised classification into a dogma: 'Since it so happens that knowledge is clearest when it bears on objects divided into species (κατὰ εἴδη), it behoves us to establish this division in every possible case and manner.' He classified plants, first of all, according to the presence or absence of stems, and then according to the habits of their branches (if any). In this way Theophrastos came to divide plants into four great classes: trees, *i.e.* plants with a single stem and branches some way above the ground; shrubs, *i.e.* plants with a stem and branches immediately above the ground; under-shrubs, *i.e.* plants with more than one stem; and finally herbs, *i.e.* plants lacking a stem, and 'coming up from the root with leaves'.

One of the most original parts of the *Historia plantarum* is Book IV, which discusses geographical distribution and plant ecology. In the six books of the *Causes of Plants*, which follows a course similar to Aristotle's *Generation of Animals*, Theophrastos investigates the generation and propagation of plants: germination, flowering, fruiting, *etc.* He also wrote a book on metals, which is not extant, and a book on stones of which a fairly long fragment has been preserved.

EUDEMOS (*fl.* 320)

Eudemos' commentary on Aristotle's *Physics*, together with that written by Alexander of Aphrodisias, was one of the main sources of Simplicios' commentary. He was also the author of a *History of Astronomy and Geometry*, which is unfortunately lost. However, some passages from it, possibly amended, have found their way, *via* Geminos, Porphyry, and Sosigenes, into the works of Theon of Smyrna, Proclos, Eutocios, Simplicios, and Clement of Alexandria. Even in its fragmentary form, Eudemos' *History* is of incomparable historical value, since no other contemporary works on the history of mathematics and astronomy are extant.

ARISTOXENOS

A disciple, first of Xenophilos the Pythagorean, then of Aristotle, Aristoxenos of Tarentum (born *c.* 360) was the greatest theorist of music in ancient times.

Lasos of Hermione (sixth century) and Hippasos of Metapontium (fifth–fourth centuries) had established a relationship between the pitch of a sound and the speed with which it was propagated through the air (the highest sounds corresponded to the fastest). This theory, though false, was nevertheless fruitful because it emphasized the role of air in the propagation of sound. Aristotle assumed its truth in the *De Anima*, but subsequently the Peripatetic author of περὶ ἀκουστῶν (possibly Aristotle himself) came to appreciate that all sounds, irrespective of pitch, travel through air with the same speed, and that the pitch varies with the frequency of vibration of the source of the sound. The new theory had been propounded by the time Aristoxenos wrote his *Harmonics*, whence he could refer with some impatience to those who 'speak of numerical ratios and relative speeds to account for high and low sounds' (*Harmonics*, II, 32).

DICAEARCHOS

Like that of all other Hellenic sciences, the history of Greek geography began in Ionia in the sixth century. True, modern critics are agreed that some of the earlier geographical notions, as far back as the Homeric poems, were substantially correct, but it was Anaximander who is said to have drawn up the first maritime charts, and Hecataeos of Miletos (*c.* 550–475) who wrote the first purely geographical work, the γῆς περίοδος. In it, the countries of the world are imagined as a vast ring of which the Mediterranean forms the centre and the ocean the outer edges.

During the fourth century, there appeared a number of purely descriptive geographies (*e.g.*, Books IV and V of the *Universal History* of Ephoros of Cyme, and the many travel reports by Massilian sailors including Pytheas' περὶ ὠκεανοῦ), side by side with the first works on mathematical geography written by Eudoxos, who made attempts to evaluate the dimensions of the terrestrial globe. Aristotle accepted his conclusions in his *Meteorologica*, which also dealt with various other questions of physical geography: the origins of the ocean and rivers, winds and fog, the distribution of the continents, and so on.

One of Aristotle's first pupils, Dicaearchos of Messina (*c.* 350–290) must be considered the only Greek geographer between the Milesian Hecataeos and the Cyrenean Eratosthenes. Only some fragments of his important and varied works are extant. He described all the inhabited regions of the world, extending from the Pillars of Hercules in the West to the Ganges in the East, and from Upper Egypt in the South to Chersonesus in the North. His world was not very different from that of Hecataeos, and measured 60,000 stadia from East to West, and 40,000 stadia from North to South. While we do not know whether he used Attic or Egyptian stadia, we can say that, in any case, he grossly underestimated the size of the earth. More precise figures were given in the next century by the first really great geographer of antiquity, Eratosthenes of Cyrene.

CHAPTER 5

Greek Medicine from the Beginning to the End of the Classical Period

ANCIENT SOURCES OF GREEK MEDICINE

THOUGH GREEK MEDICINE, at its height, was renowned throughout the civilized world, its early beginnings are rather obscure. This is all the more regrettable because we know that Hippocrates, the greatest of all Greek physicians, was heir to a long tradition.

THE HISTORICAL EVIDENCE

The *Ancient Medicine*, one of the most famous works of the *Hippocratic Collection*,[1] is an attempt to present the earlier history of that science. It is said to have stemmed from attempts to teach men how to live healthily and, particularly, to give the basis of a sound diet which they could adapt to their special needs. Hence, Greek medicine was originally the art of living—and of cooking; hygiene and gymnastics came much later. Medicine, in its strict sense, began only when specific diets were first prescribed for specific diseases, and when physicians showed that even the slightest dietetic mistake might lead to untoward consequences. Their results soon caused them to be venerated like gods.

The fifth-century author of the *Ancient Medicine* was clearly a practical man rather than a natural philosopher. He held that all systematizers trying to apply Empedocles' methods to medicine were enemies of those ancient traditions which had produced such

---

[1] The *Hippocratic Collection*, which is sometimes considered to represent the sum total of Hippocrates' own writings, is, in fact, a collection of some sixty medical texts of quite different and even opposed teachings. The individual texts were written between *c.* 450 and *c.* 350 B.C., and are our main sources of information on pre-Alexandrian Greek medicine. Our quotations from them are based on Littré's famous translation (10 volumes; Paris, 1839–61). For a critical evaluation of the *Collection*, see also L. Bourgey's *Observations et expérience chez les médecins de la collection hippocratique*, Paris, 1953.

excellent cures by following precisely observed facts. The moment anyone tried to tie these facts to theories, he ceased to be a healer and became a speculator. This traditional approach was not seriously challenged until about the middle of the fifth century, when new trends came to the fore.

HOMERIC MEDICINE

Homeric medicine has been called an exact science by many scholars, who base this claim on the many accurate clinical descriptions in the Iliad (fatal wounds, concussion, *etc.*) and on the fact that Homer's anatomical knowledge was, by and large, similar to that developed in the *Hippocratic Collection*. Hence, the two are said to have shared not only their concern for accurate observation, but also much of their positive knowledge.

Another fact worth stressing is that Homer held physicians in exceptionally high regard as men who, in a world peopled by gods, yet exercised their art in a purely rational manner. They alone could soothe wounds and bind them with healing remedies. Moreover, many of them, like Podalirios and Machaon, the sons of Asclepios, were also great heroes in battle. Conversely some of the great warriors, *e.g.*, Achilles and Patroclos, could, when the need arose, turn their hands to medicine. While Asclepios, the great healer, was the mortal prince of Triccae (*Iliad* IV, 194), some of the gods and mythological figures, too, were directly associated with medicine. Thus Apollo, the sun-god, was also a healer; Artemis, the moon-god, and hence ruler of the monthly cycle, watched over women in labour; some tasks of Hercules were clearly medical; Melampos was renowned for his famous feats of healing; and finally, the centaur Chiron, the mythological master of Asclepios and Achilles, was famed for his great knowledge of the medical properties of plants.

Evidence of the Greeks' keen observational sense is found on Mycenaean engravings, which depict men and animals with astonishing accuracy. This love for detailed observation seems to have been a fundamental and exclusive characteristic of early Hellenic civilization, and hence of their earliest medicine. Thus, while Homer described many pathological conditions remarkably well, he never so much as alluded to any medical doctrines. The same is true of the author of the *Ancient Medicine*. Though his teaching was far more elaborate and even mentioned the admixture of humours, he refused to give any systematic account of the humours. On reading the book, one cannot help feeling that this refusal was the result of an old reluctance to subordinate facts to complicated theories.

THE MAGICAL TRADITIONS IN GREEK MEDICINE

THE LATE ORIGIN OF THE TRADITION

The above comments, while substantially true, are not, however, the whole truth. For side by side with the tradition we have described there existed another, less rational, form of medicine, which looked upon diseases as having a magical or mysterious origin.

The *Iliad* largely ignored this aspect because the wounds it described had obvious causes. Not so the *Odyssey*, Book IV of which (*c.* 219–232) tells us that Helen, in order to restore gaiety during a banquet, slipped a magical potion into the wine. She explained that she had learned this art from a woman of Egypt, a country whose physicians were more knowledgeable than any others.

This magical kind of medicine was not part of the original tradition and its full development occurred very much later. A particularly significant fact was the rise of the Asclepios legend, which turned the great physician into a superhuman hero who could resuscitate the dead and was punished for it (Pindar, *Pyth.* III). Different and even incompatible traditions vied with one another to elaborate this legend, until, finally, Asclepios became one of the gods, whose busts resembled those of Zeus.

Temple medicine began in Triccae, possibly during the eleventh and tenth centuries, though it flourished only during the fifth and fourth centuries. The case of Epidauros is characteristic. Here the Asclepios cult probably began at the end of the sixth century, and had become so popular by the fifth that a branch was founded in Athens in 420. The Asclepieion in Cos, Hippocrates' native island, was established in the middle of the fourth century. These sanctuaries, which were to become medical centres in the Hellenistic and Roman epochs, were originally frequented for their magical cures of sudden or inexplicable diseases. Cawadias's excavations have unearthed characteristic inscriptions from which we learn that the patients, having participated in special ceremonies, repaired to the temple, there to dream of the appropriate cures. This practice was known as incubation.

Temple medicine went hand in hand with a number of mystical trends that played a very important role in Greece between the seventh and fourth centuries. These trends were the Orphic, the Dionysiac and, to a far less extent, the Pythagorean, all three of which were magico-mystical and devoted to miraculous cures. As P. M. Schuhl has shown, they sometimes combined the esoteric practices of, say, an Epimenides with the rational approach typical of a Solon or a Thales.

MAGICAL METHODS IN THE CLASSICAL EPOCH

Incantational and miraculous medicine coloured the views of even the philosophers—for example, Empedocles, one of the fathers of experimental medicine (famous, *inter alia*, for his clepsydra experiment). In the 112 extant verses of his great poem, the *Purifications*, he stressed the importance of all sorts of esoteric medical practices. He compared physicians to prophets and poets, and called himself the spokesman of the oracle which saved the sorely afflicted.

The evidence of Plato is more remarkable still, for the founder of the Academy was not generally a lover of mysteries. Now, not only in the early dialogues, *e.g.* the *Charmides* (155E), but also in his more mature works—the *Banquet* (202E–203A), *Theaetetos* (149C–E), *Laws* (666B–C, 790)—Plato recognized the role of charms and incantations in healing. Thus, headaches could be cured by a certain plant, but only in conjunction with the recitation of a magic formula; midwives were taught not only to administer drugs but also to recite incantations. In short, while Plato valued rational means of therapy he coupled them with the most irrational procedures.

This apparent dichotomy is due to Plato's desire to leave no phenomenon unexplained, not even the reputed magical 'cures'. The great Thucydides, too, appreciated that there were two kinds of medicine. Speaking of the great plague of Athens, he said that not only the skills of the physicians but also prayers, oracles and magic were quite impotent to dispel it (*Peloponnesian War* II, 47).

Magic and priestly medicine were thus recognized as existing in their own right, side by side with rational medicine. In this situation it is indeed remarkable that the physicians themselves refused to be drawn into discussions with magical healers, and on the one recorded occasion when they did (a case of epilepsy) they utterly confounded their adversaries (Littré, Vol. VI, pp. 352–362). Rarely were two contemporary trends so utterly opposed to each other, and all those who agree with Strabo (*Geography*, XIV, 657) that Greek medicine was born in the temples are speaking no more than a half-truth.

EXTERNAL INFLUENCES ON GREEK MEDICINE

Even so, this dichotomy presents us with a number of problems which we can solve only by a full discussion of the formation and internal organization of the great Greek medical schools.[1] That discussion will show how the positive tradition which we mentioned

[1] Since the members of the schools of Cos and Cnidos were called Asclepiads (Plato, *Protagoras* 311B, *Phaidros* 270V; Galen, Kühn ed., Vol. 18 A, p. 731) one may well ask if there was not a concrete historical connection between these schools and Homeric medicine.

at the beginning of this chapter could have maintained itself so easily, and how it managed to resist all attempts at syncretism or compromise with other trends.

An examination of the influence of Eastern on Greek medicine shows that it bore on the magical rather than on the rational component. Thus Helen's drug mentioned in the *Odyssey* (see above) was said to have come from Egypt, and Plato, speaking of incantations in the *Charmides*, claims that he did so on the authority of Zamolxis, a Thracian physician. The study of Akkadian and Egyptian texts shows that though medical cures had a rational element based on shrewd observation, they were as frequently founded on superstitions and hence were far more primitive than even the earliest Greek references to medicine (in the poems of Homer).

The recent work of Filliozat has drawn attention to certain parallels between Hindu and Greek medicine. But these parallels apply mainly to doctrines and to such theories as that of the *pneuma*, and not to practical measures. Thus, while foreign influences can be detected in the less important treatises *On Winds* and *The Regimen*, they are dismissed as dangerous by the more positive texts, *e.g.* the *Ancient Medicine* and the *Nature of Man*.

It would, however, be a great mistake to conclude that Greek scientific medicine arose in isolation. Sandrail has drawn attention to suggestive similarities between Akkadian prognostic texts, on the one hand, and the famous *Coan Prenotions* and the *Prorrhetic I* on the other, and Filliozat has emphasized their importance. We, too, have had occasion to note that Cnidean prognoses on the fertility of women and the sex of unborn children were based, almost word for word, on Egyptian papyri.

But while foreign influences on typically Hellenic medicine are undeniable, we believe that they played only a subsidiary role and that the objects and spirit of Hellenic research expressed, if only implicitly, a purely Greek ideal. On the other hand, increasing contacts with the outside world undoubtedly increased the scope of Greek knowledge and opened new vistas to it; without this contribution the magnificent seeds of Greek science would possibly never have come to fruition.

MEDICAL ORGANIZATIONS AT THE
END OF THE FIFTH CENTURY

THE IMPORTANCE OF THE MEDICAL SCHOOLS

Thanks to the *Hippocratic Collection* and many other classical references, we know that, in the fifth century, unlike Homeric times, medicine had become an independent discipline. Physicians insisted on their independence, on the value of their scientific writings—of which, Xenophon tells us in his *Memorabilia* (IV, 210), there existed a vast number—and also, as we shall see, on their humane ideals.

These ideals were common to all the medical schools, which cannot therefore be distinguished by doctrine or method but only by geographical origin—in Cnidos, Cos and Sicily. Galen likened them to so many voices in a choir. The *Hippocratic Collection* throws much light on the respective organization of the schools of Cnidos and Cos, since the writings of these two most ancient schools account for a large proportion of the *Collection*. What knowledge we have of the Sicilian school is derived from a number of Cnidean references to it (*Diseases of Women, Nature of Women*).

In all these schools, individual physicians subordinated their own work to that of the group, so much so that many texts reflected the results of collective thought. Others again, *e.g.* the famous *Aphorisms* of Hippocrates, represent the thought of successive generations. In these circumstances, it would be idle to attribute given works to given authors.

THE INDIVIDUAL CHARACTERISTICS OF THE SCHOOLS

Sharing their thought and research as they did, the members of the school were quite naturally drawn together in their social life. This is borne out by the famous Hippocratic oath, by which the physician undertakes to treat his teacher as a father with whom he will share his fortune, and whom he will aid whenever he is called upon to do so. The teacher's children he will treat as his own brothers and teach them his art without reward; he will respect the life of all his patients, and particularly of women and children. Never was professional solidarity more highly prized.

Another characteristic aspect was the quasi-scientific organization of the schools. The original aim of the schools was not the propagation and defence of certain conceptions about man and his health —or even simply of medicine. Such motives were to be introduced later, in the Alexandrian epoch, when philosophic conceptions were to have repercussions on medical concepts and theories. The original aim was the study and practice of therapeutic techniques based on observations, old and new. Hence, what differences there were between the schools bore on fine technical points. For instance, the author of the *Regimen in Acute Diseases* disagreed with the Cnideans on the exact moment when barley water or barley broth ought to be administered to patients recovering from fever (Littré II, 238–268); and the Cnideans differed from their colleagues on the significance of sandy urine (gravel in the kidney or the bladder). If the reader demands a modern parallel, the differences between the schools were comparable to the theoretical differences between, say, a medical school in New York and one in London.

ITINERANT MEDICINE
Though belonging to distinct geographical centres, physicians were great travellers and endeavoured to extend their locally acquired knowledge and skills. Travel was the more important, in that all schools believed firmly in the influence of air, water and localities on man's constitution. No wonder that physicians would stop in foreign towns for up to three years.

Physicians never travelled by themselves, but always in the company of a number of assistants, students and midwives. (In the *Laws*, 720A–C, Plato also mentions slave-physicians, charged with the more menial tasks.) Wherever he arrived, the physician would open an *iatrion*, a kind of surgery-cum-pharmacy. One of the texts of the *Collection* is entitled *The Doctor's Surgery* (κατ' ἰητρεῖον). Finally, the later distinction and conflict between surgeons and physicians had not yet been made—surgery was a fundamental and typical aspect of the art of healing.

Although the results of his travels were published as the findings of the school as a whole, every physician was alone responsible for the care of his patients, and also for his itinerary, which often took him beyond Greece into Libya, Scythia and across the Black Sea. Clearly, strict loyalty to one's school did not impose restrictions on liberty of movement.

LECTURING
Another highly original aspect of medical life in the fifth and fourth centuries was the role played by lectures, which were never mere introductions for novices but were attended by physicians as part of their normal medical life. Many texts of the *Hippocratic Collection* (*Ancient Medicine, Nature of Man, Art, Winds, Diseases I, Generation, Nature of the Child, Diseases IV*) were clearly rhetorical in character, if only because they all had an exordium and a peroration and used such characteristic verbs as λέγειν, to say. Other famous texts, too, may well have been discourses—in fact, the publication of rhetorical works seems to have been a general practice with all the schools. Thus in Xenophon's *Memorabilia*, Socrates is made to refer to the general exordia of medical discourses (IV, 2, 5). The high quality of these oral discussions is evident in a great many texts, *e.g.* in the *Nature of Man*, Littré VI, 34.

Love of oration explains the appearance of a type of man who has no equivalent in modern civilization: the 'iatrosophist' or eloquent physician, who was more concerned with oratory than with healing.

Moreover, he was a great showman who would stage spectacular operations, such as straightening a vertebral column by tying the patient to a ladder and then lowering him from a tower. The *Joints and Fractures* took him severely to task for this unprofessional lack of restraint and for misleading the public by showmanship rather than using real skill. The good sense of the classical period prevailed in the end and the period of the iatrosophist was but a picturesque interlude without any lasting effects on Greek medicine.

Even so, the love for discourse might have led to a conflict between the traditional concern for objectivity and the new taste for rhetorical perfection, in the second half of the fifth century. While the practitioner of former days had never bothered with mere eloquence, sophistry had since come to the fore and physicians were expected to be good orators into the bargain. Remarkably enough, this new requirement did little to damage their scientific ideal—*ratio* and *oratio* were in no way opposed and the lectures served but to further the pursuit of the intellectual ideals.

'INDEPENDENT' PHYSICIANS

So far we have ignored those few physicians who belonged to none of the schools, and whose independence was safeguarded by the general intellectual tolerance of the Greeks. They were generally philosophers and orators rather than physicians, and must be considered the founders of the great fifth-century medico-cosmological systems. Thus the *Regimen* bears traces of a strong personality with views of his own (Littré VI, author's preliminary statement, 466–468); and so, to a lesser extent, do the *Winds*, the *Weeks* and the *Flesh*. Unlike their organized colleagues, these individual medical philosophers bore sole responsibility for their several doctrines.

They became far more important during the fourth century, when the great traditional schools had lost their original cohesion and when the independent practitioners began to exert an increasingly powerful influence.

Werner Jaeger's studies of the considerable works of Diocles of Carystos, the famous fourth-century physician, have shown that he did not, apparently, belong to any of the schools. Diocles was a keen thinker and observer, and has been called a second Hippocrates (Pliny, *Natural History* XXVI, 6). His 193 fragments deal with such valid aspects of medicine as cooking, anatomy, fevers, hygiene, herbal remedies, and diseases of women. From the fact that he was consulted by Antigone, one of Alexander's generals and the ruler of Western Asia, on matters of hygiene (the text of Diocles' reply was found in a good state of preservation), and also because his *Hygiene* was dedicated to the Macedonian prince Pleistarchos, the son of the famous Antipater, we can judge how great his prestige must have been. Diocles, though close to Aristotle and the Lyceum by his training, was above all an individualist. With him we turn a page in Greek medical history, from the decline of the traditional family schools to the rise of medical schools in the modern sense of the word.

THE IDEALS OF CLASSICAL MEDICINE

We must now look more closely at the intellectual ideals of the schools we have described. We advisedly call them intellectual rather than scientific, though in their defence against their enemies members of the schools would always insist that healing is a true art (τέχνη), capable of being taught and yielding valuable results. Now, in fifth-century Greece all the 'skills' were held in a high repute and a technician (τεχνίτης) was one who combined art with reason. The doctors claimed to have this status, but from their texts we should find it more appropriate to call them 'scientists' and their art a 'science'. Thus, we find that the *Regimen in Acute Diseases*, criticizing the methods propounded in the *Cnidian Sentences*, describes them as 'merely technical'. This remark is extremely significant, for it shows how far the facts had anticipated their verbal expression. While 'science' as such was not yet spoken of,[1] it had already become enshrined in significant intellectual attitudes.

Let us see to what extent the medical schools merit the epithet 'scientific'. The anatomy taught at Cnidos and Cos was mediocre, the physiology full of errors. Veins and arteries were described with gross inexactitude, and surgeons famous for their elegant trepanations were apparently quite unfamiliar with the cranial sutures. The functions of the heart, the liver and the brain were almost completely unknown; what correct descriptions there are were due to chance discoveries rather than to methodical research. In this respect, natural philosophers like Alcmaeon of Croton were greatly superior to the Hippocratic physicians. The only exception was the author of *On the Heart*, who gave many correct anatomical descriptions, distinguishing between auricles and ventricles, making an accurate study of the mitral and tricuspid valves, and indicating

---

[1] Though Plato and Aristotle referred to 'science', Plato considered it tantamount to absolute knowledge (*Republic* v, 477 A, E), and hence beyond experimental investigation. Aristotle, it is true, finally held a more liberal opinion. This dogmatic view coloured the outlook of all Hellenic philosophers (notably the Stoics). The only reference to science in the *Hippocratic Collection* is found in the *Places in Man*, where science (ἐπιστήμη) is contrasted with fortune, and therefore lacks a specific connotation (Littré VI, 342).

the special properties of the left chamber; but his treatise belongs neither to the School of Cnidos nor to that of Cos and was a late addition to the *Collection*. (Bidez and Leboucq have shown that the work is related to the physiological, philosophical and medical thought of the Sicilian school.)

It is very probable that this discrepancy between observation and description was the result of the very nature of the education provided by the schools. In fact, the schools had always concentrated on wounds and diseases and their correct treatment. Physicians and diagnosticians were healers first and foremost, and must be judged accordingly, despite certain of their claims to the contrary (*e.g. Ancient Medicine* 22, *Places in Men* 2). Anatomy and physiology concerned them only in so far as they bore directly on their immediate work (for example, dislocations and fractures); in all other cases commonly held ideas or superficial appearances were accepted without very many questions.

THE EMPIRICAL TENDENCY:
THE SCHOOL OF CNIDOS

Stress On Accurate Observations

The School of Cnidos, the older of the two, though far more primitive in many respects, was rightly famed for many of its keen observations and bold procedures.

It was at Cnidos that auscultation was first practised, a fact mentioned explicitly in the *Diseases* (Littré VII, 94), whose author tells us that, by applying the ear to the ribs and listening for the sound of boiling vinegar, the physician may come to know whether a case of hydrothorax is aqueous or purulent. Elsewhere in the same book, we are told that if the chest sounds like 'the scraping of copper' the patient suffers from a disease called 'lung dropping on to the rib'— some kind of pleurisy. The 'Hippocratic fluctuations' mentioned in *Internal Complaints* (Littré VII, 226—a text consulted by Laënnec) were very light percussions of the patient's chest to find out which side had a purulent discharge. All these practices were based on remarkably accurate observations which later medical traditions, far from developing, allowed to fall into oblivion for more than 2,000 years.

This school also performed a number of remarkable surgical feats. Thus, according to *On Vision* and *On Diseases*, failing sight in otherwise normal eyes was treated by trepanation. While the texts do not give the details of this operation they do say that such operations were usually successful, from which we may infer that Greek physicians appreciated the connection between the eye and the brain.

Surgery was also commonly practised to drain pus or liquid from kidneys and lungs. In cases of hydrothorax, the *Internal Complaints* advises a very grave step: the perforation of the chest and the insertion of a linen plug, allowing the liquid to drain off for twelve days.

NOSOLOGY AND EXPERIMENT

We must also mention the accuracy of many nosological findings, some of which were to fall into oblivion only to be resuscitated very much later. These include the distinction between arthritis and gout (*Complaints*), the exact description of the successive stages of scrofula (*Flesh*), the existence of hydatic pulmonary cysts in man (*Internal Complaints*), etc. Finally, the later Cnidean texts (*Generation, Nature of the Child, Diseases IV*) described what were often very ingenious experiments that went far beyond mere clinical investigations, *e.g.* experiments in morphology, embryology and 'humoral' balance. Unfortunately, these experiments were never sufficiently controlled, so that the discovery of, say, communicating vessels was considered proof positive of the equilibrium of the body's fluids. Even so, the first experimental steps had been taken. One physician, by placing twenty eggs under some brooding hens and breaking open one egg a day, discovered that the chick embryo is surrounded by membranes like the human foetus, and that it is born 'as soon as it is strong enough to break through the shell' (*Nature of the Child*, Littré VII, 530).

Other observations gave rise to the most colourful descriptions. Phthisis was said to be accompanied by a sound like the whistling of a reed (*Internal Complaints*); one mortal fever was said to be characterized by the eyes swelling out of their orbits (*Diseases II*), and an unidentified pulmonary swelling to lead to the dilation of the nostrils 'like a running horse' and to the patient's holding his tongue 'like a dog parched by the arid heat of summer' (*Internal Complaints*).

But none of these descriptions was ever systematized by their authors, except to conclude rather vaguely that there existed three types of phthisis, four types of icterus, three types of tetanus, four types of strangury, seven diseases of the bowel, a dozen of the bladder, etc.[1]

---

[1] These numerical catalogues of various diseases were discussed by Galen who gave more precise figures (*Commentary on the Regimen in Acute Diseases*, Kühn ed. XV, 427–428). Additional groups were added later, *viz.* three types of hepatitis, five diseases of the spleen, and five types of typhus.

REMEDIES

Another peculiarity of the Cnidean school was the huge variety of remedies and prognostic tests it prescribed (*e.g.* to ascertain fertility), or rather, the huge variety of proportions in which a limited number of substances had to be administered. The last section of *Diseases III* alone gives fifty refreshing drinks for those suffering from fevers, while each of the four books on *Diseases of Women* lists thousands of concoctions covering scores of pages.

Most errhines (substances introduced into the nose) contained parsley juice, flowers of copper[1] and myrrh, and pounded leeks, in varied proportions (*Diseases II*) and were used against headaches, phthisis, fevers, *etc.* Then there were innumerable emetics, purgatives, and specifics, such as the potion administered to women after labour which consisted of five cantharides beetles, with the heads, wings and legs removed, dissolved in diluted wine together with fifteen squid's eggs and various vegetable powders (*Nature of Women*, Littré VII, 346). Equally bizarre ingredients went into the making of a vast number of fumigations, fermentations, injections and pessaries.

All these remedies represented the sum-total of 'pharmaceutical' knowledge acquired uncritically by generations of physicians. The choice of a particular remedy was almost entirely based on trial and error; 'administer and experiment', δίδου πειρώμενος, was the general motto. We may rightly call this approach pre-scientific, and the Cnidean physicians never felt impelled to go beyond that stage. They were experimenters first and foremost, who failed to master the immense multiplicity of data at their disposal. Even the explanatory attempts in certain texts, however interesting, led to no positive conclusions, no doubt because of the failure to establish a nexus between thought and experiment; whenever the Cnidean physicians turned theorists, they produced piecemeal explanations. Thus the many 'causal' explanations found in the *Internal Complaints* and *Diseases II* are all based on false inferences. For instance, the origins of the three types of phthisis are said to be the descending of curdled cerebral phlegm into the lungs, general exhaustion, and the presence of blood and bile in the spinal cord (Littré VII, 188–192).

The purely experimental approach often led to brutal interventions on the part of the physician. Some cerebral conditions and rheumatic complaints were treated by keeping the patient drunk, and diseases of the lung were treated by 'lung infusions', *i.e.* by forcing irritants down the oesophagus (and not, as the physicians thought, down the trachea) to produce violent fits of coughing. During operations, the surgeon would pull hard at the unfortunate patient's

[1] The oxides of copper.

tongue, a traditional method described by Galen in his *De sectis*. Again, the removal of polyps from the nose by means of threads, a stick and a hind's hoof, and the painting of infected throats with twisted myrtle twigs swathed in linen, though more rational, were still very crude procedures, and were used without any questions about their efficacy.

THE RATIONAL TENDENCY: THE SCHOOL OF COS

VALID OBSERVATION

The School of Cos used an entirely different approach. While Cnidos was the passive repository of a mediocre tradition and hence never advanced beyond the portals of science, Cos, though also drawing on the past, used it as a mere stepping-stone. Intensely hostile to all idle speculations and firmly wedded to the facts (descriptions of diseases abound in the writings of the school), they yet sought for the basic and rational principle underlying all medical practices.[1] Experiment had thus been raised to a much higher scientific level.

When making a diagnosis, it was the physician's first task to find out 'what it is possible to see, to touch, and to hear—all that can be grasped by the eye, the touch, the ear, the nose, the tongue and the brain, and by all other means at our disposal' (*The Doctor's Surgery*, Littré II, 272). The same instructions to the physician can also be found in *Epidemics VI*. Both texts, therefore, stress the value not only of the senses in examinations but also of bringing the mind to bear on them (ἡ γνώμη, ὁ λογισμός). The very construction of this phrase emphasizes that thought was considered a normal means of seizing upon concrete facts, an integral part of experiment and not merely something to be indulged in afterwards. This concept was soon to be developed more fully.

THE ROLE OF THE SENSES

Although it is stating the obvious to say that the knowledge of medicine, in particular, is based on sense perception, the School of Cos carried its respect for the senses much further than the Cnideans, who looked upon all diseases as already established in the existing lists. In Cos, personal observation (*e.g.* in the *Epidemics*) took precedence over all pre-established categories. General treatises like the *Prognostics* and the *Aphorisms* were based on original investigations, which, like none before, broke through the ancient prejudices.

---

[1] This principle is expressed in the *Regimen in Acute Diseases* as ἐμοὶ δ' ἀνδάνει μὲν ἐν πάσῃ τῇ τέχνῃ προσέχειν τὸν νόον (Littré II, 230); it is also mentioned in the *Wounds of the Head*, the *Prognostics*, and in the *Epidemics I*.

Accurate observation was therefore given a new and very important status. The senses, the *Ancient Medicine* tells us, are the true and indispensable guides in all complex cases. No longer was it theories or mathematical calculations which determined the precise moment of the physician's intervention, for the requirements of medicine were qualitative and complex—ποικιλώτερα—and demanded a keen training of sense perception. To provide that training young practitioners had to be educated for many years, and while good teaching was no guarantee against all errors, the very reduction of error was, as the *Ancient Medicine* pointed out modestly, a step in the right direction.

But while the senses taught the physician what symptoms and crises were indicative of a given disease, their message must be interpreted by the mind. Although the Cnideans had also made valuable observations of particular symptoms, they had described them for their own sake. The School of Cos, on the other hand, appreciated that obvious phenomena were not necessarily more important than those which had first to be interpreted by the mind, itself sharpened by experimental studies.

The Role of Thought

In effect, the Hippocratic texts invite reflection about phenomena as often as they enjoin observation. Reflection is described by the verbs, ἐνθυμέεσθαι, ἀσκέειν, μελετᾶν, προσέχειν τὸν νόον, and the very scope of the vocabulary is evidence of a broad approach. An examination of *Joints and Fractures* will make this abundantly clear.

The book deals first of all with the question of bandaging fractures, once they have been reduced. The top of the bandage must be applied to the fractured part, and the rest of the bandage so wound that the patient feels his limb is well supported yet not too strongly constricted. The feeling of constriction must increase for one day and then diminish, when a new bandage must be applied. The importance of the patient's own feelings is the only true indication that the broken bones are held in place while the humours are allowed to circulate freely, thus avoiding congestion or gangrene.

This understanding of the patient's physical reactions went hand in hand with gentle treatment, since all vigorous procedures might lead to undesirable complications. In curvature of the spine, for instance, there can be no question of routine manipulations until the nature of the complaint is fully determined: *e.g.* whether the vertebra sticks out or in, whether the condition is due to a fall, to occupational factors, or to old age, and so on. Treatment will often be futile, and in any case must differ according to circumstances.

Instruments must often be used, and their effects on the patient's individual needs must be carefully studied. Unlike the Cnidean texts, the School of Cos did not list an indiscriminate mass of therapeutic procedures; the choice of the correct technique was always based on reason allied to experiment (λογισμῷ προσήκοντι).

This alliance has many other remarkable aspects which we can mention only in passing. Thus, Hippocratic prognosis was not the mechanical attention to isolated facts, but a complex method based on scrupulous attention to the development of a multitude of related symptoms. Similarly, the treatment of acute diseases was no longer the automatic application of rigid rules, such as prescribing a total fast followed by solid food after a given number of days. What was important was to bring practice into intelligent agreement with medical principles born of long reflection on past experience— for example, to determine whether the patient was strong enough to face the almost inevitable crisis, and what diet must be prescribed to increase his individual powers of recovery. Because the patient's condition was never static, the physician could not rely on principles alone. It was this realization which led to the birth of the true art of medicine which, though based on strict principles, can never be purely mechanical.

THE SCOPE OF OBSERVATION

To appreciate the full scope of this combination of careful attention to the facts with keen reflection, we must first realize that the Cos physician felt impelled to study not only biology but also psychology, sociology, geography and even astronomy. This is illustrated best by a quotation from the *Epidemics I*:

As regards diseases, here is how we discern them. Our knowledge is based on universal human nature, on the individual nature of every person, on the disease, on the patient, on the substances administered to him, on the dispenser, and on all the good or bad signs we can deduce from these; also on the general and particular constitution of the atmosphere according to the diversities of the sky and of the place; on the habits, on the regimen of life, on the occupation, on the duration of each; on words, manners, silence, thoughts, dreams, sleep and sleeplessness, the qualities and the time of dreams; on uncontrolled manual gestures, on twitches and tears; on paroxysms, stools, urine, spitting and vomiting; on the sequence of diseases, on abscesses which herald the crises; on sweat, chills, shivers, coughs, sneezes, hiccups, belches; on breaking hot and cold winds, on haemorrhages and haemorrhoids. These are the signs and everything which they show must be examined with care.

(Littré II, 668–670.)

This passage does not mention sociology, which is, however, discussed in *Airs, Waters, Places*. This work, speaking of the behaviour of the people of Europe and Asia Minor, asserts that the temperament of men is influenced by the nature of their government (liberal or despotic). It also discusses the possible influence of fashion and customs on the human organism.

THE APPEARANCE OF THE SCIENTIFIC SPIRIT

Clearly, therefore, the kind of medicine practised in Cos may lay claim to the title of scientific in the wider sense of the word. While the particular discoveries made in Cos are difficult to specify, there is no doubt that the members of the school gave evidence in their writings of an admirably scientific approach. Thus, in *Joints and Fractures*, the author tells us that, while he himself has only observed one type of dislocation of the humerus, *viz.* in the axilla, there are others who claim that such dislocations may also appear elsewhere. Now, all these claims are based on the observation of a swelling of flesh over the alleged dislocation, which may have had quite different causes. 'I have never seen it,' declares the author, 'though I cannot state absolutely whether it is possible or impossible' (Littré IV, 80). Discussing hump-back in the same book, the author mentions the shortcomings of a method used by himself, namely placing an inflated leather bottle under the patient. 'I have especially mentioned this method, because it is most important to tell which experiments have proved useless and for what reasons' (*op. cit.*, p. 212).

Here we find submission to the facts joined to self-criticism, as a double safeguard against the causes of error. This approach, so untypical of other ancient writers, was to imbue physicians with great modesty, as they constantly remembered the greatness of their traditions, the ambiguous complexity of their experiments and the great difficulty of evaluating them correctly. Hence, they rejected all forms of showmanship and made it a principle to proceed soberly and steadily towards their aim. The physician was, above all, the servant of his art, whose simple maxim it was to be useful and never to inflict harm.

The true scientist joins accurate knowledge of the facts to the demands of reason. In this respect, too, the School of Cos led the way. It refused to accept the dead theories of the philosophers, so much so that, unlike the Cnideans, its members never even considered causal theories based on movements of bile or phlegm. Instead, and much more relevantly, they studied the development rather than the origins of diseases, introducing such notions as critical days, coctions, deposits, metastases, paroxysms and relapses. Nor did they turn these notions into absolutes, but used them only to interpret, and not to supplant, experiment. No wonder that after 2,000 years the Hippocratic doctrine of disease is still of more than purely historical interest. True, modern medicine has discarded many of its notions, but it still uses a number of the basic ideas of the Hippocratic *corpus*. While almost all other ancient systems of medicine now strike us as so many wild flights of human fancy, the ideas propounded in Cos have alone remained capable of inspiring modern experiments.

THE GREATNESS OF CLASSICAL MEDICINE: HIPPOCRATES

With the School of Cos, Greek medicine had gradually reached its scientific and philosophic apogee. Hippocratic physicians, by refusing to be drawn by wild speculations, had introduced an astonishing feeling for life and for man into the practice of their art. They knew that the human organism is a complex whole and that true wisdom consists in aiding and stimulating its natural activities; they were convinced that no one could be a true physician who ignored the psychological life of the patient. They were the first Greeks not to separate body and soul, and to consider man as a part of his physical and sociological environment. Hence their medicine was more than a mere technique; it became a high form of culture.

In due course, their outlook and ideas would come to be identified with the name of Hippocrates. We have failed to stress his own great contribution not because his historical existence is in doubt, but because in our brief summary the school is of greater importance than the man whose name it bore. Even so, the magnificent achievements of Greek medicine might never have been attained, were it not for the contribution of this man of exceptional genius, this great practitioner and outstanding scientist, renowned for his brilliant intellect. A contemporary of Plato's (and mentioned by name in Plato's *Phaedros* and *Protagoras*), Hippocrates was a product of his time, albeit an exceptional one. Though legend has added to his works and his remarkable cures, his authentic contribution has had a lasting effect on world medicine. The more we study the writings of this remarkable physician the more does our admiration grow.

BIBLIOGRAPHY

General Works on Greek and Roman Science

BRUNET and MIELI, *Histoire des Sciences, Antiquité*, Paris, 1935.
M. COHEN and I. E. DRABKIN, *Source book in Greek science*, New York, 1948. Repr. London, 1959.
ENRIQUES and G. DE SANTILLANA, *Storia del pensiero scientifico*. I: *Il mondo antico*, Bologna, 1932.

B. FARRINGDON, *Greek Science*, 2 vols., London, 1945–49.

J. L. HEIBERG, *Mathematics and physical science in classical antiquity*, Oxford, 1922.

A. MIELI, *Panorama general de historia de la ciencia*. I: *El mundo antiguo*, Buenos Aires, 1945.

PAULY-WISSOWA, *Real-Encyclopädie der klassischen Altertumswissenschaft*, Stuttgart, 1894.

A. REY, *La science dans l'Antiquité*, Vols. II–V, Paris, 1933–48.

F. RUSSO, *Histoire des sciences et des techniques. Bibliography*, Paris, 1954.

G. SARTON, *Introduction to the History of Science*, 3 vols. in 5 parts, Baltimore, 1927–48.

P. TANNERY, *Mémoires scientifiques*, 17 vols., Paris, 1912–50.

Hellenic Science

M. CLAGETT, *Greek Science in Antiquity*, London, 1957.

H. DIELS, *Doxographi Graeci*, Berlin, 1879; *Editio iterata*, Berlin, 1929.

H. DIELS, *Die Fragmente der Vor-Sokratiker*, 5th edition, Berlin, 3 vols., 1934–35 (W. KRANTZ).

P. DUHEM, *Le système du monde. Histoire des doctrines cosmologiques de Platon à Copernic*, Vol. I, Paris, 1913.

SIR T. HEATH, *A History of Greek Mathematics*, Oxford, 1921.

P. KUCHARSKI, Sur la théorie des couleurs et des saveurs dans le *De Sensu* aristotélicien, *Revue des Études grecques*, July–Dec., 1954.

P. H. MICHEL, *De Pythagore à Euclide. Contribution à l'histoire des mathématiques préeuclidiennes*, Paris, 1950.

A. MIELI, Aristote savant, *Archeion*, XIV, Rome, 1932.

CH. MUGLER, Les dimensions de l'universe platonicien d'après *Timée 32 b*, *Revue des Études grecques*, Jan.–June, 1953; *Platon et la recherche mathématique de son époque*, Strasburg–Zurich, 1948.

L. ROBIN, *Aristote*, Paris, 1944; *Platon*, Paris, 1935.

G. DE SANTILLANA, *The Origins of Scientific Thought: from Anaximander to Proclus 600 B.C. to A.D. 300*, London, 1961.

G. SARTON, *A History of science*, I, Cambridge, 1952.

G. SENN, *Die Entwicklung der biologischen Forschungsmethode in der Antike und ihre grundsätzliche Förderung durch Theophrast von Eresos*, Aarau, 1933.

C. SINGER, *A History of Biology*, Oxford, 1950.

P. TANNERY, *La géométrie grecque*, Paris, 1887; *Pour l'histoire de la science hellène. De Thalès a Empédocle*, Paris, 1930, 2nd ed.

Medicine in the Hellenic Period

J. BIDEZ and G. LEBOUCQ, Une anatomie antique du cœur humain, *Revue des Études grecques*, LVII, Paris, 1944.

L. BOURGEY, *Observation et expérience chez les médecins de la collection Hippocratique*, Paris, 1953.

CH. DAREMBERG, *La médecine dans Homère*, Paris, 1865.

A.-J. FESTUGIÈRE, *Hippocrate, l'Ancienne Médecine*. Introduction, translation and commentary, Paris, 1948.

J. GUIART, La médecine grecque aux temps héroïques de Minos a Homère, *Biologie médicale*, XV, Paris, 1925; La médecine grecque n'est pas née dans les temples d'Esculape, *Biologie médicale*, XVII, Paris, 1927.

R. HERZOG, Die Wunderheilungen von Epidauros, ein Beitrag zur Geschichte der Medizin und der Religion, *Philologus*, XXII (3), Leipzig, 1931.

W. JAEGER, *Diokles von Karystos*, Berlin, 1938; *Paideia: the ideals of Greek Culture*, Vol. III, 1st ed., New York, 1945; 2nd ed., 1947.

J. FILLIOZAT, Pronostics médicaux akkadiens, grecs et indiens, *Journal asiatique*, Paris, 1952.

J. ILBERG, *Die Ärzteschule von Knidos*, Leipzig, 1925.

W. H. S. JONES, *The Medical Writings of Anonymus Londiniensis*, Cambridge, 1947.

E. LITTRÉ, *Œuvres complètes d'Hippocrate*, 10 vols., Paris, 1839–61.

J. PRECOPE, *Iatrophilosophers of the Hellenistic States*, London, 1961. Primarily a book on Ancient Greek philosophers but with a medical interest.

E. ROHDE, *Psyché*, Paris, 1928.

E. ROBERT, *Épidaure*, Paris, 1935.

SANDRAIL, *Les sources akkadiennes de la pensée et de la méthode Hippocratique*, Toulouse, 1953.

P.-M. SCHUHL, *Essai sur la formation de la pensée grecque*, Paris, 1934 (2nd ed., 1949).

R. O. STEUER and J. B. DE C. M. SAUNDERS, *Ancient Egyptian and Cnidian Medicine*, Berkeley, Calif., 1958.

M. WELLMANN, *Die Fragmente der Sikelischen Ärzte Akron, Philistion, und des Diokles von Karystos*, Berlin, 1901.

HELLENISTIC
AND ROMAN SCIENCE

CHAPTER 1

General Survey

GREEK SCIENTIFIC THOUGHT culminated in Hellenistic and Roman science, which flourished for more than eight centuries. Despite the many political upheavals and their profound repercussions on Mediterranean thought, that science, more than any other, presents a continuous thread and must therefore be treated as a whole.

THE HISTORICAL SETTING

During the Hellenistic period, which lasted from the death of Alexander (323 B.C.) until the final destruction of the Western Roman Empire in A.D. 476, the Mediterranean world was shaken by a number of momentous events: the Wars of the Diadochi over the division of Alexander's Empire (323–281 B.C.); Rome's subjugation of the Central Mediterranean one hundred years later, and her conquest of the entire Near East by 31 B.C.; Cleopatra's defeat by Octavius; Rome's thrust into Western Europe; and the Barbarian invasions during the third and fifth centuries A.D. which eventually led to the collapse of the Roman Empire. Inevitably, these political events had grave economic, sociological, and cultural repercussions, of which the most striking were the rise of the great Eastern cities during the third and second centuries B.C., the considerable growth of Rome and to a lesser extent of Western Europe, and the decline of the Empire from the third century onwards.

THE WORK OF PTOLEMAIOS I SOTER
But despite all these many currents, science advanced smoothly throughout the entire Hellenistic period. Alexandria, the city which had done so much to encourage scientific pursuits, continued to the end to attract scientists and to offer them congenial conditions. It was the first of the Lagides (sons of Lagos), Ptolemaios Soter (Ptolemy I), who, as ruler of Egypt after the death of Alexander, turned Alexandria into the capital of the Hellenistic world, and did his utmost to

262

welcome poets, writers, philosophers, and scientists. Thus he invited the two famous Peripatetics, Demetrios of Phalera, a former pupil of Theophrastos, and Straton of Lampsacos, whom he appointed tutor to the crown prince, Ptolemaios Philadelphos, and who later succeeded Theophrastos as head of the Lyceum. Demetrios encouraged Ptolemaios' love for science, and this love together with the King's generosity were the main reasons why scientists continued to flock to his city, and thus ensured her scientific hegemony. During the reign of Ptolemaios Soter, Alexandria welcomed Herophilos, the greatest physician of his day, the astronomers Aristyllos and Timocharis, and the famous geometer Euclid.

THE MUSEUM

It is generally agreed today that it was this Ptolemaios who, advised by Demetrios of Phalera, laid the foundations of two of Alexandria's most famous cultural institutions: the Museum and the Library. Some years earlier, as Governor of Athens, Demetrios had persuaded his teacher Theophrastos to establish his Peripatetic School in an Athenian building surrounded by porticos and set in a large garden. The main building contained a large lecture hall, small living-quarters for teachers and students, and the vast library of Aristotle. The Athenian institute was called *Museum* in honour of the Muses, and its Alexandrian namesake was modelled after it, though on a very much larger scale. According to Strabo, who visited it at the end of the first century B.C., the Alexandrian museum 'contains an ambulatory, an exedra, and a great hall in which the philosophers dine in common'. In addition, the Museum must also have provided accommodation for its members, dissection theatres for its physicians, and observatories for its astronomers. Ptolemy (Claudios Ptolemaios, *fl.* A.D. 150) reports that in the second century A.D. Alexandria had a gymnasium and a quadrangular portico, each provided with a large bronze circle for making astronomical observations. These buildings were doubtless part of the Museum, and so, perhaps, were the zoological gardens in which Ptolemaios II Philadelphos (285–247 B.C.) collected all kinds of exotic animals.

In addition to their free board and lodging the members of the Museum were also paid a fee, for which the government set aside a special allocation without, moreover, demanding regular lectures in return. The teachers were meant to devote all their time to research and to discussions with their colleagues or with distinguished visitors. At its height, the school must have had several hundred teachers divided into two great categories: the 'philologists' and the 'philosophers'. The philologists were above all concerned with the principles of grammar and language, and to a lesser extent with learned research into historiography and mythography. The philosophers, who were generally called Peripatetics or Aristotelians, were far less interested in moral or metaphysical problems than in mathematics, astronomy, geography or medicine, and some of them, such as Eratosthenes, combined scientific brilliance with considerable philological skill.

All these scientists could call not only on the resources of the Museum but also on the incomparable Library, which was greatly extended under Ptolemaios II Philadelphos who also set up a smaller library in the sanctuary of Serapis. These libraries, containing more than 700,000 volumes, provided the philologists and to a lesser extent the philosophers with an incomparable wealth of reference material.

THE SCIENTISTS OF ALEXANDRIA

The Museum, which was a research institute rather than an academy of learning, became so famous throughout the world that it managed to outlive the Lagide dynasty, and to win the support of Rome. It was thanks to the Museum that Alexandria became the greatest scientific centre of all antiquity, and that the astronomer Conon of Samos, the physician Erasistratos and the engineer Ctesibios came there in the third century B.C., to teach Euclid, Herophilos, and Straton. During the second half of the third century, Alexandria welcomed Eratosthenes, the father of mathematical geography, as the custodian of its Library, and the mathematician Apollonios of Perga. In the second century B.C. Alexandria received Hipparchos, who came there to make astronomical observations, and one hundred years later she was visited by Sosigenes, who supplied Julius Caesar with all the elements needed for his calendar reform, and also by Heron, the great physicist. During the second century A.D. her guests included the mathematician Menelaos, the physician Soranos and, above all, the famous astronomer Ptolemy; and finally, during the third and fourth centuries A.D., Alexandria presented the world with three great mathematicians: Diophantos, Pappos and Theon, the father of the famous Hypatia and the last recorded member of the Museum.

SCIENCE IN OTHER HELLENISTIC CITIES

Alexandria's encouragement of scientific pursuits was emulated by other Hellenistic centres, not to mention the older seats of learning like Syracuse and Cos. New libraries were established at Pella in Macedonia, at Antiochia in Syria, at Pergamos in Asia Minor— second only to that in Alexandria—and later in Rhodes, Smyrna, Ephesos, and many other towns. While most of these cities were primarily concerned with attracting men of letters and artists, leaving the philosophers to Athens, there were some notable exceptions. Thus the tyrants of Syracuse, Hieron and Gelon, were keenly interested in science, which explains why Archimedes, himself the son of an astronomer, spent his adult life in his native city of Syracuse after having completed his studies in Alexandria; why Apollonios of Perga divided his time between Alexandria and Pergamos, and why he dedicated his works to Eudemos and to the king of Pergamos, Attalos I. The island of Rhodes, which managed to maintain its independence and prosperity during the Hellenistic period, also attracted scientists. Thus Hipparchos made most of his observations and wrote most of his works on it, and when Ptolemaios III Euergetes temporarily disrupted the activities of the Museum, Rhodes and Pergamos received many of Alexandria's former luminaries. Crates of Mallos, the famous second-century philologist and geographer, resided at Pergamos, and Posidonios, the famous philosopher and scientist, lectured at Rhodes during the first half of the first century B.C. Pergamos, with its temple to Asclepios, which was visited by throngs of people suffering from all sorts of diseases, also attracted many leading physicians, the greatest of whom was Galen of Pergamos (second–third century A.D.) who studied in his native town before going abroad to complete his training.

Since physicians depended on the patronage of a fairly large circle of well-to-do patients, important medical centres gradually grew up far from the ancient seats of Cos, of Cnidos, and of Citium (Cyprus), particularly in such highly populated cities as Ephesos and Rome, the new world capital. Since this is our first mention of Rome, we shall now pause to make a brief examination of the Roman attitude to science.

ETRUSCAN SCIENCE

Before they came under the influence of the Greeks, the Romans had been civilized by the Etruscans, a people more immersed in religious rites than any other Western nation. Moreover, unlike the Greeks and Romans, the Etruscans were so enmeshed in irrational taboos and observances that, throughout their history, they never managed to proceed to any kind of distinction between their religious and secular life.

While all rational and scientific thought is based on the appreciation that natural processes are governed by natural laws, primitive thought looks on natural phenomena as the effects of divine whims. Unlike the Greeks and Romans, who gradually came to recognize that appearances could be explained without the agency of transcendental forces, the Etruscans held fast to the belief that the phenomenal world was the result of mystic forces unleashed in heaven or hell.

COSMOLOGY

Despite their ritualistic outlook, however, the Etruscans were never guilty of mental inertia or lack of intellectual curiosity. They simply ignored the principle of causality, the basis of all scientific thought, holding that all causes were equally divine and that all phenomena were sent by the gods to acquaint men with their demands.

In his *Naturalium Quaestionum* (II, 32, 2), Seneca illustrates this finalist outlook of the Etruscans with particular force, when he says: 'There are differences of interpretation between our countrymen and the Tuscans, who possess consummate skill in the explanation of the meaning of lightning. While we think that because clouds collide therefore lightning is emitted, they hold that clouds collide in order that lightning may be emitted. They refer everything to the will of God; therefore they are strong in their conviction that lightning does not give an indication of the future because it has occurred, but occurs because it is meant to give this indication.'

Such, in short, were the principles of Etruscan 'science', which though basically false nevertheless merits our attention, for had the Etruscans applied their keen observation and shrewd deductions to the facts themselves, rather than to their ominous 'significance', they might well have made a lasting contribution to scientific knowledge.

THE PRINCIPLES OF DIVINATION

In the sacred books containing the entire doctrine revealed miraculously to the Etruscans by the genius Tages and the nymph Begoe, divination took pride of place. The books taught the diviners—haruspices—how and where to look for divine signs, and what predictions to derive from them. These signs fell into three main categories: thunderstorms, the entrails of victims, and unusual events, all of which had to be observed and interpreted carefully, then to be acted upon. This is how Seneca described the diviner's art: '*ars in haec tria dividitur, quemadmodum exploremus, quemadmodum interpretemur, quemadmodum exoremus*' (*ibid.*, II, 33, 1).

THE OBSERVATION OF THUNDERSTORMS

Seneca, and Pliny the Elder in his *Natural History* (II, 137–148), described the Etruscan principles of observing thunderstorms in some detail. The Etruscans divided the sky into eight eastern and eight western sectors, the former foreboding good fortune and the latter evil. Nine gods were responsible for releasing thunderbolts. Jupiter alone kept three different kinds in his armoury. To assess the significance of a particular thunderbolt its origin and path had to be observed with great care, for, as in Chaldaean astrology, celestial

sectors played a paramount role in this pseudo-science. The brontoscopic Etruscan calendar, of which a Greek version by John Lauren-
tios Lydos (based on an older Latin translation) is extant, has rightly
been compared with the Babylonian hemerologia, in which the
meaning of lightning depends on the day on which it has struck.

HARUSPICY

Now, the notion that the meaning of a phenomenon is related to its
'place' was an inherent part not only of the art of interpreting
thunderbolts, but also of haruspicy. Thus the Tuscans held that the
liver of a sacrificial animal—the animal's 'seat of life'—reflects the
state of the universe at the moment of sacrifice. The surface of the liver
was thought to represent the divine mansions, from which the future
could be predicted. The Piacenza bronze liver, discovered in 1877,
was a model for teaching future haruspices the secret of their trade.
It was divided into a great number of 'heavenly compartments' from
which the god's intentions could be divined, just as they could from
the celestial 'places' of thunderbolts.

We have seen that there is a close connection between Etruscan and
Assyrio-Babylonian haruspicy. Recent work by M. Nugayrol on a
clay liver discovered at Fallerona has thrown fresh light on this
connection, though we are still unable to tell by what precise route a
technique practised during the second millennium B.C. reached Italy
during the seventh century B.C. (or later). Scholars are, however,
gradually supplying the missing links.

MARVELS

A great number of phenomena were looked upon as marvels, and
were thought to have exceptional divinatory significance. Servius,
Macrobius, and Ammianus Marcellinus have described fragments of
Etruscan *ostentaria* in which the doctrine of marvels was presented. All
animals and trees were thought to fall into two categories: *animalia
felicia* and *infelicia*, and *arbores felices* and *infelices*—presaging good or
evil much like the various parts of the liver and the 'places' of
thunderstorms. Clearly, all nature had a mysterious and profound
connection, which the Etruscans tried to discover by various related
techniques.

Etruscan 'science' therefore had much in common with ancient
Eastern science, and both together exerted a significant influence
on Rome. Thus, under the reign of the Tarquinius family Rome
adopted a finalist philosophy based on magic. Even during the first
Republican centuries, Etruria, though by then the enemy of Rome,
continued to seduce the Romans with its magical world view. The
impact of Greek philosophy never quite overcame the influence of

the priests, whose magical interpretations were much closer to popular belief than the apparent abstractions of the scientists.

TECHNOLOGY

Their primitive scientific outlook notwithstanding, the Etruscans showed great skill when it came to practical matters. They were masters of the art of civil and funereal architecture, of land irrigation and of swamp drainage. It was because of them that Rome could boast an outstanding sewage system in the sixth century B.C. Their concern with places led them to concentrate on dividing the land by strict principles, and in doing so they laid the foundations of the Roman system of cadastration so well known from the writings of the Roman *agrimensores*, and still detectable in aerial photographs of Italy. As goldsmiths they were often far superior to the Greeks, and even modern craftsmen have been unable to fathom the secret by which they managed to decorate jewellery with perfect little gold balls, whose diameter was sometimes less than 0.02 mm.

All we know of Etruscan medicine is based on hearsay. Thus Theophrastos and Martianus Capella state that Etruscan physicians were skilled in compounding remedies. According to an ancient legend repeated by Hesiod in verse 1,014 of his *Theogony*, the sons of Circe, herself renowned for her philtres, became Etruscan princes. Etruscan physicians relied on the curative virtues of the many thermal springs of Tuscany and Umbria, which are frequented by sufferers to this day. Dentistry was highly developed, thanks to the exceptional talent of the goldsmiths, and seventh-century Tuscan tombs were found to contain a great number of gold-crowned teeth. (In the middle of the fifth century the enactment of the Twelve Tables entitled all Romans to inter their dead together with 'what gold was found in their mouths'.)

Hence, while Etruria made a rather poor contribution to scientific thought, there is no doubt that she provided Rome with many of her technical skills.

THE ROMANS AND SCIENCE

The Roman contribution to theoretical science was as negligible as the Etruscan, though for quite different reasons. In fact, it is restricted to some lucid though fairly unoriginal discussions by Seneca of meteorological and geographical questions, to modifications of Greek ideas, to such compilations as Pliny's *Natural History*, and to works on agriculture and on art. On the other hand, Roman engineers perfected methods of building roads, bridges, aqueducts, canals, vaults and steps, and of manufacturing glass and metal articles, which redounded greatly to Rome's credit. This does not mean, as so many critics have claimed, that the Romans despised pure science, for we know that Lucretius, Cicero and Virgil were great admirers of its leading teachers. Moreover, we saw that Rome continued to support the Museum and the Library in Alexandria. Science, and particularly arithmetic, geometry and cosmography, had a place in Roman teaching which, though limited, was enough for technicians to acquire what theoretical knowledge they needed. But it remains a fact that, preoccupied as they were with literature, morals, and Platonic ideas, the Romans tended to leave science to the Greeks, and lacked the ability to bring to mathematics the intellectual acumen in which they so excelled when it came to jurisprudence. In short, there was no such thing as Roman science, and Rome's conquest of the East caused no break in the scientific tradition. Rome may at best be said to have influenced the development of medicine by attracting a number of physicians and then forcing them to adapt their methods to the tastes of the Roman public. Even so, the theoretical study of medicine and the training of Roman physicians remained the almost exclusive prerogative of the Eastern school, so that the vast majority of the great physicians continued to be recruited among the Greeks.

OUTLOOK AND METHODS

PERIPATETIC INFLUENCES

Because of the unity imposed upon Hellenistic and Roman science by the scientific pre-eminence of Alexandria, the views and methods of the leading Aristotelian philosophers and scientists gathered in Alexandria by Ptolemaios I Soter became the predominant views of the time. The fathers of the Museum, Demetrios of Phalera, the King's counsellor, and Straton of Lampsacos, the tutor of the heir apparent, were pupils of Theophrastos and of Aristotle. Moreover, in building the Museum and the Library, Ptolemaios had merely emulated the example of Alexander the Great, whom Aristotle had imbued with a love for science and who had used all his power to propagate his teacher's doctrines. Finally, and above all, the beginnings of Alexandrian science coincided with the very period when the seed sown by Aristotle had begun to sprout. The preceding chapters have shown how scientific research gradually threw off its former shackles as Aristotelian supplanted Platonic ideas, and as they were in turn modified by Theophrastos. We shall see that Straton of Lampsacos, though following in Aristotle's footsteps, arrived at many conclusions diametrically opposed to those of his teacher.

Let us briefly summarize the general principles held by Hellenistic science. First of all, science came to be considered as being independent of, though not necessarily opposed to, the metaphysical concerns of the philosophers. Instead of trying to synthesize explanations involving cosmic forces into one vast theory, Hellenistic science concentrated on the study of natural phenomena and their mathematical interpretation. Various specialized branches of science began to emerge, and while some exceptionally brilliant men excelled in more than one of these, most of them no longer tried to embrace all nature in one narrow viewpoint. Aristotelian *a priori* assumptions were gradually superseded by careful observations, and the frantic search for 'causes' and universal principles by the study of laws governing the behaviour of related phenomena. In short, the facts were no longer made to fit the theories—the science of Aristotle and Theophrastos may be said to have come into its own only during the Hellenistic and Roman epoch.

THE PLATONIC HERITAGE

Though Plato's influence on Hellenistic science was less marked than Aristotle's, it was Platonism which was indirectly responsible for the third-century stress on geometry and astronomy, at the expense of physics and biology. While Aristotle and Theophrastos were mainly interested in the observational sciences, Plato, heir to the Pythagorean tradition, had a marked preference for intelligible rather than sensible phenomena, and hence for logic rather than observation. In astronomy, Plato had raised circular and uniform motion into a dogma, and many texts—such as the introduction to the *Almagest*, in which Ptolemy defined his astronomical postulates—were clearly inspired by Platonic views. But then Aristotle, too, had assumed that circular motion provided the best explanation of celestial phenomena. In fact, as Neugebauer has stressed, it was the most rational of all ancient hypotheses claiming to account for the observed phenomena.

THE INFLUENCES OF NEW PHILOSOPHICAL SYSTEMS

Science is never immune from hasty generalizations nor from illuminism. In Alexandria, its emancipation from metaphysical bondage was far too recent to secure it from occasional retraction. Thus, at the height of its expansion at the beginning of the third century, new philosophical systems were propounded which had a marked and generally deleterious effect on scientific progress. The Epicureans, heirs to the ancient atomic tradition, were vociferous opponents of the leading astronomers, whom they accused of ignoring the plurality of worlds, the infinity of space, and the non-geometrical character of sidereal phenomena. While they failed to formulate their cosmology in scientifically valid terms, the Epicureans nevertheless had a stimulating effect on the work of physicists like Straton of Lampsacos and of physicians like Erasistratos and Asclepiades. Stoicism, again, which was based on Platonic and Peripatetic doctrines, also had a strong effect on the development of scientific thought. A number of Stoics, and above all Posidonios of Apamea, were true scientists who, by propagating their philosophic ideas, helped to spread the most important findings of Hellenistic science—together with such grave errors as the notion of universal sympathy. While that notion helped Posidonios to explain the tides, it introduced into cosmology a mysterious force acting at a distance and smacking of astrology. Again, the Stoic theory of *pneuma* acted as a brake on medicine. But it was not until the advent of Scepticism, a doctrine first propounded by Pyrrhon and adopted during the second century by the Academy, that scientific progress was directly attacked by philosophy, and that physicians were encouraged to found the so-called 'empirical' school, whose very name shows how opposed it was to earlier Alexandrian medical trends.

IRRATIONAL FORCES

Much graver than Scepticism, which used reason to attack science, was the gradual emergence of irrational theories which, together with other factors, were to bring ancient science to the brink of ruin. From the third century B.C. onwards, the influence of these theories began to undermine all attempts to explain natural phenomena by rational means; astrology and (later) alchemy challenged astronomy and natural science, and magic insinuated itself into medicine. Ptolemy still drew a clear distinction between astronomy and astrology, in both of which he was equally well versed, but others, like Pliny the Elder, were no longer able to sift fact from fancy, reason from occult explanation, or medicine from sorcery. Particularly at the beginning of the Christian era, when Oriental mysticism took Greece and Rome by storm, such exotic sects as the Gnostics and the Hermetics managed to find a ready audience for their distorted and over-simplified cosmologies, ostensibly revealed to them by God. Popular credulity gradually helped such doctrines to gain the upper hand over critical and scientific ideas.

THE INFLUENCE OF THE EAST

Such, in brief, was the outcome of Alexander's and his successors' attempts to graft Eastern concepts forcibly on Greek scientific ideas. While the Greeks had always absorbed what they thought worth while from the Egyptians and Persians, Alexander's attempts to intensify this process was undoubtedly the main cause of the decline of rationalism in the following centuries. Before that, however,

Alexander's conquests and unification of the East, Rome's later conquest of the Mediterranean countries and the Roman explorations of distant lands had greatly helped to widen the horizons of naturalists, geographers and astronomers. Travellers and traders were everywhere on the move, from Scotland to the Somali coast and from the Canaries to India and even China; and the crossroads of the main trade routes met precisely in the Eastern Mediterranean, at the very point where the axes of the world were said to intersect.

SCIENTIFIC PROGRESS

As a result, many branches of science were given a tremendous impetus. From Euclid to Pappos and Theon of Alexandria, mathematicians took unprecedented steps in developing geometry and arithmetic, in inventing trigonometry, in perfecting algebra, in studying optics and acoustics, while the astronomers, led by Aristarchos, Hipparchos and Ptolemy, made splendid discoveries including the heliocentric doctrine (unhappily not retained). They brought the geocentric theory to a high degree of geometrical perfection and at the same time founded mathematical geography. Straton of Lampsacos and, particularly, Archimedes formulated some of the fundamental laws of physics; Alexandrian physicians, beginning with Herophilos and Erasistratos, applied Aristotle's and Theophrastos' biological ideas to man, thus founding scientific anatomy and physiology and clearing the path for the majestic work of Galen. However, Aristotle and Theophrastos had no worthy successors in physics, zoology and botany, which were finally stifled by occultism. Strangely enough, it was in those branches of science in which Aristotle's own contributions were least fruitful that Aristotelian ideas produced the most striking and unexpected results.

CHAPTER 2

Pure and Applied Mathematics

WHILE THE HISTORY of Greek science must be carefully pieced together from sparse documents, generally written during a later period, Hellenistic science produced three monumental works which have reached us in a perfect state of preservation.

They stand out, majestic and alone, like Greek temples in a desert. These amazing relics of an ancient science had so lasting an influence on all future developments that we shall discuss them in some technical detail.

EUCLID

For the last four centuries, historians have been generally agreed that Euclid, the greatest Hellenistic mathematician, was born at the dawn of the third century B.C., even though the first explicit mention of Euclid appeared no earlier than in a preface by Apollonios.

Again, though Euclid is generally considered a precursor of Archimedes, some references by Archimedes suggest strongly that he may have been Euclid's contemporary.

In any case, all studies of Alexandrian mathematics must begin with the study of Euclid.

PLANE GEOMETRY

First and foremost among Euclid's writings were the *Elements*, a gigantic work of thirteen books which remained a standard text until the nineteenth century.

The *Elements* can be divided into five parts. The plane geometry of polygonal and circular figures is discussed in Books I–IV. These books do not deal with similarity, which is treated in the second part, consisting of Book V, dealing with the theory of proportions, and Book VI, in which that theory is applied to geometrical figures. The theory of integers (whole numbers) is the subject of the third part, contained in Books VII, VIII and IX. Book X, the longest of all, is devoted to the study of the simplest incommensurables (irrationals).

The fifth and last part, on solid geometry, is covered by Books XI, XII and XIII.

Euclid prefaced Book I with a number of definitions, with five postulates, and with 'common notions', whose number varies in different editions but could not, originally, have been more than five. The most famous postulate is the last:

That if a straight line falling on two straight lines makes the interior angles on the same side less than two right angles, the two straight lines, if produced indefinitely, meet on that side on which the angles are less than the two right angles.

This famous postulate is generally quoted in J. Playfair's abridged eighteenth-century version: 'Through a given point only one parallel can be drawn to the given straight line.' From the third century B.C. until the eighteenth century A.D. that postulate was considered a necessary assumption for applying mathematical arguments to geometry. We know today that that is not so, but since non-Euclidean geometries can be expressed only by means of circular and exponential functions, and since the Greeks were restricted to Babylonian algebra which they adapted to geometry by the technique of applying areas, they had either to assume Euclid's postulate or else to abandon all geometrical studies. What is remarkable is that Euclid should nevertheless have realized that what was needed was a postulate, and not a demonstration. His was therefore the first purely mathematical approach in all history.

The subject-matter of Book I, which begins (by way of a proposition formulated as a problem) with the construction of an equilateral triangle and concludes with the Theorem of Pythagoras, is mainly based on very ancient material.

Book II, which is very short, deals with the foundations of geometrical algebra, the only kind of algebra known to the Greeks. The first ten propositions give the geometrical equivalents of a number of algebraical identities, and discuss such topics as the relations between rectangles of equal height or between squares constructed on the sum or the difference of two line segments. The Book also shows how to solve equations of the second degree, though by methods that have long since been discarded. The same subject is treated in a more comprehensive manner in Book IV, which studies the determination of areas by successive approximations and makes an exhaustive examination of the equation $ax^2 + bx + c = 0$.

Book III, still very elementary, deals with the properties of the circle. In particular it establishes, by algebraic geometry and not by similarity, that, if from any point O a straight line is drawn to cut a circle at P, Q, the rectangle OP . OQ is constant. The study of the tangent leads to the first enunciation of the very important concept of the angle of contingence.

Book IV, which has a Pythagorean flavour, also deals with circles, but in relation to the inscription and circumscription of them by all those regular polygons which can be so constructed with ruler and compass, namely, equilateral triangles, squares, pentagons and hexagons. By such constructions as the inscription of the pentagon, without recourse to similarity, Euclid revealed the hand of a great master.

Proportion

The second part of the *Elements* is much less elementary. Thus Book V represents one of the high-lights of Greek mathematical thought, so much so that its contents were not fully digested until the nineteenth century. The Book deals with ratios which are defined as follows:

[3] A ratio is a kind of relation in respect of size between two magnitudes of the same kind.

[4] Magnitudes are said to have a ratio to one another if they are capable, when multiplied, of exceeding one another.

[5] Magnitudes are said to be in the same ratio, the first to the second and the third to the fourth, when, if any equimultiples whatsoever be taken of the first and the third and any whatsoever of the second and the fourth, the former multiples alike exceed, are alike equal to, or alike fall short of, the latter equimultiples, taken in corresponding order.

[7] When, of the equimultiples, the multiple of the first magnitude exceeds the multiple of the second, but the multiple of the third does not exceed the multiple of the fourth, then the first is said to have a greater ratio to the second than the third has to the fourth.

The most important definition is the fourth. While Book V legitimately refers to it as a definition, Books VI, X, XI and XII assume implicitly that line segments, plane areas, volumes, and rectilinear angles obey it as a law. But Archimedes felt that it should be merely a restricted postulate, for curvilinear angles and particularly the angle of contingence are not satisfied by it as a definition.[1]

Definitions 5 and 7 enable one to formulate a general theory of ratios of supreme elegance, on a par with the modern concept of cuts introduced during the last century. Apart from an anonymous scholium to that effect, there is no evidence that the theory goes back to Eudoxos.

Book VI is important though elementary. It deals with similar triangles, the theorem wrongly known as that of Thales, the proportionality of arcs of a circle to central and inscribed angles, and the

[1] *See p. 221 f.*

general solution of equations of the second degree by purely geometrical methods. Henceforth algebraical geometry would have a sound basis, which Archimedes and Apollonios knew how to exploit.

ARITHMETIC

The arithmetical Books of the *Elements* are the oldest extant texts on the theory of whole numbers and remained the most rigorous writings on this subject until the beginning of the nineteenth century.

Book VII continues the discussion in Book V of the theory of ratios, but applies them exclusively to commensurables. Its approach is, moreover, far less incisive. The Book as a whole is based on the following considerations: numbers being magnitudes, they can be assumed, without any explicit postulate or proof, to have the general properties of all magnitudes—existence, uniqueness, commutativity, and associativity. It is on these intuitional properties and on the discrete nature of whole numbers that all the proofs are based. This discrete character is expressed in two main axioms: (1) unity 'measures' every number, and (2) below any given number there exists only a finite series of numbers. It is from the second axiom that Euclid derived his algorithm for determining the greatest common measure of two numbers by approximate simplification of fractions. This algorithm, the basic tool of elementary number theory, thus made its first appearance in connection with the theory of proportions. It was used subsequently by Aristarchos of Samos and by Archimedes, and was also the basis of the theory of continuous fractions which was to play so important a role from the seventeenth century onwards. Book VI also contains propositions about numbers prime to one another, and discusses prime numbers in much the same way as elementary textbooks still do. The final propositions (33–39) are directed to the problem of finding the least common multiple of two or three numbers.

Book VIII, which is much more homogeneous than Book VII, is almost entirely devoted to geometric progressions. Its main object is to establish a general criterion as to whether the nth roots of integers or fractions are rational.

Book IX consists on the one hand of outworn propositions on odd and even numbers based on weak arguments, and on the other hand of subtle and elegant solutions including the proof that the series of prime numbers is infinite. It also gives the criterion for *perfect numbers*.

IRRATIONALS

Book X, the largest of all, contains 114 propositions! Its study makes great demands on modern mathematicians, who are, however, amply repaid for the trouble they may take over it. Its main object is to make a careful classification of irrational straight lines, based on the method of applying areas to any assigned straight line, assumed to be rational.

Many scholars have attributed this Book to Theaetetos, the hero of one of Plato's dialogues. Now, though a number of its simplest propositions may, in fact, have been written in the fourth century, the Book as a whole is clearly the work of a professional mathematician, closer to Apollonios than to Archimedes.

The first proposition, which may be due to Eudoxos, is the basis of the method of exhaustion which we shall discuss below. This is how it was formulated:

Two unequal magnitudes being set out, if, from the greater there be subtracted a magnitude greater than its half, and from that which is left a magnitude greater than *its* half, and if this process be repeated continually, there will be left some magnitude which will be less than the lesser magnitude set out.

The next three propositions use Euclid's algorithm for finding the G.C.M. of two or three numbers, to show that whenever the process does not come to an end the magnitudes are incommensurable. There follow some general propositions on magnitudes, and the rest of the Book is devoted to line segments. It investigates every possible variety of straight line which can be represented by $\sqrt{(\sqrt{a}+\sqrt{b})}$ where a and b are two commensurable lines. It then goes on to simplify and classify the results. Proposition 36 is the beginning of Euclid's classification of compound irrationals, the first of which was called 'binomial', a term which has survived in modern mathematical language.

SPACE

Book XI opens Euclid's study of solid geometry. What little we know of the work of Archytas and Eudoxos makes it probable that this Book combined fourth-century knowledge of this subject with some fifth-century developments.

Of the initial definitions, those concerning spheres, cones and cylinders all involve the concept of motion, for these bodies are said to be generated respectively by the rotation of a semicircle about its base, of a right triangle about one of its legs, and of a rectangle about one of its sides. Such kinematic considerations were entirely absent in the previous books. The first three propositions are easily shown to be inadequate and they are, in fact, postulates. They state that:

A part of a straight line cannot be in the plane of reference and another part in another plane.

If two straight lines cut one another, they are in one single plane; and every triangle is in one plane.

If two planes cut one another, their common section is a straight line.

However, the Book as a whole—concerned with parallel straight lines, planes at right angles to one another, solid angles and parallelepipeds—is of a high standard. It is remarkable for its complete neglect of the related notions of direction and symmetry.

Book XII deals with the areas of circles and the volumes of pyramids, cones, cylinders and spheres, on the basis of the method of exhaustion, which, according to Archimedes' formal statement, goes back to Eudoxos. The Book does not discuss the problem of squaring the circle or duplicating solid figures, but merely defines their ratios:

Circles are to one another as the squares on their diameters.

Every prism which has a triangular base is divisible into three pyramids equal to one another.

Spheres are to one another in the triplicate ratio of their respective diameters.

The equivalence of two volumes is proved by showing that the first is neither greater nor smaller than the second, *i.e.* by the method of exhaustion (Prop. 1, Book X) which, in effect, amounts to proving that what difference there may be between the two volumes is too small to be significant.

PLATONIC BODIES

Book XIII, which is very elegant and highly technical, is entirely devoted to Plato's five regular polyhedra.

In the second century B.C., Hypsicles added a Fourteenth Book which deals with the relations between a dodecahedron and an icosahedron inscribed in the same sphere. The author admits in his preface that the subject had been previously investigated by Aristarchos and by Apollonios. The Byzantines added a rather poor Fifteenth Book, also dealing with Platonic bodies. It consists of two parts, one apparently written in the fifth century A.D. and the other later still.

MINOR OR LOST WORKS

The list of other books attributed to Euclid is very great, though only some of these are extant. Among the latter is the *Data*, a sort of complement to the *Elements* though more analytical in character. The work contains ninety-four propositions, the first of which treat of the properties of proportional magnitudes, or of proportional increases, *i.e.* of the properties of linear functions. The following, more geometrical, propositions deal with similar figures, the application of areas (*i.e.* the solution of second-degree equations) and with circles. All in all, the work is fairly elementary.

According to Pappos' rather vague account, Euclid's *Porisms*, which are lost, were of a much higher standard. From Pappos' descriptions modern mathematicians, and particularly Simson and Chasles, have tried to reconstruct that work, though their reconstruction, like all such attempts, is highly hypothetical. Even so, they seem to have shown convincingly that, in his *Porisms*, Euclid tackled a number of problems related to projective geometry and the theory of transversals, such as were studied by mathematicians during the first half of the nineteenth century.

Euclid also wrote two other lost works: the *Conics* and the *Surface Loci*, which we shall have occasion to mention later.

ARCHIMEDES

In 212 B.C., during the sack of his native town, Roman soldiers killed Archimedes, the 75-year-old sage of Syracuse. Archimedes was famous for his mathematical writings, his mechanical inventions and for the brilliant way in which he defended his country.

The following of his writings (in as nearly chronological order as we can give) have come down to us:

> *On Plane Equilibrium*, Book I.
> *The Quadrature of the Parabola.*
> *On Plane Equilibrium*, Book II.
> *On the Sphere and Cylinder*, Books I and II.
> *On Spirals.*
> *On Conoids and Spheroids.*
> *On Floating Bodies*, Books I and II.
> *The Measurement of a Circle.*
> *The Sand Reckoner (Arenarius).*
> A letter to Eratosthenes on *The Method*, a kind of scientific testament in which he partly reveals the secrets of his discoveries.

In addition, a *Book of Lemmas*, translated from the Arabic, though apocryphal in its present form, nevertheless contains elegant if elementary propositions related to some of Archimedes' lost works.

According to Pappos, Archimedes was also the first to describe the thirteen semi-regular polyhedra, and he is said to have been the author of the famous 'Cattle Problem' (involving eight unknown quantities) which leads to the equation $x^2 - 4,729,494\, y^2 = 1$, y being a multiple of 9,314. The complete solution of the problem would have taken up 744 pages, each containing 2,600 numbers, so that

Archimedes naturally preferred to show what equations were involved and to leave it at that!

THE METHOD

The letter to Eratosthenes on *The Method*, which was discovered in 1907, is the key to Archimedes' main discoveries. It is chiefly from this and also from the chronological order of his writings, established from their prefaces, that we can form an approximate idea of his intellectual progress.

Familiar with the laws of statics (for it must be remembered that Syracuse was one of the main technical centres of the time), Archimedes assumed that all bodies have a centre of gravity, and he tried to formulate the laws governing them with a minimum of postulates in Book I of *On Plane Equilibrium*. That book gives clear evidence of his mathematical skill even though we may say, in general, that mechanical rather than mathematical considerations inspired his theories. In fact, it was on the basis of his laws of leverage that he began his studies of the centres of gravity of simple plane figures, and of the triangle in particular.

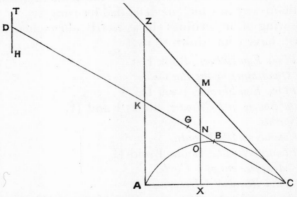

fig. 27 Archimedes' quadrature of a segment of the parabola.

In the course of these studies, he arrived at procedures which were to lead mathematics into the most fruitful paths. To illustrate this point, we shall look at his letter to Eratosthenes (*Method*, Proposition 1), in which he discussed the squaring of a segment of the parabola, the first quadrature which he had been able to perform precisely.

Let ABC be a segment of a parabola. Draw the straight line AZ parallel to the axis of the parabola, and draw also the tangent to the parabola CZ. Then draw XM parallel to the axis, to meet the parabola at O and the tangent at M, so that, as Archimedes knew, OX.AC = AX.XM, and OX.KC = KN.XM.

This last relation put him in mind of the balance. He produced CK to D, making DK = KC, and took a straight line TH = OX and placed it with its centre of gravity at D. Since TH = OX and DK = KC, it follows that TH.DK = KN.XM, whence it is evident that TH must balance XM about the fulcrum K according to the law of levers. But all possible lines OX make up the segment of the parabola, and all possible lines XM form the triangle ACZ. Therefore the entire area of the segment, if placed at D with its centre of gravity on D, will balance the entire triangle ACZ, whose centre of gravity is at G (one-third of the distance KC from K). Since DK = KC, KG is one-third DK, and it follows that the area of the triangle must be three times that of the segment.

These inductive steps, which Archimedes also used for a host of other quadratures described in *The Method*, call for two comments: (1) Archimedes was no purist and had no scruples about introducing fruitful mechanical analogies into geometry, and (2) he realized that any area could be represented by a series of parallel lines, any volume by a series of planes, and any continuous figure in general by an infinite sum of indivisible parts.

In the seventeenth century, when Cavalieri used the same approach, Archimedes' method proved fruitful once again. Unfortunately, the otherwise brilliant Italian mathematician kept somewhat too strictly to the letter of his illustrious predecessor's work and hence failed to provide a rigorous synthesis of his intuitive step. Now, Archimedes himself did, in fact, go on to make that synthesis—another clear proof of his brilliance.

THE PARABOLA

In his *Quadrature of the Parabola* he showed how this synthesis was made. While at first using the same figure which he had submitted to Eratosthenes, he no longer analysed the segment of the parabola into an infinity of straight lines. Instead, he inscribed and circumscribed it with two series of trapezia and then showed, by Eudoxos' method of exhaustion, that the segment is neither smaller nor larger than one-third of the triangle.

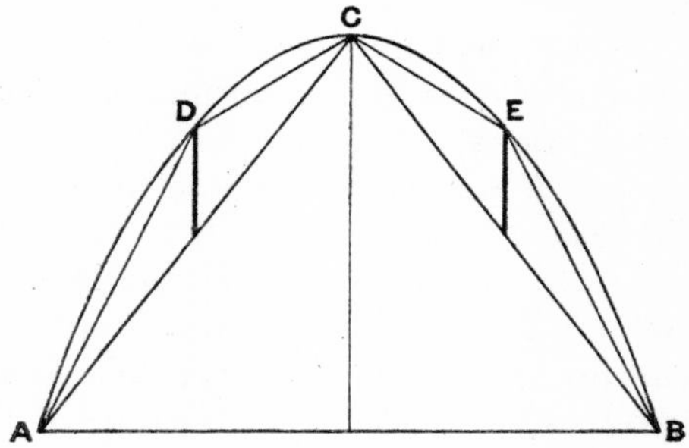

fig. 28 Archimedes' quadrature of the parabola.

His rigorous proof was nevertheless still based on mechanical principles and hence did not fully satisfy him. He therefore gave a purely geometrical proof, in which he simply *exhausted* the parabolic segment by Eudoxos' method:

ACB is a segment of a parabola, whose tangents are parallel to AB at C, to AC at D, and to BC at E. The triangles ADC and CEB, which are congruent, are each equal in area to $\frac{1}{8}$ the area of the triangle ACB.

Repeating this process, and showing that the series $1 + \frac{1}{4} + \frac{1}{16} + \ldots$ has the limit $\frac{4}{3}$ (though he did not use modern terms), Archimedes demonstrated that the segment cannot be either greater or smaller than $\frac{4}{3}$ times the area of the triangle ABC.

Book II of *On Plane Equilibrium* discusses the centres of gravity of parabolic segments, and gives a series of increasingly rigorous proofs, all based on the inscription of triangles in the segment. Archimedes begins by demonstrating on exhaustive principles that the centre of gravity must lie on the axis. Proposition 5 then gives a remarkable proof that the centre of gravity of the segment is nearer to the vertex of the segment than is that of the triangle inscribed over its base. This proof, which is the first recorded attempt to present a mathematical argument based on complete induction or recurrence, amounts to showing that, no matter how small we make the segment, its centre of gravity will always divide the diameter in the same ratio of 3:2.

Sphere and Cylinder

In his *Method*, Archimedes explains how mechanical considerations enabled him to find the ratio of a sphere to a cylinder circumscribed about it, and adds:

From the examination of that theorem, I conceived the notion that the surface of a sphere is four times as great as a great circle in it, for judging from the fact that any circle is equal to a triangle with base equal to the circumference and height equal to the radius of the circle, I apprehended that, in like manner, any sphere is equal to a cone with base equal to the surface of the sphere and height equal to the radius.

Archimedes had previously established these results in his *On the Sphere and Cylinder*, one of his most famous works. It begins with five assumptions:

(1) Of all lines which join the same two points, the straight line is the least.

(2) If there are two curved lines in a plane joining the same two points, and convex in the same direction so that one is wholly embraced by the other, then that which lies inside is the lesser of the two.

(3) Similarly, with surfaces whose limits coincide on the same plane, the plane surface is smaller than any other.

(4) Of two convex surfaces whose limits coincide on the same plane, and which are curved on the same side of that plane, the one that encloses the other is the greater.

(5) The postulate which we have already given (p. 275).

Assumptions 1 and 3 subsequently became the definitions of the straight line and of the plane of other mathematicians, such as of Heron of Alexandria. After the publication by Campanus (thirteenth century A.D.) of an edition of Euclid's *Elements*, the straight line came to be quite generally defined as the shortest distance between two points.

Using these definitions, Archimedes proceeded to show by strict application of the method of exhaustion that the surface of any cone or right cylinder is greater than that of the inscribed pyramid or prism, and smaller than that of the circumscribed pyramid or prism.

Hence he evaluated the surface areas of the cone and the right cylinder as proportions of the area of a corresponding circle, and not by means of formulae or independent figures, which were then thought to be the exclusive province of geodesy or applied geometry. On the whole, our own elementary texts, though they lack his rigour, have followed Archimedes' method in extending these findings to the evaluation of the area and volume of the sphere.

Book II goes on to treat various problems connected with spheres and cylinders according to the methods of algebraical geometry. In order to find a sphere of volume equal to that of a cone or a cylinder, Archimedes reduced the problem to that of finding two mean proportionals between two given lines. We shall see that this was also the method used by Apollonios in Book V of *The Conics*, and since neither mathematician bothered to explain this method (which is expounded in Eutocios' commentary on Archimedes) it must have been common practice in their day. The fact that the proportionals could not be constructed with ruler and compass was apparently considered no disadvantage.

Archimedes then went on to show how a given sphere can be cut by a plane so that the volumes of the segments may have a given ratio. This he did by dividing a line AB at X in such a way that

$(AX)^2:(XB)^2 = m:n$. Archimedes pointed out that, if this problem is propounded in this general form, it requires a *diorism* (the

investigation of its limits of possibility) which he promised to give later. Unfortunately, that explanation was either omitted or else it is lost.

This subject is also broached in the *On Conoids and Spheroids*, whose last proposition is, in fact, a diorism showing that of all the segments of a spheroid the hemisphere has the greatest volume.

CONOIDS AND SPHEROIDS

On Conoids and Spheroids introduces three new bodies of revolution: (1) the *spheroid*, which is produced by the revolution of an ellipse about one of its axes, and which is called *oblong* or *flat* according to whether it revolves about the major or minor axis; (2) the obtuse-angled conoid, which is produced by the rotation of a section of a hyperbola about its transverse axis; and (3) the right-angled conoid, produced by the rotation of a parabola about its axis. While *The Method* evaluates the ratio of the volumes of these bodies to those of cones by means of mechanical procedures, *On Conoids* deals with them by pure geometry.

Archimedes' procedure has a strong resemblance to the integral calculus. He inscribed and circumscribed the volumes under consideration with two series of cylinders, which could be made to differ less and less from each other and so approach the intermediate form to any desired degree of accuracy. To evaluate the results Archimedes used the inequalities

$$\frac{n^2}{2} < 1+2+3+ \ldots +n < \frac{(n+1)^2}{2}$$

and

$$\frac{n^3}{3} < 1+4+9+ \ldots +n^2 < \frac{(n+1)^3}{3}$$

He may thus be said to have used a form of integration based on his mechanical method of breaking figures down into parallel segments. In the *Conoids* he introduced this principle purely mathematically, combining an algorithm based on Pythagorean figured numbers with Eudoxos' method of exhaustion.

FLOATING BODIES

On Floating Bodies, Book I, laid the foundations of the science of hydrostatics. In his *Analytical Mechanics*, Lagrange has given an excellent summary of this work:

Archimedes based his experiments and hence his theories on two principles:

(1) That the character of fluids is such that the part under less thrust is driven along by the part under greater thrust, and that each part is compressed by the entire weight of the fluid which is above it.

(2) That bodies which are thrust upwards in a fluid are forced upward along a perpendicular line which passes through their centres of gravity.

From the first principle, Archimedes concluded first that the surface of a fluid, all of whose parts tend to move towards the centre of the earth, must be spherical if the fluid is to remain in equilibrium, and second that a body with the same weight as an equal volume of fluid will sink until it is just covered, since, if we consider two equal pyramids of the fluid in equilibrium about the centre of the earth, a pyramid which is partly immersed will exert a greater pressure on the centre of the earth, or in general on any spherical surface whatever above this centre, than the other. In the same way, Archimedes proved that if solids lighter than an equal volume of fluid are placed in a fluid, they will be immersed so that the weight of the solid will be equal to the weight of the fluid displaced; whence he deduced the two hydrostatic theorems: that if a solid lighter than a fluid be forcibly immersed in it, the solid will be driven upwards by a force equal to the difference between its weight and the weight of the fluid displaced, and that a solid heavier than a fluid, if placed in it, will be found lighter than its true weight by the weight of the fluid displaced.

Archimedes immediately seized upon the second principle to establish the law of equilibrium of floating bodies. He showed that every segment of a sphere lighter than an equal volume of fluid must necessarily float in the fluid with its axis vertical to the surface, since, were the base inclined, the weight of the projecting part, considered to be concentrated in its centre of gravity, and the vertical upthrust of the fluid, considered to be concentrated in the centre of gravity of the submerged part, would tend to turn the segment until its base assumed a horizontal position.

In Book II Archimedes applies the same principle to the equilibrium of a segment of a right-angled conoid, *i.e.* a paraboloid of revolution. He assumes implicitly that, for practical purposes, the water surface is a horizontal plane. The book as a whole is a delightful expression of Archimedes at his best, full of creative zest and anxious to give his readers intellectually stimulating exercises.

On Spirals

On Spirals is devoted to the study of a kinematically defined curve—the 'spiral of Archimedes'. The section on quadratures is treated in much the same way as it is in the *Spheroids*, and need not detain us here. On the other hand, the tangent propositions may be called the most ancient texts on the differential calculus.

For the Greek mathematicians a curve is generated by the movement of a point, and a first example is given by the definition of a spiral. Other examples are furnished by the curve of Hippias or Dinostratos, and the cylindrical spiral of Apollonios. According to Eutocios (reported by Diogenes Laertios), Archytas (fourth century) was the first to use motion for solving and describing geometrical problems; hence the kinematic method could not have been new to Archimedes. Apollonios, too, though he considered conics as plane sections, obtained them from the continuous motion of a straight line. On the other hand, in all known Greek texts a plane curve is always considered as the entire or partial boundary between two regions in a plane, of which one, 'the figure', is generally convex and may contain only line segments and not lines of unlimited length. Now, a tangent to a curve is a line of unlimited length and, though it is not contained by the 'figure', its existence must be demonstrated. It must also be shown—if it exists—that there can be only one tangent to any point on the curve, and that any other straight line meeting the curve must necessarily cut the figure. This problem was treated by three great Greek mathematicians: Euclid, who considered the case of the circle, Apollonios, who considered conics, and Archimedes, who considered spirals.

While the ancients were also greatly interested in left-handed curves, they left no texts dealing with their tangents.

Archimedes does not mention by what analytical steps he obtained the tangent to his spiral. However, that analysis was not nearly as delicate a task as his synthesis. For while it is fairly easy to prove that a particular straight line touches a circle externally at a particular point, it is much more difficult to establish that it is the only one which does so. Archimedes' argument was of characteristic lucidity and elegance but, characteristically, made great demands on his readers. In fact, he proved the proposition by replacing one transcendental problem with two others involving algebraic expressions higher than the second degree and left the rest to the reader, considering it too trivial for himself. Pappos has criticized him for this, but the remaining problem is, in fact, easily solved if one reduces the higher expressions to first degree equations, which is done nowadays by successive differentiation.

MEASUREMENT OF A CIRCLE

While *On Spirals* may be said to bear on the theoretical aspects of squaring the circle, the small *Measurement of a Circle* deals with the practical aspects and, moreover, provides an excellent example of Greek geodesy or practical geometry.

We know that the Egyptians equated the area of a circle with that of a square with a side 8/9 its diameter, giving $\pi = 256/81 \simeq 3\frac{1}{6}$. The most accurate Babylonian figure was 3,7,30 (in sexagesimal notation), which is $3\frac{1}{8}$. Although there are no extant texts to this effect, we have every reason to assume that the Greeks arrived at similar figures.

Proposition 1 of *Measurement of a Circle* proves that the two problems of rectifying and squaring the circle are identical. More precisely, it uses the method of exhaustion to show that a circle is equivalent to a right-angled triangle in which one of the sides about the right angle is equal to the radius, and the other to the circumference of the circle. Proposition 2 then shows that if the circumference is $3\frac{1}{7}$ the diameter, then the area of a circle is to the square of its diameter as 11 is to 14. Proposition 3 shows that the ratio of the circumference to the diameter is less than $3\frac{1}{7}$ but greater than $3\frac{10}{71}$. (The latter value is correct to within $\frac{1}{500}$.)

The weak point of third-century Greek arithmetic was the absence of systematic fractions. (It was only in the second century that astronomers adopted the Babylonian sexagesimal system.) Hence Archimedes was forced to use common fractions throughout his work. While he handled these with his customary skill, he omitted to fill in the 'trivial' details. Thus he adopted, without further explanations, $\sqrt{3} < \frac{1351}{780}$ and $> \frac{265}{153}$, two excellent approximations, obtained by continuous fractions.

NOTATION: THE *Arenarius*

The last of Archimedes' treatises which we shall examine here, the *Arenarius* (or *Sand Reckoner*), deals with notational problems. The Greeks used two methods of writing down numbers. In the Attic or Herodian system, which was similar to the Roman, the letters I, Π, Δ, H, X, M stood for 1, 5, 10, 100, 1,000, and 10,000, respectively. Hence, for instance, the numbers 6, 14, 50 and 2,541 would be written as:

$$\text{ΠI; ΔIIII: } \boxed{\Delta}\text{ ; XX } \boxed{H} \text{ ΔΔΔΔI}$$

Like the later Roman numerals, the Attic numerals were extremely clumsy when it came to complicated calculations, which had to be performed on counting-frames and similar devices.

It was probably in the middle of the fifth, and above all in the third century, that the Greeks began to use, *inter alia*, a decimal and semi-positional notation. In it, nine letters of the Greek alphabet represented the first nine numbers, nine other letters represented the tens, and another nine letters the hundreds. Thousands were expressed by unit letters with a mark below the letter. Thus 1, 10, 100,

1,000 and 274 were expressed respectively by: α; ι; ρ; ϙ and σοδ. Ten thousands were expressed by the letter M with the multiple above. Thus 40,000 was written $\overset{\delta}{M}$. In the course of time, this notation was modified a great deal. Diophantos, for instance, separated ten thousands from thousands by a simple point, *e.g.* τϛ.ϑ̇ = 3,069,000.

Archimedes set himself the task of developing this system of notation which, though less practical than ours, was nevertheless a great improvement on the Attic. He managed to express a number which, in our notation, would require 800 million cyphers. The pretext for this exercise was to find the number of grains of sand contained in the universe and, incidentally, to give a succinct account of the astronomical system of Aristarchos of Samos (see below).

Archimedes' method of expressing very large numbers was not adopted by later mathematicians, who preferred Apollonios' much simpler method of using powers of 10,000, which we have described. That notation, subsequently augmented with sexagesimal fractions, remained the chief tool of all mathematicians and astronomers until the introduction of the so-called Arabic numerals. Even when Arab mathematicians had adopted a place-value notation, Arab astronomers preferred the old Greek system, though they substituted their own alphabet. Meanwhile the West, after its rupture with the Eastern Empire, continued to use the exceedingly cumbersome Roman notation.

APOLLONIOS

Apollonios of Perga, the 'Great Geometer', lived at Alexandria, Ephesos and Pergamos from about the middle of the third to the beginning of the second century. Of his main work, the *Conics*, the first seven of the eight books have come down to us, four in the original Greek and three in an Arabic translation.

His many other works, not one of which is extant, are known mainly from Pappos' commentaries. They were: *On the Cutting Off of a Ratio, On the Cutting Off of an Area, On Determinate Section, On Inclinations, On Plane Loci, On Contacts,* and the *Ocytocion* (containing a more practical system of notation than Archimedes', and possibly the one which prevailed in Greece). Geminos also mentions a work called *On the Cochlias* which dealt with the cylindrical helix, and Marinos of Naples speaks of a critical *Universal Treatise* on the foundations of mathematics, fragments of which have found their way into Proclos' *Commentary* on Euclid, Book I, and also into the *Definitions*, attributed to Heron.

21 Etruscan haruspicy

22 The Athens 'Tower of the Winds'

THE CONICS

We have described the earliest references to conic sections in the work of Menaechmos, Aristaeos and Euclid. Study of the works of Archimedes shows that the theory was already far advanced. The conic sections were associated with acute-angled, right-angled, and obtuse-angled cones, the terms 'ellipse', 'parabola' and 'hyperbola' being introduced by Apollonios, who showed that the three curves could be obtained as sections of the same cone.

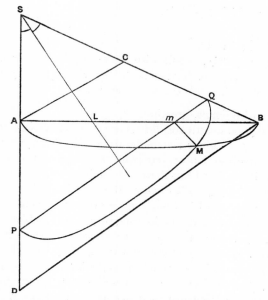

fig. 29 The classical theory of conics before Apollonios.

In *fig. 29*, let the acute-angled cone with vertex S, axis AL, and generatrix SA be cut by the plane AMB, perpendicular to SA. From M, the point we wish to study, draw Mm perpendicular to the plane ASB, *i.e.* to the diameter PQ of the circular section passing through M, and lying on the axis AB of the section under consideration. From Euclid, we know that $(mM)^2 = mP . mQ$. But $mP:BD = mA:AB$, and $mQ:AC = mB:AB$. Whence: $(mM)^2:mA . mB = BD . AC:(AB)^2$. Since $BD:AB = 2AL:AC$, we can also put: $(mM)^2:mA . mB = 2AL:AB$. We may state the result obtained by the Greeks in modern terms as follows: In the section of the acute-angled cone, the ratio of the square of the ordinate to the rectangle formed by the two abscissae on the diameter is twice the ratio of the part of the diameter as far as the axis to the whole diameter.

When the Greeks considered points in a plane, their algebraic geometry enabled them to reduce first and second degree equations to a canonical form which they now saw how to apply to the conic sections. Once that fact was appreciated, the kinematic definition of conoids of revolution was abundantly plain.

Our remarks on the parabola have shown how highly developed the theory of conics had become in Archimedes' day. We have also seen to what extent Archimedes may be said to have anticipated Newton's method of fluxions.

The Conics, BOOKS I–IV

In Book I of his *Conics*, Apollonios systematized and generalized the work of his predecessors. The general preface to the second (the only extant) edition makes this quite clear:

Apollonios to Eudemos, greeting.

If you are in good health and things are in other respects as you wish, it is well; with me two things are moderately well. During the time I spent with you at Pergamos I observed your eagerness to become acquainted with my work in conics; I am therefore sending you the first book, which I have corrected, and I will forward the remaining books when I have finished them to my satisfaction. I dare say you have not forgotten my telling you that I undertook the investigation of this subject at the request of Naucrates, the geometer, at the time when he came to Alexandria and stayed with me. When I had covered the ground in eight books I gave them to him at once—in too much haste because he was on the point of sailing and they had therefore not been thoroughly revised; indeed, I had put down everything just as it occurred to me, postponing revision till the end. Accordingly I now publish, as opportunities serve from time to time, instalments of the work as they are corrected. In the meantime it has happened that some other persons also, among those whom I have met, have got the first and second books before they were corrected; do not be surprised therefore if you come across them in a different form.

Now, of the eight books the first four form an elementary introduction. The first contains the modes of producing the three sections in the opposite parts (of the hyperbola), and the fundamental properties subsisting in them worked out more fully and generally than in the writings of others. The second book contains the properties of the diameters and the axes of the sections as well as of the asymptotes, with other things generally and necessarily used for determining limits of possibility (*diorismoi*); and what I mean by the diameters and axes respectively you will learn from this book. The third book contains many remarkable theorems useful for the syntheses of solid loci and for *diorismoi*; most of these theorems, and the most beautiful, are new, and it was their discovery which made me aware that Euclid did not work out the synthesis of the locus with respect to three and four lines, but only a chance portion of it, and that not success-fully; for it was not possible for this synthesis to be completed without the aid of the additional theorems discovered by me. The fourth book shows in how many ways the sections of cones can meet one another and the circumference of a circle; it contains other things in addition, none of which has been discussed by earlier writers, namely, the question of in how many points a section of a cone or the circumference of a circle can meet a double-branched hyperbola, or how two double-branched hyper-bolae can meet one another.

The rest of the books are more by way of appendices; one of them deals somewhat fully with *minima* and *maxima*, another with equal and similar sections of cones, another with theorems of the nature and determination of limits, and the last with determinate conic problems. But, of course, when all of them are published it will be open to all who read them to form their own judgements about them, according to their individual opinions. Farewell.[1]

Apollonios' reference to 'the locus with respect to three or four lines' deserves our special attention, since these lines became the basis of Descartes' geometry in the seventeenth century. They were discussed in detail by Pappos:

If from a given point straight lines be drawn to meet three straight lines given in position at a given angle, and if the ratio of the rectangle contained by two of these straight lines to the square of the third is given, the point will lie on a solid locus given in position, *i.e.* on one of the three conic lines. Again, if straight lines be drawn to meet four straight lines of given position at a given angle, and if the ratio of the rectangle contained by two of these to the rectangle contained by the other two is given, the point will also lie on a conic section of given position.

The preface to Book IV tells us that the Book itself is based on the work of Conon, an Alexandrian mathematician and astronomer and a friend of Archimedes. Nicotelos of Cyrene, who is otherwise un-known, questioned the value of Conon's work, thus giving clear proof of the intense interest in conics in his day.

Books V–VIII

Books V, VI and VII were not known in the West until the middle of the seventeenth century. The first Latin translation was published in 1662, when, by curious chance, Huygens had just presented the theory of involutes as an aid to horology. Book V dealt with just that

[1] Adapted from Heath's translation.

question, though in quite a different spirit. For while the Dutch genius had come to his discovery from applied mathematics, Apollonios had arrived at it by a detailed examination of a problem in pure geometry. This is how he put it himself:

In this fifth book I have laid down propositions relating to *maximum* and *minimum* straight lines. You must be aware that my predecessors and contemporaries have but briefly investigated the shortest lines, and have only proved which straight lines touch the sections and, conversely, by virtue of what properties they are tangents. For my part, I have proved these properties in the first book (without however making any use, in the proofs, of the doctrine of the shortest lines), inasmuch as I wished to connect them closely with that part of the subject in which I treat of the production of the three conic sections, the better to show that in each of the three sections countless properties and necessary results appear, with respect to the original (transverse) diameter. I have separated the propositions in which I discuss the shortest lines into classes, and I have dealt with each individual case by careful demonstration; I have also related this investigation to the investigation of the maximum lines above mentioned, because I considered that those who pursue this science need these for obtaining an understanding of the analysis and the determination of the limits of possibility of problems, as well as for their synthesis. In addition, the subject is one of those which seem worthy of study for their own sake.

This book, together with the fifth book of Euclid and with Archimedes' *Method* and *Spirals*, is one of the greatest masterpieces of Greek geometry. It makes very difficult reading, mainly because of Apollonios' meticulous synthetic approach. Nevertheless, the argument is simple enough and developed with rare brilliance. The book deals with normals to conics regarded as maximum and minimum straight lines, and considers various points and classes of points from which such lines can be drawn to the conics, *i.e.* as the feet of normals to the curve. The points through which only three (and not the usual four) normals can be drawn, since two of the normals coincide, are constructed by a method which is tantamount to assuming that they satisfy, for instance, the equation

$$(ax)^{2/3} + (by)^{2/3} = (a^2 + b^2)^{2/3}$$

and for the case of the ellipse

$$\frac{x^2}{a^2} + \frac{y^2}{b^2} = 1.$$

Modern mathematicians would thence have deduced the existence of an evolute of the ellipse, but Apollonios failed to do so, possibly because he could find no kinematic method of describing the curve.

Book VII, finally, gives the two 'theorems of Apollonios' on conjugate diameters.

OTHER WORKS OF APOLLONIOS

Apollonios' lost works, which sixteenth-, seventeenth- and eighteenth-century mathematicians have tried to reconstruct more or less successfully, are known to us from Pappos' commentaries. The two books of *On the Cutting Off of a Ratio*, dealt with the general problem: Given two straight lines parallel to each other or intersecting, and a fixed point on each line, to draw through a given point a straight line which shall cut off segments from each line bearing a given ratio to one another. *On the Cutting Off of an Area* dealt with the same problem, except that the two segments had to be constructed into a rectangle of given area. In other words, both works dealt with the tangential properties of conics, while *On Plane Loci* dealt with the kinematic properties of the conics themselves.

According to Pappos, the two books of *On Determinate Section* discussed other problems of a similar type, *i.e.* problems involving second-degree equations, to which Greek algebraic geometry lent itself particularly well.

The *Inclinations* (two books) dealt with a problem developed in Archimedes' *Spirals*: Given two straight or curved lines and a point, to draw through the point a straight line such that the given lines cut off a segment of given length. In algebraic form, the resulting equations are usually of degree higher than 2, and were called solid (degree 3 and 4) or linear (degree higher than 4). According to Pappos, Apollonios considered only the class of problems which could be solved by the plane method (degree 1 or 2).

On Contacts discussed the following: Given three things, each of which may be a point, a straight line, or a circle, to draw a circle which shall pass through each of the given points (so far as it is points that are given) and touch the straight lines or circles.

On Plane Loci (two books) dealt with linear and circular loci. In modern terms, most of the contents of the first book can be said to have treated of the homothetic, translational, rotational, similar and inversional transformations of plane loci. The book also showed that the locus of points whose distances from any number of straight lines bear a linear relation to one another is a straight line. Book II dealt with the following problems: If from two given points A, B, two straight lines are drawn to a point P, then (1) if $AP^2 - BP^2$ is given, the locus of P is a straight line; (2) if AP, BP are in a given ratio, the locus is a straight line or a circle; and (3) if AP^2 'is greater by a given ratio than a given ratio' to BP^2, *i.e.* if $AP^2 = a^2 + m \cdot BP^2$, the locus is a circle in position.

SPHERICS AND TRIGONOMETRY

The Greeks were the inventors not only of conic sections but also of trigonometry, though their progress here was much slower. The reason is easy to find: while algebraic geometry, which was a Greek adaptation of Babylonian arithmetic, lent itself admirably to the study of plane geometry including conics, it could not be applied to spherical geometry and hence to trigonometry. We shall see how Hellenistic mathematicians overcame the difficulties in their path.

SPHERICS
In the fourth century, the discovery of the sphericity of the heavens and of the earth led to the birth of a new science: spherics. Autolycos' *On the Moving Sphere* and Euclid's *Phenomena* are nearly conclusive evidence that Eudoxos and his school must have consulted a manual of the fixed sphere.

Both works dealt with the discrepancies in the risings and settings of the signs of the Zodiac and similar problems, and their conclusions were used in such works as Hypsicles' *On Ascensions* which, in the second century, became the basis of crude but fairly satisfactory astronomical calculations and clearly required some knowledge of spherical geometry.

In fact, we have an elementary treatise on the subject, namely three books by Theodosios which go back to about 200 B.C., but which are based on an earlier tradition, including Euclid's *Elements*.

But while spherical geometry was known, trigonometry was not, though the first signs of it had appeared in the works of Aristarchos, in Archimedes' *Arenarius*, in the *Optics* attributed to Euclid and in Dinostratos' quadratrix. In particular, all these writers had noticed that, for $0 < x < \pi/2$, the function sine $x:x$ approaches zero, and the function tan $x:x$ approaches infinity.

STEREOGRAPHIC PROJECTION
Moreover, Apollonios had suggested the method of projecting spheres on planes in *Conics*, I. (Synesios of Cyrene attributed the actual discovery of the method to Hipparchos who lived just after Apollonios.) Stereographic projection was used in the construction of that remarkable astronomical instrument, the plane astrolabe, described by Philoponos in the fifth century A.D., which the Arabs took over from the Greeks. One part of the instrument was called the 'spider', and since Vitruvius mentions that a clock by that name was said to have been invented by Apollonios, we have reason to believe that Apollonios may have invented that astrolabe as well.

Remarkable in itself though the theory of stereographic projection was (today it is a particular case of inversion in space), its exponents lacked the necessary means of calculation.

Now the construction of a table of chords, an indispensable tool in trigonometry, is attributed to Hipparchos. We do not know on what principles it was based, but the ninety-third proposition in the critical edition of Euclid's *Data* might well have served his purpose. In any case, this proposition enables one to construct a sine table of the kind worked out by the Hindu mathematician, Âryabhaṭa, at the beginning of the fourth century A.D. But all this is so much speculation, and it is only at the end of the first century A.D. that we have any definite evidence of trigonometrical investigations, in the work of Menelaos of Alexandria.

THE CONTRIBUTION OF MENELAOS

Menelaos, an astronomer who flourished in Rome in 98, was the author of a (lost) work *On the Calculation of Chords*, and a treatise in three books, the *Spherics*, which has come down to us in Arabic translation.

The first book of the *Spherics* may be considered the first two-dimensional non-Euclidean geometry. In it the great circle plays the same role as does the straight line in plane geometry. The book defines spherical triangles, called 'three-sides', cases of congruency between them, and the relations between their sides and angles. No distinction is made between congruency and similarity.

Book II is more astronomical, and Book III deals with spherical trigonometry as such, the only kind of trigonometry studied systematically by the Greeks. It is based on Menelaos' two theorems on the plane and on the sphere.

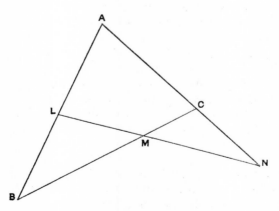

fig. 30 Menelaos' plane theorem.

If, as in *fig. 30*, the plane triangle ABC is cut by the line LMN, Menelaos' proposition in plane geometry shows that

$$LA : LB = (NA : NC)(MC : MB).$$

This proposition may well have been based on Euclid's *Porisms*, but its real importance was only brought out when Menelaos applied it to his theorem for the sphere.

For, if ABC is a spherical triangle and LMN an arc of the great circle, the Greek geometer showed that:

$$\text{chord of 2 LA} : \text{chord of 2 LB} = \frac{\text{chord of 2 NA}}{\text{chord of 2 NC}} \cdot \frac{\text{chord of 2 MC}}{\text{chord of 2 MB}}.$$

Menelaos deduced a host of consequences from this theorem, which for centuries was to remain the master-key to trigonometry, a Greek science which was not to be given its (Greek) name until the dawn of the seventeenth century.

PTOLEMY'S CONTRIBUTION

The best preserved documents on Hellenistic trigonometry are Chapters 9 and 11 of Book I of Ptolemy's great *Syntaxis* or *Almagest*, written during the second half of the second century A.D. This is how Chapter 9 begins:

How to obtain the lengths of chords inscribed in a circle.

For speedy practice, we shall now construct a table of values of these chords by dividing the circumference into 360 degrees. Our table will list all the arcs by half degrees and for each of the arcs we shall show the values of the subtending chord by dividing the diameter into 120 equal parts. It will appear that this number is the most convenient. We shall show, first of all, how by the uniform use of the smallest possible number of propositions, we may obtain a general and speedy method of obtaining these values. We shall not confine ourselves to giving a table of values, but we shall show an easy means of proving and verifying these values, by demonstrating how they were obtained. We shall employ the sexagesimal system of notation, to avoid the embarrassment of fractions; and in our multiplications and divisions we shall always take the nearest result, so that what we neglect will not in any way affect the appreciable correctness of our figures.

After having shown, by an elegant construction based on Euclid, how to inscribe a pentagon and decagon in a circle, Ptolemy demonstrates that their sides are respectively $70^p\ 32'\ 3''$ and $37^p\ 4'\ 55''$ (where p refers to the parts marked on the diameter). Similarly, he evaluates the side of the inscribed hexagon, square, and equilateral triangle.

He goes on to establish, by what has remained a classic method, the theorem bearing his name, namely that, in an inscribed quadrilateral, the product of the two diagonals equals the sum of the products of the opposite sides. (The theorem itself may well go back to Menelaos or to an even earlier author.) From it, he could calculate the chord of the difference or sum of two arcs, the chords of each of which were known individually.

This theorem will help to find most of the other chords corresponding to arcs measured in half-degrees. . . . We shall find by calculation that chord $1\frac{1}{2}°$ contains approximately 1^p 34' 15" of the parts of which the diameter contains 120, and that chords $\frac{1}{2}°$ and $\frac{1}{4}°$ contain 0^p 47' 8".

Ptolemy had to evaluate chord $1°$ by interpolation, incidentally giving an elegant demonstration of the propositions of Aristarchos and of Archimedes that (in modern terms) sine $x{:}x$ is a decreasing function of the arc. He showed, in fact, from comparisons with arcs $1\frac{1}{2}°$ and $\frac{3}{4}°$, that chord $1°$ must be both smaller and greater than 1^p 2' 50", which is the value he adopted.

To appreciate just how accurate this value is, we need only consider the length of chord $1°$ as the length of the arc and multiply it by 360 to obtain the length of the circumference. We find that $\pi = 3° 8' 30''$ (or $3 + \frac{8}{60} + \frac{1}{120}$), a value almost identical with 3.1416. It is in fact correct to three sexagesimal places.

Henceforth, Greek trigonometry was truly established. It was based on sexagesimal fractions, and on tables rigorously computed. Its main object of study was always the sphere, to which Menelaos' theorem applied particularly well. This theorem, which involved the chord not of an arc, but of the double arc, paved the way for the later appearance of the sine. The main fault of this early kind of trigonometry was its failure to develop adequate algorithms. Nevertheless, the main step had been taken, and the successors—Hindus, Arabs, Europeans—had simply to follow along the trail which the Greeks had blazed for them.

GEODESY: HERON OF ALEXANDRIA

Before we discuss the creative contribution of the last of the great Greek mathematicians, Diophantos, we shall quickly glance at some of the more elementary works on applied mathematics, commencing with those of Heron of Alexandria.

Heron, to whom we owe much of our knowledge of the history of Greek mechanics, physics and above all technology, was also an important historian of geodesy or practical geometry. Now, geodesy together with logistic or numerical calculation had always been the basis of all mathematical studies. Among the vast collection of texts on geodesy, chiefly Byzantine, which form the so-called Heronian collection, Heron's own work is of a much higher standard than that of the other contributors. His birth date is rather uncertain, and all we can say is that he lived after Apollonios and before Pappos, *i.e.* between *c.* 150 B.C. and A.D. 250, though, from Heron's evaluation of the distance between Rome and Alexandria by means of two observations of an eclipse of the moon, O. Neugebauer has concluded that he must have lived in A.D. 62 and hence have been a contemporary of Menelaos.

METRICS

His own authentic work on geodesy, the *Metrics*, a work in three books, was not discovered until 1896. Book I deals with measurements of areas, Book II with volumes, and Book III with the division of areas and volumes in given ratios and under various conditions. Each book has an introduction, and all the problems are arranged in order of difficulty.

While the statement of each problem involves numerical data, the proof itself is usually presented in a Euclidean or geometric manner. In most cases his proof is tantamount to reducing the problem to another, previously solved, and assumes acquaintance with Euclid's *Elements*, which are not, however, explicitly mentioned. Nevertheless, Heron solved many problems by other methods, particularly those whose scope went beyond the *Elements*, in which case he generally referred the reader to the relevant theorems of Archimedes and, in the volume on the torus and for the chord tables, to Apollonios and Dionysodoros.

Among his most remarkable results was the proof of what is now called the 'formula of Heron', *viz.* $\triangle = \sqrt{[s(s-a)(s-b)(s-c)]}$, whereby the area of a triangle is expressed as a function of its sides. Unlike his great predecessors, Heron had no objection to expressing the product of two or more areas, probably because he worked with numbers, that is with measurements rather than with the magnitudes themselves. His extremely elegant proof of the formula strikes one as based on prior geometrical demonstration, rather than being an original discovery. In effect, his formula may be said to be the result of steps in numerical logistic similar to those by which modern mathematicians could solve the same problem using 'specious logistic'. In that case, Heron would have expressed an otherwise unknown trend of mathematical thought, going back to Babylonian procedures.

Another interesting aspect of the *Metrics* is found in Book III, which contains such problems as the division of a triangle into parts having a given ratio, by a straight line passing (a) through the vertex, (b) parallel to one side, and (c) through any point in one side. This book has much in common with a little book *On Divisions* attributed to Euclid and also with Babylonian texts. Moreover, its subject-matter was to be treated by Arab and European mathematicians in the twelfth and thirteenth centuries, by Tartaglia in the sixteenth, and by all modern elementary textbooks. It may well be that the methods of applying areas and of Greek algebraic geometry were developments of such simple themes, the final fruits of which were the masterpieces of Euclid, of Archimedes and, above all, of Apollonios, whose lost work *On Cutting Off an Area* mentions the subject by name.

ACOUSTICS

The Greeks have left us only two works on acoustics: the *Division of the Canon*, written at the beginning of the Hellenistic period and attributed to Euclid, and Ptolemy's *Harmonics*.

The very brief Euclidean text follows the mathematical tradition begun by Eudoxos in astronomy and adopted by physicists, especially at the turn of the nineteenth century. Whenever a phenomenon or a series of phenomena cannot be explained, a plausible hypothesis is put forward and its mathematical consequences are investigated. If, as the Greeks were wont to say, the hypothesis 'saved the appearances', all was well; if not, it had to be modified or rejected.

The *Division of the Canon* puts forward the following hypotheses. Sound is invariably associated with motion, the pitch of the emitted sound varying with the number of motions occurring in a given time. Sound is therefore thought to consist of distinct entities, the sizes of which are in commensurable proportions to one another. Certain sounds are simple and give a pure note: these are the exact multiples and simple fractions. Harmonious sounds correspond to simple ratios, and the mathematical consequences of this assumption are then investigated. The last part of the work, which deals with stringed instruments, assumes that the number of vibrations is inversely proportional to the length of the vibrating string.

Ptolemy's *Harmonics*, in three books, is a much more comprehensive work. In it, he presents, criticizes and develops the various musical theories of his day, and then goes on to psychological discussions and to a mystical comparison of sound with the 'music of the spheres', based on astrological ideas and on Pythagorean and Platonic theories.

OPTICS AND PERSPECTIVE

In optics, the main Hellenistic texts that have come down to us are
Euclid's *Optics*, Heron's *Catoptrics*, another *Catoptrics* by a pseudo-
Euclid (Theon of Alexandria?), and Ptolemy's *Optics*. Of these four
works, the most remarkable are the first and the last.

All these authors believed that the eye emits visual rays which are
propagated with great speed in straight lines. 'On opening one's
eyes,' Heron wrote, 'one immediately perceives the fixed stars.' Only
luminous bodies or illuminated bodies are visible, and while their
rays, too, are propagated in straight lines, they must not be confused
with the visual rays. Euclid held that the individual rays are distinct
and do not form a continuous cone. In this way he explained why a
series of distant objects could not be taken in with a single glance.

From the Platonic assumption that all visual rays travel with the
same speed, Euclid was able to construct a theory of perspective,
which must not, however, be confused with what fifteenth-century
Italian painters understood by that term. For while modern perspective is the projection of space on a flat surface as apparent to mono-
cular vision, Euclid was more concerned with qualitative laws than
with the construction of a picture. What rules of perspective he
suggested are of little practical use to painters. The real ancestors of
modern perspective were the founders of stereographic projections
(whom we mentioned earlier) and of *gnomonics*, the theory of sundial
construction, on which the only extant systematic treatise is Book IX
of Vitruvius' *Architecture*. Gnomonics was a purely Greek science and
must be considered one of the sources of the theory of conic sections.

PTOLEMY'S *Optics*

Ptolemy's *Optics* is known to us in the obscure Latin translation of
Eugenius of Palermo (twelfth century), which was based on a mutilated Arab manuscript.

Ptolemy's basic hypotheses were slightly different from Euclid's,
for while he, too, believed that the eye emitted rays, his visual cone
had become continuous, thus explaining how the eye is able to
estimate distances.

The laws of reflection were discussed by Heron, Ptolemy, and
Theon. Heron explained reflection by the principle of the shortest
path, which Fermat used in the seventeenth century to study
refraction. Ptolemy said that the visual (incident) ray and the
reflected ray are in the same plane, that the angle of incidence is
equal to the angle of reflection and that 'the image of a point on a
mirror is at the point of concurrence of two lines, one of which is
drawn from the luminous point to the centre of curvature of the

mirror, while the other is a line from the eye to the point on the mirror where the reflection takes place'.

Ptolemy also made a systematic study of refraction and, according to Cleomedes, he even mentioned the existence of atmospheric refraction and pointed to the observational errors to which it might give rise. His laws of refraction were that the visual (incident) ray and the refracted ray are in the same plane, that the angle of incidence is not equal to the angle of refraction, and that the image is at the point of concurrence of two lines, one of which is the incident ray produced, while the other is the perpendicular from the luminous point to the plane of the boundary between the two media.

For reflection and refraction alike, Ptolemy mentioned control experiments with simple but ingenious instruments. He even published three refraction tables for rays passing from air into water and into glass, and from water into glass, giving the angles of refraction for incident rays of from 0°–80°, by steps of 10°. The fact that the corresponding differences are constant (30′) suggests that the results were extrapolated from a very limited number of experimental findings. These tables are but one of the many numerical tables known since the Babylonian ephemerides, and it is wrong to consider them, as so many have done, the first attempts to establish physical laws by extrapolation. Greek mathematics was not advanced enough to be used for that purpose.

ALGEBRA: DIOPHANTOS

Like the masterpieces of Euclid, Archimedes and Apollonios, Diophantos' *Arithmetica* appeared quite suddenly. That work seemed to run counter to all previous mathematical trends, a fact which would have continued to puzzle historians, were it not for some recent discoveries about Babylonian science. But while his indebtedness to Babylonia has now been established beyond doubt, it would be a gross exaggeration to consider Diophantos a mere compiler of ancient Mesopotamian findings. His analytical style alone puts his work on a par with Euclid's *Method* and some of Pappos' writings.

All we can say with certainty about his biographical dates is that he lived between 150 B.C. and A.D. 350, though most historians follow Tannery in putting his time near the middle of the third century.

Of the thirteen books said to have formed his *Arithmetica* only six are extant. This is how Book I began:

Knowing you, most revered Dionysios, to be keenly interested in numerical problems, I have attempted to explain the nature and power of numbers by starting with the foundation on which all things are built.

The subject may appear to be more difficult than it really is, because it is new and because beginners often despair of succeeding. You, however, should have no difficulty in understanding it, by virtue of your own zeal and my proof, for ambition joined to teaching leads rapidly to knowledge.

Since, as you know, all numbers are composed of given quantities of units, you will understand that their composition may be extended to infinity. Among numbers we know particularly: the squares, which are formed when a number, which we call the side of a square, is multiplied by itself; then the cubes, which are formed by multiplying a square by one of its sides; then the squaro-squares, which are formed when squares are multiplied by themselves; then again the cubo-squares, which are formed when squares are multiplied by cubes having the same side; and finally the cubo-cubes, which are formed when cubes are multiplied by themselves. Now it so happens that many arithmetical problems involve either the sum of these numbers, or their difference, or their product, or their quotients, or their square roots; and all these problems can be solved by following the path which I show below.

While some of his numerical problems were determinate, by far the great majority were not. Only rational and positive solutions were admitted, and Diophantos was generally satisfied with particular solutions (often obtained by elegant manipulations) which did not lend themselves to generalization. His rather rudimentary algebraic notation, restricted as it was to mere abbreviations, could express no more than one unknown, its powers from 1 to 6, and their reciprocals. The only operator was a subtraction sign; additions were indicated by simple juxtaposition. The inadequacy of this notation did not stop Diophantos from tackling very difficult problems, by manipulations from which later mathematicians were to derive much benefit. To illustrate Diophantos' algebraic procedures, we shall now describe one of his simple solutions, though in modern notation. This illustration will tell the reader much more about the *Arithmetica* than any summary of this apparently unsystematic work could hope to do.

Find two numbers, such that the difference between the square of either and the other number forms a square

$$(x^2 - y = u^2; \; y^2 - x = v^2)$$

Let the smaller number, x, be increased by any number of units but particularly by one unit, and let the greater number be the square of the smaller less x^2, such that the square of the smaller number minus the greater number will form a square (if the smaller number is $x+1$, the greater number will be $(x+1)^2 - x^2$, and the square of the smaller number minus the greater number will be x^2).

Since the square of the smaller number is x^2+2x+1, it follows that the greater number is what has been added to x^2, *viz.* $2x+1$. Hence the square of the smaller number minus the larger number is a square. Now, the square of the larger number, *i.e.* $4x^2+4x+1$, minus the smaller number must also be a square. In fact, the square of the larger number minus the smaller number is $4x^2+3x$, which must be a square. Let it be equal to $(3x)^2$, *i.e.* $4x^2+3x=9x^2$. Hence $x=\frac{3}{5}$, the smaller number $(x+1)=\frac{8}{5}$, and the larger number $(2x+1)=\frac{11}{5}$. These numbers satisfy the conditions.

(*Arithmetica*, II, 21.)

Some of the propositions are clear evidence that Diophantos did not shrink from tackling even the most complicated fractions. Some historians have considered this love for calculation as being out of keeping with Greek thought, but we must disagree with them. The work of Aristarchos, of Archimedes (*Arenarius, Measurement of a Circle, Cattle Problem*), of Euclid (*Division of the Canon*), and of Heron or Ptolemy, abounds with complicated and elegant numerical examples. In fact, the Babylonian love of numbers and calculations was inherited by the great Greek geometers, and only the scarcity of records of that part of their activities has led to the false impression that it was not. Algebraic geometry is far too closely related to the algebraic arithmetic of the Babylonians to leave any doubts on that subject.

Nevertheless, Diophantine algebra is a far cry from pure Greek geometry. Modern mathematics was born from the synthesis of these two trends by Vieta, which showed quite clearly how different and yet how closely related they really were. The synthesis also brought out the full richness of Diophantine analysis and its relevance to three new mathematical currents: its fusion with the classical methods of applying areas led to geometrical analysis; the systematization of its purely algebraic procedures gave a tremendous impetus to modern algebra; and the development of its purely numerical part involving certain properties of integers became the basis of Fermat's theory of numbers.

Having been the forerunner of Bombelli, of Vieta, and Fermat, and the inspirer of some of Jean Bernoulli's developments of the integral calculus, Diophantos must, undoubtedly, be considered one of the fountainheads of mathematical thought.

THE COMMENTATORS

Diophantos was the last great Hellenistic mathematician. His successors, great and small alike, are famous mainly for their commentaries on the work of the earlier writers.

The most famous of these was Pappos of Alexandria, who probably lived under Diocletian at about A.D. 300. His main work, the *Collection*, contained eight books, of which Book I and the first part of Book II are lost. In the *Collection*, Pappos discussed the work of all the great mathematicians of the past, though perhaps not as systematically as one might have wished. Still, his analyses of and comments on many of these works are our only evidence of their existence. Moreover, he was often not content with mere descriptions but went on to draw original conclusions from them. Thus he is said to have anticipated Guldin's theorem on the relation between the centres of gravity and the areas or volumes generated by the rotation of plane figures.

Proclos and his pupil, Marinos of Naples (end of the fifth century), both of whom made original contributions to mathematics, are also known much better because of their comments. Thus Proclos wrote a *Commentary* on Euclid, Book I, and Marinos a preface to Euclid's *Data*.

With Eutocios, who lived at the end of the fifth and beginning of the sixth centuries, and who wrote extremely perspicacious commentaries on Archimedes and Apollonios, we have reached the point where Hellenistic science gradually made way for Byzantine science. Thus it was to Anthemios, the architect of the Church of St. Sophia, that Eutocios dedicated his commentary on Apollonios' *Conics*.

When Byzantium finally ousted Alexandria and Rome completely, Greco-Roman science died without much fuss, and Western mathematics entered its long winter sleep, not to re-awaken until the Renaissance.

23 The Denderah zodiac

24 The signs of the zodiac

CHAPTER 3

Astronomy and
Mathematical Geography

PTOLEMY'S PREDECESSORS

It is, perhaps, surprising that we know very little of the history of Hellenistic astronomy. True, Ptolemy's *Almagest* presents a planetary theory in the final form which its author gave it in the middle of the second century A.D., but most of the earlier works on which many of his theories were based are lost and must therefore be reconstructed from fragments, and from what are often contradictory accounts in the writings of Ptolemy himself, his commentators and his popularizers. Meagre though these sources are, they leave no doubt that astronomy made great strides during the third and second centuries B.C. But again, while we know that Aristarchos of Samos upheld the heliocentric system eighteen centuries before Copernicus, and that Hipparchos, the greatest astronomer before Ptolemy, added greatly to the store of accurate observational knowledge and to interpretative methods, we cannot say how original their work really was. Similarly, we know very little about astronomical developments during the three centuries separating Hipparchos from Ptolemy except that little progress was made in them, largely because of political unrest and the growing influence of astrology. Chaldean horoscopy had spread first to the East and then to Alexander's empire with astonishing rapidity and was responsible for the publication of a spate of pseudo-scientific works. The only real astronomical progress, slight as it was, concerned planetary theory, the evaluation of stellar distances and sizes, and tidal theory. Mathematical geography, too, which had been given a great impetus by Eratosthenes and Hipparchos during the third and second centuries B.C., apparently stood still until Marinos of Tyre and Ptolemy infused it with new vigour in the second century A.D.

ARISTARCHOS OF SAMOS:
PRECURSOR OF COPERNICUS

In about the year 300 B.C., when Alexandria began to flourish with the active support of Ptolemaios I Soter, few scientists questioned

305

the prevailing cosmology, which, as they knew, had received the blessings of Plato and Aristotle. In it, an immobile and spherical earth occupied the centre of a uniformly revolving sphere of stars. Between that sphere and the earth the seven planets, including the sun, followed orbits complex and contrary to the diurnal revolution, being pulled along by the movement of the sphere. Beyond that there was nothing, for the universe was thought to be finite.

Then, during the third century, there appeared a work which challenged all these notions. Its author, Aristarchos of Samos, had been the pupil of Straton of Lampsacos, who became Theophrastos' successor as head of the Peripatetic School (287–279). Like his teacher, Aristarchos was keenly interested in physics, and particularly in optics, though he was above all an astronomer. We know that he observed the summer solstice in 281 or 280 B.C., and that Vitruvius called him the inventor of the *scaphe*, a sundial with a hemispherical surface and a vertical gnomon.

DIMENSIONS AND DISTANCES OF THE SUN AND THE MOON

One of Aristarchos' extant writings, *On the Sizes and Distances of the Sun and the Moon*, re-examined an earlier problem first posed in the middle of the fourth century. Whereas Eudoxos, using Pythagorean musical intervals, had concluded that the sun's diameter was nine times greater than the moon's, and Phidias, the father of Archimedes, that it was twelve times as great, Aristarchos was the first to put these speculations to the geometrical test. He considered the triangle MES, formed by the centres of the moon M, of the earth E, and the sun S, at the precise moment of quadrature, *i.e.* when the angle EMS is a perfect right angle. Having measured the angle MES, he then calculated the ratio of the three angles of the right triangle, and hence determined the ratio of its three sides by quasi-trigonometrical calculations. He also used another method, based on the apparent diameters of the moon and the sun and on the shadow-cone during eclipses of the moon. With remarkable mathematical skill he then deduced that, taking the diameter of the earth as 1, the diameter of the moon was 0.36 (instead of 0.27), that the distance of the moon from the earth was 9.5 (instead of 30.2), that the diameter of the sun was 6.75 (instead of 108.9), and that the distance of the sun from the earth was 180 (instead of 11,726). The discrepancies were due to three grave observational errors: Aristarchos made the angle MES—which is very difficult to measure—equal to 87° instead of 89° 50'; the ratio of the diameter of the shadow-cone to the diameter of the moon equal to 2 instead of 2.6; and, worst of all, the apparent angular diameters of the moon and the sun equal to 2°, which is roughly four times larger than they are. The last error is the more surprising because Archimedes claimed that 'Aristarchos discovered that the apparent dimensions of the sun were roughly equal to the 720th part of the zodiac', *i.e.* to 30'. The only explanation is that the *On the Sizes* was written during Aristarchos' youth, which is corroborated by the fact that it was still based on the geocentric system.

ARISTARCHOS' HELIOCENTRIC THEORY

According to the evidence of his contemporary, Archimedes, and of many later writers, Aristarchos put forward the hypothesis that the fixed stars and the sun were immobile; the earth described a circle amidst the other planets about the sun; and that the centre of the sun coincided with the centre of the sphere of fixed stars. According to Plutarch, Aristarchos also held that the earth rotated on its own axis, thus explaining the apparent diurnal revolution of the celestial vault. Beyond that, we know nothing about Aristarchos' ideas, not even if, as seems probable, he considered the moon to be a satellite of the earth. Even so, there is no doubt that he must be considered an early forerunner of Copernicus, and that, together with the Atomists and the Epicureans, who believed in the plurality of worlds and an infinite universe, he provided antiquity with the elements of a scientific cosmography.

ORIGINS OF THE HELIOCENTRIC THEORY

Historians of science disagree on the question of Aristarchos' original authorship of the heliocentric theory, and also on its subsequent fortunes. We saw that Philolaos and other Pythagoreans had, long before Aristarchos, considered that the earth described a circle about a central fire, which was not, however, the sun. Furthermore, according to Heath and Gundel, Heraclides of Pontos and not Aristarchos was the author of the theory that the earth rotates on its own axis every twenty-four hours, and taught also that the sun, moon and the superior planets (Mars, Jupiter, Saturn) revolve about the earth, Venus and Mercury being satellites of the sun. On the other hand, P. Tannery identifies the system of Heraclides with that of Tycho Brahe, who held that the five extraterrestrial planets revolved about the sun, and the sun, with this huge attendant family, revolved about the earth. Yet other scholars, and Schiaparelli in particular, cite a doubtful passage from Geminos, which contradicts all the other evidence, to prove that Heraclides was, in fact, the real author of the heliocentric theory, or else that, starting from Philolaos' theory, Heraclides came to hold that the sun, Venus, Mercury, the earth, and the superior planets all turned about a central point in that order. In that theory, we have only to reduce the radius of the sun's orbit to zero to obtain the heliocentric system, a step which Schiaparelli claims was probably taken by Heraclides himself. In that case, Aristarchos would have been an advocate rather than the inventor of the theory, though it seems most odd that, with one doubtful exception, all ancient authors should have attributed the heliocentric system to him rather than to the far better-known Heraclides. In particular, we cannot believe that Archimedes, a man so well-versed in astronomical questions, in such close contact with all his colleagues, and only some twenty years younger than Aristarchos, would not have mentioned it if Aristarchos had borrowed his theory from another author. We may therefore take it that it was, in fact, Aristarchos who first propounded the theory that the sun is the common centre of the earth and of the planets, even if there is some doubt whether he was also the first to state that the earth rotates about its own axis.

FORTUNES OF ARISTARCHOS' THEORY

Although he was a well-known figure, Aristarchos failed to convince other learned men of the validity of his theory. Apart from the astronomer Seleucos (second century B.C.), scientists and philosophers alike rejected it out of hand and called it an outrage. The geocentric, and hence anthropocentric, doctrine had become a philosophic and moral dogma, so much so that Cleanthes of Assos, the famous Stoic and a contemporary of Aristarchos, felt impelled to ask the Greeks to charge Aristarchos with blasphemy. And while the philosophers attacked the theory on the ground that it impugned the divine perfection of the celestial sphere, scientists opposed it on physical grounds. If the earth moved about the sun, the stars were bound to undergo angular displacements, which they did not (the vast distances involved were not appreciated at the time). Moreover, the earth, being the heaviest of all celestial bodies must necessarily sink to the bottom, *i.e.* to the centre of the universe; and how could one believe that the stars, made of pure fire, would remain unmoved while the heavy earth circled and turned in space? No wonder that the leading astronomers and scientists, including Archimedes, Apollonios of Perga and Hipparchos, preferred the geocentric system which alone struck them as being capable of 'saving the appearances'.

FROM ARCHIMEDES TO HIPPARCHOS

ARCHIMEDES AND ASTRONOMY

Archimedes, the great mathematician and physicist, was also a keen astronomer. His planetarium was famous in antiquity, and he was well-versed in the astronomical literature of his time. It is mainly due to him that we know anything at all about Aristarchos' theory, and to his *Arenarius*, in particular, that we know what ideas were held regarding the sizes of the stars and their distances from the earth. Archimedes was not, however, an original astronomer, and he failed to explain how the motions of the planets fitted into his geocentric views. Now, it was precisely such explanations which crowned the work of the Hellenistic and Roman astronomers.

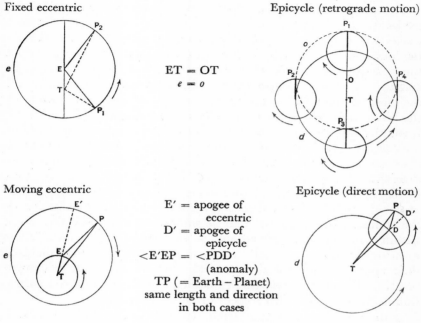

fig. 31 Eccentrics and Epicycles.

ECCENTRICS AND EPICYCLES

The system of homocentric spheres first proposed by Eudoxos, perfected by Callippos, and further elaborated by Aristotle, failed to 'save' one of the appearances. At the end of the fourth century Autolycos of Pitane pointed out that since Venus and Mars, for example, clearly changed their apparent distances from the earth in the course of their revolutions, they could not possibly describe perfect circles concentric with the earth. Thus the theory of the spheres had to be discarded in favour of the theory of eccentrics and epicycles, which began to take form in the third century and combined the Platonic dogma of circular motions with increasingly accurate observations.

The eccentric element of the theory, *i.e.* the doctrine that the planets described circles of which the earth was not at the centre, enabled astronomers to explain not only the 'zodiacal anomaly', namely the fact that the planets, sun and moon move through equal arcs in unequal times, but also the 'solar anomaly' of the smaller planets (stations and retrogressions). The latter arose from the fact that the centres of the eccentrics described small circles about the earth, in a sense opposite to the motion of the planets, their radii being equal to the degree of eccentricity.

The theory of epicycles, which was at first used independently, explained the anomaly in a different way. Epicycles were small circles whose centres moved along a very much larger circle called the 'deferent'. In this system, the direct motion of the epicycle along the deferent represented the movement of the planet through the zodiac (the planet's proper orbit), while the planet's motion round the circumference of the epicycle, in the same sense, accounted for the 'solar anomaly' of the small planets (nowadays explained by the revolution of the earth about the sun). Whenever a planet moved outside the deferent, *i.e.* away from the earth, its apparent diameter decreased, and its motion was added to that of the epicycle along the deferent. Whenever it moved closer to the earth, its apparent diameter increased and, its motion being in an opposite sense to that of the epicycle along the deferent, it showed a retrograde motion in the zodiac. Planets appeared to be stationary only while they were within the deferent circle and only when their angular displacement towards the east was exactly equal to the angular displacement of their epicycle along the deferent. The inclination of the planetary orbits to the ecliptic was easily explained by giving an equal inclination to the epicycles with respect to the deferents.

If the epicycle itself completed one revolution while its centre travelled along the deferent in the opposite (retrograde) sense, each point on the circumference of the epicycle could be shown to describe a circle which was equal and eccentric to the deferent, while the distance between the centres of the two circles was equal to the radius of the epicycle. In that case, the theory of epicycles became a simple geometrical variant of the theory of eccentricity. It could also be shown that there was no geometric distinction between the two systems other than their respective dimensions, *i.e.* the ratio between the two circles was larger when the smaller was the mobile eccentric. Hence the ancient distinction between the two theories was historical rather than factual.

ORIGIN OF THE THEORIES OF ECCENTRICS AND EPICYCLES

The original authorship of the two theories is still under dispute. According to the 'classical' view, upheld particularly by Heath, the theory of epicycles goes back to Heraclides of Pontos. Now, if

Heraclides did, in fact, teach that Venus and Mercury revolved about the sun, while the sun revolved about the earth, his doctrine was but a short step from the geometric system in which the ecliptic was represented by the deferent, and the orbit of each of the two planets by epicycles with the sun as their centre. As for the eccentric, it must have been invented later by an unknown astronomer in the late fourth century, who realized that the superior planets came into annual 'opposition' on a circle about the earth.

As against Heath, many students of the *Timaeos* have held that Plato was fully conversant with the theory of epicycles, which, they say, together with the theory of the eccentric circles, was a Pythagorean invention. While this claim is interesting it is, however, based on somewhat tenuous arguments. In short, it is difficult to settle the question of original authorship, and all we can state is that on Ptolemy's evidence, Apollonios of Perga was not only familiar with the theory of epicycles but also produced a geometrical construction of them. From Ptolemy we also know that even before Hipparchos (first half of the second century) mathematicians had already thought of combining the two theories into one in order to account for the two anomalies in the motions of the small planets—epicycles to explain the solar anomaly and eccentrics to explain the zodiacal anomaly. The ground had therefore been well prepared by the time that Hipparchos appeared on the scene.

HIPPARCHOS

All we know of the life of this illustrious scientist is that he was born in Nicaea in Bithynia, and that he made most of his astronomical observations in Rhodes and in Alexandria between 161 and 127 B.C. Only the least important of his works is extant: the *Commentaries* on a famous third-century astronomical poem by Aratos of Soli, the *Phenomena*. Hence, it is difficult to say precisely what place must be assigned to Hipparchos in the history of astronomy. While many scholars have called him a mere imitator of the Chaldeans, of Apollonios and of Ptolemy, others consider him the real author of the *Almagest*, and Ptolemy a shameless plagiarist. There is no doubt that he was held in great authority as an astronomer, both during his life and after his death.

By his stress on observation, Hipparchos was a most representative scientist of the Alexandrian period. His strong censure of Eratosthenes' findings in mathematical geography shows to what lengths he carried his demands for rigorous methods and his respect for observable facts. His work is not so much remarkable for its theories as for its precise data and the resulting discoveries.

Observational Instruments

Like most scientists Hipparchos combined his own observations with those of his predecessors, though, as we have said, he was markedly critical of the older material. He measured variations in the apparent diameters of the sun and the moon by means of a diopter of his own invention which was greatly superior to that of Archimedes. This instrument consisted of a horizontal support on which were mounted vertical plates: a fixed one with only one hole, and a sliding one with two holes in vertical alignment. The eye was placed against the hole of the fixed plate and focused on the rising or setting star, and the slide was moved until its two holes, seen through the first hole, coincided with the upper and lower edges of the star, when the star's angular diameter could be determined. Archimedes' diopter had no fixed plate, and used a small vertically mounted cylinder as a slide. Ptolemy said that he obtained far better results from Hipparchos' instrument than from a clepsydra, by which he measured the interval between the transit of the upper and lower edges of a star across a fixed line. Hipparchos also used earlier astronomical instruments, no doubt after having improved them: a diopter for measuring the ascension or angular displacement of the stars, which could be moved horizontally and vertically by means of two graduated wheels; probably a plane astrolabe, also called the 'universal instrument' (which some historians claim was not invented until the second century or even—which is most unlikely—the sixth century A.D.); possibly an armillary sphere, called the 'naval astrolabe' during the Middle Ages but mentioned by Geminos in the first century B.C.; certainly a planetarium similar to that used by Archimedes a century earlier, and by Posidonios fifty years later; and also a sphere of fixed stars depicting the known constellations.

Babylonian Observations

Hipparchos compared most of his personal observations with data collected not only by such Alexandrian astronomers as Aristyllos and Timocharis, who had determined the positions of numerous stars at the beginning of the third century, but also (though less certainly) by the Babylonians. Ptolemy has pointed out that the Babylonian lunar ephemerides, the earliest known of which were established in the third century B.C., listed the very constants on which Hipparchos based his lunar tables. However, Hipparchos (and also Ptolemy) may have arrived at his results by using Babylonian 'linear functions', for many later astrological texts (some of doubtful value) mention this expressly, and we know that Hipparchos adopted the Babylonian division of the circle into 360 degrees, each divisible into 60 minutes of 60 seconds. In the third century,

Babylonian 'magi' like Berossos, and Alexandrians like the astronomer Conon of Samos, acted as the intellectual intermediaries between Mesopotamia and Greece, and, even later, 'Chaldean' methods continued to influence the development of astrology and of certain mathematical trends, though never of geometrical astronomy, which was an exclusively Greek contribution.

Principles and Methods of Alexandrian Astronomy

In fact, Hipparchos adhered to the Hellenistic tradition, fully accepting the Pythagorean and Platonic method of explaining celestial phenomena by circular and uniform motions. The originality of Alexandrian astronomy was to attempt the reconciliation of these motions with absolute respect for the facts. Hipparchos—like Ptolemy—was aware of contradictions between the two, and like Aristotle he held that these contradictions were inherent in mathematics, which was rooted in both the metaphysical sphere of pure understanding and the physical sphere of sensible phenomena. Now, following Plato, he also held that the sensible world was governed by divine laws, which, being eternal and immutable, were also rationally explicable. The only perfectly beautiful and rational motion was circular and uniform, and it was the astronomer's task to show that circular motion governed all celestial phenomena and that all heavenly bodies revolved about their centres at a uniform rate. This *a priori* dogma may be said to have played much the same role in antiquity as the law of universal gravitation does nowadays.

Hipparchos was therefore not satisfied with his predecessors' attempts simply to formulate geometric systems such as epicycles, eccentrics, or combinations of both. According to him, the real system hidden beneath the apparent disorder of the sensible world could be discovered only by careful *observation* of the characteristic motions of every celestial body, from the analysis of the various anomalies, and from the determination of the magnitudes and periods involved. Only then could one formulate the geometrical laws governing the number, size, position and circular velocity of the stars. Finally, the astronomer must show that these laws were not only necessary but also sufficient, and then construct accurate tables listing future events by which the value of the system could be determined.

The Theory of the Sun and the Moon

Such was the difficult task that Hipparchos set himself. He first adopted two solar theories, one based on the eccentric and the other on the epicycle, and then showed that they were equivalent, since either sufficed to explain what seemed to be the only important solar anomaly, *i.e.* the inequality of the seasons (though not the precession of the equinoxes). The sun was said to describe a circle with radius *r*, the earth being at a distance from the centre equal to *er*, where *e* = 0.4166. The longitude of the sun's apogee was said to be 5° 30′ in Gemini. From these figures, Hipparchos constructed tables giving the position of the sun during every day for a number of years (600 according to Pliny the Elder). Ptolemy was unable to improve on these results.

The case of the moon proved more difficult—and no wonder, when we consider that our satellite continues to elude the predictions of astronomers even to this day. According to Ptolemy, Hipparchos arrived at rather imperfect results, based mainly on Babylonian tables and particularly on those of the astronomer Ki-din-nu (the Cidenas of Strabo and Vettius Valens), though he improved the Babylonian dates of eclipses by introducing a period of 4,267 months. (His calculation of the mean synodic month—29 days, 12 hours, 44 minutes, 2.5 seconds—differs by less than one second from the exact value.) But, according to Ptolemy, who discussed Hipparchos' errors at length, his geometric analysis of the anomalies was incomplete and, above all, his eccentric circles and epicycles led to discordant results, most probably because of errors in observing eclipses.

As for the 'small' planets, modern scholars agree with Ptolemy that Hipparchos contented himself with demonstrating the inadequacy of his predecessors' results and with outlining the task of his successors. He himself felt unable to follow the path he had mapped, no doubt because he realized that his data were insufficient. The work was first tackled in the course of the following centuries and finally completed by Ptolemy.

THE PRECESSION OF THE EQUINOXES

It was probably while elaborating his solar theory that Hipparchos made his greatest discovery: he noticed that in its annual motion the sun took a longer time to return to its original position in the zodiac than it did to return to the equator from one spring to the next, *i.e.* that one sidereal year was equal to 365 days, 6 hours, 10 minutes (actual value: 365 days, 6 hours, 9 minutes, 10 seconds) while one solar year was equal to 365 days, 5 hours, 55 minutes, 12 seconds (actually: 365 days, 5 hours, 48 minutes, 46 seconds). He explained correctly that this discrepancy was due to an annual displacement of the equinoctial points, which are the points of intersection between the ecliptic and the equator. Since, according to the geocentric view, the plane of the ecliptic was immovable, the sphere of the fixed stars was assumed by Hipparchos to slip back very slightly along the ecliptic, for only in that way was it possible to explain why the equinoctial point advanced on the zodiac—why there was an annual 'precession of the equinoxes'. He calculated that this annual displacement was 36″, which is 14.26″ short of the correct figure. The spring equinox, which had been in Taurus at the time of the old Babylonian empire, had moved to Aries by Hipparchos' day, and has since moved to Pisces. While some historians have attributed the discovery of the precession to a fourth- or third-century Mesopotamian astronomer, it is now generally agreed that the credit must go to Hipparchos.

THE STAR CATALOGUE

This great discovery went hand in hand with another important contribution by Hipparchos: his *Star Catalogue*. In his *Commentary* on the *Phenomena* of Aratos, Hipparchos had previously corrected a great number of the poet's errors regarding the position of the stars and the dates of their heliacal risings and settings. Pliny the Elder tells us that it was the discovery of a new star which first gave Hipparchos the idea of compiling his *Catalogue*—and, in fact, a nova did appear in Scorpio in 134 B.C., according to the *Chinese Annals*. In any case, the *Catalogue* was compiled after the discovery of the precession; for while the *Commentary* on the *Phenomena* lists the positions of the stars by references both to the equator and to the ecliptic, the *Catalogue* lists their latitudes and longitudes with respect to the ecliptic alone, and in such a way that the precession of the equinoxes does not affect the latitudes but changes all the longitudes by the same fixed annual value. Before Hipparchos, Eudoxos and Eratosthenes had published inaccurate descriptions of the constellations, and other astronomers, *e.g.* Aristyllos and Timocharis, had given the position of a few stars; Hipparchos listed more than 800 stars, no doubt in order to check whether they were really 'fixed', a task which he fulfilled punctiliously.

To explain the great renown which this astronomer enjoyed in antiquity we need only add that he gave a tremendous impetus to mathematical geography, and that he was the first to construct a table of chords. When he died there was no scientist great enough to enter into his heritage and complete his task. But his work and his example were not lost.

THE APOGEE OF ANCIENT ASTRONOMY

Though there were no great astronomers between the time of Hipparchos and that of Ptolemy, a growing interest in Babylonian astrology brought some knowledge of celestial phenomena to a wide public and a number of astronomical advances were made during that period by serious researchers.

THE DIAMETER OF THE SUN ACCORDING TO POSIDONIOS

The best of all ancient measurements of the diameter of the sun and of its distance from the earth were those made by the Stoic philosopher Posidonios, a man of wide interests and great intellectual brilliance. Posidonios investigated many aspects of science and particularly of meteorology and geography. Hipparchos had previously improved Aristarchos' values by making the diameter of the sun equal to $12\frac{1}{3}$ terrestrial diameters (instead of $6\frac{3}{4}$) and the distance of the sun from the earth equal to 1,245 terrestrial diameters (instead of 180). Posidonios probably based his own calculations on Archimedes, according to whom the diameter of the solar orbit was roughly 10,000 times the diameter of the earth; at all events, Pliny tells us that he calculated the average distance of the earth from the sun to be 500,000,000 stadia, *i.e.* some 57 million miles (real distance is about 93 million miles) and the diameter of the earth to be 76,400 stadia, which gives a ratio of about 6,550 (instead of the correct 11,726). According to Posidonios, the diameter of the sun was equal to 39.25 terrestrial diameters (instead of 108.9), and he was the first to have pointed out that the sun looks much larger on the horizon than it does in mid-sky. Ptolemy failed to appreciate the value of these results and reduced to 1/605 and 1/5.5 the ratios of the diameter of the earth to the distance and the diameter of the sun, respectively. On the other hand, he gave better values for the moon, making its mean distance from the earth and its diameter respectively 29.5 and 0.29 terrestrial diameters (correct values: 30.2 and 0.27), as against Posidonios' 26.2 and 0.157 and Hipparchos' 33.6 and 0.33.

Posidonios must be called the discoverer of atmospheric refraction, the cause of the so-called 'horizontal' eclipse, *i.e.* the simultaneous presence above the horizon of the eclipsed moon and the setting sun. This may be inferred from the fact that atmospheric refraction is described and explained by Cleomedes, a popularizer who lived at the beginning of our era, and who based most of his writings on the work of Posidonios.

PLANETARY THEORY
AFTER HIPPARCHOS AND BEFORE PTOLEMY

During that period, slight advances were also made in planetary theory, as we know from a rather confused passage of Pliny the Elder —written towards A.D. 77. In his analysis of planetary motion, Pliny points out that because of their eccentric orbits the planets keep approaching and receding from the earth, and lists the points in the zodiac corresponding to their respective apogees and perigees. Now, while Pliny was apparently ignorant of the system of epicycles, and while he associated absurd astrological 'causes' with his geometrical explanations, his longitudes correspond within a few degrees with Ptolemy's figures, at least for the sun, Mars, Jupiter, and Saturn. (For the inferior planets, the apogees were more difficult to determine on the geocentric hypothesis, and Pliny's results were therefore valueless.) Pliny was clearly indebted to Hipparchos for his solar data, but the other information must have been established by unknown astronomers between the end of the second century B.C. and the middle of the first century A.D. Moreover, in the second century B.C., Babylonian astronomers had already determined the apogees of the sun and of Jupiter, giving figures in close agreement with Ptolemy's. Hence, Pliny's account may have been no more than a pseudo-geometrical rendering of the latest findings of Babylonian astronomy.

BABYLONIAN ASTRONOMY AND HELLENISTIC SCIENCE

In effect, side by side with Greek geometrical mathematics and astronomy, Hellenistic and Roman scientists also developed a mathematics and an astronomy of purely Mesopotamian origin, based on simple arithmetical methods. This tradition has survived, above all, in a number of extant papyri on popular astronomy, and also in astrological texts, in all of which latitudes are expressed as the ratio between the longest and the shortest day experienced at the place in question. Thus the latitude of Alexandria was said to be 7/5, because the sun is visible for fourteen hours during the summer solstice and for ten hours during the winter solstice. The astronomers calculated the number of daylight hours at a given place, by adding the times which the six signs of the zodiac following the solstitial points on the ecliptic took to rise above the horizon. To evaluate the period of each sign the Greek astronomers, at least from the time of the *Almagest*, used complicated but exact trigonometrical calculations leading to a curve with two peaks, whereas in the Babylonian lunar ephemerides these periods increased uniformly from Aries to Virgo, and decreased uniformly from Libra to Pisces, thus leading to a curve with only one peak. But though he used a trigonometrical method in his *Almagest*, Ptolemy went back to linear methods in the later *Tetrabiblos*, in accordance with astrological usage. Similarly, the lunar calendars of Geminos and other contemporary astronomers were calculated from simple Babylonian parameters obtained by purely arithmetical methods.

ASTROLOGY

Though astrology in the narrow sense of the word (*i.e.* as the art of determining the influence of the seven planets on any part of the earth, and particularly on man, from their position in the zodiac) was born in Mesopotamia at about the end of the fifth century, it did not really come into its own until the third century. For while the practical rules of casting horoscopes were Babylonian, the elaboration of the theory, particularly in Ptolemy's *Tetrabiblos*, seems to have been the result of Hellenistic reflection. Thus, though the idea that each day of the week was influenced by planets is of Babylonian origin, the actual correlation of the seven planets (Saturn, Jupiter, Mars, Sun, Venus, Mercury and Moon, in that order) with given hours of the day was a purely Hellenistic innovation. Here the sun was said to govern the first hour of the first day, which was therefore called Sunday. Twenty-four hours later it was the moon's turn and so the second day became Monday, *etc.* Unlike the Greeks, the Babylonians did not divide the day into twenty-four hours, and so the order of the planets given in cuneiform texts of the Seleucid epoch (Jupiter, Venus, Mercury, Saturn, Mars) was quite unlike that of the Greeks, which corresponded to the order of the planets in the geocentric system.

It follows that Babylonian astronomy could at best have had a marginal influence on Greek geometric cosmology. Even zodiacal astrology, a Babylonian invention which captured the entire Greco-Roman world, owed its theoretical developments to the Greeks, so that Babylonian and Greek notions have continued to coexist in it to this day. This surprising fact is easily explained when we consider that most Hellenistic and Roman astronomers adhered firmly to the doctrine of the divine nature of the stars first propounded by the Pythagoreans, then adopted by Plato, and handed down to the Peripatetics and particularly to the Stoics. The direct action of the stellar gods on the course of terrestrial events seemed clearly borne out by the rhythm of the seasons and later by that of the tides and by the regular occurrence, between the heliacal risings and settings of certain constellations, of common meteorological phenomena.

POPULARIZERS AND POLYGRAPHS

However, this doctrine did not stop true scientists like Ptolemy and Hipparchos from developing geometrical astronomy and from arousing public interest in celestial phenomena as such. Following in their footsteps came a host of astronomical popularizers. Side by side with such confused cosmological accounts as those of Cicero's *De Natura Deorum* and of the numerous Stoic texts, there were the lucid *Phenomena* by Geminos (possibly a pupil of Posidonios in the first century B.C.); Cleomedes' *On the Circular Motion of Celestial Bodies* (probably early second century A.D. and not, as has been claimed, first century B.C.), which was a valuable guide to the geographical methods of Eratosthenes and Posidonios; Theodosios of Bithynia's *On Days and Nights* and *On Habitations* (first century B.C.), in which the author explains variations of stellar visibilities as functions of changes in latitude; Theon of Smyrna's *On the Mathematical Knowledge which is Needed to Read Plato* (early second century A.D.), Part IV of which is devoted to astronomy and describes the lost writings of Adrastos of Aphrodisias, a Peripatetic who lived at the beginning of the second century A.D.; Plutarch's short dialogue *On the Face which Appears in the Disc of the Moon* (end of first century A.D.), which gives the correct explanation that the markings on the moon are shadows; the Roman Senator Manilius' long poem on astrology (beginning of the first century); and finally Pliny's account of cosmology in his *Natural History*, which is a mine of information and also bears witness to what extent Babylonian concepts held sway in Greek science.

THE WORK OF PTOLEMY

After these three relatively lean centuries, Claudios Ptolemaios, who lived at the height of Rome's power, produced a work so brilliant that it was to remain the bible of astronomers for the next fourteen centuries. Although all we can say of his life is that he flourished in Alexandria from 127 to 151, his work is exceptionally well-known since most of his writings have been preserved, either in the original version or in Latin or Arabic translations. The chief of these are: the *Mathematical Treatise*, a masterpiece of ancient astronomy; the *Planetary Hypotheses*, a new and concise presentation of the theory of the planets; the *Apparitions of the Fixed Stars*, a sort of calendar of the risings and settings of the stars (similar to the ancient parapegms) for five main latitudes from Syene (Aswan) to the Black Sea; the *Tetrabiblos*, the canon of Hellenistic astrology; the *Geography*, in eight books, and the *Optics* and *Acoustics*, which we discussed in the last chapter.

At the beginning of the *Mathematical Treatise* (called the *Almagest*, the 'Great' Book, by medieval Arab scholars) Ptolemy explains his desire to give a complete account of the geocentric system. He deals first with the structure of the universe, with the different kinds of celestial motions, and with the terrestrial latitudes (Books 1 and 2), then with solar and lunar theories (Books 3 to 6), with the structure of the celestial spheres and the catalogue of the stars (7 and 8), and finally with the theory of the planets (9 to 12). Ptolemy never pretended to be writing an original work and frequently acknowledged his sources. Hence, many critics have claimed that even when he made no such acknowledgements his arguments were borrowed from other writers. However, careful investigations have shown that this criticism is quiite unwarranted and that Ptolemy made a considerable number of original contributions to astronomy.

PTOLEMY'S PLANETARY THEORY

Thus, Ptolemy is now generally credited with having completed and perfected Hipparchos' planetary theory, utilizing the approximate determinations of the apogees and perigees of the eccentrics which were not available to Hipparchos. In solar theory Ptolemy added nothing to Hipparchos, though, like him, he proved the equivalence of the theories of the epicycles and the eccentrics. Unlike Hipparchos, however, who preferred epicycles in all cases, Ptolemy preferred eccentrics when it came to the case of the sun, because this entailed only a single motion instead of two. On the other hand, Ptolemy made basic changes in Hipparchos' theory of the moon and of the small planets. Except for the case of Mercury, for which his method was more complicated still, Ptolemy explained his differences from Hipparchos in the following way.

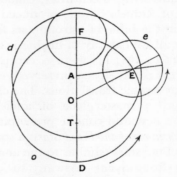

fig. 32 Ptolemy's equant.

According to Hipparchos, the great circle *o* with centre O, eccentric with respect to the earth T, carries an epicycle *e* (*see fig. 32*). Planetary motions along this epicycle explain the 'zodiacal anomaly', otherwise called the variations in the apparent velocity of the planet, due to changes in its distance from the earth. The 'solar anomaly', *i.e.* the stations and retrogressions of the planets which are explained in the heliocentric system by the annual revolution of the earth about the sun, are here explained by the direct motion of the planet P along the epicycle. To this scheme, traditional from at least the second century B.C., Ptolemy added a new element. According to

Platonic principles ackowleged in the introduction of the *Almagest*,
both the planet on its epicycle and also the centre of the epicycle on
its deferent must describe uniform motions. To 'save appearances'
Ptolemy therefore used a subterfuge: he constructed a third circle
$d = o$ about A, a point on the axis TO, making OA = OT. He then
assumed that the motion of the epicycle on its deferent was constant
with respect to the centre A of the circle d, and not with respect to
the centre O of the deferent o. In other words, constructing the
straight lines OE and AE to join the centres of the circles o and d to
the centre E of the epicycle e, and calling D and F the points of
intersection between the axis TOA and the deferent o, he showed
that the angle DAE and not the angle DOE increases uniformly.
The circle d was called the *circulus aequans* or *equant*, and it is easy to
see that its effect on the motion of the epicycle, and consequently on
the planet, varies according to whether the planet is near the perigee
D, or near the apogee F. Whenever the angle DOE is greater than
the angle FAE, the motion of E is retarded by the equant, since to a
given portion of the arc of the deferent, for instance EF, there
corresponds a greater angle at the centre of the equant FAE;
conversely when DOE is smaller than FAE, the equant acts as an
accelerator.

Now, as Duhem has stressed, Ptolemy's introduction of the equant
was, in fact, tantamount to endowing a mobile point with a variable
circular velocity, whereby Ptolemy sinned against—or at least
twisted—the law of circular and uniform motion. Still, Ptolemy was
too great a scientist to allow theories to override facts.

'The astronomer', he wrote in the *Almagest*, 'must try his utmost to
explain celestial motions by the simplest possible hypotheses; but if he
fails to do so, he must choose whatever other hypotheses meet the case.'

In the case of the moon and Mercury things were further
complicated by the fact that the eccentric deferent, instead of being
fixed, itself revolved in a small circle, equally eccentric, but in the
opposite direction to the other movements. Ptolemy's analysis of
the motion of the moon was so exact that he was able to discover the
'evection' and 'nutation', two phenomena which Hipparchos had
overlooked. He also calculated the parallax of the moon, *i.e.* the
angle between the line joining the centre of the moon to a point on
the surface of the earth, and the line drawn from the centre of the
moon to the centre of the earth. Archimedes, too, had noticed this
phenomenon and Hipparchos had vainly tried to make a similar
determination of the solar parallax.

Finally, to explain by circular motion the regular variations in the
inclinations to the plane of the ecliptic of the planes of the planetary

21

orbits, Ptolemy suggested the inclinations could be represented by inclinations of the epicycles to the eccentrics. He joined the point of the epicycle nearest the centre of the deferent to the circumference of a small circle, perpendicular to the plane of the deferent but having its centre in the same plane; the small circle, while revolving about its own centre, followed the epicycle in its motion along the deferent, thus causing the epicycle to oscillate about the plane of the deferent. A complete oscillation concided with one full revolution of the epicycle on the deferent, *i.e.* of the planet through the zodiac; at the nodal points (the points of intersection of the planetary orbit and the ecliptic) the plane of the epicycle coincided with the plane of the deferent. (For Mercury and the moon, the solution was more complicated still.) In his *Planetary Hypotheses*, Ptolemy simplified the method by substituting an epicyclic sphere for the combination of epicycle and perpendicular circle.

THE STAR CATALOGUE

The originality of Ptolemy's star catalogue has been no less hotly disputed than that of his planetary theory. Thus, some critics claim that he was merely an imitator of Hipparchos, and point out that Pliny mentioned the existence of another catalogue of 1,600 stars some 75 years earlier than Ptolemy's. Still, there is no doubt that Ptolemy's catalogue contained at least 300 more stars than that of his predecessor, and that 90 per cent of his data were based on original observations and calculations. Hipparchos had divided the stars into six classes, which he called 'magnitudes', according to their apparent brightness, and Ptolemy recognized at least two intermediate grades between any two of Hipparchos' broad divisions.

PTOLEMY AS THE LAST ASTRONOMER OF ANTIQUITY

So brief a summary cannot do full justice to Ptolemy's considerable contributions to astronomy. Each of his propositions was based on rigorous demonstrations, on countless observations and on shrewd mathematical arguments. Moreover, Ptolemy either reconstructed or, more often, produced himself the complete analysis of all the motions involved in his planetary theories. Thus, to solve a number of geometrical problems connected with his work, Ptolemy had to improve the spherical trigonometry of Hipparchos and Menelaos.

Ptolemy's work represents the summit of ancient astronomy, for though the subsequent decline was momentarily interrupted by the Theodosian Renaissance at the end of the fourth century, most of his successors like Bardesanes, Censorinus, Firmicus, Maternus, Hephaestion of Thebes and Paul of Alexandria were primarily concerned with astrology, while real astronomers like Pappos and

Theon of Alexandria contented themselves with commentaries on Ptolemy's work. No wonder, then, that until the end of the fifteenth century Ptolemy's authority was never questioned except by Aristotelian diehards, who preferred perfect spheres to Ptolemaic circles on principle.

MATHEMATICAL GEOGRAPHY

Different Conceptions of Geography

The fourth century, during which the sphericity of the earth came to be generally accepted by the scientific world—only Epicureans and uneducated people refused to believe in it—saw great developments in geography, which Aristotle and, above all, Dicaearchos had previously tried to turn into a scientific discipline. The first Alexandrian geographers pursued the same aims which Ptolemy was to propound four centuries later:

Geography must first consider the form of the whole earth as well as its size and its position with reference to the heavens, so that it may be able to tell the size and nature of the known portion of the earth and under what parallel circles of the celestial sphere each part lies. From this it will be possible to learn the length of nights and days, the fixed stars that are overhead and those that at all times are above or below the horizon, as well as other information that we include in accounts of the habitable regions.

This essentially mathematical conception of geography struck some as being far too narrow. Thus Polybios in his *History* (second century B.C.) and Strabo in his *Geographia* (first century B.C.) added not only the contours of countries and their natural resources, but also descriptions of their commerce and politics. Unfortunately both works are studded with errors.

Eratosthenes and the Size of the Earth

Mathematical geography had three illustrious representatives: Eratosthenes, Hipparchos and Ptolemy. Eratosthenes of Cyrene (*c.* 275–195) was a typical Alexandrian scientist. He was summoned from Athens by Ptolemaios III Euergetes to take charge of the education of the future Ptolemaios IV Philopator, and to act as custodian of the Library. He also excelled as a man of letters, historian, poet, grammarian, mathematician, astronomer and geographer. Of his scientific works, only some fragments and summaries are extant. A small text, criticized by his posthumous opponent, Strabo, was an attack on all those who held that Homer was infallible and who made desperate attempts to fit all discoveries to his sacrosanct verses.

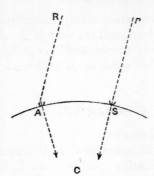

fig. 33 Measurement of the arc
Alexandria–Syene by means of a
hemispherical gnomon.

Cleomedes tells us by what method Eratosthenes estimated the dimensions of the earth. His procedure, which was a great advance on that of Dicaearchos, was based on estimates of the arc of the great circle through Alexandria and Syene (Aswan), which had three advantages: the two towns were more or less on the same meridian (longitude was not thought to affect the measurements); the distance between them had been measured by Egyptian survey-ors; the sun was known not to cast a shadow on the day of the summer solstice in Syene, and hence it sufficed to measure at Alexandria the angle which the shadow of the needle of a hemispherical gnomon made with the vertical. Let R, r be parallel rays from the sun at Alexandria (A) and at Syene (S), and let C be the centre of the earth. At S the ray rS will be vertical and will pass through C, while at A the radius RA will make an angle α with the vertical AC, equal to the angle ACS. In the given case, the gnomon showed that the meridian zenith-distance of the sun at Alexandria was $\frac{1}{50}$ of the circumference of the heavens, while the linear distance of the two places had been determined to be 5,000 stadia. Consequently the circumference of the earth was found to be 250,000 stadia, which the ancient astronomers amended to 252,000 stadia as likely to be nearer the truth. Since Eratosthenes probably used Egyptian stadia of 516.73 feet each, his 252,000 stadia were equivalent to 24,662 miles. Unfortunately, the impressive accuracy of this result arose from two compensating errors: Syene and Alexandria are not quite on the same meridian, and the distance between them is really 5,346 Egyptian stadia. The error in latitude is exactly offset by the error in distance. (Eratosthenes' approximation would have been fairly accurate even had he used Olympic stadia of 606 feet.)

ERATOSTHENES AND THE PROBLEM OF THE INHABITED EARTH
The second problem was to determine and map the dimensions and the shape of the inhabited earth. Eratosthenes solved it by a method traditionally attributed to Dicaearchos, by marking off known

distances on two rectangular co-ordinates crossing at Rhodes. Eratosthenes improved his predecessor's evaluation of the actual distances, particularly along the N.–S. axis. Thus, while Dicaearchos had taken the distance between Syene and Lysimachia (Thracia) to be 20,000 stadia (1,864 or 2,236 miles) Eratosthenes made it 13,100 stadia, which is 1,242 or 1,500 miles (the correct figure is 1,087 miles). Since the gnomon was by then being used correctly to measure the altitudes of stars above the horizon, latitudes could be calculated fairly accurately provided only that the chosen observational points were accessible or that reliable correspondents could be found.

Longitudes, on the other hand, were far more difficult to determine, for, lacking accurate chronometers for comparing the time in two places, geographers were forced to rely on the rough and ready calculations of sailors and of Persian or Greek surveyors working in Asia. They even lacked the means of determining the precise interval between the occurrence of a given eclipse of the moon over different meridians—a phenomenon independent of the longitude. (In any case, that method does not seem to have been considered by anyone before Hipparchos.) No wonder, then, that Eratosthenes' First Parallel, which ran from Cape St. Vincent to the mouth of the Ganges and passed through the Strait of Messina, Rhodes, Thapsacos (on the Euphrates), the 'Caspian Gates' and the Himalayas, placed the Strait of Messina as far south as Malta, and misplaced the Himalayas (which were thought to run W.–E. instead of NW.–SE.). Moreover, its 70,800 stadia were 20–30 per cent too long. Errors in the determination of longitudes even affected what were otherwise accurate calculations of latitude, because geographers drew meridians through points that were far from being in alignment. Eratosthenes concluded that the habitable world was an irregular oblong running from east to west, and occupying roughly 130° (*i.e.* just over one-third of the globe), though tapering off towards the north and the south. This region was thought to be surrounded by water on all sides.

Apart from this, Eratosthenes gave free reign to his imagination, particularly in his poems, where he also mentioned two other inhabited regions, one in the northern hemisphere between Cape St. Vincent and the eastern edge of Asia, and another in the southern hemisphere. In the second century B.C. Crates of Mallos drew up a more symmetrical model of the earth which met with great success: its four continents, two in the northern and two in the southern hemisphere, were separated by two oceanic ribbons circling the earth, one along the equator and the other along a great circle passing through the poles.

HIPPARCHOS

Eratosthenes' writings were severely criticized by Hipparchos in three books, of which only fragments have come down to us. Even these have to some extent been distorted by Strabo, who failed to understand them fully. It appears that Hipparchos concentrated on showing which of Eratosthenes' contributions to astronomy and cartography were purely speculative and hence non-scientific. Thus, he accused Eratosthenes of having based his determinations of distances and latitudes on the hearsay evidence of travellers and soldiers. The only correct way of mapping the world was to rely exclusively on astronomical observations: the ascension of stars, the shadow of the gnomon, and the interval between the occurrence of an eclipse of the moon at various places. Before making a model of the inhabited world scientists must collect a wealth of authentic astronomical data, for only then could they hope to avoid false conclusions. Hipparchos knew only too well how justified his critique was, for he himself had committed a great many errors in trying to correct those of Eratosthenes (for instance, he had made the Indus run towards the south-east). Still, his suggestions could have been implemented only by a huge staff of scientific observers stationed in appropriate places, and even nowadays the determination of geographic coordinates is handicapped by the lack of personnel. But Hipparchos was more than a critic; he was also the first to place cartography on a mathematical basis by showing how to project the grid of meridians and parallels on to a plane, and he may well have been the first to represent meridians by convergent straight lines cutting across curved parallels, three centuries before Ptolemy.

MATHEMATICAL GEOGRAPHY AFTER HIPPARCHOS

Like astronomy, scientific geography stood still between the second century B.C. and the second century A.D. The work of Agatharchides, Scymnos and even Artemidoros can safely be passed over in silence. In the last century B.C., Posidonios 'improved' on earlier measurements of the diameter of the earth: he assumed the arc of the Rhodes-Alexandria meridian to be $1/48$ of a great circle (*i.e.* $7\frac{1}{2}°$ instead of $5\frac{1}{4}°$) and its length to be 5,000 stadia (a sailor's estimate which was 25 per cent too high); the two errors cancelled out so that the result, which is reported by Cleomedes as 240,000 stadia (23,546 miles), though less accurate than Eratosthenes', was nevertheless not so very far out. Strabo, on the other hand, claimed that Posidonios' figure was really 180,000 stadia, a result which both he and Ptolemy adopted. Tannery and Duhem have pointed out that it seems most unlikely that both these great men should have committed so grave an error, and they have therefore suggested that Strabo and Ptolemy must have used the Ptolemaic or Royal Egyptian stade of 693 feet; however, this assumption raises serious difficulties which many historians have judged insurmountable.

We shall ignore the geographical comments found in the astronomical works of such popularizers as Geminos and Cleomedes, in Pliny's *Natural History*, in the *Chorography* of Pomponius Mela (first century A.D.) or in the descriptive poem of Dionysios Periegetes (second century A.D.), since none of these texts, though interesting in many respects, merits the term 'scientific'.

THE AUTHORSHIP OF THE *Geography*

Like the *Mathematical Treatise*, Ptolemy's *Geography* marks a turning-point in the history of science, not only by its scope and by the fame it enjoyed right up to the Renaissance, but also by its scientific quality. Unfortunately, the origins of this work are so shrouded in mystery that historians have to be most circumspect before making any final pronouncements on the matter.

We have seen that uncertainty on one essential point, the unit of length which Ptolemy employed, led to estimates differing by as much as 30 per cent. There are graver discrepancies still when it comes to those six books of the *Geography* which classify places into regions and give their geographical co-ordinates. (Book I is a sort of methodological introduction, and Book VIII deals with map-making.) All the extant manuscripts, of which the oldest were written at the end of the twelfth century, contain marked differences not only in their numbers—in Greek literal notation—but also in classification. While some scholars claim that these differences are due to revisions and additions made during the fourth and fifth centuries, others go so far as to assert that the *Geography* itself was a compilation by an unknown Byzantine scholar who, during the tenth–eleventh century, used Ptolemy's data to write the work. The whole problem has remained highly controversial, but there can be no doubt that the extant manuscripts are not as Ptolemy himself would have written them—if, indeed, he wrote any of them at all. Thus the maps were probably made in the thirteenth- to fourteenth-century Byzantine drawing offices, such as that of Maximos Planudes, based on older material some of which dates back to the end of the Roman Empire.

PTOLEMY AND MARINOS OF TYRE

Finally, it is impossible to say to what extent Ptolemy based his work on Marinos of Tyre, whom he often cites—or rather criticizes. It was Marinos who, at the beginning of the second century B.C., tried to meet Hipparchos' criticism that geography lacked adequate astronomical data. From Ptolemy we know that Marinos developed cartography by projecting a grid of meridians and parallels on a plane map according to the 'orthogonal' method, later called 'Mercator's projection', which uses a rectangular grating formed of parallel straight lines. As we know, this method leads to grave distortions north and south of the projected regions, but that did not matter so much at a time when the areas near the equator and the Arctic Circle were practically unknown. Thus, the gravest errors were not so much due to the maps themselves as to false determinations of the geographic co-ordinates, and particularly of the longitudes. According to Marinos the length of the known world, from the Fortunate Islands (Canaries) in the west to the City of Sera in China in the east, was 228°, whereas in reality it is about 130°. Similarly, he made the length of the Mediterranean 62° instead of 42°.

ERRORS AND CORRECTIONS OF PTOLEMY

While Ptolemy undoubtedly made many improvements to the methods of Marinos of Tyre, he committed and incorporated many errors of his own, and for the same reasons. Lacking an adequate number of astronomical observations over a wide enough area, he, like Marinos, was forced to rely on travellers' reports and existing charts. Beyond that, he often failed to consult the best available and most recent sources—hence the many errors in the 8,000 or so numerical data of his *Geography*. Because of these errors, it did not greatly matter that he replaced Marinos' eight parallels (between the equator and Thule, 63° North) with 29 parallels in the *Almagest*, and with 21 in the *Geography*. He misjudged the location of even the most familiar towns, placing Marseilles in the latitude of Byzantium, Babylon $2\frac{1}{2}°$ north of its real position, and extending Ceylon south of the equator. While he drew his meridians 5° apart instead of 15°, as Marinos had done, thus reducing some of the worst errors, he nevertheless left a most misleading picture of the inhabited world: its length from the Canaries to Sera became 180° (as against 228° in Marinos and 126° in reality) and, according to him, a southern continent joined the east coast of Africa, at Mozambique, to China. Ptolemy's distortion of Asia, coupled with Aristotle's even faultier picture, was to have serious geographical repercussions, particularly during the Renaissance.

Even so, Ptolemy's mathematical brilliance led to considerable developments of previous cartographical procedures, such as Marinos' orthogonal projection. Ptolemy devised four systems, the first of which applied to regional maps only. In this, he continued to use Marinos' method of drawing the parallels of latitude and meridians of longitude as straight lines. In the second system, he represented the lines of latitude by parallel curves about the pole as their centre, much as Hipparchos did. The third system was much more complex and was the forerunner of Bonne's projection. It was a modification of the simple conic, in which all the parallels were divided truly, and the meridians were curves drawn through these dividing points. Since these curves became wider the farther removed they were from the central North–South axis, the maps became very distorted towards the western and eastern edges. Ptolemy's fourth system was a plane map inside an armillary sphere; it seems never to have been used.

Before condemning Ptolemy's *Geography*, as Hipparchos would undoubtedly have done, we must remember that a number of errors imputed to him are due to later changes, and that some of his ideas were quite correct, such as that the Asiatic continent extended to the north and east of the Himalayas, and that the equatorial region was habitable (as Polybios and Posidonios had asserted earlier). Ptolemy also came much nearer than his predecessors to the truth of such delicate problems as the sources of the Nile and the shape of South-East Asia. In any case, geography benefited as greatly from his adventurous hypotheses as from Hipparchos' rigour, though Ptolemy may be rightly reproached for having presented as established facts the results of poor deductions drawn from questionable data.

Like the *Almagest* in astronomy, Ptolemy's *Geography* marks the end of ancient science. Subsequent centuries produced a host of descriptions, itineraries, guides, summaries and compilations, like those of Agathemeros and Solinus, none of which led to any advances in real geographical knowledge. What information was obtained from closer contact with distant people and from voyages to mysterious regions, and particularly to Asia, was at best fragmentary and inaccurate, and was never recorded in special works. In the course of the brief fourth-century scientific revival, Pappos, the great commentator on the *Almagest*, also wrote a *Geography* which may well have contained additions and corrections to Ptolemy's work on the subject.

THE PROBLEM OF THE TIDES

We must now say a few words about an important geographical and astronomical phenomenon, namely the tides. Though they were familiar with Herodotos' detailed descriptions of tides in the Red Sea, and though they were intrigued by the nature of the capricious currents prevailing in a number of Mediterranean straits, the Greeks failed to appreciate the true nature of this phenomenon until they ventured beyond the Mediterranean, *i.e.* until Pytheas of Massilia sailed the Atlantic and Alexandrian sailors reached Indian waters about 325 B.C. It was only then that they began to relate tides to the motions of the moon, and that Antigonos of Carystos and the great geographer Eratosthenes became interested in that connection. Eratosthenes tried, in particular, to relate ocean tides to the currents in the Strait of Messina and pointed out that the semi-diurnal ebb and flow was closely connected with the position of the moon above or below the horizon. In the second century, the astronomer Seleucos of Seleucia discovered that tides were not uniform in all oceans and at all periods of the year, and he put forward a meteorological explanation of the phenomenon which agreed with his heliocentric views: in revolving about the earth, though in the opposite sense, the moon compressed the air, which in turn alternatively compressed and decompressed the ocean.

The best of all ancient explanations of the tides was given in Posidonios' *On the Ocean*. Posidonios, on the basis of personal observations at Cadiz, was the first to distinguish the three tidal periods: the semi-diurnal inequality (he showed how the semi-diurnal ebb and flow in the Atlantic depends on the superior and inferior culminations of the moon); the fortnightly inequality (he knew that every syzygy corresponds to a period of high water and every quadrature to a period of low water); and finally, the semi-annual inequality. According to Strabo, Posidonios had learned from the inhabitants of Cadiz that the tides grew larger between equinoxes and solstices, and smaller between solstices and equinoxes, whereas the opposite does in fact occur; but Seneca and Pliny the Elder in the first century A.D., and Priscianus of Lydia in the fourth, all three of whom based their writings on the tides on Posidonios, described the semi-annual inequality correctly, so that it seems likely that Strabo misreported Posidonios. Posidonios even observed the lunitidal interval, *i.e.* the interval between the moon's transit and the occurrence of high water, which, at Cadiz, he gave as two hours, a figure in close correspondence with the actual value at that port. Naturally, neither Posidonios nor any of his Roman or Greek successors suspected the correct explanation. Posidonios thought that the moon, being humid and hot, caused a swelling of the water mass (?), and the tides were to him, above all, one example among many of the doctrine of universal sympathy. While tidal theory made little further progress until the sixteenth century, there was one scientist to improve upon Posidonios' analysis: the Venerable Bede, who, in the seventh century, made a great number of personal observations on the English coast.

CHAPTER 4

Physics and Biology

WHILE THE EXACT SCIENCES—mathematics, astronomy and mathematical geography—rose to great heights during the Hellenistic and Roman epochs, biology and physics remained very much as Aristotle and Theophrastos had left them. Not that books on these subjects were no longer being written or read—on the contrary, the two rival schools of philosophy, the Stoics and the Epicureans, produced a spate of such writings and there were many more popular books as well. But scientific research as such made little progress, for it lacked men of mark and a reliable method. Hence our discussion will be extremely brief.

PHYSICS

Hellenistic physics dealt with two distinct topics: speculations about matter and nature in accordance with metaphysical ideas, and investigations of the laws governing particular phenomena. The Stoics, like the Epicureans, greatly preferred philosophic discussion to the search for scientific truth. The Stoics looked upon the world as the temporary result of a transitory crystallization of the celestial ether, the eternal, pure and active emanation of Zeus. It was the fiery breath or *pneuma* inherent in the divine ether which engendered and supported life and endowed all nature with reason, joining all parts of the universe by the mysterious force of *sympathy*. Periodically, the cosmos was reabsorbed into the pure fire which was, in fact, its material soul and the necessary law of the universe—the great conflagration ensuring palingenesis. As for the Epicureans, we saw earlier that they were quite satisfied with borrowing older atomic theories, adding to them as they went along, though never developing their fruitful implications.

STRATON OF LAMPSACOS

There was, however, one physicist, Straton of Lampsacos, who tried to combine the theories of Democritos and Aristotle into one scientific framework. Of the numerous writings of this important Alexandrian scholar, only some fragments and unauthenticated summaries are extant, but even these few gleanings suffice to show how original and

331

brilliant a man he must have been. In his *On the Vacuum* he adopted Democritos' hypothesis that all substances contain empty spaces, but he rejected the notion that an infinite void surrounded the world, and also the atomic hypothesis, since for him, as for Aristotle, matter was infinitely divisible. He also dismissed two fundamental Aristotelian articles of faith: the theory of natural places, and the theory of the Prime Mover. According to Aristotle, each of the four elements was carried towards a given region of the cosmos by its inherent character. Fire, being 'absolutely light', moves spontaneously towards the edges of the cosmos; the earth, being 'absolutely heavy', moves towards the centre of the universe; air and water, being 'relatively light or heavy', move towards intermediate places. As against this view, Straton held that all elements, fire included, have weight; the lightest bodies are those which contain the largest voids; all bodies move towards the centre of the universe but the heaviest, exercising a greater pressure, come to lie beneath the others. He also presented a purely mechanical interpretation of nature in which there was no need for a Prime Mover or for the teleological conceptions of Aristotle. From Heron's preface to the *Pneumatics*, we know that Straton made a number of experiments with vacuums and airfilled tubes, which, though elementary (the plunging of a tube into water, air or a vacuum, and experiments with cupping glasses), nevertheless show how much Straton wanted to rid himself of all preconceived ideas—how much he tried to rely on the observed facts alone and how he added systematic laboratory experiments to his regular observations of nature.

ALEXANDRIAN ENGINEERS

Unfortunately, Straton's theories were far less well-received by his fellow scientists than by those Alexandrian engineers who, from the third century B.C., devoted much of their energy to the practical application of scientific discoveries. The most famous of them were Ctesibios, his disciple Philon of Byzantium (third century A.D.), and Heron of Alexandria (first century A.D.). In addition to their practical work, they also produced theoretical treatises, some of which have come down to us, for example the *Pneumatics* of Philon, and of Heron, both of which were based on Straton's *On the Vacuum*. Like Straton, they explained the elasticity of fluids, the expansion of bodies and differences of densities by infinitely small voids, but, unable to apply this theory to siphons, they denied the existence of large vacuums. Philon performed a remarkable experiment which, when repeated in the seventeenth century, was to help solve the problem of the nature of air. Lighting a torch in an inverted vessel plunged into water, he found that air was gradually used up by the flame, with the consequent extinction of the flame and a rise in water level inside the vessel. (Lavoisier was the first to explain this phenomenon correctly.) Heron discussed theoretical problems of optics, mechanics and even mathematics, in special works or in special chapters devoted to these subjects.

ARCHIMEDES AND SPECIFIC GRAVITY

It was only when they were able to apply known mathematical methods to the problems to be investigated that Alexandrian physicists obtained their best results. Since we have already discussed their contributions to mechanics, optics and acoustics, we shall merely recall Archimedes' work on statics and hydrostatics in the third century B.C. The greatest merit of his *On the Equilibrium of Planes or of their Centres of Gravity* was that it placed statics on a sound geometrical foundation, even though its discussions of the lever and the centre of gravity as physical phenomena were no more advanced than Aristotle's, which had, moreover, been based on a more adventurous and no less fruitful method. On the other hand, with his *On Floating Bodies* Archimedes became the quite original founder of scientific hydrostatics.

As we know from Vitruvius, Archimedes was also the first to define specific weight. When Hieron, tyrant of Syracuse, suspected that a craftsman whom he had commissioned to make a golden crown as a temple offering to the immortal gods had substituted a measure of silver, he asked Archimedes to settle the question. Archimedes immersed in water successively (1) a quantity of gold equal in weight to the crown; (2) a quantity of silver equal in weight to the crown; and (3) the actual crown, measuring the overflow in each case. Since (1) and (3) did not tally, he was able to calculate from (1) and (2) that the goldsmith had, in fact, stolen some gold, and how much silver he had substituted. From this and a great many similar stories we know that, quite apart from being a brilliant theorist, Archimedes was also a man of practical genius, rightly famed for his scientific inventions and formidable machines of war.

METEOROLOGY

In antiquity, meteorology was considered a brand of physics and held to embrace all the 'atmospheric' phenomena of the sublunary world, including even such purely geographical or geological problems as the sources of rivers, volcanic eruptions and earthquakes, and the structure of mineral deposits.

Aristotle's *Meteorology* and the writings of Theophrastos were the main sources of what, in the Hellenistic and Roman period, were generally mediocre studies and books. Peripatetics, Stoics and even

Epicureans vied with one another to popularize or plagiarize the *Meteorology*, or, as Epicuros and Lucretius did, to temper it with their own cosmology. The only meteorologists meriting special mention were the Greek Posidonios of Apamea (135–*c.* 51 B.C.) and the Roman Seneca (first century A.D.), both of whom were Stoics. While we know that the latter was a brilliant compiler rather than an original scholar, we are not at all certain what Posidonios' contribution was, since none of his meteorological texts is extant. Thus, scholars are still disputing which of his alleged theories influenced subsequent Hellenistic and, above all, Roman writers. We know that on the important question of comets Posidonios agreed with Aristotle in holding that they were formed by the condensation of masses of dry air in the neighbourhood of the ether, there to be set aflame by the celestial fire, just like meteors. Posidonios also agreed with the early Stoics that stars increased in size by absorbing substances which rose up from the earth and penetrated through the layers of air. It is this view which distinguished him most clearly from Aristotle, for it involved a monistic and vitalistic conception of the universe. To Posidonios, the atmosphere was *the* place in which all the constituent elements of the universe intermingled. All these elements were active, dynamic, and were moved by a characteristic *vis vitalis*, acting between the earth and the heavens. As for Seneca, it was his great lucidity, particularly in his *Natural Questions*, which made him a great meteorologist and an expert on comets. He was the only Greco-Roman scientist who adopted the thesis of one Apollonios of Myndos—an Eastern scholar otherwise quite unknown—that comets were planets of a particular kind. But like his colleagues, Seneca was quite wrong when it came to explaining the nature of earthquakes.

SEISMOLOGY

From the beginnings of Greek science, 'physicists' took a keen interest in earthquakes and other seismic phenomena, which so often laid waste parts of Greece, Asia Minor and Southern Italy. They realized clearly that the causes were subterranean, but attributed them to underground lakes and rivers or to pockets of compressed air. Aristotle, in his *Meteorology II*, and his disciples Theophrastos, Callisthenes and Straton, presented a variety of pneumatic explanations, one of which was adopted by Posidonios, whose studies of seismology were more systematic than those of any other scientist of antiquity. From his widespread travels and his extensive knowledge of the literature he was able to classify earthquakes in far greater detail than Aristotle, and hence to appreciate the related phenomena far better. He also investigated the effects of earthquakes on the contours of the earth, while continuing to adhere to the notion that all tremors were caused by the presence of compressed masses of air in underground 'caverns'. Perhaps he was one of those Stoics mentioned by Seneca who equated the earth with the human body and who, under the influence of physicians like Erasistratos, believed that it contained special ducts for carrying its vital humours. Other scientists of unknown name and date substituted a subterranean fire for the cavernous masses of air, and explained that this fire consumed parts of the subsoil, thus causing the earth to subside. According to others again, this fire evaporated the subterranean waters, thus producing explosions of steam and compressed air and hence violent disturbances of the earth's crust. Seneca adopted the pneumatic theory, though he added another explanation of 'simple' tremors: the sudden fall of rocks which had broken away because of their own great weight or because of erosion caused by subterranean waters.

CHEMISTRY

We cannot speak of progress in chemistry, for that science did not see the light of day until the seventeenth century. Nevertheless, the technical literature of the Hellenistic and Roman epoch contains references to what we would call chemical techniques, applied particularly to industrial and pharmaceutical processes. Thus, the geographer Agatharchides of Cnidos (second century B.C.) described the purification of gold by melting the metal with lead or salt, whereas Theophrastos, a century and a half earlier, had mentioned salt but not lead. Pliny was the first to give an accurate account of the manufacture of glass by fusing sand and soda-ash; Dioscorides the first to describe a healing ointment compounded of litharge and oil, the processes of distillation, sublimation and crystallization, and the water bath; Vitruvius, Dioscorides and Pliny added to Theophrastos' accounts of the production and the poisonous effects of mercury. In short, innumerable chemical, and particularly metallurgical, procedures were discussed and often recorded. But the study of these procedures and of their development does not concern the history of science as such, except to show that those who wrote them were interested in scientific questions. None of these writers made the least attempt to explain the facts he reported, or to discuss the nature of chemical composition and decomposition. Chemical phenomena were never studied for their inherent interest, but were simply used to illustrate the philosophical speculations (particularly) of Aristotle, such as that original matter is amorphous, and that each of the different elements to which it gives rise may, in certain circumstances, be transformed into an element of 'related nature', *e.g.* air into water, water into earth, or *vice versa*. Chemistry was simply expected to bring forward corroborative proofs of these hypotheses.

THE ORIGINS OF ALCHEMY

It was this general belief in the interchangeability of the elements, strengthened by uncritical explanations of metallurgical or dyeing techniques and the growing acceptance of mystical illuminism, which led to the remarkable flourishing of alchemy. The term 'alchemy' is derived from the Arabic *al kimiya*, which in turn is derived from the Greek *chuma* ('fusion' of metals) or from the Egyptian *chemi* (black), Hellenized into *chemia*, by which the Greeks referred either to Egypt (the 'black land') or to black lead, the basic substance of all alchemical operations. Alchemy was primarily though not originally concerned with the transmutation of the four 'base' metals—copper, iron, tin, lead—into gold or silver. Research during the past fifty years, particularly by E. O. von Lippmann and Max Wellman, has done much to unravel the tangled skein of the history of ancient alchemy. It made its greatest strides in Egypt during the Ptolemaic period, when generations of artisans attached to the temples developed secret recipes for gilding, silvering, or staining sacred objects—metal, stone, or fabrics—and all these processes came to be called 'dyeing' techniques. At that stage there was no question of transforming common metals into gold. At the beginning of the second century B.C. an occultist scholar from Mendes in Egypt, one Bolos, published a treatise on dyeing, divided into four parts: gold, silver, precious stones, and purple. Fragments of this work have been recovered in a tomb at Thebes. In all probability Bolos was also the pseudo-Democritos to whom a great number of alchemical texts were subsequently attributed, including particularly the *Physica et Mystica*, though what fragments of this work have come down to us seem to have been published, or rather re-published, during the first three centuries of our era, together with other writings of the same type. A careful comparison of the *Physica et Mystica* with the treatise on dyeing and with other known fragments of the writings of the pseudo-Democritos (*i.e.* Bolos) shows that they are related, at least in substance. Since he was the first to combine time-hallowed Egyptian methods with Greek metaphysical and physical conceptions, Bolos may justly be called the real father of alchemy.

However, there is a more recent hypothesis contending that the idea that copper could be changed into gold, and the search for the 'elixir of life' (Arabic version of the Greek ξηρίον = desiccative powder), arose many centuries earlier. Its proponents point out that

25 Animals of the Nile

26 The Anatomy Lesson (?)

magical symbols recalling a number of alchemical formulae were discovered in Syria, whence they are said to have spread, in about the third century B.C., both to China, where the transmutation of cinnabar (mercuric sulphide) into gold seems to have been attempted during the second century, and to Egypt, where mysticism was then at its height. But even if this rather tenuous hypothesis were to be proved correct and the idea of the transmutation of metals did arise before the end of the third century, the role of Bolos would still remain fundamental, since, according to P. Festugière, he established the 'canon' of alchemy: the laws of sympathy and antipathy governing the combinations and separations of all substances or 'natures' in the physical world. It was this canon which led to the enunciation of the traditional alchemical formula: 'One nature is charmed by another', and to the principle that all primary matter is one and hence transmutable. Now the primary substance of all alchemists was black lead, and later mercury, which were to be united with substances having a natural affinity for them and able to confer on them the properties of the noble metals, and so produce gold and silver. Of these properties, the easiest to transfer seemed to be colour, a misconception based on the observation that metals could be gilded and silvered without much difficulty.

For eighteen centuries the alchemists, some of whom were extremely skilful experimenters, gave free reign to their wildest fancies and produced a mountain of texts on their exploits. The Roman Empire was flooded with apocryphal writings attributed by their authors to the revelations of various divine or human sources: Hermes Trismegistes, Isis, Cleopatra, *etc*. In about A.D. 300 Zosimos of Panopolis (Lower Egypt), the greatest ancient alchemist next to Bolos, wrote a chemical treatise in twenty-eight books which was suffused with mystical notions. While his anonymous predecessors had largely ignored mystical influences, Zosimos turned alchemy into a veritable esoteric religion, based on mysterious ceremonies, secret initiations and long spiritual preparation. Henceforth alchemists would be divided into two schools: practitioners and mystics; and it is the latter who accounted for the majority of writers with whom the history of ancient alchemy closes during the fourth and fifth centuries.

THE BIOLOGICAL SCIENCES

While chemistry had never exercised the minds of the greatest scientists of antiquity, biology had made great strides under Aristotle and Theophrastos. Hence its decline in the Hellenistic and Roman era seems particularly marked. Fortunately, while botany and zoology went into a steep decline, anatomy and physiology made remarkable advances which we shall discuss in the next chapter. In other words, there was a change of emphasis in favour of the study of man and away from Aristotelian attempts to fuse all the branches of biology into one overall theory. The only possible exception was Nicolas of Damas, who, in the first century B.C., tried to subordinate botany and biology to Peripatetic ideas in his *On Plants*. This work, which has often been wrongly attributed to Aristotle, was in no way comparable to Aristotle's own writings.

BOTANY

Botany had fallen into the hands of farmers and pharmacologists, and particularly of 'rhizotomists' (root-cutters), some of whom wrote catalogues of plants accompanied by what were generally accurate therapeutic and toxicological indications. Thus Nicander of Colophon, a third-century poet, listed 125 plants in his *Theriaca* and *Alexipharmaca*; Crateuas, court-physician to the famous Mithridates VI (132–63) who himself was the author of a treatise on toxicology, was apparently the first botanist to accompany all his descriptions with illustrations, while restricting the text itself to pharmacological comments. It was probably his drawings which later artists used as their models when they illustrated the famous *De Materia Medica*, a work written in the middle of the first century A.D. by the military surgeon Dioscorides of Anazarbos (Cilicia). Three and a half of its five books give descriptions of some 600 plants, stating for each one the various names by which it was known, the structure of its various parts and its habitat, properties, and therapeutic indications. The rest of the work deals with animals, animal products like milk and honey, and with simple chemical techniques. Plants are classified by their medical properties, and generally divided into families. The work, which is remarkable for its method, was regarded very highly until the end of the Renaissance, and played a great role in the history of descriptive botany. In antiquity, it was frequently reproduced, summarized or amended. Thus the famous sixth-century *Codex Aniciae Julianae* was a (poorly executed) alphabetical list of known plants, accompanied by numerous coloured drawings based on models which probably go back to the time of Dioscorides and certainly to the time of Crateuas (first century B.C.). The work of Dioscorides, despite its restricted scope, was far more accurate and based on more careful personal observation than the botanical works of Pliny the Elder. Of the sixteen books of Pliny's *Natural History* devoted to plants and plant remedies—representing nearly one-half of the work—the most interesting are those dealing with arboriculture and agriculture. While they contain a great deal of valuable information on ancient methods of growing trees and edible plants, they are devoid of critical spirit and personal observations—which is only to be expected from a scientifically unschooled state official.

ZOOLOGY

Hellenistic zoology could not even boast a Dioscorides. After Aristotle, the love for knowledge receded before the love of marvels which fed on the fabulous accounts of voyagers from all parts of the world. Nothing except their repute has remained of Callimachos' *Catalogue of Birds* and the *Compendium* of the writings of Aristotle and his disciples by Aristophanes of Byzantium (both published in the third century). The founders of the literature on zoological marvels were Antigonos of Carytos (*c.* 200 B.C.) and Alexander of Myndos (first century A.D.). Pliny's *Natural History*, Vols. VIII–XI, which deals with terrestrial animals, 'fishes', birds and insects, is a perfect example of this type of writing. It is uncritical, based entirely on hearsay, lacks any order, is full of errors and repeats the most preposterous fables. Even so, Pliny, not content with relying on Aristotle, added more than forty mammals, fifteen amphibians and reptiles, about twenty-five fishes and some thirty insects to Aristotle's classification, thereby increasing our knowledge, if not of ancient science, at least of ancient folklore and of ancient culinary methods. His influence was considerable throughout the Middle Ages and even during the Renaissance. Thus it is from him and from Alexander of Myndos that the author of the *Physiologus* borrowed most of his notions. The *Physiologus* was a collection of Christian allegories based on the marvellous peculiarities of animals, and was the forerunner of the many medieval bestiaries; it was published at Alexandria towards the end of the second century. Similarly, Aelion, who wrote a treatise *On Animals* in seventeen books and *Variae Historiae* (or *Miscellanies*) in fourteen books at about the same time, also based most of his ideas on Pliny and Alexander. All these 'marvellous' texts are clear evidence of great public interest in animals and plants, which, moreover, also expressed itself in works of art and particularly in frescoes and mosaics. The artists of the time produced scrupulously accurate reproductions of the colour and shapes of a great number of vegetables and animals, and especially of birds, fishes, crustaceans and molluscs; clearly their patrons demanded close likenesses. However, art appreciation is no substitute for hard scientific effort.

ANTHROPOLOGY

On the whole, therefore, botany and zoology had greatly declined since the time of Aristotle. Before investigating the contributions of

Alexandria and Rome to anatomy and physiology, we must briefly discuss a science which sprang from biology, geography and philosophy, and which was an original contribution of the Hellenistic age: anthropology. Its founder was the versatile Posidonios (135–51), though even before him historians like Herodotos and Polybios had studied the differences between the various Mediterranean peoples. Still, Posidonios was the first to investigate not only the physical but also the psychological characteristics of different nations, and to propose an explanatory theory. According to him all these differences were due to climatic factors. For instance, southern races were darker than northern because they were more exposed to the sun. Excesses of cold or heat paralysed intelligence, which was therefore most highly developed in temperate zones. Similarly, climatic factors were held responsible for the contrast between the *thymos* of the Celts and Germans, which caused them to be over-excitable, and the *logos* of the Mediterranean people, which represented the victory of reason over instinct. Posidonios also held that men, like animals and plants, prosper only in their natural regions. When they are transplanted they must try to adapt themselves to the new conditions (which is often impossible) or perish. This theory may be called the forerunner of the modern theory of adaptation for, though oversimplified and very inaccurate, it contained a large grain of truth.

CHAPTER 5

Medicine

MEDICAL SCHOOLS

AT ABOUT 300 B.C., medicine, like all the other sciences, was given a
sudden impetus in Alexandria, the capital and leading scientific
centre of the Hellenistic world.

THE TWO ALEXANDRIAN SCHOOLS
Two of the greatest physicians of antiquity, Herophilos and Erasistratos, came to Alexandria to establish medical schools. Both men
were guided by the desire to study the human body and its functions,
and to fit therapeutic procedures to their patients' needs. The new
schools represented no break with their fourth-century predecessors:
Herophilos and Erasistratos had been taught by Praxagoras of Cos
and by Chrysippos the Younger who, as a member of the Neo-
Cnidean School, was strongly influenced by the Sicilian School and
the atomic doctrine of Democritos. Nevertheless, the Alexandrians
did a great deal to develop anatomy and physiology, mainly by
their systematic dissections. In fact, even in Galen's day (second
century A.D.) physicians still came to Alexandria to study their
method. Alexandria eclipsed all other medical centres, of which only
that of Cos, reinvigorated by Praxagoras, and the Dogmatic School
of Athens, founded by Diocles of Carystos in *c.* 380, had survived as
guardians of the Hippocratic tradition. The Alexandrian schools
flourished until the second century A.D., and that of Herophilos,
in particular, produced a number of brilliant physicians including the famous Rufus of Ephesos (beginning of the second century
A.D.).

THE EMPIRICAL SCHOOL
During the second half of the third century physicians began to rebel
against the theoretical conceptions of both the Dogmatic School,
which was considered too much a slave to Hippocratic dogmas, and
the Alexandrian School, whose ideas were held to be too academic. The new physicians were more concerned with the thera-

peutic aspects of medicine. Medicine does, in fact, owe its greatest advances to the fusion of the two views. Still, one trend would often prevail over the other, and at the end of the third century the empirical approach, supported by philosophical scepticism, gained the upper hand over the theoretical approach. Its victory culminated in the founding, at Alexandria, of Serapion's Empirical School. In time, the empiricists began to relent and ceased to frown upon the study of anatomy and the practice of dissection. Up to the time of Galen the school had a large following and included such versatile practitioners as Heraclides of Tarentum.

THE METHODIC SCHOOL

Contempt for theoretical speculations and for the Hippocratic tradition also characterized the third school founded during the Hellenistic and Roman period. This was the Methodic School, established during the second half of the first century B.C. by Themison of Laodicea. Themison was the pupil of Asclepiades of Prusa (Bithynia), who was responsible for the success of Greek medicine in Rome during the first half of the first century. An expert on Epicurean atomic theory, which had taken Rome by storm, Asclepiades explained diseases as the result of disorganizations of the body's atoms. The cure was an appropriate regimen—hydrotherapy and gymnastics—of a kind which delighted his patients. Some of the Methodists came to repudiate all learning and trained their pupils within a few months, while others more wisely returned to the experimental method. The greatest gynaecologist of antiquity, Soranos of Ephesos (beginning of the second century A.D.) was a member of the Methodist School, which flourished until the third century.

THE PNEUMATIC SCHOOL

But a new wind had begun to blow against the obscurantism and Epicureanism of the Methodic School and, at the beginning of the first century A.D., the Pneumatic School was founded by Athenaeos of Attalia. This school, which restored theory to honour and which followed in the footsteps of the Stoics and the Dogmatic School, explained that physiological equilibrium was due to the influence of the *pneuma*, the vital breath animating all parts of the body. The leading member of the school was Archigenes of Apamaea (early first century A.D.).

THE ECLECTIC SCHOOL

The Pneumatists, as firm believers in training and scientific research, lent a ready ear to the theories of other great physicians, past or present. At the end of the first century, a pupil of Athenaeos, Agathinos of Sparta, founded the Eclectic or Episynthetic School, which appropriated all that seemed best in the doctrines of the other sects. While some of its members, for example Herodotos (end of first century), tended towards the Methodic School, others, such as Aretaeos of Cappadocia, were closer to the Pneumatic.

GALEN

Eclecticism, which appeared the wisest of all doctrines, was practised in fact, though not in theory, by the greatest physician of antiquity after Hippocrates, Galen of Pergamos, whose work dazzled his contemporaries. He was taught by Hippocratic, Empiricist and Methodist teachers, and frequented most medical centres of his day. Thus his work, though steeped in Aristotelian principles, transcended the doctrinal differences among the various sects. Galen was the last great figure in ancient medicine, for while many of his successors were good practitioners and capable commentators, they contributed little that was original or valuable.

CHRONOLOGICAL SURVEY

The curve depicting the history of scientific medicine during the Hellenistic and Roman period has a different shape from that of the exact sciences. At first the ups and downs are less marked, and the third-century peak reflecting the establishment of the Alexandrian schools and the resulting advances in anatomy and physiology, followed by the empirical reaction and its beneficial effects on therapy, does not continue into the second century, whereas the peak of the other sciences does. On the other hand, even during the least brilliant period, from the second century B.C. to the beginning of the second century A.D., there were many excellent practitioners, especially between 150 B.C. and 50 B.C. Again, the establishment of the Pneumatic School was the signal for a scientific rebirth which culminated in the work of the two great men from Ephesos, Rufus and Soranos, both of whom flourished at the beginning of the second century A.D. Finally, at about the same time that Ptolemy wrote his great encyclopaedic work on astronomy, the *Almagest*, Galen produced his monumental synthesis of ancient medicine.

Rather than discuss the various sects in detail, we shall, in what follows, describe the chronological progress of Hellenistic medicine as a whole, and close with a discussion of such special branches of medicine as ophthalmology, surgery, and hippiatry. Throughout, we shall stress the purely scientific aspects of medical study.

THE BEGINNINGS OF ALEXANDRIAN MEDICINE

DISSECTION

We have seen that the first of the Lagides, Ptolemaios I Soter and and his son Ptolemaeos II Philadelphus, counselled by two able Aristotelians, Demetrios of Phalera and Straton of Lampsacos, did their utmost to attract the best scientists of the time to Alexandria. Though no one can tell whether the Museum contained a special medical section, physicians flocked to Alexandria not only because they knew that liberal treatment awaited them there, but mainly because she offered them unequalled possibilities of dissecting human bodies. For while there is evidence of occasional dissections as early as in the fourth century B.C., it seems that public dissections of the human body were a Ptolemaic innovation and remained an almost exclusive privilege of the school of Alexandria. The general explanation of this phenomenon is that the Alexandrians were familiar with the Egyptian tradition of embalming bodies and hence felt no revulsion at the sight of corpses. A number of ancient authorities, including Celsus, have even accused Erasistratos of performing vivisection on prisoners condemned to death, and Galen's silence on this point does little to clear his predecessor's name.

HEROPHILOS

Herophilos, born in Chalcedon in the last third of the fourth century, and the somewhat younger Erasistratos were respectively responsible for turning anatomy and physiology into scientific disciplines. Both men came to Alexandria to teach and practise medicine and to found rival schools. A former pupil of Praxagoras, who had restored the school of Cos to its former greatness, Herophilos wrote a number of works, now lost, including an *Anatomy* and treatises on the eye and the pulse. What little we do know of him makes it quite clear that he was a shrewd observer and singularly free of preconceived ideas, even those based on the authority of Hippocrates. He shared with Theophrastos and Straton a contempt for the Aristotelian notion of 'cause', and his scepticism extended to all theories. No wonder, therefore, that the Empirical School was largely founded by Herophileans.

In anatomy, Herophilos was particularly interested in the nervous and vascular systems, in the reproductive and digestive organs, and in the eyes. He identified the brain as the centre of the nervous system and reaffirmed with Alcmaeon and Hippocrates that it was the seat of the intelligence, which Aristotle had placed in the heart. He recognized the importance of the fourth ventricle, which, according to him, housed the soul; he discovered the *calamus scriptorius* (a lozenge-shaped region in the hinder part of the rachidian bulb), the *torcular Herophili*, the four vessels where the cerebral veins unite, and gave a precise description of the meninges. He was also the first to distinguish sensory nerves from the mass of nerves and tendons which his predecessors had lumped together, and to show that they ran from the skin to the spinal cord and to the brain. He failed, however, to isolate the motor nerves.

Herophilos made the first clear distinction between arteries and veins; arteries, 'six times' thicker than veins, contained blood in addition to *pneuma*, but lost their fluids after death. They received their blood and their impetus from the heart, the pulse-beats and rhythm of which Herophilos determined by means of a clepsydra. According to him, the pulse was directly related to respiration; he noticed the existence of a pulmonary systole and diastole, comparable with the arterial pulse but doubled. This rhythm explained the four phases of the respiratory cycle: intake of fresh air, distribution of the fresh air to the body, intake of foul air coming from the body, evacuation of the foul air. His explanation is clear proof of Herophilos' remarkable physiological aptitude.

He was also the first physician to isolate the lacteal vessels, whose function was to be explained by Aselli in the seventeenth century. Above all he was responsible for considerable theoretical and practical advances in gynaecology, obstetrics and embryology. Though keenly interested in pathology and therapy, he failed to make contributions on a par with his work in anatomy. Of Herophilos' numerous disciples who helped to maintain the renown of his 'first' school during the third century, the foremost was Demetrios of Apamaea, a famous gynaecologist and the first physician to give a precise description of dropsy.

ERASISTRATOS

Erasistratos was born in Iulis on the Isle of Cos at the end of the fourth century. He studied medicine, first in Athens where he was the pupil of Metrodoros, the third husband of one of Aristotle's daughters, and where he became steeped in Peripatetic methods, and then at Cnidos, where he was greatly influenced by the teachings of Chrysippos the Younger and, later, by the Atomists. Finally he settled in Alexandria where, as we saw, he remained until his death. He wrote a number of works, all lost, notably on fevers, haemoptysis, abdominal pathology, anatomy and hygiene.

Though known as a great physiologist, Erasistratos was first and foremost the Father of Comparative Anatomy, a discipline that Aristotle had merely outlined, and of Pathological Anatomy, *i.e.* the study of structural changes due to morbid conditions. He extended Herophilos' studies of the nerves and the brain and, in particular, made a detailed investigation of the cavities and the convolutions in the brains of man, hare and stag, whence he rightly concluded that the number of convolutions varied with the degree of intellectual development. He was the first to distinguish between motor and sensory nerves, and took a keen interest in the heart and the vascular system. A great many physiological terms describing various aspects of the circulatory system were originally coined by him.

ERASISTRATOS ON THE CIRCULATION OF THE BLOOD

The main obstacle to the full understanding of the circulatory system had always been ignorance of those reversible chemical processes by which the blood absorbs and releases oxygen and absorbs and rids itself of carbonic acid. Erasistratos took over from Praxagoras and Chrysippos the belief that only the veins contained blood, while the arteries were filled with air—a notion based on post-mortem observations. He also held that blood was formed in the liver. Despite these grave errors, his work led him to discoveries that were not to be excelled until more than eighteen centuries later, when Harvey discovered the continuous circulation of the blood. Erasistratos appreciated that the heart was the motor which caused the blood to flow. He asserted that the left ventricle contained pure air which was carried from the lungs by the pulmonary vein, 'a vein resembling an artery', that the right ventricle contained blood coming from the liver by way of the vena cava, and that, with every contraction of the heart, the blood from the right ventricle was sent into the lungs by the pulmonary artery, 'an artery resembling a vein'. While the air of the left ventricle was expelled into all parts of the body through the aorta and the arteries during the systole, the blood from the vena cava and the air from the pulmonary vein was drawn into the heart during the diastole, when the sigmoid valves of the pulmonary artery and of the aorta prevented the reflux of blood and air into the heart. A 'tricuspid' valve in the vena cava and a 'bicuspid' valve in the pulmonary vein were said to close the two vessels during their dilatation. Thus, unlike Herophilos, Erasistratos wrongly attributed the functions of the auricles to the two pulmonary vessels, and believed that most of the blood supplied by the liver to the vena cava was distributed to the entire body—with the exception of the lungs—by the veins. Obstructions of the bile duct caused the bile to be diverted into the vena cava, causing jaundice. Because of these ideas Erasistratos might easily be dismissed, were it not that he put forward a brilliant hypothesis: finding that the arteries of living men released blood when they were cut, he assumed that the veins were joined to the arteries by minute vessels, and that the sudden cutting of an artery caused an escape of air and hence an influx of blood from the nearest vein, because 'nature abhors a vacuum'. The same influx also occurred during certain diseases. Erasistratos' hypothesis could not be verified, for there was no optical means of demonstrating the presence of capillary networks. Hence Galen rejected it when, four and a half centuries later, he showed that the arteries of living beings carry blood continuously.

In the course of developing his capillary theory, Erasistratos also made considerable contributions to the physiology of respiration. He recognized that the epiglottis closes the larynx during swallowing, thus preventing liquids and solids from entering the trachea. He gave an accurate description of the structure and function of the gastric muscles. According to him, peristalsis was responsible for mashing the food and for mixing it with air introduced by the gastric arteries; he was therefore an opponent of Diocles, who held that food was fermented or broken down in the stomach, and of Aristotle, who had likened digestion to cooking. From the stomach and the intestine, the alimentary juice was transported to the liver which transformed it into blood. Erasistratos also discovered lymphatic vessels in the mesentery, but failed to appreciate the nature of the lymphatic circulation.

THE *pneuma*

Pneuma, rather than blood, played the main role in Erasistratos' physiology. He distinguished between a vital *pneuma* and a psychic *pneuma*, located respectively in the left ventricle of the heart and in the ventricles of the brain. Both were formed from the air which passed into the lungs during respiration—which he described with great care—and thence into the heart by the pulmonary veins. In the heart, that part of the air which had become vital *pneuma* was carried either to the brain, where it underwent a second transformation into psychic *pneuma*, or else into other parts of the body by the arterial system. The psychic *pneuma* was carried to various parts of the body by the nervous system, there to cause muscular movements. Blood nourished the tissues and the organs; *pneuma* moved them. In short, Erasistratos' system was a kind of synthesis between the pneumatic theory, so dear to physicians of the Dogmatic School like Praxagoras, and the atomistic naturalism of Democritos. The 'occult' forces found in the physiology of the Peripatetics and of Herophilos were discarded, nor was there any question of the body consisting of atoms separated by small voids, for nature was said so to abhor a vacuum that it continually filled those empty spaces which suddenly form in the living body. In this way, Erasistratos managed to explain the incessant renewal of tissues and body fluids by appropriate nourishment and, as we say, the sudden appearance of venous blood during arterial injuries.

PATHOLOGY AND THERAPY

Being a mechanist physiologist, Erasistratos rejected the humoral theories of the Dogmatic School, and explained that while deficiencies in nourishing juice (chyle) might account for apoplexy, paralysis and jaundice, most other diseases were due to plethora, *i.e.* to the accumulation of misdirected substances in various parts of the body. Plethora was generally accompanied by fever, due to the transfer into the arteries of venous blood under high pressure, and hence by pneumatic disequilibrium.

Holding these views, Erasistratos quite naturally preferred preventive hygiene to therapy. Thus he prescribed a vegetarian diet for plethorics and rich meat food for hydropics. He also prescribed baths, massages, walks and the moderate use of wine. Nevertheless, for particular cases he prescribed a series of strange ointments, such as a liniment containing copper, grilled truffles, myrrh, saffron and honey. Many of Erasistratos' main conclusions were based on keen observation and original investigations, as, for instance, the famous weighing experiment. Having weighed a bird, he locked it in a cage and then weighed it again as well as its droppings, after it had fasted for a number of days. From the fact that its weight had decreased, he concluded correctly that some of its substance had been volatilized. Unfortunately, he paid greater attention to *a priori* assumptions and metaphysical speculations than Herophilos or Theophrastos had done, and his successors accentuated this tendency to such an extent that, not surprisingly, none of them has left his mark on the history of medicine.

Nevertheless, the influence of the two founders of Alexandrian medicine went far beyond the confines of their two schools: their works and the controversies which they provoked, the impetus which they gave to further research, and the success of the experimental procedures initiated by them, were the main causes of subsequent advances and of increasing medical specialization.

THE FIRST EMPIRICISTS

All attempts to raise medicine to the level of a true science were keenly opposed by those physicians to whom medicine was, above all, the art of healing diseases. Celsus has told us that they considered it 'idle to search for the obscure causes of natural actions, because nature is impenetrable; the proof of which is the disagreement between all those who discuss such questions'. Moreover, since the treatment had to vary from place to place, they pointed out that the causes of diseases could not be universal, nor could understanding the causes of wounds, for example, ever lead to the correct cure. The only thing that counted was practical experience, and according to Celsus:

Medicine, in its infancy, was never the child of reason but of experiments . . . if physicians have been successful it is because they have sought for cures not in obscure causes or natural actions, which they all interpret in different ways, but in fruitful experiment.

Because of its exclusive reliance on experiment, a new school, founded in about 200 B.C., came to be known as the Empirical. Many of its members kept in close contact with Sceptic philosophers (*cf.* Galen's *Sermo adversus empiricos*), and the famous Sceptic Sextos Empiricos was himself an empirical physician. The founders of the school were Philinos of Cos and Serapion of Alexandria, who was undoubtedly the author of the three principles of the art of medicine which Glaucias of Tarentum popularized towards the turn of the second century B.C. as the *empirical tripod*. These were (1) personal observation (*autopsy*) and personal experiment (*teresis*); (2) the transmitted body of older observations (*history*); (3) the application of remedies, proven in similar diseases, to the treatment of new diseases (*analogy*). All the rules were clearly based on experience and not on theories or logical deductions.

Luckily this school, which pretended to turn its back on theoretical science, never succeeded in doing so completely. One of its two founders, Philinos of Cos, a former pupil of Herophilos, developed his teacher's experimental approach, as we have seen, and while hostility against Hippocratic ideas was very marked in the beginning, it became less severe under Glaucias, who concentrated his attacks on the theoretical part of Aristotle's writings. We shall see that Heraclides of Tarentum managed to reconcile theoretical research with the empirical approach, and it is largely due to this wisdom that the Empirical School produced, if not the greatest, yet some of the leading physicians of antiquity.

ROMAN PHYSICIANS BEFORE GALEN

ROMAN MEDICINE
During the second century B.C. the centre of Mediterranean cultural life shifted to Rome from the East. The repercussions of this move which, as we saw, were felt by all the sciences, were particularly marked in the history of medicine. At the beginning of the third century, Archagatos the Peloponnesian was the first trained physician

to settle in Rome, which had previously known only quacks. In the following century medicine suffered a setback as a result of Cato's vigorous campaign against Greek ideas. Then, at the beginning of the first century B.C., the great Asclepiades of Bithynia founded the first Roman medical school, and in A.D. 14 came the creation of an official *Scola Medicorum* which continued until the reign of Theodoric (late fifth century). Similar schools were opened in Marseilles, Bordeaux and Saragossa. Rome attracted physicians from all over the world because of its wealthy clientele, and also because of growing Roman interest in medicine which is vouched for by Celsus. Most of the physicians were Greeks who found Rome favourable to their study of therapeutic, though not of theoretical, problems. The only medical sect to originate in Rome was the Methodist, which was clearly anti-scientific in its principles and in their application; all the other sects had their 'Schools' or leaders in the East—the venerable school of Cos, the Dogmatic School, the schools of Herophilos and of Erasistratos, the Empirical School, and finally the Pneumatic and Eclectic schools. Strangely enough, this proliferation of schools went hand in hand with a lessening of rivalry, as may be seen in the very name of the youngest and in the fact that a number of famous physicians owed allegiance to more than one sect. Hence it was not so much competition between sects as the trend towards specialization (*e.g.* the development of gynaecology and ophthalmology, and the existence of a number of great physicians, particularly during the reign of Trajan) which ensured the vitality of medical science.

ASCLEPIADES OF BITHYNIA

Apart from two disciples of Herophilos, Demetrios of Apamaea (a famous gynaecologist) and Andreas of Carystos (an oculist and pharmacologist), both of whom lived at the end of the third century B.C., three men merit the attention of historians. The first of these is Asclepiades of Bithynia, born at Prusa in 124 B.C. Having studied medicine in various Eastern cities, no doubt including Alexandria, he finally settled in Rome. His medical theory, which was based on the teachings of Erasistratos and on Neo-Cnidean mechanistic theories, also bore the marks of Epicureanism, a philosophy then in great vogue in the capital. In one of his *Elements*—of which he wrote some twenty, all lost—he explained that the human body is a compound of particles called *oncoi*, *i.e.* special atoms of different form and properties. While the *oncoi* of the soul were said to be smooth and round, others were square, triangular, or oval. Respiration was the intake of atoms of air, and good health was dependent on smooth evacuation of atoms by the pores. Blocked pores were the cause of fever and plethoric diseases, while distended pores gave rise to various forms of debility. Asclepiades also subscribed to humoral and pneumatic theories, and his keen observations enabled him to isolate malaria and to distinguish between pleurisy and pneumonia. But his fame rests mainly on the originality of his therapeutic methods. Faithful to his theories and anxious, according to Pliny the Elder, to please his Roman clients, he scorned the brutal procedures of his colleagues and became the great advocate of 'the curative action of nature'. He held that it was the physician's task to 're-establish the symmetry of atoms quickly and agreeably' by means of fasting, wine or water, gymnastics, baths and massages. Hence, Asclepiades has been called 'the first of the hygienists'.

METHODISM AND EMPIRICISM DURING THE FIRST CENTURY B.C.

Pliny's and Galen's adverse opinion notwithstanding, Asclepiades himself was no charlatan. However, his reputation was ruined by the charlatanism of most of the Methodists, who, because the founder of their school, Themison of Laodicea, had been a pupil of Asclepiades, wrongly cited the latter's authority for their own over-simplified views. Themison recognized two, and only two, pathological conditions: *status strictus* and *status laxus*, caused respectively by constriction or dilatation of the pores, to be cured by revulsives or tonics. No wonder that the school could turn out fully-fledged physicians within six months!

A contemporary of Asclepiades, Heraclides of Tarentum, is said to have been the best physician of the Empirical School. He was trained by Herophilians and wrote a number of works on dietetics, surgery, therapeutics, military surgery, and on Hippocrates. His research bore mainly on pharmacology and toxicology, and he substituted for the imported and complicated remedies prescribed by other Empiricists such well-known substances as cinnamon, pepper, balsam and, above all, opium, both as a sedative and also as a hypnotic. In fact, Heraclides remained much closer to Herophilos than to the Empiricists. He probably performed dissections of the human body and was bold enough to deduce the psychological consequences of certain of his clinical findings, after first subjecting his conclusions to independent verifications.

Apollonios of Citium, another Empiricist of the first half of the first century B.C., owes his fame to the destiny of one of his books. In the fourth century A.D. his *Commentary* on the Hippocratic *Articulations*, which dealt chiefly with the reduction of dislocations, was used by the Byzantine physician Nicetas as part of his collection of surgical treatises. The manuscript, containing remarkable illustrations, some of which go back to a much earlier tradition, was discovered in Crete in the fifteenth century by Johannes Lascaris and greatly influenced physicians during and after the Renaissance.

CELSUS

Celsus was another physician who, though officially an Empiricist, was receptive of other doctrines, particularly those of Hippocrates, Erasistratos and the Methodists. At the beginning of the Christian era he wrote the *De re medica*, which was intended to familiarize Rome with the history of the precepts of medicine. The Latin text of this work mentions that the author, the patrician Aulus Cornelius Celsus, was a contemporary of Tiberius. Max Wellmann has claimed that the work was a translation of a Greek original. In fact, Celsus was a writer on many subjects, not a professional physician, and his book was part of an encyclopaedia of which the other volumes, unhappily lost, dealt with such varied subjects as agriculture, military science, rhetoric, philosophy and law. Even so, modern scholars have rejected Wellmann's opinion, which they claim is supported neither by the text nor by what is known of Celsus' life.

The *De re medica*, which is second in importance only to the Hippocratic Collection and the works of Galen and on a par with the *Pathology* of Aretaeos of Cappadocia, consists of eight books. Book I begins with a most interesting history of the medical schools and goes on to discuss methodology and dietetics; Books II, III, and IV deal with prognosis and therapy; Books V and VI with pharmacology (historical summary and remedial theory); Book VII with surgery; and Book VIII with bone diseases. The author makes no claim that his work is anything more than a compilation. The work is lucid, well-documented, written in clear and elegant Latin; the symptoms of diseases and the therapy (dietetic and pharmaceutical) are described with great accuracy; there are quite remarkable pages on the history of medicine, on clinical indications, on abdominal and eye surgery—Celsus was the first to describe the removal of a cataract—and much sound advice on daily conduct and healthy living. While Celsus was admittedly no physician himself, and made no original contributions to medical science, it is difficult to understand why his writings were ignored until the Renaissance, for few other authors have shown so much good sense, judgment and impartiality.

By the side of his work, the collections of remedies and extravagant prescriptions scattered in Pliny's *Natural History* or combined into the *Compositiones medicamentorum* of Scribonius Largus are of very minor importance.

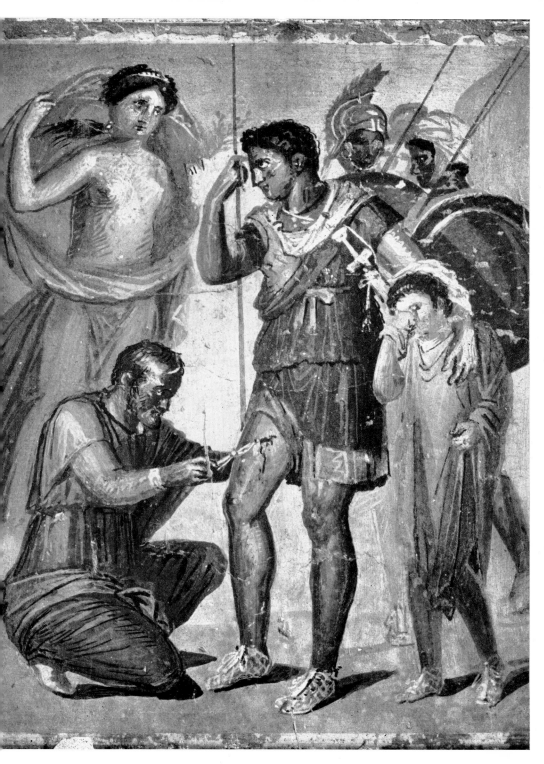

27 Surgeon tending Aeneas

28 Woman pharmacist (Gaul)

THE SCIENTIFIC REACTION IN THE FIRST CENTURY OF OUR ERA

The popularity enjoyed by 'Methodist' and other quacks was a threat not only to public health but also to the very future of medicine. Fortunately there was a reaction against their worst abuses and their philosophical prejudices. The theorists of the first century A.D. founded their physiology and pathology on the system taught by the Stoics. The reader will recall the importance they attached to the *pneuma*, which also played an important role in some Hippocratic texts of Erasistratos, and in the Neo-Cnidean school. The *pneuma*, or rather the *spiritus*, as the Romans called it, gradually became an all-embracing principle, said to endow all animals, and especially men, with the vital forces contained in the celestial ether; it was this principle which preserved health, provided only that its tension, reflected by the pulse, was regular. While the pneumatic theory was rather narrow, its adherents were wise enough not to ignore observations and to adopt what was best in the other schools, so much so that Agathinos of Sparta, a pupil of Athenaeos of Attalia, the founder of the Pneumatic School, established the Eclectic School, whose members were free to choose among the doctrines of the Empiricists, the Methodists or the Pneumatics. Some members of the new school appear to have been good practitioners and authentic scientists, though we know very little about their work. Athenaeos wrote a medical treatise in thirty books which was highly praised by Galen, and Agathinos was an (over-zealous) advocate of cold baths. Of his many pupils, Herodotos, Leonides and, above all, Archigenes, a friend of the Methodists, became famous. Herodotos was undoubtedly the first physician to have identified smallpox and to have stressed its epidemic character; Leonides of Alexandria is known for his keen observations and for his surgical descriptions; and Archigenes, who was a very popular physician at the beginning of the second century, became the best and most illustrious representative of the Pneumatic School. As such, he concentrated on the pulse and established ten criteria for measuring it: amplitude, speed, pressure, beat, frequency, precision, evenness, regularity, flow and rhythm. He distinguished between dicrotic, ardent, formicant, capricant, and vermicular pulse-beats—a remarkable classification which Galen extended even further. Archigenes was also a student of pathology and classified fevers, analysed the course and causes of diseases, described leprosy and a number of Indian diseases, and so on.

RUFUS OF EPHESOS

Nevertheless his fame was eclipsed by that of three other pre-Galenic physicians: Rufus, Soranos, and Aretaeos. Rufus of Ephesos spent a number of years in Alexandria, where he became imbued with

Aristotelian ideas and the tradition of Herophilos and Erasistratos. Then he settled in Rome, where he practised medicine during the reign of Trajan (beginning of the second century). He wrote some forty medical works which were rediscovered by the Arabs during the Middle Ages. Twelve of these works are partially preserved, including his treatise *On the Names of the Parts of the Human Body*, *On the Anatomy of the Human Body* (which may be apocryphal), *On the Pulse*, and *On Diseases of the Kidneys and the Bladder*. Although dissections in Rome were generally performed on monkeys, Rufus managed, *inter alia*, to give a striking description of the human eye, including an account of the structure and the function of the crystalline humour, which remained unequalled—and misunderstood—until the seventeenth century. His description of the heart was very similar to that of Erasistratos, though he realized the arteries contained blood as well as *pneuma*; above all, he was the first physician, practically the only one before Harvey, to appreciate that the apex of the heart touches the chest wall during the systole and not during the diastole; for more than fifteen centuries physicians continued to believe that the arterial pulse-beats coincide with the period of dilatation of the heart. Similarly, while his description of nerves was based on the anatomy of Herophilos and Erasistratos, he distinguished clearly between sensory and motor nerves and described the optic chiasma. In pathology, Rufus made a detailed study of leprosy, bubonic plague, erysipelas and epithelioma. He discovered the salutary function of fevers (which he tried to induce artificially), and described the main diseases of the male genitourinary organs, giving, among other things, a remarkable account of the removal of bladder stones. He also made interesting observations on psychological conditions and on some diseases of women.

SORANOS OF EPHESOS

One of Rufus' contemporaries and compatriots, Soranos of Ephesos, was the greatest gynaecologist of antiquity. A Methodist by affiliation, but well-versed in anatomy and close to the Empiricists, Soranos wrote some thirty books on different medical subjects, the most famous of which, *On Diseases of Women*, was rediscovered in the nineteenth century. An abridged version of the work by Moschion published in the fifth or sixth century for the use of midwives was, however, well-known during the Middle Ages, and a tenth-century manuscript of that version contained interesting anatomical drawings illustrating the ideas of the times. In his original work, Soranos gave a remarkably accurate description of the female genitalia and of the possible positions of the foetus. He was a keen opponent of the brutal methods of the Cnidean School and of the common superstitious methods of dealing with pregnancy and childbirth. He recommended the use of the speculum, of the obstetric chair—depicted on many ancient statues—and of intra-uterine injections, and gave an exceptionally lucid account of such conditions as metritis, metrorrhagia, amenorrhœa, scirrhus, uterine fibroma, hysteria, nymphomania, *etc.*, for all of which he suggested reasonable methods of treatment. He also gave valuable advice on the care of the new-born child. Nor were his contributions restricted to gynaecology and obstetrics, for among various other extant fragments of his works is a treatise *On Acute and Chronic Diseases* in the Latin adaptation of Caelius Aurelianus, a fifth-century African physician. Despite his adherence to the Methodist principle of considering all morbid states to arise from contractions or dilatations of the pores, Soranos made a large number of meticulous clinical studies and hence a host of differential diagnoses. But his fame rests mainly on his work in gynaecology, for, as a clinician, he was overshadowed not only by Galen but also by a member of the Pneumatic School, Aretaeos of Cappadocia, who flourished just before, or at about the same time as, Galen.

ARETAEOS OF CAPPADOCIA
Aretaeos, of whose life little is known, was the author of two treatises of four books each, written in the Ionian dialect: *On the Causes and Signs of Acute and Chronic Diseases* and *On the Treatment of Acute and Chronic Diseases*. These two works, which have been handed down to us in a somewhat mutilated state, are rightly considered the best ancient texts on their subjects. In them, Aretaeos tried not only to give an accurate account of the symptoms of a great number of diseases, but also to determine their external or internal causes and the appropriate therapy. He gave outstanding descriptions of pleurisy, phthisis and pneumonia, and also dealt with asthma, various forms of paralysis (ataxia, anaesthesia, paraplegia, apoplexy), tetanus, epilepsy, hysteria, cholera, dysentery, migraine, icterus, *etc*. He was the first to identify and describe diabetes; he associated fainting with cardiac conditions and distinguished between the effects of spinal and of brain lesions; that is, he realized that the latter, unlike the former, affect the opposite side of the nervous system. He gave brilliant descriptions of such psycho-pathological conditions as mania and melancholia. His remedies were few and mainly based on manipulation and diet—laxatives, emetics, enemas, cupping glasses, leeches and blood-lettings, douches and frictions. Against phthisis he prescribed trips to the seaside; against debility a change of diet, walking and distraction. All in all, it would appear that Aretaeos did not adhere closely to the precepts

of the Pneumatic School to which he is said to have belonged, for though he stressed the importance of the *pneuma* and the *tonus*, he also considered the effects of the humours—as Hippocrates had done. Moreover, he classified diseases according to Methodist precepts and based his etiology on a detailed knowledge of anatomy, like the Alexandrians. While some scholars have therefore suggested that Aretaeos was no more than an imitator of Archigenes of Apamaea, to whom, in fact, he bears some resemblance, their view is generally rejected today. The modern view is that, while Aretaeos was un-doubtedly *influenced* by Archigenes, he was a great physician in his own right and by his own original contributions. We must end this brief list with Marinos of Alexandria, heir to the tradition of Hero-philos and of Erasistratos, who also flourished during the reign of Trajan. He was the author of an excellent anatomy in twenty books, wrote brilliant studies particularly of the cranium and the vertebral column, and was the teacher of the great anatomist Quintos, and —through his pupils Satyros and Numisianos—of Galen. Galen him-self was a great admirer of Marinos, to whom he acknowledged his indebtedness.

GALEN

By the scope and quality of his work, and by his tremendous influence on the history of medicine, Galen shares with Hippocrates the honour of having been the greatest physician of antiquity.

THE MAN
Galen's life is well-known from the many personal remarks scattered throughout his writings. He was born at Pergamos in A.D. 129–30, and his father, who was an architect, gave him his first introduction to scientific and philosophic thought. One night, Asclepios, the god of medicine, whose famous temple was in Pergamos, came to Galen's father in a dream and instructed him to make a physician of his son, then seventeen years old. Pergamos was a city in which physicians abounded, and young Galen had no difficulty in finding highly qualified teachers. After his father's death, he spent nine years visiting the great medical centres of Smyrna, Corinth and Alexandria, where he completed his training. While he concentrated on anatom-ical studies, he also attended the lectures of Julianos the Methodist and of the philosophers belonging to other sects. When he returned to Pergamos at the age of twenty-eight years he became physician to the College of Gladiators, where he practised surgery and dietetics for the next four years.

In 161–162, he went to Rome. His public lectures and his great clinical skill quickly brought him fame, powerful friends and no less powerful enemies. We do not know whether it was his enemies or the terrible epidemic which forced Galen to flee the capital in 166, just as he was about to be appointed physician to the emperor. If it was to escape the epidemic, as many scholars have claimed, he miscalculated badly since, far from removing him from the plague, his visits to Cyprus, Palestine and Syria took him nearer to its centre. He returned to Pergamos, where he had barely resumed his work with the School of Gladiators when Marcus Aurelius summoned him to assist in preparing the campaign against the Germans in Aquileia (Northern Italy). On the sudden death of Lucius Verus, the joint-emperor, Marcus Aurelius took Galen back to Rome and appointed him personal physician to Commodus, the heir-apparent. For the next twenty years, Galen divided his time between administering to the needs of the Roman nobility and the publication of his works. In 192, a fire destroyed the temple of Pax in which most of his manuscripts had been stored. Shortly afterwards Galen left Rome, most probably for Pergamos, his native town, where he died in about A.D. 200 at the age of seventy years.

GALEN'S WORK

Full of ambition and overriding pride, energetic and violent, given to intrigue and anxious to impress the world, Galen lived a tempestuous and exceptionally brilliant life. Apart from more than 500(!) medical works, he wrote a number of books on rhetoric, philology and philosophy, including a treatise *On Scientific Proof*, of which only some fragments are extant, and a treatise *On the Passions of the Soul and its Errors*, which was largely autobiographical. Since it would take us too far afield to discuss the chronological order of all his many works—he himself compiled two annotated bibliographies—we merely record that he began to write at the age of eighteen years, when he was still a pupil of the anatomist Satyros of Pergamos, and that he apparently wrote his works on philosophy, anatomy and physiology before his first departure from Rome in 165–166, and his treatises on pathology and therapy after his return to Italy. The purely medical writings of Galen can be grouped under the following headings.

(1) Introductions to medicine, including particularly the *De Sectis*, the *De Optima Doctrina* and the *Sermo Adversus Empiricos*, in which he gave a vivid account of the main schools of medicine.

(2) The many *Hippocratic Commentaries*.

(3) The works of anatomy and physiology, which contain the most substantial part of Galen's doctrine and include the *De Usu Partium Corporis Humani*, the fifteen books of the *De Anatomicis Administrationibus*, and four smaller books of the *Synopsis de Pulsibus*.

(4) The less important writings on etiology and diagnosis.

(5) The numerous works on hygiene (notably the six books *On Hygiene*) and on dietetics, pharmacology and, above all, on therapy. The fourteen books on therapeutic method (*Megatechne* or *Ars Magna*) remained the medical Bible for many centuries to come.

SCIENTIFIC AND METAPHYSICAL SYNTHESIS

In considering Galen's general works, one is struck by their synthetic character, by the solidity of their scientific framework, and by the important part which metaphysical principles played in them. Quick to criticize the theses of his predecessors, Galen, nevertheless, borrowed freely from all, except the Methodists, whatever he considered valuable. In philosophy, too, he was under the triple influence of Aristotle, Plato and the Stoics, and might therefore be called an eclectic were it not that, far from merely borrowing, he integrated his many gleanings into a highly personal, vigorous and coherent doctrine.

Raised by a father who loved science, obsessed with the elegance of mathematics, trained by the best physicians of his time, Galen tried to raise medicine to the level of an exact science. He expressed keen regret that he had to base his anatomy on dissections of animals, and that his physiological investigations were hampered by the lack of adequate techniques in examining tissues. Even so, some of Galen's experiments have remained famous; for instance, his demonstration that the arteries carry a pulse-wave originating from the heart. He first freed the artery and then tied it, to show that no pulse-wave passed through it. Having done that, he replaced part of an artery with a tube, and showed that the wave was being propagated through it. Again, tying an artery in two places, he showed that the section between the ligatures contained blood at all times, thus refuting Erasistratos. These and other brilliant experiments led Galen to remarkable physiological discoveries. They also convinced him that careful clinical examinations were needed to determine the relative significance of symptoms and to prescribe appropriate treatment.

Unfortunately, Galen combined insistence on accurate observations with a stultifying metaphysical dogmatism. What is regrettable is not that Galen was a philosopher, but that he allowed his prejudices to blind his eyes and to distort his conclusions. Galen's fundamental postulate was the Aristotelian teleological notion that all parts of the body were expressly created by God for pre-established purposes, and that all organs functioned in accordance with the divine scheme. This naïve absolutism was bound to lead him into ridiculous paths. He was a sworn enemy of all mechanists, evolutionists and atheists—in short, of all those who denied God or who tried to explain nature by more mundane precepts. His love for metaphysical argument and his Aristotelian preconceptions caused Galen to commit grave blunders in biology, notably in his enunciation of the theory of temperaments, which we shall discuss. They explain why this otherwise brilliant scientist produced works that were in many respects inferior to those of earlier anatomists and physiologists.

ANATOMY

As an anatomist, Galen excelled above all in his descriptions of bones, muscles and nerves, and to a less extent of joints, blood-vessels and the intestines. He was particularly successful in his distinction between apophyses, epiphyses and diaphyses, and in his description of the cranial box. Despite certain inconsistencies in nomenclature, Galen's myology, based on the study of monkeys of the genus *macacus* and on other animals, is greatly superior to that of all his predecessors, and his descriptions of the spinal muscles and the Achilles tendon are admired to this day. He made many personal observations of the nervous system, in particular of the cranial nerves, which he divided into seven pairs; he identified recurrent, spinal and cervical nerves, the nervous ganglia and a part of the sympathetic system. On the other hand, he failed to locate the olfactory and the pathetic nerves, and he was wrong in his anatomical view of the trigeminal nerve, which was not described correctly until the eighteenth century.

PHYSIOLOGY

In Galen's physiology we must distinguish between far-fetched biological theory and brilliant individual discoveries. The theory is a complex edifice based on the *pneuma*, the four elements, the humours and mysterious forces. Higher life exists in three forms—echoes of Plato!—the psychic, the animal and the vegetative, each supported by a special kind of *pneuma*. The psychic *pneuma* is centred in the brain and is transmitted through the nervous system, the vital *pneuma* is distributed by the heart and the arteries, the natural *pneuma*, which resides in the liver, is transmitted through the veins. But just as the pagans of his day imagined that Jupiter was represented on earth by a series of minor gods, so Galen introduced a series of special forces—attraction, retention, alternation, expulsion, secretion —to govern such physiological activities or functions as digestion, nutrition or growth. These were the elder sisters of those 'dormitive virtues' which Molière ridiculed as explaining everything and explaining nothing. The same may be said of Galen's theory of temperaments, at least in the form in which he related it to the older theory of humours. The reader will remember that in the fifth century the theory of the four elements was said to reflect in the human body the correspondence between the macrocosm and the microcosm. Thus the four elements—fire, air, water and earth—and their four characteristic qualities—heat, cold, humidity and dryness—were said to produce the four main humours of living beings: blood, phlegm, yellow bile and black bile. In the blood the four elements were mixed in equal quantities, but in the other humours one element was predominant—water in phlegm, fire in yellow bile, earth in black bile. This is where the theory of temperaments came in. It was first suggested in the Hippocratic treatise *On the Nature of Man*, adopted very discreetly by Erasistratos and Asclepiades, and finally formulated by Galen. According to their predominant humour, all individuals could be grouped into four physiological groups: the sanguine, the phlegmatic, the choleric and the melancholic. While modern psychologists have retained these terms for describing various human temperaments, they utterly rejected Galen's physiological justification of the theory.

Observation and practical experiment on the bodies of certain animals led to better results. Galen's vascular theory was based on that of Erasistratos, with whom he agreed in holding that the blood was manufactured in the liver out of chyle and natural *pneuma*, that it was distributed to the rest of the body by the venous system which left the right side of the heart through the vena cava. On the other hand, we saw that, unlike Erasistratos, Galen knew that the arteries, too, always carried blood. According to him, the blood entered the right ventricle, where it divided into two streams. While the larger was led by the pulmonary arteries to the lungs, there to be purified and to be returned to the venous system, the smaller stream crossed the wall betwen the two ventricles to be mixed in the left ventricle with *pneuma* introduced by the pulmonary vein from the trachea, thereupon to become vital *pneuma* and to be distributed by the arteries. Blood carried by the arteries to the brain was there transformed into psychic *pneuma* by a 'wonder-network' (*rete mirabile*) and then distributed by the nerves. This brings us to Galen's physiology of the nervous system. His explanation of the functions of the spinal cord in particular was not surpassed until the beginning of the nineteenth century, and his correlation of injuries to various parts of the spinal cord and the cranial and cervical nerves with paralysis of given organs, or given parts of the body, are rightly considered among the most brilliant medical observations of all times. By comparison, his embryology seems very feeble indeed.

PATHOLOGY AND DIETETICS
According to P. Seidmann, Galen looked upon life as 'a harmonious

resultant' and upon health as a state of equilibrium based on the correct functioning of all the organs and the correct distribution of *pneuma*. Galen's pathology is therefore inseparable from his physiology; like the latter, it combines a complicated theoretical synthesis of many ancient doctrines, including those of Hippocrates, with the shrewd pragmatic findings of the skilled practitioner. In his famous *Therapeutica* he covered pathological conditions, organ by organ, on the assumption that every functional disorder was due to an organic lesion.

We cannot analyse this vast work in detail and merely note that he divided diseases into three categories according to whether they affected the humours, the 'similar' parts (*i.e.* paired parts of the body) or the unpaired organs. He also distinguished between four groups of pathological phenomena: (1) the direct causes of 'pathological movement', (2) the 'pathological movement' itself, *i.e.* functional disorders, (3) results of this 'movement' in the affected parts, and (4) various symptoms. Galen subscribed to the ancient theory of 'critical days' in the development of diseases and, in the case of chronic diseases, to the Hippocratic cycle: indigestion—coction—crisis.

Like the Hippocratic school, Galen preferred dietetic and prophylactic to therapeutic measures wherever possible, holding that it was far better to maintain the body in good health than to try to re-establish lost equilibrium. He prescribed baths and massages, changes of climate, and physical exercise in moderation (for his life among the gladiators had shown him the danger of gymnastic excesses) and, when necessary, moderate blood-lettings and purges. When these methods failed, he had recourse to the vast collection of natural remedies listed in his *De Simplicium Medicamentorum Temperamentis et Facultatibus* (eleven books). The most famous of all his remedies was a 'theriac', containing opium and seventy other ingredients, alleged to be a panacea. To his works on therapy Galen added treatises on surgery, ophthalmology and otology, thus showing that his practical gifts were as universal as his theoretical views.

This versatility is the partial explanation of his considerable influence on his contemporaries and successors right up to the seventeenth century. Another reason is that Galen was the last great physician of antiquity, and that no worthy successor appeared to continue the work he had begun. Finally, he might not have been as popular with Christians, Moslems and Jews alike, had he not subscribed to a finalist philosophy and had he failed to proclaim his belief in a merciful, wise and omniscient God, whom it behoves all men to worship.

PARA-MEDICAL SPECIALITIES

The end of the second century marked the decline of medicine,
though it was less profound than that of the other sciences. Thus the
fourth-century Renaissance saw a brief revival of medicine and particularly of veterinary science.

A history of medicine cannot deal at length with all those related
branches which, despite their theoretical foundations, are based
largely on skill (surgery, dentistry), or which belong to other disciplines. For example, veterinary science and pharmacology may be
said to belong to biology and botany and not to medicine as such.

SURGERY

As we saw, many Hellenistic and Roman medical discoveries
resulted from surgical operations. Conversely, ophthalmology owed
some of its most notable advances to anatomical theory. However,
Celsus tells us that, after Hippocrates, surgery became an independent discipline with its own teachers, especially from the second
century B.C. onwards. Among the leading surgeons, most of whom
belonged to the Empirical or the Pneumatic schools, were Philoxenes,
an Alexandrian who lived at the beginning of the first century B.C.
and who wrote a number of surgical works frequently quoted by
Soranos and Galen; Ammonios, another Alexandrian of the same
period, who invented a forceps for removing large stones from the
bladder; and Meges of Sidon, a Methodist who lived at the end of
the first century and who apparently specialized in abdominal
surgery. At the beginning of the second century A.D., two great
surgeons continued the great tradition begun by Rufus and Soranos:
Heliodoros, who wrote a treatise on surgery in five books, and Antyllos,
of whom we know no more than that he must have been one of the
best, if not the best, surgeon of antiquity. Some of the extant fragments of his writings deal with aneurisms and the removal of
cataracts.

It is difficult to say whom we should admire more: the surgeons
or their long-suffering victims. Trepanations, tracheotomies, laparo-
tomies, lithotrities and amputations were commonly performed
without antiseptics, and with no anaesthetics other than mandragora juice, sometimes mixed with henbane, or opium mixed with wild
lettuce juice. Another method of reducing suffering was to squeeze
the carotid arteries (from *caros*, 'numbness') and the jugular veins.
(Galen and other physicians were openly opposed to the use of
narcotics.) On the other hand, surgical instruments were highly
developed, as we know from the descriptions of Celsus and from many
archaeological finds at Pompeii and especially in Gaul, where

scalpels, probes, forceps, tweezers, saws, hooks, catheters, drills of all kinds, *etc.*, were discovered in great numbers.

Eye Surgery and Dentistry

From a host of signets and special instruments unearthed in Gaul, we know that eye surgery was also practised by specialists. In the first century A.D., Celsus described the surgical treatment of pterygium, cataract and exophthalmus, and in the reign of Nero, Demosthenes Philalithes, a disciple of the Neo-Herophilian school, wrote an important treatise on ophthalmology which remained the chief textbook until the end of the Middle Ages. Celsus is also our most important witness about the dental practices of his day. Though he dealt mainly with stomatology, recommending, for instance, cauterization as a means of treating alveolar pyorrhoea, he also described the successive phases of dental extraction and the treatment of dental caries by prepared cotton plugs. Moreover, from skeleton finds we have learned to appreciate the marvellous prosthetic feats of Roman dentists: bridges attached by golden rings and supporting up to four false teeth are not uncommonly dug up in Italian, and especially in Etruscan, tombs, and the finds even include crowns made of the enamel of human teeth from which the dentine was removed.

Roman Veterinary Science

In all ancient civilizations domestic animals and slaves provided the main sources of power. No wonder, therefore, that veterinary science, and especially hippiatry, was pursued so vigorously during the Hellenistic age. Its history is difficult to outline, since many of the relevant texts have been lost. We know that not only the Hippocratic physicians, but also Xenophon, and Aristotle in his *History of Animals*, dealt with the subject at some length, but after them there is a gap, at least in the Greek literature, until the third century A.D. Even so, we know that veterinary science was pursued in Hellenistic countries during the interval. Thus the *Georgics* of the famous occultist, Bolos, *alias* Democritos of Mendes, written in about 200 B.C., contain a section on animal welfare, and we know from Varro and Pliny the Elder that Epicharmos (second century B.C.) discussed the same topic and that Paxamos (first century B.C.) wrote a book on bovine diseases. In Italy, too, veterinary science was seriously pursued from the first century B.C. onwards and discussed by such writers as Varro and Virgil in the first century B.C., Columella and Pliny the Elder in the following century, and Palladios in the fourth century A.D. Moreover, Virgil's *Georgics* give an exact description of various identifiable diseases, and Columella's *De Re Rustica* (which

Palladios merely plagiarized) was based on extensive knowledge and gave a great many practical hints to stock-breeders. Columella's clinical descriptions are so precise and yet so inapplicable to modern diseases that historians like S. Leclainche have assumed that he must have dealt with pathological conditions that have since disappeared, such as goat-pest, ovine pneumonia and epizootic plague. In general, he dealt with symptoms—fever, cough, vomiting, colic, _etc._—rather than with causes, but he also gave excellent advice on animal hygiene.

GREEK HIPPIATRY

Ancient veterinary medicine rose to its greatest heights in the collection of Greek texts written in the third, fourth and fifth centuries A.D., which were partly combined in the Middle Ages, perhaps as early as the tenth century, into the _Hippiatrica_. Its main sources were earlier documents, including the Hippocratic—and even Egyptian and Asiatic—texts. The best known of its authors was Apsyrtos who, according to the Byzantine lexicographer Suidas, was born towards A.D. 300, was Constantine the Great's chief veterinary surgeon during the campaign against the Sarmatians and the Goths, and later practised in Bithynia. (Modern historians have tried to show that Apsyrtos lived between A.D. 150 and 250, though their case is disputable.) The extant part of his work consists of some sixty letters addressed to various people of whom some twenty were veterinary surgeons. In the best manuscripts, these letters are arranged to cover, successively, general diseases (fevers, glanders, peripneumonia, saddle-gall), various methods of blood-letting in particular diseases, potions and ointments. Equine diseases are described in detail, and the treatment prescribed is more rational than that of any earlier works. Compared with Apsyrtos, Pelargonios, who lived in the second half of the fourth century and who wrote 48 articles in the _Hippiatrica_, cuts a very poor figure. On the other hand, the 107 articles by Hierocles (_c._ 400) make an excellent manual of hippology (breeding, hygiene, selection and training of horses). We had best say nothing at all about the anonymous _Mulomedicina_, a compilation in barbarous Latin published about the same time under the aegis of Chiron the Centaur. The four books of the _Veterinary Art_ attributed, perhaps falsely, to Vegetius, the author of a _Summary of Military Art_, deserve mention, for though they repeat, and repeat badly, the ideas of the _Mulomedicina Chironis_ and of Columella, they give us some idea of the scope of veterinary knowledge at the end of antiquity.

THE LAST PHYSICIANS OF ANTIQUITY

While hippiatry flourished in Rome, medicine was given a new impulse in the East under Constantine. Despite the assaults on culture and 'pagan' science by fanatical Christians, Alexandria continued to reward the intellectually curious. Thus, Oribasos, born in Pergamos *c.* 325, could still receive a sound medical training in Alexandria. In Athens he met the future emperor, Julian the Apostate, whom he accompanied to Gaul and who became his patron. Because of his support for Julian's attacks on the Church, Oribasos was exiled after the emperor's death in 363, but he was recalled soon afterwards to Constantinople, where he led an active and peaceful life. Though no great scientist or original writer, Oribasos is remembered for having handed on the teachings of Galen in his systematic *Medical Collection* in seventy books, of which some twenty are extant. Because of the immensity of that work, he later condensed it into nine books and added the four books of the *Euporista*, a kind of popular guide to dietetics and therapy. These two texts, which were shortly afterwards translated into Latin, enjoyed immense popularity in their day.

Other famous Greek physicians of the time included the neurologist Philagrios, and the psychiatrist Posidonios, whose works, together with those of Oribasos, heralded a new movement which was to have its apogee in sixth-century Byzantium. In the West, on the other hand, constant invasions and internal chaos during the third century wiped out all vestiges of medical research. The best physicians of the fourth and fifth centuries restricted their activities to compiling or to translating the works of the Methodists, and especially of Soranos of Ephesos. The most famous of these compilers were Vindicianus, a friend of St. Augustine, who wrote the *Gynaecia* and the *De Expertis Remediis*, and Caelius Aurelianus, born in Numidia, whose fifth-century version of Soranos' work, the *Acute and Chronic Diseases*, deserves special mention.

THE END OF ANCIENT SCIENCE

From the end of the second century, science underwent a general decline. Even during the fourth century, when Constantine and Theodosios gave it a new lease of life, it merely stood still. The reasons must be sought on the one hand in ideological and spiritual, and on the other in political and ethnic, upheavals.

ANTI-SCIENTIFIC TRENDS
The rationalist approach which is the basis of all truly scientific thought has two sworn enemies: credulity and visionism. Now from the third century B.C. onwards, and particularly at the beginning of the Christian era, irrational ideas under various guises took the

entire Greco-Roman world by storm. During the first four centuries of our era scientific research, as such, was under constant attack from sceptics and dogmatic philosophers alike, and people became increasingly receptive to such important mystical practices as the cults of Dionysos, of Cybele, of Isis, of Baal and of various solar divinities. Thaumaturges such as Apollonios of Tyana and Alexander of Aboniteichos became very influential; the powerful Gnostic movement invaded the most unlikely circles; Pagans, Jews, Christians, Greeks and Barbarians, all tried to explain the secrets of the Creation by 'revelations'—for example, those which the Greco-Egyptian god Hermes-Thoth revealed to his son Asclepios and which inspired the famous (and extant) 'hermetic' writings. Knowledge was no longer considered the result of reason, observation, and objectivity but of a pure heart, blind faith and—wild imagination.

No wonder the occult sciences, astrology and alchemy, flourished in the manner we have already described. While magic had always been practised clandestinely, particularly by the ignorant, it emerged into broad daylight at the beginning of the Christian era and captured the attention of even the most educated. Hence astrology eclipsed astronomy; alchemy thwarted chemistry; botany was degraded into the listing of ridiculous 'remedies'; and zoology became a collection of incredible 'marvels'. The philosophers, too, fell in with the new trend. While the Platonists embraced mysticism, the Stoics turned to omens and astral influences, looking, like Pliny the Elder, for mysterious and celestial causes rather than for natural explanations.

On the other hand, the second century, in which these new tendencies began to come to the fore, may be called the golden age of Roman astronomy and medicine—and also of the Roman Empire —and the fourth century produced a number of brilliant scientists. It would therefore be wrong to say without qualification, as so many historians have done, that ancient science surrendered without a struggle.

THE INFLUENCE OF CHRISTIANITY

Undoubtedly the early Christians treated 'pagan' science with a reserve ranging from indifference to frank hostility. From the end of the second century this contempt gradually faded, though violent attacks were made by Tertullianus and Lactantius, and there were outrages such as the sack of the Library and the Museum in Alexandria. But when the majority of the Christian Fathers came to appreciate the value of Greek thought, they also accepted those scientific findings of the Greeks which did not contradict Scripture and which did not turn the faithful from the path of true salvation.

St. Basil, St. Gregory and St. Augustine stressed the uses of science and recommended the study of nature as the work of the Creator. Admittedly, Christian attempts to fit biological and geographical facts to Genesis I—interpreted either literally or allegorically—led to singular difficulties. Thus St. Augustine was forced to deny the existence of the antipodes, and a century later Cosmas Indicopleustes contested the sphericity of the earth. It is also true that Christian philosophers did not consider science to be their business and that they subordinated worldly to spiritual knowledge. But, with certain exceptions, they no longer raised systematic objections to science as such. Moreover, we need only recall the names of Cassiodorus, of Isidore of Seville and of the Venerable Bede, to realize how interested many leading churchmen were in scientific problems.

THE DESTRUCTION OF GRECO-ROMAN CIVILIZATION

In reality science, like the Western Empire, succumbed to the Barbarians and not to Christianity. Just as the moral and material conditions set up by the Ptolemaic dynasty had laid the foundations of the great upsurge of Hellenistic and Roman science, so the destruction of these cultural foundations by the German invaders, the resulting political and economic upheaval, and the introduction of 'barbarian' values robbed science of its material and moral framework. Preliminary attacks during the third century and the great invasions of the fifth century put a stop to all cultural activities in the West, while the Byzantine Empire, safe for another few centuries but deprived of the great Alexandrian impetus, witnessed a gradual decline of its scientific activities.

THE LAST ANCIENT SCIENTISTS

The last scientists of the ancient West played a very important part in transmitting the heritage of the past to future generations. The fourth century produced a host of translators, compilers and commentators, especially of mathematical, geographical and medical works. Three of them deserve special mention. Martianus Capella of Madaura (Numidia) wrote *The Marriages of Mercury, Philology, and the Seven Liberal Arts* (*c.* 470), which was a compendium of cultural knowledge. Anticipating the Scholastics, he divided all useful learning into the *trivium*—grammar, dialectics and rhetoric— and the *quadrivium*—geometry (including geography), arithmetic, astronomy and music (including poetry). His work, though mediocre, was very popular in the Middle Ages. The other two were far more intellectually distinguished. Boëtius, born *c.* 480 and appointed Consul by Theodoric, King of the Ostrogoths, in 510, was subsequently incarcerated and executed in 524 for having advocated the re-establishment of 'Roman liberty'. Apart from his famous *Philosophic Consolations* written shortly before his death, he published an adaptation of Nicomachos' *Arithmetic* and a *Summary* of the writings of Nicomachos, Euclid and Ptolemy on music, both of which are extant. In addition, he is known to have written summaries of Euclidean geometry and Ptolemaic astronomy, thus completing the *quadrivium*. It was mainly through Boëtius that the Middle Ages learnt about ancient science. Finally, there was Cassiodorus, who was also made a Consul (in 514). He survived the expulsion of the Goths, spent some time in Constantinople and then returned to his native town of Scylacium in Calabria, where he founded the famous *Vivarium*, in which he became a monk. His fame is due less to his encyclopaedic compilations—the *Institutiones Divinarum et Humanarum Litterarum* and the *Variarum Epistolarum Libri XII*—than to his monastic activities. It appears that his fellow monks were given the task of copying out all the manuscripts for which Cassiodorus, profiting from the expulsion of the Barbarians and the re-union of Rome and Byzantium, had patiently combed the Empire. Without Cassiodorus, his monks and all the others who during centuries busily copied out texts (most of which were incomprehensible to them), all the works of antiquity, scientific and literary, would have been lost for ever, and there would never have been a Renaissance.

BIBLIOGRAPHY

General Works

See bibliography on p. 259 *for* BRUNET and MIELI, COHEN and DRABKIN, ENRIQUES and SANTILLANA, HEIBERG, A. MIELI, A. REY, F. RUSSO, G. SARTON and P. TANNERY.

See also:

J. BEAUJEU, Report to the Grenoble Congress of the G. Budé Association on Technical Literature of the Greeks and Latins, Proceedings, Paris, 1949, pp. 21–77: critical evaluation of research during the period 1920–46.

P. BOYANCÉ, Les Romains et la science, *L'Information Littéraire*, Vol. III, 1951, p. 60.

PAULY-WISSOWA, *Real-Encyclopädie der Klassischen Altertumswissenschaft* (especially the articles *Erasistratos*, *Eratosthenes*, *Geodesy*, *Galen*, *Herophilos*, *Hipparchos*, the *Museum*, *Planets*, *Posidonios*, *Rufus*, *Soranos* and *Straton*).

G. A. SARTON, *A History of Science: Hellenistic Science and Culture in the Last Three Centuries B.C.*, Cambridge, Mass., 1959.

W. TARN and G. T. GRIFFITH, *Hellenistic Civilisation*, London, 1952.

29 Maya observatory

30 Inca *quipu*

Etruscan Science

C. O. THULIN, *Die etruskische Disciplin*, 3 Theses, Gothenburg, 1905 to 1909; Die Götter des Martianus Capella und der Bronze-leber von Piacenza, *Religiongeschichtliche Versuche und Vorarbeiten*, 1906.

S. WEINSTOCK, Martianus Capella and the cosmic system of the Etruscans, *Journal of Roman Studies*, XXXVI, 1946.

A. GRENIER, L'orientation du foie de Plaisance, *Latomus*, 1946, pp. 293 ff.

A. PIGANIOL, Brontoscopic Calendar of Nigidius Figulus, in *Studies in Roman economic and social history in honour of Allan Chester Johnson*, Princeton, 1951, pp. 79–87.

The chapter on Greece, Etruria and Rome in the Catalogue of the Exhibition on Cosmic Symbolism and Religious Monuments which took place in the Musée Guimet in 1953–54.

M. NOUGAYROL's paper on the Clay Liver of Villa Guilia, in the *Proceedings of the Académie des Inscriptions et Belles-Lettres*, 1956.

A complete bibliography up till 1948 can be found in A. GRENIER, *Les Religions étrusque et romaine*, 'Mana', Paris, 1948. Cf. also M. PALLOTTINO, *Etruscologia*, 3rd ed., Milan, 1955.

Hellenistic and Roman Mathematics

T. HEATH, *A History of Greek Mathematics*, 2 vols., Oxford, 1921; *A Manual of Greek Mathematics*, Oxford, 1931; *The Thirteen Books of Euclid's Elements*, 3 vols., Cambridge, 1926; *Mathematics in Aristotle*, Oxford, 1949.

G. LORIA, *Histoire des sciences mathématiques dans l'Antiquité hellénique*, Paris, 1929.

B. L. VAN DER WAERDEN, *Science Awakening*, Groningen, 1954.

H. G. ZEUTHEN, *Histoire des mathématiques dans l'Antiquité et au Moyen Age*, Paris, 1902; *Die Lehre von den Kegelschmitten im Altertum*, Copenhagen, 1886.

Astronomy

F. BOLL, *Sphära*, Leipzig, 1903; *Sternglaube und Sterndeutung*, 3rd ed., 1926.

F. CUMONT, *Astrology and Religion Among the Greeks and the Romans*, New York, 1912.

J. B. J. DELAMBRE, *Histoire de l'astronomie ancienne*, 2 vols., Paris, 1817.

P. DUHEM, *Le Système du Monde*, 6 vols., Paris, 1913–54.

W. GUNDEL, *Sterne und Sternbilder im Glauben des Altertums* . . ., Bonn, 1922; *Dekane und Dekansternbilder*, Hamburg, 1936; the article *Planeten*, in *Real-Encyc.*, 1950.

T. HEATH, *Aristarchos of Samos*, Oxford, 1913.

O. NEUGEBAUER, The Alleged Babylonian Discovery of the Precession of the Equinoxes, *Journal of the Amer. Or. Soc.* I (1950); The Early History of the Astrolabe, *Isis*, XL (1949), p. 240; *The Exact Sciences in Antiquity*, Providence, R.I., 1957.

G. V. SCHIAPARELLI, *Scritti sulla storia della astronomia antica*, I, Bologna, 1925.

P. TANNERY, *Recherches sur l'histoire de l'astronomie ancienne*, Paris, 1893.

B. L. VAN DER WAERDEN, *Die Astronomie der Pythagoreer*, Amsterdam, 1951.

Mathematical Geography

R. ALMAGIA, La conoscenza del fenomeno delle maree nell'antichità, *Arch. Inst. Hist. des. Sci*, II (1949), p. 887.

L. BAGROW, *Geschichte der Kartographie*, Berlin, 1951.

H. BERGER, *Geschichte der wissenschaftlichen Erdkunde der Griechen*, Leipzig, 1887.

A. DILLER, The Ancient Measurement of the Earth, *Isis*, XL (1949), p. 6.

J. O. THOMSON, *History of Ancient Geography*, Cambridge, 1948.

H. F. TOZER, *History of Ancient Geography*, Cambridge, 2nd ed., 1935.

Physics and Chemistry

M. BERTHELOT, *Collection des anciens alchimistes grecs*, 4 vols., Paris, 1888.

P. DIEPGEN, *Das Elixir*, Ingelheim-am-Rhein, 1951.

E. J. KIJKSTERHUIS, *Archimedes*, Groningen, 1938.

A. G. DRACHMANN, *Ktesibios, Philon and Heron*, Copenhagen, 1948.

A. M. J. FESTUGIÈRE, *La Révélation de l'Hermès Trismégiste*. I: L'astrologie et les sciences occultes, Paris, 1944.

O. GILBERT, *Die meteorologischen Theorien des griechischen Altertums*, Leipzig, 1907.

E. O. VON LIPPMANN, *Entstehung und Ausbreitung der Alchimie*, 2 vols., Berlin, 1919–31.

S. SAMBURSKY, *The Physical World of Late Antiquity*, London, 1948.

H. STROHM, Theophrast und Poseidonios, *Hermes*, LXXXI (1953), p. 278.

L. THORNDIKE, *A History of Magic and Experimental Science During the First Thirteen Centuries of Our Era*, 2 vols., New York, 1923.

Biology

W. E. MUEHLMANN, *Geschichte der Anthropologie*, Bonn, 1948.

C. NISSEN, *Die botanische Buchillustration* . . . , Stuttgart, 1951.

G. SENN, *Die Entwicklung der biologischen Forschungsmethod in der Antik*, Aarau, 1933.

E. E. SIKES, *The Anthropology of the Greeks*, London, 1914.

C. SINGER, *A History of Biology*, Oxford, 1950.

M. M. THOMSON, *Textes grecs inédits relatifs aux plantes*, Paris, 1955.

Medicine

A. CASTIGLIONI, *History of Medicine*, New York, 1947.

G. BJOERCK, *Apsyrtus, Julius Anicanus et l'Hippiâtrique grecque*, Uppsala, 1944.

H. DEICHGRAEBER, *Die Griechische Empirikerschule*, Berlin, 1930.

M. LAIGNEL-LAVASTINE, *Histoire générale de la médecine*, 3 vols., Paris, 1936–49.

E. LECLAINCHE, *Histoire de la médecine vétérinaire*, Toulouse, 1936.

M. NEUBURGER, *Geschichte der Medizin*, 2 vols., Stuttgart, 1906–11.

C. SINGER, *Greek Biology and Greek Medicine*, Oxford, 1922.

G. SARTON, *Galen of Pergamon*, Univ. of Kansas, 1954.

PART III

The Middle Ages

HAVING EXAMINED THE CRADLES OF SCIENCE in the Near East, India, China, Greece, Alexandria and Rome, we can now turn our attention to scientific developments during the long era known as the Middle Ages. We begin with a discussion of science in pre-Columbian America, from its vague beginnings to the *conquista* in the fifteenth century, and go on to consider Arabia, which scored its most brilliant scientific successes between the eighth and twelfth centuries, Byzantium, which took over the torch of Hellenism in the sixth century and helped to spread its light until Constantinople was taken by the Turks in 1453, and finally India, China and Western Europe, where the medieval period was less clearly delimited.

In India, the Middle Ages may be said to have begun with the ninth century Moslem invasions which impeded the spontaneous dissemination of Indian culture, and to have ended in the fifteenth century, when Indian science had lost all remnants of its original vigour. In China, the medieval period began with the capture of the capital by the Barbarians at the beginning of the third century and ended at the end of the fifteenth century when the first missionaries introduced Western notions into the Far East. In Western Europe, finally, the Middle Ages lasted from the Barbarian invasions of the fifth century until 1450, and may be divided into four main periods: the Dark Ages, during which science marked time; the eleventh and twelfth centuries, when Moslem contributions led to a marked increase of scientific activity and knowledge; the thirteenth and fourteenth centuries, when scholastic ideas were first formulated and began to spread; and the late Middle Ages (first half of the fifteenth century), which brought a decline of scholasticism and an increasing need to adapt science to everyday needs.

The chronological and geographical divisions we have been forced to adopt are bound to obscure the close contact between different medieval cultures. Thus Arabic science had direct repercussions on India and Europe, and so, to a lesser extent, did Jewish, Byzantine and Chinese science. Hence, if the reader wishes to gain a fuller understanding of medieval science, he must look on Part III as an indivisible whole, and on our subdivisions as necessary evils. For despite its many differences, medieval science was the prelude to modern science, which transcends all national barriers.

CHAPTER 1

Science in Pre-Columbian America

WHEN COLUMBUS FIRST DISCOVERED the American continent, it was inhabited by a variety of people, the most backward of whom were still in the Palaeolithic stage, while the most advanced had reached a level of civilization comparable to the early Egyptian. Though it would be misleading to call the religious systems and technical achievements of these people 'scientific', even the most primitive among them made practical contributions that no historian of science can ignore.

LIVING MATTER

THE VEGETABLE KINGDOM
The American Indians were remarkably shrewd observers of nature and, by domesticating such plants as the potato, maize, manioc, haricot beans, tomatoes, pineapple, *etc.*, made a considerable contribution to the world's agriculture. In addition, they grew a variety of intoxicants (cocoa, tobacco, coca, peyote, maté, datura, *etc.*), and were famed for their medical knowledge. In the sixteenth century, Philip II of Spain sent the famous physician and naturalist Francisco Hernandez to Mexico to gather medical information from the natives, and similar knowledge could have been obtained in Peru and other parts of the continent. In fact, medicinal plants were known and used throughout the New World, and included emetics, cathartics, diuretics, anthelmintics, antidiarrhoetics, sudorifics, abortives, febrifuges, analgesics, *etc.* Among those whose properties have been investigated by modern physiologists were: ipecacuanha, an emetic; jalap, a hydragogue cathartic; wormseed (*Chenopodium ambrosioides* L.), an anthelmintic; cihuapatli (*Montanoa tomentosa*, Cerv.), an ocytodinic; balsam of tolu, a stimulant expectorant; balsams of Peru and of Copahu, two cicatrizants. In surgery the Indians practised amputations, trepanations and, in Mexico, even embryotomies.

Other discoveries were made in related fields. Thus, some Amazonian tribes prepared the very effective paralysant, curare, from certain members of the *Strychnos* family. Curare, which was originally intended as an arrow poison, has been used successfully in cases of hydrophobia and tetanus. The modern rubber industry is based on the Indian discovery of a substance that lent itself to the making of hollow balls, squirts and sticks for beating the great xylophone drums. From Peru to Mexico it was common practice to burnish alloys of gold and copper by heating their surfaces and then applying the acid sap of certain plants, notably of *Oxalis pubescens* H. B. K.

THE ANIMAL KINGDOM

American Indians are credited with having been the first to domesticate turkeys, llamas, vicuñas and guinea-pigs. The Mexicans were expert at rearing the tiny insects *Coccus axin*, from which they obtained lac, and *Coccus cacti*, which supplied them with cochineal, a splendid red dye greatly coveted by Europeans until the middle of the nineteenth century. Finally, naturalists have paid tribute to the skill with which the people of Guiana and Amazonia changed the colour of the plumage of living birds by feeding them a special diet and applying special substances to their epidermis.

The study of nature was greatly helped by the existence of botanical and zoological gardens maintained by the Aztec state. Even so, the Indians failed to make discoveries which one might have expected them to hit upon quite naturally. Thus it has often been pointed out that they failed to appreciate the important medical properties of quinine.

COUNTING AND ASTRONOMY

Since interest in mathematics and astronomy invariably goes hand in hand with a fairly high degree of culture, these disciplines remained the exclusive concerns of only the more civilized Incas and Middle American Indians.

THE INCA EMPIRE

The Inca Empire, which extended from the Equator to Northern Chile and North-Western Argentine, was greatly superior to Mexico both in its technical and its social achievements. However, in the theoretical field the Incas were handicapped by their inability to write. Though they took an interest in the stars for religious purposes, they were unable to record and interpret their observations systematically.

Still, it must be stressed that the mere absence of records is no evidence that they were backward. For instance, we know that they set up special markers for observing the times of rising and setting of the sun on the Cuzco horizon, and that they must therefore have

looked for some sort of regularity in these events. We also know that
the early Peruvians used a decimal system of counting in conjunction
with their *quipus*, or knotted cords. Unfortunately, what *quipus* have
been found in coastal tombs tell us little about the actual values they
were meant to express. Erland Nordenskjöld has suggested that some
of them referred to a solar cycle of 365 days, and others to the synodic
revolutions of Venus, Mars, and Jupiter. However, his assumptions,
though attractive, are rather tenuous and, in fact, all judgments of
Peruvian science are bound to be highly speculative until further
evidence is unearthed.

MIDDLE AMERICA
The Middle American cultural zone extended mainly to Guatemala
and Northern Mexico, and for our purposes it is best divided geographically by the Isthmus of Tehuantepec into the Aztec Empire in
the West and the Mayan civilization in the East.

Though different in many respects, the Aztecs and Mayans shared
a cultural basis. Among the common elements were the painting of
pictographs or hieroglyphs on copper and beaten bark; the use of a
decimal notation with special signs for units, scores, scores of scores,
scores of scores of scores, *etc.*; and the reckoning of time by a highly
involved combination of a ritualistic and a divinatory calendar. The
ritualistic year consisted of 365 days, divided into eighteen months of
twenty days each, and a five day unlucky period; the divinatory year
consisted of 260 days, each represented by the combination of twenty
day-names and thirteen numbers, in the following way:

```
1A   2B   3C   4D   5E   6F   7G   8H   9I   10J   11K   12L   13M
1N   2O   3P   4Q   5R   6S   7T   8A   9B   10C   11D   12E   13F
1G   2H   3I   4J, etc.
```

When the two calendars were combined, only four of the twenty
day-names could begin the year, as a simple mathematical calculation will show: 365 (the number of days in a year) divided by 20 (the
total of day-names) leaves a remainder of 5. Moreover, since 365
divided by 13 leaves a remainder of 1, each of the thirteen numbers
could begin the new year, so that the number of the New Year's Day
increased by one each year. Hence, it was not until fifty-two years
had elapsed that a year was begun with the same day-name and
number. The Aztecs called this fifty-two year cycle a 'bundle of years'
and two such cycles 'an age'.

In astronomy, the Middle American people were mainly interested
in the duration of the tropical (solar) year, of the synodic (lunar)
month, and of the Venusian cycle. There is no proof that they
identified any of the other planets or calculated their motions; they

were certainly ignorant of the fact that the earth and Venus revolve
about the sun. We know that some of them at least attached special
ritualistic, divinatory and agricultural importance to the star
Aldebaran (α Tauri) and also to Orion and the Pleiades.

Pre-Columbian drawings depict astronomer-priests in their temples,
eyes fixed to a slot, apparently observing the precise rising or setting
of a star on the horizon. In the ancient city of Uaxactun, a pyramid
facing the rising sun stood behind a temple whose centre marked the
equinoctial line and behind two other buildings in line with the
solstitial points. At Chichen Itza a round tower, now half in ruins,
was a veritable observatory. Its very thin walls were studded with
narrow slots looking out on the true south, the true west and the
setting moon at maximum declination.

Lacking accurate clocks, the Indians seem to have calculated the
mean duration of the day from astronomical observations over very
long periods. When they established their calendar, the Middle
American Indians took the solar year to be 365 days, and the Venus
cycle to be 584 days. References to ceremonies every 8 or 104 years
make it clear that feast days were held whenever the end of a solar
cycle coincided with that of the Venusian cycle, since:

$$8 \text{ solar years of 365 days } = \; 5 \text{ Venusian years of 584 days;}$$
$$104 \text{ solar years of 365 days } = 65 \text{ Venusian years of 584 days.}$$

Subsequently, the Indians began to appreciate the increasing discrepancy between their calendar and the celestial phenomena which
it was meant to reflect. Even then they were reluctant to meddle with
their sacred calendar and preferred to keep more accurate records of
the discrepancies, to be used in conjunction with it.

It seems that various tribes in the Aztec Empire specialized in
calculations of this kind, but their results have not come down to us,
nor do Spanish, Aztec or Mixtec documents throw any further light
on the matter.

The Mayans, on the other hand, have bequeathed to us a fairly
large number of documents which, however, are unhomogeneous and
hence difficult to interpret. The oldest are stone (and more rarely
wood and stucco) inscriptions dating from the 'Old Empire' *i.e.* from
about the fourth to the ninth century A.D. The *Codex Dresden*, an
important astronomical manuscript, probably dates back to the
twelfth century, but is generally considered to be based on a much
earlier 'Old Empire' copy. The 'New Empire' did not produce any
further calendrical inscriptions, but some of its traditions have come
down to us, albeit in distorted form, through the Spaniards. The
native calendar, though completely forgotten by the modern
descendants of the Mayans in the Mexican valleys, has survived to

some extent among southern highland people, who are therefore excellent witnesses to the ancient tradition.

There are marked differences between calendars of various date and provenance. Moreover, all inscriptions before the *conquista* were made with ideographs that are extremely difficult to decipher. Since Mayan epigraphy lacks a Rosetta stone, it is forced to rely on the brief explanations of a sixteenth-century Spanish missionary, who often misunderstood what the natives told him. On this fragile basis, Americanists have been able to reconstruct the essential elements of the Mayan calendar, though their ignorance of the context and of subtle religious distinctions has made some of their conclusions rather doubtful.

MAYAN NUMERATION AND TIME RECKONING

We know more about the numerical data in Mayan texts than about any other of their contents. The ancient Mayans could handle very large numbers, possibly because they used cocoa-beans as their (very lowly) monetary unit. But though they could count orally, they apparently recorded none but calendrical data. With certain exceptions (marked by a special sign on the manuscripts but not on the bas-reliefs), time was calculated from the fixed date *4 Ahau 8 Cumku*, which experts are generally agreed to place on or about August 12th, 3113 B.C. In the 'New Empire' this method of time-reckoning was no longer used except in the *Codex Dresden*, which was, in fact, an archaistic document.

Chronological Mayan inscriptions reckoned time intervals in days (or *kins*), *uinals* (of 20 days), *tuns* (of 18 *uinals* or 360 days), *katuns* (of 20 *tuns* or 7,200 days), *baktuns* (of 20 *katuns* or 400 *tuns*), *pictuns* (of 20 *baktuns* or 8,000 *tuns*), *calabtuns* (of 20 *pictuns* or 160,000 *tuns*), *kinchiltuns* (of 20 *calabtuns* or 3,200,000 *tuns*), and *alautuns* (of 20 *kinchiltuns* or 64,000,000 *tuns*). This was clearly a decimal system with the *tun* as the unit, and *kins* and *uinals* as subdivisions.

The use of such large units of time took the Mayans into mythological realms, and we have no valid explanation why a Quirigua stele refers to a period of five *alautuns* (*i.e.* more than 300,000,000 years), giving the precise dates of its beginning and end in terms of the ritualistic and divinatory calendars. J. E. S. Thompson has taken this as evidence that the Mayan astronomer-priests must have looked upon time as infinite.

Texts written after the *conquista* in Roman characters do not mention such large units of time, and epigraphists have, in fact, reconstructed their names by combining the names for 400, 8,000, 160,000, *etc.*, with the word *tun*. (*Katun* stands for *kal-tun* = 20 *tuns*.) However, the larger units also appear in the *Codex Dresden* and in bas-reliefs, and their numerical value could be deduced from their position in the various series listed.

'Old Empire' dates starting from *4 Ahau 8 Cumku* were always written or engraved in decreasing order of units, while the bas-reliefs invariably recorded dates in increasing order. Confusion was avoided since each unit was depicted by a characteristic glyph.

In the *Codex Dresden*, time intervals are invariably set out in decreasing order, in one vertical column, thus obviating the need for repeating the names of the units. For instance, an interval of 8 *baktuns*, 18 *katuns*, 13 *tuns*, 5 *uinals* and 11 *kins*, *i.e.* 3,573 *tuns*, 5 *uinals*, 11 *kins* (or 1,286,390 days), was simply expressed by five figures arranged in one column, of which the uppermost gave the *baktuns*. The numbers were expressed by points and strokes, according to the Mayan system of representing 1 by a point and 5 by a stroke. The whole system was clearly comparable to a system of place-value notation, in which individual symbols have different values corresponding to different positions:

8 ••• (*baktuns* of 20 *katuns*)   •••• 9

18 ═══ (*katuns* of 20 *tuns*)   ••• 8

13 •••═ (*tuns* of 18 *uinals*)   ⊜ (0)

5 ─── (*uinals* of 20 *kins*)   ⊜ (0)

11 •═ (*kins* or days)   ⊜ (0)

(*Total:* 1,286,391 days)   (*Total:* 1,353,600 days)

In these numerical series, it often happened that the last spaces had to be filled with special signs, which scholars have called terminal zeros. Thus the Mayan expression shown on the right has often been rendered as 9.8.0.0.0.: 9 *baktuns*, 8 *katuns*, 0 *tun*, 0 *uinal*, 0 *kin*. In fact, the Mayans were exclusively concerned with the lapse of time—for them, twenty days was simply one more *uinal*, 18 *uinals* one more *tun*, *etc.* Thus Dr. Thompson has shown that the so-called zero glyph simply signified completion of given units, and that the date transcribed by archaeologists as 9.8.0.0.0. merely told the Indians that 9 *baktuns* and 8 *katuns* (*i.e.* 3,600 *tuns* or 1,353,600 days) had passed since the beginning of the period, and that no further *uinals* and *kins* were needed to complete the eighth and last *katun*. It is therefore a clear mistake to credit the ancient Mayans with the discovery of the abstract zero concept as we know it.

The Mayans sometimes employed a special sign for representing the completion of half a unit of time—their only venture into fractional arithmetic. As Dr. Thompson has emphasized so well, they based their number theory not on fractions but on the search for the smallest common multiples of two or more periods. These periods were measured in days simply because no practical means existed for evaluating shorter intervals.

MAYAN DETERMINATIONS OF ASTRONOMICAL PERIODS

Thanks to their persistent observations, their system of writing and their search for common multiples, the ancient Mayans produced surprisingly accurate calculations of some astronomical cycles in order to co-ordinate them with their calendar. In a very suggestive study, L. Satterthwaite has shown how the priests arrived at their remarkable results by very simple arithmetical methods.

THE SYNODIC REVOLUTION OF THE MOON

From the most ancient bas-reliefs, we know that the Mayans were in the habit of associating dates with the 'age' of the moon, *i.e.* with the number of days that had passed since the last new moon. These were the supplementary C, D and E glyphs which have been studied by J. Teeple. From a great number of such observations the priests of Palenque inferred during the seventh century A.D., that eighty-one lunations (or synodic revolutions of the moon) are equivalent to 2,392 days, or that one lunation = 29.53086 days (as against 29.53059 days in reality).

Inscriptions show that, during the first half of the eighth century, another system of reckoning was introduced in the city of Copán. In it 149 lunations = 4,400 days, or one lunation = 29.53020 days. This system was abandoned later in favour of the earlier and more accurate one.

ECLIPSES

The *Codex Dresden* (pp. 51–58) contains a table of dates covering more than 32 years, and listing 405 consecutive lunations, namely 5 × 81 lunations or 2,392 days, divided into 69 groups of 5 or 6 lunations each. Now, this grouping is remarkable, since each group ends on a date on which an eclipse of the sun might have occurred. Teeple has thought that the origin of these tables may be found in the fact that, during the years covered by them, eclipses of the sun always fell at the end of three brief periods of the divinatory calendar, whence their periodicity must have become obvious to the Mayans. As we saw, the divinatory year was 260 days and two such years coincide fairly well with three eclipse periods. Teeple has pointed out that after 405 lunations there would be an error of approximately 1.6 days, and Thompson has mentioned certain indications showing that the Mayans were conscious of this discrepancy and that they corrected it periodically.

TROPICAL YEAR

Since the Mayan ritualistic year of 365 days kept advancing on the seasons, it failed to reflect agricultural and religious events. Some adjustment had to be made and at Copán numerous inscriptions set out the discrepancy between the real solar (or tropical) year and the ritualistic year which had accumulated since the beginning of the Mayan calendar over a period exceeding 3,800 years. Hence the Copán estimate of the tropical year must have been at least as accurate as that of the Gregorian Calendar. Other Mayan cities seem to have arrived at very similar results.

Experts are not certain about the methods by which these discrepancies were evaluated. J. E. Teeple, who has done most of the spade work, thinks that the priests must have worked backwards from common multiples between solar and lunar periods; he notes that the bas-reliefs very frequently refer to a period corresponding to nineteen tropical years. Hence the Mayans may have been familiar with the Metonic cycle: 19 years = 235 lunations. We have also seen that the Copán priests had found that 149 lunations = 4,400 days. Now, while each one of these two equations contains a slight error, the errors cancel out and give a solar year of 365.2420 days which is more exact than the Gregorian year of 365.2425 days (the real tropical year is 365.2422 days). Needless to say, this figure is not found on any inscriptions since, as we saw, the Mayans were unfamiliar with fractions. Different Mayan cities are said to have obtained slightly different figures by different methods, though Dr. Thompson has expressed serious doubts on this assumption.

THE VENUSIAN CYCLE

Since the ancient inhabitants of Mexico believed that Venus as the morning star was an evil omen, they were most anxious to predict its future course. Now, the synodic revolution of Venus varies most disconcertingly between 580 and 587 days, from which, as we saw, the early Indians inferred that its mean period was 584 days. Venus was said to be visible for 236 days as the morning star, invisible for 90 days when at superior conjunction, visible for 250 days as the evening star, and invisible for 8 days at inferior conjunction.

The Mayans and other people of ancient Mexico considered a period of 37,960 days containing 65 Venusian cycles of 584 days each, 104 ritualistic years of 365 days each, and 146 divinatory years of 260 days each. At the end of this period, the heliacal rising of the morning star was therefore expected to coincide with a fixed day and month of the ritualistic calendar and also with a fixed year of the cycle of fifty-two years combining the two calendars. This day, called *1 Ahau* in the divinatory calendar, was dedicated to Venus and the god reigning over the planet was often called by the same name (in Mayan: *hun ahau*).

Subsequently, Mayan astronomers noticed that the earlier approximation was inexact, and that the Venusian cycle was slightly less than 584 days. (The correct figure is 583.92 days.) The discrepancy accumulated over 37,600 days was, in fact, greater than half the normal variation of the synodic period, and could not pass unnoticed. To correct the error by making the period of 37,960 five days shorter would not only have failed to eradicate the discrepancy completely, but would have meant losing sight of the cycle's divinatory significance. The Mayans therefore preferred to abandon all attempts to relate Venus with the ritualistic calendar, and concentrated instead on its correlation with the divinatory calendar of 260 days, thus preserving the importance of the day *1 Ahau*. The results were listed in a table of corrections covering pages 46–50 of the *Codex Dresden*.

These corrections bear on a total of 240 Venusian cycles of approximately 584 days each, the total of which is reduced from 140,160 days to 140,140 days. Eight days are subtracted at the end of the fifty-seventh cycle, and four days each at the end of three further periods of sixty-one cycles each (the 118th, 179th, and 240th cycles). These four deductions had the advantage of re-establishing calendrical harmony, and the total subtraction of twenty days (instead of the correct 19.2 days) represented a small error over a period of almost 384 years.

Teeple, who discovered this interesting correction, mentions that it would have been almost perfectly accurate had the table contained a further period of sixty-one cycles and a further deduction of four days. The totals subtracted would then have been twenty-four days over 301 cycles, and the error during 175,784 minus 24 days would have been roughly two hours in 481 years. J. E. S. Thompson has shown that page 25 of the *Codex Dresden* may be considered as evidence that the Mayans did in fact introduce the additional cycles, and that the apparent omission is due to a copying error on the part of a scribe.

One cannot help marvelling at the accuracy of these results, obtained as they were by such primitive methods. There is no doubt that, despite their preoccupation with mystical and divinatory problems, the Mayans were well on the road to rational science.

BIBLIOGRAPHY

Handbook of South American Indians, 6 vols., Smithsonian Institution (Bureau of American Ethnology, Bulletin 143), Washington, 1946–50.

Plants and plant science in Latin America, Waltham, Mass., 1945.

R. PARDAL, *Medicina aborigen americana*, Buenos Aires, 1937.

R. D'HARCOURT, *La Médecine dans l'ancien Pérou*, Paris, 1939.

M. MARTINEZ, *Las plantas medicinales de México*, Mexico, 1944.

R. C. GILL, *A bibliography on curare*, New York, 1940.

L. L. LOCKE, *The ancient quipu or Peruvian knot record*, New York, 1923.

E. NORDENSKIÖLD, *The secret of the Peruvian quipus*, Gothenburg, 1925; *Calculations with years and months in the Peruvian quipus*, Gothenburg, 1925.

S. G. MORLEY, *An introduction to the study of the Maya hieroglyphs*, Smithsonian Institution (Bureau of American Ethnology, Bulletin 57), Washington, 1915.

J. E. TEEPLE, *Maya astronomy*, Carnegie Institution (Contributions to American archaeology No. 2), Washington, 1931.

J. E. S. THOMPSON, *Maya arithmetic*, Carnegie Institution (Publication 528, Contribution 36), Washington, 1941; *Maya hieroglyphic writing. Introduction*, Carnegie Institution (Publication 589), Washington, 1950.

L. SATTERTHWAITE, *Concepts and structures of Maya calendrical arithmetics*. University of Pennsylvania, Philadelphia, 1947.

E. FÖRSTEMANN, *Die Maya-Handschrift der Königlichen Bibliothek zu Dresden*; 2nd edition, Leipzig, 1892.

31 Aztec calendar

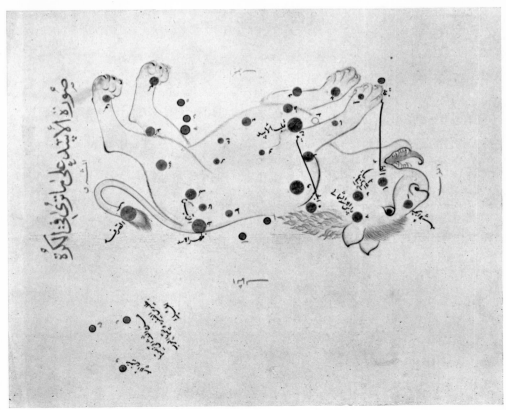

32 Ursa Major and Centaurus

CHAPTER 2

Arabic Science

AT THIS STAGE of our historical knowledge, it would be idle to pretend that any account of Arabic science could do justice to its immense intellectual scope and repercussions in the rest of the world. Most overall surveys make do with a list of the leading authors and their works, using such Arabic compilations as, for instance, the *'Uyūn al-Anbā' fī Tabaqāt al-Aṭibbā'* ('Sources of Information on the Classes of Physicians') of Ibn Abī Uṣaibi'a, the *Ta'rīkh al-Hukamā'* ('History of Scientists') of Ibn al-Qifṭī, or more general summaries like the *Fihrist* of Ibn al-Nādim and the *Kashf al-Ẓunūn* by Hājjī Khalīfa. But while all these source-books provide the historian with an excellent framework, many of the texts quoted are lost or unidentified, and some of the most important exist only in (inaccessible) manuscript form. Moreover, the interpretation of even those texts which are more readily available involves a great deal of prior research into language, context and sources.

Again, while there are many excellent studies of Arabic science as such, their very generality plays down the existence of opposed philosophical currents and the specific theories and methods of great individuals. Conversely, writers like Carra de Vaux and Meyerhof have concentrated on just these aspects, and hence have tended to ignore the general trend.

Since it would therefore be presumptuous to pass final judgment on the original contributions of Arabic science, all we can hope to do is describe the general climate and the general attitude towards science of the Moslem world.

THE INTELLECTUAL CLIMATE

RELIGIOUS FACTORS

There is a clear distinction between Arabic and Moslem science, though both contributed greatly towards scientific progress during the Middle Ages. The Moslem conquerors were most anxious to learn what they could from their ancient subject peoples, if only because the Koran enjoined them to study the sky and the earth to find proofs of their faith. The Prophet himself had besought his disciples to seek knowledge from the cradle to the grave, no matter if their search took them as far afield as China, for 'he who travels in search of knowledge, travels along Allah's path to paradise'. True, the knowledge the Koran preached (*'ilm*) was above all knowledge of the religious laws, but Islam never made a clear-cut distinction between the sacred and the profane. Hence, for instance, there are many *hadīths* (sayings attributed to Mohammed) concerning medicine in general and remedies in particular, on which Moslem scientists and philosophers based many of their dicta and actions. Thus when Averroës wrote that the Koran invites men to observe nature and to seek rational knowledge, he expressed the opinion of all Moslem scholars that the earth was given to man for constant and reverent study.

INFLUENCE OF GREECE AND INDIA

When we speak of Arabic science, we refer to works in the Arabic language. Hence all the peoples conquered by Islam and taught the sacred language of the Koran had a share in Arabic science, particularly those who, like the Indians and Persians, could look back on a long scientific tradition of their own. Much more important still was the contribution of ancient Greece and of Alexandria, which came down to the Arabs through Byzantium, not only in Syriac texts but also in early Arabic translation.

Thus, though its scope was much wider, Arabic science may rightly be considered the heir of Hellenistic science. Great scientists like Galen and Ptolemy were acknowledged as masters by Greeks and Arabs alike, and Arabian schools were organized on the pattern of the Greek, publishing commentaries, encyclopaedias, dictionaries and scientific manuals. The scholars versed in more than one science if not in all, whose most illustrious Greek counterparts were such men as Eratosthenes and Galen, were the rule rather than the exception among the Arabs, many of whom were philosophers *cum* astronomers *cum* physicians *cum* biologists, and often historians, geographers, jurists and poets, as well. The best-known of these encyclopaedic minds were Avicenna (Ibn Sinā) and al-Bīrūnī.

Though the Greek influence was tempered with Indian and Persian ideas, the view that Arabic science was a hotch-potch of notions imported from all over the world does not stand up to critical examination: the framework of Arabic science was exclusively Greek.

Speaking of Indian culture in his *Ṭabaqāt al-Umam*, Sāʿid al-Andalusī admitted that it was 'a mine of wisdom, a source of law and of politics'. Indian scientists were acknowledged to be masters of the science of number (*'ilm al-'adad*), of geometry and astronomy, and to have surpassed all other peoples in their knowledge of medicine. But while Indian scientific texts were revealed to their authors by the stars, Greece learned her science from 'men of the highest rank, and of the greatest scholastic merit, with an authentic concern for the various branches of knowledge'. We must stress the expression 'authentic concern' (*al-i'tinā' al-ṣaḥīḥ*), by which Sā'id acknowledges the unique character of Greek science: its objectivity and disinterested aims.

THE ORGANIZATION OF SCIENCE

Only if we consider the combined influence of religious and social conditions can we explain the great impetus given to science by the Moslem world. Science was part and parcel of the life of every Moslem city; every Caliph took a personal interest in its progress. Among the best-known of these patrons were Khālid, the 'philosopher prince', whose work may have been legendary; al-Manṣūr, the founder of Baghdad; and al-Ma'mūn, who sent his emissaries in search of manuscripts worth translating into Arabic. Doubtless, there were many who, in the name of their religion, objected to all foreign ideas, but the love of science triumphed over their objections. In their search for truth, Arabian scientists were primarily interested in gathering knowledge which had stood the test of time, possibly on the assumption that nothing new could be discovered. But this very search gave them a taste for methodical investigation and opened up unsuspected avenues.

Their classifications of previous results, for instance, led them to revise the very concept of science. While the Greeks, under the influence of Plato and Aristotle, had divided the sciences according to their essential character and methods of investigation, the Arabs, even when they adopted the Greek labels, used classification not only as an inventory but also as a programme. They held that scientific methods could not be defined from the *a priori* intelligibility of their objects, but that the appropriate methods emerged in the course of scientific research. This change of view marked an important step towards a truly experimental approach; only by investigation can we discover what methods lead to the truth. While Aristotle distinguished between theoretical, practical, and 'poetic' science, and though Averroës maintained this classification, most other Arabs attempted to synthesize the three. This effort led to a complete reversal of the prevailing views; science was no longer held to be a synonym for contemplation—it became active effort.

AL-FĀRĀBĪ'S CLASSIFICATION

In his *Iḥṣā' al-'Ulūm*, al-Fārābī classified the sciences into five branches: (1) philology; (2) logic; (3) mathematical sciences (arithmetic, geometry, perspective, astronomy, weights and measures, mechanics); (4) physics and metaphysics; (5) politics, law and theology. Science thus covered all branches of human knowledge. Most of the disciplines listed under headings (3) and (4) involve theory and practice alike, and al-Fārābī made a clear distinction between them only in pure mathematics, where he considered pure arithmetic as the theoretical basis of practical calculation, and pure geometry of surveying and allied occupations. Again, when it came to weights and measures, he distinguished between theoretical metrology and the practical study of 'instruments that can raise heavy objects and transport them from one place to another'. Mechanics was defined both as the science of applying known mathematical laws to natural bodies and also as the science of deriving these laws from the behaviour of these bodies, that is to say, both as rational and as physical mechanics.

Al-Fārābī's classification, though devoid of any analytical divisions, was therefore an interesting attempt to combine theory and practice. Science (*'ilm*) and art (*ṣinā'a*) had become inseparable.

AVICENNA'S CLASSIFICATION

Avicenna's *On the division of rational knowledge* (*Aqsām al-'Ulūm al-'Aqliyya*) seems much closer to the Greek view. Avicenna returned to the distinction between theoretical and practical science, holding that the aim of the former was to obtain certain knowledge (truth) of objects whose existence did not depend on human action, while the aim of the latter was to study those objects on which man's actions could have direct effects, and hence to further the welfare of the community. The adjective 'practical' was therefore used in the Greek sense, as bearing on human action. However, the 'poetic' sciences of Aristotle had disappeared from Avicenna's classification. The theoretical sciences were subdivided into three 'levels': natural sciences, mathematics and, highest of all, metaphysics. These levels reflect the inherent nature of the objects they describe.

Either the definition and existence of objects are both related to corporeal matter and to motion ... or else only their existence but not their definition is related to matter and to motion ... or else neither their existence nor their definition is related to matter or motion.

Though this method of classification is clearly analytical and enables one to construct a hierarchy of the sciences, Avicenna soon afterwards preferred to substitute a classification into fundamental and derived sciences. The fundamental branches of natural science deal with the general principles of beings, matter and form, pure elements, generation, corruption, growth, alteration, accidents affecting the elements before they enter into compositions, meteors, atmospheric phenomena, earthquakes, oceans, mountains, the mineral, vegetable and animal kingdoms, and finally man and his immortal soul. The derived branches, on the other hand, deal with medicine, court astrology, physiognomy, oneiromancy, the science of talismans, magic, and alchemy. Of the mathematical sciences, pure arithmetic, geometry, astronomy and music are fundamental, while the 'four rules' and algebra are derived from them. Similarly, surveying, mechanics, weighing, perspective, the science of mirrors and of the equilibrium of liquids are derived branches of geometry.

Behind what appeared to be an elegant Greek façade, Avicenna had, in fact, listed all the then existing branches of science, and had implicitly retained the close connection between theory and poetics; only the names differ, for Avicenna's fundamental and derived branches were basically none but the pure and applied sciences. Avicenna's classification is therefore by no means as far removed from al-Fārābī's as it appears at first sight, though Avicenna himself would not have said so. Thus he criticized al-Ghazālī for calling medicine an applied branch of natural science. However, if we bear in mind what role medicine played in Arabic science, we find this objection unconvincing.

THE CLASSIFICATION OF THE BRETHREN OF PURITY
Another system of classifying the sciences was that of the Brethren of Purity (*Ikhwān al-Ṣafāʾ*). It was based on Pythagorean and Neo-Platonic mystical notions, and divided science into the study of: (1) mathematics; (2) physical bodies; (3) rational beings; (4) divine laws, whose order reflects the soul's progress towards divine wisdom. This classification would be of no interest to the historian of science were it not that it stressed even more strongly than al-Fārābī's the subordination of mathematics to natural science. Mathematics had become a propaedeutical step towards physics, which was no longer considered the lowliest science, tainted by corruptible matter and fleeting appearances.

Our first epistle concerns number. Its aim is to engage the soul of those who study philosophy . . ., who contemplate reality and seek the causes of all beings.

The study of proportion, in particular, was considered a means towards the study of the structure of natural bodies, and mathematics in general had become a means towards an end.

These examples will suffice to show that though the Arabs were not always as logical in their classifications of the sciences as they might have been, they nevertheless showed signs of what we may call a pragmatic approach. The views on mathematics of the Brethren of

Purity developed an important conception of mathematics which would bear fruit when concern with algebraic operations replaced interest in numerical and geometrical 'essences'.

THE SPIRIT OF ARABIC SCIENCE

SCIENCE AND PHILOSOPHY

Arabic science never severed the link with its philosophic antecedents. Aristotle, Plato and the Neo-Platonists inspired the cosmology and the fundamental scientific approach of the Arabs, and scientists like al-Kindī and Avicenna continued to be philosophers in their own right.

But like Galen, their acknowledged master, Arabic scientists allowed their scientific attitude to temper their philosophy and hence to free them of their metaphysical strait-jackets. This is notably true of their traditional beliefs, since nothing so shakes our preconceived notions as the need for resolving their contradictions.

AL-FĀRĀBĪ

A clear sign of this development is found in the work of al-Fārābī. In a chapter on natural science he distinguishes between natural and artificial (manufactured) bodies, and concludes that we come to know the former through the latter, the only bodies whose structure and material processes we can perceive. So far, he is well within the bounds of Aristotelean 'artificialism'. But al-Fārābī goes on to consider the intermediate cases, for instance:

> There are, however, a number of artificial bodies of which the structure is imperceptible; one such is wine, which is a body produced by art and yet the force which causes it to ferment is not perceptible; its existence is known only by its action, and that force (*quwwa*) is the form (*ṣūra*) and the structure (*ṣīgha*) of wine; it is to wine as the edge is to the sword, since it is by that force that wine exerts its action. . . .

> Thus medicaments like theriac and others which are compounded (*murakkaba*) by the skill of the physician do not act on the human body except through those forces which their composition engenders in them; these forces are not perceptible; our senses can only perceive the actions resulting from them. Hence any medicament becomes a medicament only by virtue of two things: the complex mixtures (*ahklāṭ*) of which it is composed and the force by which it exerts its action. The mixtures constitute its matter and the force by which it acts, its form.

These quotations are extremely important, for if the mixture whose composition engenders the force is called 'matter', and the force itself 'form', we must conclude that the form proceeds from matter, and is the effect of a particular organization of matter which thus exhibits new properties. Aristotle's attempts to bring intelligible form down to earth from the Platonic heavens had finally borne fruit. Scientific intelligibility is obtained by the study of material combinations— hence the stress on action and on active properties in the definition of form. Whereas the term *quwwa*, which we have translated as 'force', was commonly used by Arabic philosophers in the Aristotelian sense of potential energy,[1] al-Fārābī used it in the modern sense. In all man-made articles the force involved is active: linen by itself has no tendency to turn itself into a tunic, nor a slab of marble to turn itself into a statue. Yet what is matter for art, is form for nature.

It is according to these examples (wine, compounded remedies) that we must understand the form and matter of natural bodies. Even if they are not detectable by the senses, they play the part of imperceptible matter and form in artificial bodies.

The force causing a tree to grow is well beyond our grasp and must be likened to the force causing wine to ferment, which is equally undetectable except by its effects. There is therefore a perfect analogy between natural bodies and those produced by man with the help of nature. This view is but a short step from a science which considers the effects of man's actions on nature, namely experimental laboratory science.

AL-RĀZĪ

Abū Bakr Muḥammad ibn Zakariyā al-Rāzī (or Rhazes as the Romans called him), a critic of natural philosophies, provides yet another example of the same intellectual revolution. According to Aristotle, φύσις was the principle of motion of inanimate beings; all actions and all properties of natural bodies, unlike human actions, could be reduced to their 'natures'. Al-Rāzī knew the impasse to which this view had led the sciences, and therefore attacked its proponents.

We observe that you endow nature with the same attributes as living beings: choice, knowledge and wisdom, because you claim that nature acts always with wisdom and fitness; that it aims towards a goal, that it does no thing aimlessly, creating the eye of an embryo so that the child might see ... that it sets all things in their right places, organizing them perfectly, forming the foetus in the womb and then guiding its development most delicately towards perfection; also that it governs man, lends

[1] Galen had previously used the term δύναμις to refer to active force. Under the influence of Joannes Philoponos, Yaḥyā ibn 'Ādī, Avicenna, and Abū l-Baraqāt al-Baghdādī revised Aristotelian physics accordingly.

him health, dispels his diseases, since, as Hippocrates has said, nature is the physician of all our ills. And yet you say that nature is inanimate and without life . . . without capacity of choice, without knowledge, which is an evident contradiction and a manifest absurdity.

(*Opera Philosophica*, ed. P. Kraus, I, p. 120.)

From this protest we must not infer that al-Rāzī was a teleologist who had turned his back on science. What he criticized was merely the view that, nature being blind, man could not possibly control or analyse it. Thus he attacked Galen, saying:

You teach us that nature governs living beings. . . . The contrary is true, for it is the living who govern nature. Having been stricken by fever once, a man will know what remedies have helped him, and use them should he be stricken a second time. (*Ibid.*, p. 120.)

Al-Rāzī had therefore realized that there is an intelligible order in the world, and only because it is intelligible can man grasp it and use it for his own ends—as, indeed, does God himself. Nature and art are inseparable, and this view is stated explicitly in an attack on Alexander of Aphrodisias:

As for Alexander's pretensions that the operations of nature are superior to art, let me reply by asking him how the marvellous and sublime feats (of human art) can spring from a dead and impotent reality?

Al-Rāzī concluded that if art can so readily be grafted to nature, for instance in alchemy and medicine—two disciplines in which he was particularly interested—it might well be that nature herself contains the elements of those arts which human actions create.

All these views are clear signs of an intellectual ferment that was bound to have the most far-reaching effects on future scientific thought and research.

Avicenna, too, gave unmistakable proof of a wish to guide Aristotelian concepts into more resolutely experimental paths.

Arabic Translations

One of the most important aspects of Arabic science was its concern with translations. Arabic scientists translated Indian, Persian and, above all, Greek works, and the names of Euclid, Ptolemy, Galen, were household words among them. Many of these translations are our only sources of a number of Greek texts, since lost.

This deference to ancient authority, this desperate hunt for manuscripts, as if all wisdom began and ended with them, has led many to conclude that the Arabs themselves contributed nothing at all to science. Now, while it is true that they made relatively few new discoveries, there can be no doubt at all that they did yeoman service in widening the scientific horizon, and breaking down age-old barriers to scientific progress.

Al-Kindī

The Arabs never looked upon translation as a purely mechanical and menial task. This is best shown by the work of al-Kindī, one of the greatest of the Moslem scholars. Al-Kindī, who has been called *the* Arab philosopher, was also an authentic scientist. Thus, in two *Epistles* (*Rasā'il al-Kindī al-falsafiyya*) he explained that ice and hail were formed in the upper layers of the atmosphere, whenever the aqueous parts of the clouds consisting of water vapour hardened (*jamadat*) by contraction (*inḥiṣār*) of the external surface of the vapour because of the cooling of the surrounding air. This explanation was taken from Aristotle. But al-Kindī also discussed another aspect of the problem which, though noticed by Aristotle as well, was not discussed by him nearly as lucidly:

Why does vapour freeze in the atmosphere, and why does water raised into the air freeze, when the nature of air is composed of heat and humidity, and when air is heated by the movement of the sphere . . . ? (II, page 90.)

These questions, though trivial and simple for those who are conversant with the science of beings and nature and though very nearly solved, elude those who do not follow along the paths of natural science and who do not know its principles. Thus they hold that such questions present great difficulties and embarrassments, and are so many contradictions impossible to reconcile; they say in effect: How is it possible that the heat below should cause the motion of the sphere, when what is closer to the motion is colder than what is further away from it? This is a contradiction and an absurdity. (II, p. 91.)

Al-Kindī realized that the mere reading of ancient texts—in Greek or Arabic—could become an obstacle to clear thought, unless it was used as a call to consult nature herself, and to solve the apparent contradictions in that way. Mere book-learning is inadequate and even pernicious; we must 'follow along the paths of nature' to understand her.

When we do not know the principles, causes and reasons of things, we cannot understand them, and perhaps there is no man more ignorant in this respect than he who has delved into the writings of ancient scientists and considers them sufficient for obtaining the truth about scientific problems, without reviewing the sciences in their proper order. . . .

(II, p. 91.)

Accepting the wisdom of the ancients is futile unless their principles are first reconsidered and brought into harmony. It is vain to keep to the letter of their writings unless the letter is first understood and evaluated, and this is the translator's primary function.

Al-Kindī's own explanation of the apparent paradox of the cooling of air in the sky shows how the Arabs, while preserving Greek concepts, could by suitable commentaries enhance their explicative value. Only fire is absolutely hot, air is hot only relative to water, just as water is not absolutely cold but cold only with respect to air.

The earth is heated because of the circular motion (of the sphere), in such a way that it becomes hotter than the surrounding air. . . . The same thing occurs when we pour tepid water over one of our limbs previously exposed to the cold. The water feels hot, though, had we just stepped out of a hot bath and poured the tepid water over our body, it would feel cold.

(II, p. 97.)

We see how flexible the Greek concept of elementary qualities had grown—cold, hot, dry and humid had ceased to be absolutes. Moreover, while al-Kindī and the other Arabic translators undoubtedly kept to the spirit of the originals, their search for suitable Arabic equivalents of Greek terms inevitably forced them to reformulate and hence to clarify those concepts which were vague in the original.

LINGUISTIC AND LEXICOGRAPHIC PROBLEMS

The Arab translators' first task was to set up a Greek-Arabic scientific dictionary, and to coin appropriate scientific terms from existing Arabic vocabulary, or from Syriac and other Semitic languages. This work was not purely philological, for it often involved redefining, verifying and elucidating the original concepts.

Arabic is an exceptionally expressive language, rich in fine shades of meaning and poetic nuances. Thus when Abū Zayd al-Anṣārī wanted to list various kinds of rain in his *Kitāb al-Maṭar*, he went to the poets for his definitions. While the lexicographers established an inventory of the Arabic language, the scientists provided an inventory of knowledge. We may smile at al-Aṣmaʿi's classification of vegetables into three kinds: vegetables that are eaten uncooked (*aḥrār al-baql*), bitter vegetables (*dhukūr*), and sour vegetables (*ḥamḍ*). But we cannot help being impressed by his distinction between the palm and the vine, which was both scientific and highly poetical.

TRANSLATION AND VERIFICATION

The translations posed many problems of identification. Thus the πομφόλυξ of Dioscorides, meaning a kind of metallic bloom, was identified by Ibn-al-Bayṭār with the alchemists' *tūtīyā*, *i.e.* zinc oxide. When it came to Dioscorides' names for rare plants and animals the translators and commentators were forced to look not only into their dictionaries but into nature herself. The Spanish physician Ibn Juljul tells us that the first translator of Dioscorides' *Materia medica*, Iṣṭifān ibn Basīl, 'rendered into Arabic those Greek terms of which he knew the Arabic equivalents, but left all others in Greek'. His translation was later corrected by Hunayn ibn Isḥāq. Max Meyerhof, who has made a special study of Arabic translations, tells us that, later still, when the Emperor of Byzantium offered an illustrated Greek manuscript of the *Materia medica* to 'Abd al-Rahmān III, Caliph of Cordova, 'scientists and polygraphs set to work verifying those botanical and other terms which had not been translated into Arabic by the Baghdad translator-physicians. These men were joined by a number of Moorish physicians and herbalists and between them they managed to identify most of the drugs mentioned by Dioscorides. Ibn Juljul himself continued their work. . . .' (*Sharḥ* . . ., Introduction, p. vii.)

At the same time, the Arabic pharmacopoeia was being augmented with plants and plant-products from Persia, India and Spain. The great geographer al-Idrīsī professed that Dioscorides' book was his Bible and that he had learned 'all its contents by heart, the better to know what Dioscorides had omitted' (Meyerhof, *ibid.*, p. x).

In their mathematical translations, Arabic scientists checked and corrected Greek calculations and measurements. Thus they remeasured the arc of the terrestrial meridian in order to improve upon Eratosthenes' value. Al-Battānī (Albategnius) made a number of corrections to Ptolemy's calculations, and his work was continued right up to the thirteenth century and, though incorporating new discoveries and improved evaluations, all the (subsequent) texts preserved 'the style and manner of Ptolemy' (F. Strunz).

Their respect for the Greeks did not blind the Arabs to their predecessors' shortcomings. Their critical spirit was so highly developed that, in time, they made a point of verifying all the Greek texts by personal observations.

So far, we have not spoken of the work of Arabic geographers, travellers and cosmographers, who, while describing the various regions of the earth, also recorded unusual natural phenomena, crops, animals and agricultural and manufacturing methods. Some of these geographers, like al-Bīrūnī, were also well-versed in the other sciences, and it is from them that the alchemists, physicians and apothecaries must have learned of the original sources of their drugs.

CONCLUSION

In brief, the Arabs did a great deal to turn science from metaphysical speculation into experimental and operational paths. Their concern with identification and verification, and hence with observation, accurate descriptions and measurements, did much to develop an objective scientific attitude. Joining great intellectual curiosity to a love of knowledge, they not only preserved and transmitted the science of antiquity, but gave it a new foundation. P. Kraus has shown how Al-Rāzī, in particular, propounded a new theory of scientific progress (*cf.* Rāzī, *Dubitations, i.e. Doubts about Galen*).

HISTORICAL SUMMARY OF
ARABIC SCIENCE

DISSEMINATION OF ARABIC SCIENTIFIC IDEAS

Arabic science may be said to have flourished between the eighth and twelfth centuries of our era, during which time it was, in fact, the almost exclusive repository of Greek learning. Latin translations of Arabic texts sparked off the great Western intellectual rebirth and it is from them that Christian philosophers and scholars took their cue. But with the capture of Cordova, the cultural centre of the Moslem West, by Ferdinand III in 1136, and of Baghdad by Hūlāgū's Mongol hordes in 1258, Arabic science was effectively cut short, even though eminent Arab scientists continued their researches.

The history of Arabic science can be divided chronologically and geographically. In the beginning, the East was the main centre of learning, scholars from Persia, Egypt, Syria and India flocking to Baghdad. Then, with the conquest of Spain by the Omayyads, Cordova began to supplant Baghdad, so that it is mainly through Spain that Arabic learning has come down to us, and this despite the fact that the Crusades brought the West into close contact with Eastern Arabia.

GROWTH OF ARABIC SCIENCE

Arabic science took some time to reach its apogee. Lacking means of exchanging information with scholars from other countries, Arabic scientists were at first left to their own resources. At the time there was no such thing as 'science', but only Greek, Persian, Indian and Chinese sciences. Loath to adopt any one to the exclusion of the others, the Arab conquerors were the first to give science the international character which we consider one of its fundamental characteristics. Neither Alexander nor the Romans made as profound an impression on their subject races as did the Arabs, who taught them the sacred language of the Koran as a profound religious duty. Arabic became *the* international scientific language; any scientific text of importance was written in Arabic and read all over the cultured world.

NON-ISLAMIC SCIENCE IN ARABIA

It has often been said that those Arabian tribes which did not adopt the Islamic faith remained utterly ignorant of science. Now, while their scientific contribution was admittedly restricted to the concoction of remedies and the development of special practical skills, they were bound to be affected by their neighbours' scientific activities. The Koreish tribe, in particular, handled the drug and spice trades, and hence came into frequent contact with India and Persia. Bīrūnī, in his *Introduction to the Book of Drugs*, mentions that merchants were called after the regions or parts in which they practised their trade. Thus amber merchants were called either *al-Shalāhiṭi*, from Baḥr Shalāhiṭ (the southern part of the Malacca trade route) or else *al-Shiḥrī*, after al-Shiḥr, the name of a district and port in Hadhramaut. Makalla and Aden were in continuous contact with India, and drug merchants had to supply not only 'directions for use' but possibly medical, pharmacological, botanical and mineralogical explanations as well. The first Arabic physician, al-Ḥārith, a contemporary of the prophet Mohammed, was born in Ṭayf, which lay on the caravan route. Al-Ḥārith travelled to India and to Persia, where he studied and taught in the famous school at Jundīshāpūr.

JUNDĪSHĀPŪR AND BAGHDAD

From the life of al-Ḥārith we know that Jundīshāpūr was famed throughout Arabia. It was to this town, in which the Sassanians had set up a medical school, that the Nestorians fled from Edessa when they were persecuted by the Byzantine Church in the fifth century. Similarly, when Justinian closed the Athens School in 525, its teachers were welcomed in Jundīshāpūr by Nūshīrwān the Just. Nūshīrwān also invited Indian teachers, thus turning his capital into a meeting-place for Greek, Syriac, Persian and Indian scientists. Here the work of translating Greek texts into Syriac was first begun, and here also some of the first translations into Arabic were made after the Moslem conquest.

Soon after Baghdad was founded in 762 by the Abbasid caliph Abu Ja'far al-Mansūr, it began to eclipse Jundīshāpūr. Baghdad also absorbed the Alexandrian tradition, *via* Harran, the Sabian capital, famous for its astronomers, mathematicians and translators. The Baghdad Academy of Science was founded by al-Ma'mūn, who was especially interested in biology and who encouraged cultural exchanges with India. From the *Fihrist* we know that the Barmecide prince Yaḥyā ibn Khālid invited Indian physicians and philosophers to teach in Baghdad, which had become the greatest scientific centre of the East and which continued to flourish until the final disappearance of the Abassid caliphate.

THE NINTH AND TENTH CENTURIES

In the history of Arabic science, it is impossible to distinguish sharply between an era of pure translation and an era of original research. Thus the greatest of all translators, including Ḥunayn ibn Isḥāq (ninth century), wrote original treatises as well. All we can say, therefore, is that there were two main waves in the history of Arabic science. Sarton has called the first, which occurred at the end of the eighth century and continued during the ninth, a 'wave of enthusiasm' for learning and research. During the first half of the tenth century this wave began slowly to recede, to give way in the second half of that century to a new wave, not only in the East but also in Egypt, where a Fatimid caliph founded the Cairo Academy of Science, based on the Baghdad model, and in Spain, where al-Ḥakam II set up an immense library.

THE ELEVENTH CENTURY

The eleventh century was the most brilliant of all, for in it flourished some of the greatest Arabic scientists: the astronomer Ibn Yūnus, the physician Ibn al-Haytham, known particularly for his work in optics, and the two most famous men of them all: Ibn Sīnā (Avicenna) and Bīrūnī. During the twelfth century, Arabic science continued to flourish especially in the West, under the leadership of Ibn Rushd (Averroës), Ibn Ẓuhr (Avenzoar) and Maïmonides, the 'Jew of Cordova' who settled in Cairo in about 1165. By the thirteenth century the great period of Arab science had passed; the Christian West, profiting from the many Latin translations of Arab writings, began to take over where the Arabs had left off and to prepare for the Renaissance.

We conclude this brief survey with Sarton's succinct list of the most important Arabic scientists and of their main works:

1 Time of Jābir Ibn Ḥayyān (second half of eighth century)

Al-Aṣma'ī, philologist and naturalist, flourished at Baghdad and Basra.

The Persian astronomers Ibrahīm al-Fazārī, his son Muḥammad, and Ya'qūb ibn Ṭāriq, studied Indian mathematics.

The Jewish astronomer Mashallah.

The Persian astrologer al-Naubakht and his son al-Faḍl, chief librarian to Harūn al-Rashīd.

The Sabian alchemist Jābir ibn Ḥayyān. P. Kraus has shown that the body of his alleged work consists of the later writings of various authors.

The Christian philosopher Theophile of Edessa, astrologer and translator of medical works from the Greek into Syriac.

The Nestorian-Persian physician Ibn Bakhtyashū‛, first of a leading family of physicians, head of the hospital of Jundīshāpūr.

2 Time of al-Khwārizmī (first half of ninth century)
Yaḥyā ibn Baṭrīq, Christian translator.

Al-Naẓẓām, natural philosopher. Suggested evolution.

Al-Kindī, Arab 'philosopher king' born in Basra. Taught at Baghdad; treatises on geometrical optics and physiology; criticized the alchemists.

The three sons of Mūsā ibn Shākir, mathematicians and translators.

Al-Ḥajjāj ibn Yūsuf, astronomer (Baghdad).

Al-‛Abbās, astronomer (Baghdad and Damascus).

Abu Sa‛id al-Ḍarīr, astronomer at Junjan, near the Caspian Sea. Treatise on the drawing of the meridian.

Al-Khwārizmī, mathematician and astronomer, founder of algebra (born in Khiva, Southern Aral Sea).

Aḥmad al-Nahāwandī, astronomer (Jundīshāpūr).

Ḥabash al-Ḥāsib, astronomer from Merv, taught at Baghdad. Drew up a table of tangents.

Sanad ibn ‛Aly, builder of the observatory at Baghdad.

‛Aly ibn ‛Īsā al-Aṣṭurlabī, maker of astronomical instruments at Baghdad and Damascus.

Yaḥyā ibn Abī Manṣūr, Christian Persian astronomer, taught at Baghdad.

Al-Farghānī, born in Farghana (Transoxiana), astronomer at Baghdad.

Al-Marwarradhī, born in Khurāsān, astronomer at Baghdad and Damascus.

‛Umar ibn al-Farrukhān, astronomer, born in Tabaristān, flourished in Baghdad.

Abū Ma‛shar, born in Balkh (Khurāsān), astrologer at Baghdad.

Ibn Sahdā, translator of medical works, Baghdad.

Jibrīl ibn Bakhtyashū‛, Christian physician at Baghdad.

Salmawayh ibn Būnān, Christian physician.

Ibn Massawayh, son of a pharmacist of Jundīshāpūr, Christian physician of Baghdad.

‛Aly (Rabban) al-Ṭabarī, Moslem physician, son of a Persian Jew.

Among the Jews, the astronomer Sahl al-Ṭabarī, and the astrologer Sahl ibn Bishr, born in Khurāsān.

3 Time of al-Rāzī (second half of ninth century)
Al-Māhānī, mathematician and astronomer from Māhān (Kirmān). Tried in vain to solve the Archimedean problem of dividing a sphere by al-Māhānī's equation.

Al-Nairīzī, from Nairiz near Shīrāz, astronomer and mathematician, wrote commentaries on Ptolemy and Euclid.

Thābit ibn Qurra, of Harrān (Mesopotamia), astronomer. Founder of the school of translators of Baghdad.

Qusṭā ibn Lūqā, Christian of Greek origin, from Baalbeck (Syria), flourished in Baghdad.

Al-Battānī (Albategnius) of Harran, astronomer.

Abū Bakr, Iranian astrologer.

Aḥmad ibn Yūsuf, Egyptian mathematician. Wrote a book on proportions.

Ḥamīd ibn 'Aly, of Wasit (Lower Mesopotamia), astronomer.

Sabūr ibn Sahl, of Jundīshāpūr. Author of an antidotary.

Yaḥyā ibn Sarāfyūn, author of a medical encyclopaedia in Syriac. Flourished in Damascus.

Ḥunayn ibn Isḥāq, physician and translator, head of a school and a famous medical family.

Ibn Khurdadbeh, geographer, flourished in Samarra.

Al-Ya'qūbī, geographer, flourished in Armenia and Khurāsān.

Al-Rāzī, the greatest clinician of the Middle Ages, alchemist and physicist, born at Ray, near Teheran, flourished at Ray and later at Baghdad.

4 Time of al-Mas'ūdī (first half of tenth century)

Al-Fārābī, born near Turkestan, philosopher and scholar, flourished at Aleppo and Damascus. Wrote a treatise on music.

Mattā ibn Yūnus and Yaḥyā ibn 'Adī, Christian translators.

Abū Kāmil, developed Khwārizmī's work on algebra.

Abū 'Uthmān, the Damascene, taught at Baghdad; translated Euclid's Book X and Pappos' *Commentary* on it.

Sinān ibn Thābit, mathematician, physicist, astronomer and physician, flourished at Baghdad.

Ibrahim ibn Sinān, mathematician; quadrature of parabola.

Al-'Imrānī, astrologer, commentary on the algebra of Abū Kāmil, born at Mosul (Upper Mesopotamia).

Ibn Waḥshīya (pseudonym), alchemist and agriculturist, born in Iraq.

Numerous geographers: Ibn Rusta, *fl.* Ispahan; Ibn al-Faqih, born in Hamadhān (Persia); Abū Zayd, *fl.* Sīrāf (Persian Gulf); Qudama, *fl.* Baghdad; al-Hamdānī, a Yemenite; Abū Dulaf, born near Mecca; al-Mas'ūdī, born at Baghdad.

5 Time of Abū'l-Wafā (second half of tenth century)

Encyclopaedia of the Brethren of Purity, a secret society formed at Basra, in about 963.

Abū Ja'far al-Khāzin, born in Khurāsān, solved the so-called al-Mahānī equation.

Al-Kūhī, native of Tabaristan, treated Archimedean and Apollonian problems leading to equations of degree higher than two.

Abū'l-Fath, of Ispahan, mathematician and astronomer.

Al-Sijzī, born at Sigistan, studied conic sections and the trisection of an angle.

'Abd al-Rahmān al-Sūfī, astronomer, flourished at Ray. Book of fixed stars.

Abū'l-Wafā, born Qūhistan, flourished at Baghdad. Wrote commentaries on Euclid, Diophantos, and al-Khwārizmī; contributed greatly to the development of trigonometry.

Al-Khujandī, of Sir Daria, proved (imperfectly) that the sum of two cubes cannot be a cubic number.

Abū Nasr, born in Iraq, mathematician.

Al-Qabisi, of Mosul, mathematician.

Maslama ibn Ahmad, of Madrid, flourished at Cordova, mathematician and astronomer.

'Aly ibn 'Abbās, famous physician from Southern Persia, flourished at Baghdad.

Abū Mansūr Muwaffak, flourished at Herāt; wrote a Persian *Materia medica*.

Abū'l-Qāsim, famous physician and surgeon, of Zahrū near Cordova.

Ibn Juljul, physician to the Spanish caliphate.

Al-Istakhrī, of Persepolis, geographer.

Buzūrg ibn Shahriyyar, from Khūzistān, geographer.

Al-Muqaddasī, of Jerusalem, traveller and geographer.

(N.B. This was the period of the first great Moslem contributions to the Christian West. Gerbart of Auvergne (later Pope Sylvester II) studied in Catalonia and taught at Rheims from 972. The Jewish physician Donnolo studied Arabic at Palermo, taught at Otranto and Rossano, and died *c.* 982.)

6 *Time of al-Bīrūnī (first half of eleventh century)*

Al-Bīrūnī, of Khwārizm (Khiva), mathematician, astronomer and geographer.

Ibn Sīnā (Avicenna), born in Afshana near Bokharā, philosopher, astronomer, physicist and physician.

(N.B. Sarton said of these two great scientists: 'Al-Bīrūnī represents the more adventurous and critical spirit, Ibn Sīnā the synthetic spirit. Al-Bīrūnī was more of a discoverer and in that respect he came nearer to the modern scientific ideal. Ibn Sīnā was essentially an organizer, an encyclopaedist and a philosopher.')

Al-Karmānī, born at Cordova, died at Saragossa, introduced the mathematical ideas of the Brethren of Purity into Spain.

Other Arab mathematicians and astronomers in Spain were Ibn al-Samḥ (Granada); Ibn Abī'l-Rijāl of Cordova (?) who flourished in Tunis; Ibn al-Saffār (Cordova).

Arab mathematicians and astronomers in the East were Kūshyār ibn Labbān from Jīlān, south of the Caspian Sea; al-Karkhī (Baghdad); al-Nasawī, born in Khurāsān.

Ibn Yunus, of Cairo, worked at the Dār al-Ḥikma observatory.

Ibn al-Wafīd, physician of Toledo, and the Jew Ibn Janāḥ. Wrote treatise on simple remedies.

Ibn al-Haytham, the most famous physicist and optician of the Arab world, born at Basra, taught at Cairo.

Massawayh al-Mārdīnī, Christian physician of Upper Mesopotamia, flourished at Baghdad, then at Cairo.

'Ammār, of Mosul, one of the most original Islamic oculists.

'Aly ibn Riḍwān, of Cairo, physician.

Al-Kathi, chemist, of Baghdad.

Abū Sa'id 'Ubayd Allah, physician of the family of Bakhtyashū'.

Ibn Buṭlān, physician of Baghdad.

'Aly ibn 'Īsā, oculist of Baghdad. Wrote treatise on ophthalmology.

7 Time of Omar Khayyām (second half of eleventh century)
(This period marks the last upsurge and the beginning of the decline of the Moslem world. It produced the first scientific works written in the Hebrew and Persian languages.)

Al-Zarqālī, astronomer of Cordova.

Yūsuf al-Mu'tamin, King of Saragossa, mathematician.

Muhammad ibn 'Abd al-Bāqī, mathematician of Baghdad.

Omar Khayyām (the tentmaker), poet and mathematician. Cubic equations with some geometric solutions.

Abū 'Umar ibn Hajaj, of Seville, writer on agriculture.

Ibn Jazla and Sā'id ibn Hibat Allah, physicians of Baghdad.

Zarrin Dast, Persian oculist.

Al-Bakrī, geographer (Cordova).

Al-Mawardī (Basra and Baghdad) 'sociologist'.

(The influence of Arabic and Moslem culture grew as a result of the Latin translations of Constantine the African. The first Latin-Arabic glossary was published in Castille'.)

THE EXACT SCIENCES

INTRODUCTION

The exact sciences which made up the medieval *quadrivium* were arithmetic, music, geometry and astronomy. Together with the *trivium* (grammar, dialectics and rhetoric) they constituted the 'Seven Liberal Arts'.

The concept of 'exact science' was given a new meaning by the Arabs. Their language, as we have seen, had become the language of international communication. To make that possible, all the Asiatic elements of the Arabic vocabulary had to be fitted into a conceptual framework which, though based on the Greek model, had to conform to the peculiar structure of the Arabic language. Now all Arabic words are triliteral—that is to say, they are made up from 3,726 'immortal' root-words of three consonants each. Inflection is by internal vowel changes and, since vowels are not written down, reading calls for prior thought and selection. Names, verbs and prepositions alike are subject to trivocal flexional endings (*i'rāb*).

Because of these structural properties, Arabic favours the expression of analytic, atomistic, occasionalist and apophthegmatic thought. A recent technical study on the 'semantic involution of concepts' (*taḍmīn*) has shown how much Semitic languages tend towards shortened and abstract formulations—how they 'algebraize', while Aryan languages 'geometrize' (see *Arabica*, vol. 1). In fact, just as thought may be projected into space (as in Pythagorean figured numbers), so it can be turned back on itself at appropriate times to construct its object (compare the time-scheme of Kant).

Arabic, which facilitates this 'interiorization' of thought, is particularly suited to expressing exact scientific concepts and to developing them, in much the same way as mathematical concepts have evolved historically. These began with the intuitive and almost contemplative arithmetic and geometry which, with Plato, preceded the contemplation of intelligible 'natures' and essences, and proceeded to the science of algebraic constructions in which arithmetic and geometry are fused together. Arabic is a language in which thought is expressed paratactically, as a flow of ideas without connectives; hence many lovers of Greek have claimed that Arabic is far less incisive than the Aryan languages, with their choice of well-defined conjunctions and conjugations. But then all Semitic people have a marked aversion to a linguistic framework in which all the consequences and associations of thought are incorporated. In logic, Arabic does not start with the method of classification by dichotomy known as the 'Tree of Porphyry'. It eschews *a priori* black-and-white distinctions, and concentrates on the various shades of grey—the so-called *Shāwadhdh* or anomalous qualities. The Arabs were therefore closer to the Stoics than to Aristotle.

Hence it is not surprising that early Arabic philosophers used the 'Stoic' syllogism of the Greek and Hindu atomists; it was only later, and not without religious scruples, that they came to adopt

Aristotelian logic. The entire history of Arabic science reflects the permanent conflict between two opposing grammatical views: Stoic logical atomism *v.* Peripatetic hylomorphism; the school of Kufa *v.* the school of Basra (*cf.* the conflict between the Greek grammarians of Pergamos and of Alexandria).

The consequences of these linguistic arguments made themselves felt not only in logic but also in mathematics. In arithmetic, numbers became personalized; they ceased to be 'natures' and became active beings capable of acting in concert with others. By extending to mathematics the occasional atomism of the first Islamic scholastics, the Arabs ceased to confine numbers within the closed and static spatial continuum of the Greeks, and projected them instead into unlimited time where they became so many discontinuous instants (*ānāt*) of intensity. Arabian mathematicians considered numbers as isolated 'grains of quantity' which, in their appropriate spheres, were endowed with action and efficacy according to their fixed rank in the finite series of numbers. No matter whether the Arabs considered the famous Fibonacci series (0, 1, 1, 2, 3, 5, 8, 13, 21, 34 . . .) which is so important in biology (phyllotaxis), the law of definite proportions discovered empirically by the alchemists, or the periodic law of stellar phenomena (cycles of 140, 280, 960 solar years), they invariably tended to look upon certain numbers as particularly 'helpful' to experimental research.

Hence they were not so much interested in 'natural' series as in the rank of particular numbers in them. In other words, they were more concerned with ordinals than with cardinals; unlike the Greeks, they had no aversion to odd or irrational numbers, so much so that Pinès has claimed that Thābit ibn Qurra was familiar with the Cantor discontinuum.

Having examined the influence of the Arabic language on scientific development, we shall now look at another aspect: the algebraization of the alphabet. The twenty-eight letters of the Arabic alphabet not only represent all the numerals but also the twenty-eight classes of ideas of Arab philosophers. Thus Ibn Sīnā's arguments in the *Nayrūziya* are based on a philosophic alphabet; and, forty years before him, the philosopher Abū'l-Hasan Deilemī asserted that there were two classes of irrefutable arguments, the series of twenty-eight letters of the alphabet and the series of integral numbers. By that he meant that it was legitimate to fit the twenty-eight alphabetical symbols into some kind of mechanical scheme which would reflect any series of real events.

In this way, Arabic science managed to produce abstract 'arguments' based on alphabetical numbers—every word can 'release' a number of objects designated by letters adding up to the same total (for example: 'AYN, the 'essence', originally meaning 70, is equivalent to YA+SAD = 10+60 = 70). In this connection, it is interesting to note that Arabic astrologers constructed a 'thinking machine', the *zairja*, which was discussed by ibn Khaldūn, described by Raymond Lull in his *Ars Magna* and admired by Leibniz.

Although Aristotelian logic gradually replaced the philosophical alphabet until its use was restricted to the syncretic Shīite sect, it remained latent in all the many gnostic currents of Islamic thought. Developed by Lull, Leibniz and Lambert, it paved the way for the logical calculus, which, together with modern algebra, is therefore one outcome of the philosophical alphabet and its peculiar features.

ARITHMETIC
Arabic arithmetical texts usually classify their subject-matter into integers, fractions, and other numbers, and the study of some of their properties (friendly and perfect numbers, magic squares) may be called the study of number theory in embryo. The oldest of all known magic squares, made up of the first nine integers in three rows (4/9/2; 3/5/7; 8/1/6), which the Chinese had carved on the back of a tortoise (see *fig. 22*, page 173), attracted the attention of many leading Arab thinkers, including Ghazālī.

OPERATIONS
The Arabs adopted the Greek definitions of arithmetical operations, but used methods of their own. Some of their procedures which strike us as unnecessarily complicated and rather unnatural are so only because they were based on the prior analysis of number construction. Take, for instance, al-Amūlī's division by 2 of a number:

Dividend	1,365	
Intermediate quotient	0,132	−1
Add	55	
Final quotient	682	$(682 \times 2) + 1 = 1,365$

The figure 5 is written below and to the right of the intermediate quotient of every odd number of the dividend and the two are added, on the implicit assumption that $\frac{1}{2} = 0.5$ (though decimal fractions were unknown to the Arabs).

Following in the footsteps of the Greeks, Arab mathematicians extracted square and cube roots by successive approximations, and even constructed root tables. They also used the abacus for the same purpose, and were not slow in observing that numbers ending in 2, 3, 7, 8, or in an odd number of zeros could not be perfect squares. In particular, they developed practical rules of arithmetic and demonstrated the existence of numerous identities, though they failed to bring out the general commutative, associative and other laws involved, *i.e.* that $am+bm = (a+b)m$; $\sqrt{a}\sqrt{b} = \sqrt{ab}$; *etc.*

FRACTIONS

It must be emphasized how much number theory was originally tied to linguistic problems. Arabic had no special terms for unit fractions smaller than $\frac{1}{10}$. Hence fractions in general were expressed by '*m* parts of *n*'. Moreover, the Arabs regarded fractions either as unit parts or else as ratios between the several parts of a number and the number itself (*cf.* the Epistle of the Brethren of Purity). Only the first of these views corresponds to a mathematical extension of the concept of number, and its general acceptance was impeded by the metaphysical belief in an indivisible and absolute unit that was not a number, the monad of certain Pythagorean doctrines. Hence the Arabs never adopted the modern way of writing fractions, except when numerator and denominator consisted of only one digit each. Moreover, whenever the denominator could be broken down into aliquot parts lower than ten, they expressed each fraction by a series of fractions and of fractions of fractions, whose successive denominators were the aliquot parts.

$$\text{Thus } \frac{19}{35} \text{ became } \frac{4}{5}\frac{3}{7}, \text{ } i.e. \text{ } \frac{3}{7}+\left(\frac{4}{5} \text{ of } \frac{1}{7}\right), \text{ or } \frac{3}{7}+\frac{4}{5\times7} = \frac{15+4}{35}.$$

When the denominator was a prime number, or when its aliquot parts contained a prime number higher than ten, it was looked upon as an ordinary divisor. This complex approach was one of the main reasons why the Arabs failed to develop a general theory of fractions. In passing, we might mention that Arab astronomers often used sexagesimal fractions.

PRACTICAL PROBLEMS

The Arabs had to solve a number of concrete problems, such as the division of taxes, the calculation of tithes and the division of estates according to the Koranic law. Most of their practical rules were therefore based on proportions. Furthermore, practical problems also brought them face to face with such progressions as the sum of even or odd numbers, though they failed to prove their generality. Arabic arithmetical texts also refer to weights and measures, to the purity of coins and to methods of counting (*cf.* the system of *siyāq* cyphers).

ALGEBRA: ḤISĀB AL-JABR WA'L-MUQĀBALA

According to Ruska's translation of the term, algebra was originally no more than a method of calculating complements (*jabr*) and redintegrations (*muqābala*), two terms which have also been translated as 'restoration' and 'equalization'. Al-Amūlī said that whenever a member of an equation contains a negative number it must be 'completed'. In effect, the Arabs looked upon negative terms as being incomplete; *jabr* was needed to balance them, after which equal or homologous terms could be removed from the two members by *muqābala*. For example:

In the equation: $5x^2 - 6x + 2 = 4x^2 + 7$
jabr gives: $5x^2 + 2 = 4x^2 + 6x + 7$
and *muqābala*: $x^2 = 6x + 5$

Arab mathematicians could manipulate unknown quantities and hence solved concrete problems by solving the appropriate equations.

'ARABIC' NUMERALS

The so-called Arabic numerals (*ghubar*) are in fact of Indian origin and made their first appearance in 830. In Arabic, they were written from right to left and, according to their position (from the right), they represented units, tens, hundreds, *etc*. Whenever the number to be expressed lacked units, tens or hundreds, a point was written in the appropriate place of the 'word'. This point was our zero.

Unlike the Greek and Semitic literal notation, the Indian notation was unlimited, for by it any number, no matter how large, could be expressed. Instead of assigning one symbol to each number, the Indians had introduced a place-value notation—the symbols had lost their quiddity and had become relative. Numbers could henceforth be engendered *ad infinitum* by a simple mathematical law. P. Boutroux has shown how their arithmetic quite naturally led the Arabs to algebra.

THE DEVELOPMENT OF ALGEBRA

The process of algebraization was begun by al-Khwārizmī (early ninth century) and was not, as Wiedemann has called it, 'a primitive method of applied calculations based on numerous examples . . .'. True, some of al-Khwārizmī's solutions were accompanied by geometrical figures, but not those of his successors, Abū Kāmil and the great Abū'l-Wafā'. Omar Khayyām's classification of equations has justly remained famous and, in the West, Fibonacci's *Flos* was the first textbook of algebra.

MUSIC

Arabic musical texts were mainly devoted to the classification of the musical intervals between the seven fundamental notes obtained on the four strings of the lute, and to a lesser extent to the study of modes (whose originally Persian names were first mentioned in the eleventh century, when Ibn Sīnā discussed three of them: *nawā, isfahān,* and *salmakī*). Al-Fārābī was the first to 'hellenize' Arabic musical concepts.

But the origins of Arabic music go back to the introduction, in about the fifth century, of rhymes ending in nasal vowels by the Jewish poet Yannây and by Arabic poets, and to the Arab love of popular refrains (*zajal*) set to music. Arabic music was rhythmical rather than melodic, and was based on the alternation of muffled (*tik*) and resounding (*tum*) drumbeats. Its concern was with tempo and its neglect of musical flow made it atomistic, reflecting the tick of the clock rather than the even course of the Greek clepsydra.

GEOMETRY

The Arabic contribution to geometry was largely restricted to the translation of the works of Euclid (Book X of the *Elements* and a number of lost works). However, their experimental approach caused the Arabs to present many problems where Euclid had deemed one sufficient. Their work also bore unmistakable traces of the Indian *Siddhāntas* and of the works of Heron, translated by Qustā ibn Lūqā, who taught the Arabs what applied geometry they knew. Arabic geometers were also influenced by Archimedes and Apollonios.

Hence we must clearly divide Arabic geometry into constructional and arithmetical branches. When it came to constructions, the Arabs expressed the elements of geometrical figures in terms of one another, *i.e.* by the methods of Greek geometry, and investigated the same problems which their Alexandrian predecessors had studied (such as mean proportionals and the trisection of an angle). The Banū Mūsā, in particular, were representative of this approach; their solutions involved no arithmetical or algebraic techniques.

But the numerical approach was the more characteristic of the two, so that Suter could write, 'In the application of arithmetic and algebra to geometry, and conversely in the solution of algebraic problems by geometrical means, the Arabs far surpassed the Greeks and the Hindus.' The most famous contributions to this field were Ibrahīm ibn Sinān's writings on the quadrature of the parabola, Abū'l Wafā's writings on the construction of regular polygons involving cubic equations, and Abū Kāmil's writings on the pentagon and the decagon. Nāṣir al-Dīn al-Tūsī's discussions of Euclid's propositions led to G. Saccheri's first attempts to formulate a non-Euclidean geometry (1733).

In cartography, Arabic geometers used the Persian method of the six *kishwârs*. In this, a central region was represented by a circle, surrounded by six circles of equal radius which touch the central circle and their neighbours. The resulting honeycomb pattern has a far less distorting effect on the peripheral regions of a map than have other methods of projection (Ptolemy, Peutinger, Mercator). Al-Balkhī's atlas was constructed on this principle.

Another sphere to which geometry was applied was surveying; some Arabic textbooks have discussed this subject in conjunction with such tenth-century Persian mechanical inventions as mills, Persian wheels, mangonels and traction engines. Finally, such geometrical concepts as the point, the line and space were the subject of many arguments between those Arabic philosophers who looked upon space as a cover or support (Aristotelian space) and those who considered it as a container (the Platonic space of Abū'l-Baraqāt).

ASTRONOMY

In astronomy, the Arabic experimental method proved exceptionally successful. Not only could the Arabs call on their own meticulous observations, but they could also gather information from the Chaldean observatories, which the Persian, Greek and Moslem dynasties had successively equipped with the latest instruments.

Towards the end of the eighth century, Arabic astronomers based their ideas on al-Fazārī's translation of the Sanskrit *Siddhānta*, but more generally, they adopted Persian and especially Greek sources, so much so that most of their best-known astronomical tables can be shown to have been inspired by Ibn al-Biṭrūji's translation of Ptolemy's *Almagest*.

The Moslems looked upon astronomy as the noblest, the most exalted and the most beautiful (al-Battānī) of sciences, if only because the study of the stars was an indispensable aid to religious observance. They helped to determine the month of Ramadan, the hours of prayer and the orientation of mosques towards Mecca. Moreover, the Koran enjoined the faithful to contemplate the glory of God in the construction of His universe.

According to Nallino, who based this opinion on Birūnī's *al-Qānūn al-maṣʿūdi*, Arabic astronomy was subdivided into spherical astronomy, chronometry, spherical trigonometry and mathematical geography. It completely ignored such subjects as we should include under astro-physics and celestial mechanics.

Under the reign of al-Ma'mūn (ninth century), astronomers of the Baghdad and Damascus observatories busied themselves with verifying and correcting Ptolemy's tables, and established the so-called *Verified Astronomical Tables* of Yaḥyā ibn Abī Mansūr (A.D. 830). Unlike Ptolemy's, these Tables took into account the precession of the equinoxes. Observations of Venus and the sun led the same astronomers to adopt a non-Ptolemaic model which, according to Nallino, was tantamount to 'transforming the orbit of Venus into an epicycle whose constant centre was the real position of the sun'. Unfortunately, the Arabs failed to conclude that Venus was a satellite of the sun. Similar studies were being pursued throughout the Moslem world, and led to such influential writings as the works of Farghānī, Battānī, Ibn Yūnus (*Hakemite Tables*), Zarqālī, Nāṣir al-Dīn al-Tūsī (*Tables of the Ilkhān*), and finally to the construction of the Alphonsine Tables (1272), the first astronomical tables of the West.

From their observations, the Arabs also constructed a solar calendar as a guide to harvests and tax collections. A very inaccurate, archaic, and purely Arabic calendar, which has been used in south-east Asia from time immemorial, and later in the desert, was based on the *Anwā*, the twenty-eight zodiacal or 'dewy' mansions of the moon. It arose from the 'Pleiadic' calendar, studied by Fraser.

Trigonometry, which was at first treated as a branch of astronomy, was later studied independently. The trigonometrical tables of al-Khwārizmī (ninth century) were translated into Latin by Adelard of Bath in 1126. From al-Battānī (858–929) to al-Tūsī (1201–74) trigonometrical studies proceeded apace, particularly when Abū'l Wafā' (940–98) published his works on spherical trigonometry. In trigonometry the Arabs were vastly superior to the Greeks and the Indians, to whose sine and cosine tables they added tables of the other trigonometrical functions, and then established the fundamental relations between them. Even before Abū'l Wafā', Aḥmed ibn 'Abd Allah was familiar with tangents, cotangents, secants and cosecants needed for calculating the correct hour for holding the *'asr* prayers.

The Arabs also used astronomy as an aid to navigation in the Indian ocean. Pelliot has pointed out that, while sailing to Madagascar, Arab navigators were the first to observe the Magellanic Clouds.

In addition to theoretical works, the Arabs also published textbooks on the manufacture and handling of astronomical instruments, particularly of the astrolabe. Even today, Moroccan mosques employ a special official whose duty it is to fix the hour of prayer by means of an astrolabe.

Finally, we must not overlook the purely astrological aspect of Arabian astronomy, which was so much admired in the Holy Roman Empire, where the works of Abū Ma'shar and of Ibn Abī'l Rijāl were translated and studied with keen interest. The Persian Banū Naubakht family was renowned among the Arabs for having cast the horoscope of the newly founded city of Baghdad, and for publishing a table of astrological predictions up to the year 933 which was in great demand. Astrology, the 'judicial' science of the 'decrees of the stars' ('ilm aḥkām al-nujūm), was thought to be very closely related to astronomy. The study of conjunctions and oppositions for horoscopic purposes led to precise observations and tables, and such scholars as al-Battānī had no hesitation in solving astrological problems according to strict trigonometrical principles.

All in all, Arabic astronomers were original thinkers whose systematic research enabled them to revise many of Ptolemy's findings. The leaders of this movement were Ibn Bājja, and later Jābir ibn Aflaḥ, who worked in Spain. In addition, the apparently irregular revolutions of the planets, observed by means of Chaldean hemispherical gnomons, caused the Arabs to make a radical revision of such Aristotelian concepts as impetus, acceleration and velocity. However, this philosophical reassessment which began with Ibn Sīnā and was continued by Abū'l-Baraqāt is only of marginal interest in a history of the 'exact' sciences.

MECHANICS AND OPTICS

Mechanics and optics occupy a half-way position both between mathematics and biology and also between theoretical and applied science.

According to al-Khāzinī, mechanics is the study of centres of gravity (*marākiz al-thiql*) and of equilibrium, as taught by Aristotle, Archimedes and Pappos. Mechanics was also said to govern the art of constructing and manipulating spring balances (*mīzān*) and scales (*qarasṭun*), which could be used for measuring time (by counterbalancing the residual sand in a sand clock) and for establishing the specific weights of various substances (Ibn al-Haytham and al-Bīrūnī). This was the purely physical or chemical aspect of mechanics. On the other hand, mechanics can also be used to demonstrate the validity of mathematical theories; for example, the law of inverse proportions can be demonstrated by showing that the ratio of two weights in equilibrium on a lever is inversely proportional to the ratio of their distances from the fulcrum. Al-Bīrūnī even used the balance to demonstrate the rules of *jabr* and of *muqābala*, and conversely, al-Khāzinī used the laws of proportion to determine the accuracy of balances.

Another aspect of Arabic mechanics was the study of pulleys, based on the work of Heron of Alexandria, whose writings were translated by Qusṭā ibn Lūqā. Finally mechanics was held to hold the key to the art of building automatic machines, a subject studied by the Banū Mūsā family.

For theological reasons, Arabic atomistic philosophers returned to the concept of rectilinear motion, and divided circular orbits into a series of small line segments. However, they failed to appreciate the tremendous mathematical implications of this procedure.

Optics which, *inter alia*, was the art of constructing mirrors, was

studied quite especially by Ibn al-Haytham, who discussed physiological optics and presented a philosophical theory of the nature of
light. He was familiar with reflection and refraction, made experiments with plane, spherical, cylindrical and parabolic mirrors, wrote
a treatise on the measurement of the paraboloid of revolution, and
investigated the light of the stars, the rainbow, colours, shadows and
darkness. Clearly, therefore, he broke down the barriers between
mathematics, physics and biology, and was equally familiar with all
three.

PHYSICS AND BIOLOGY

DEFINITION AND FUNDAMENTAL CONCEPTS

The Arabs held that all the natural sciences were but different applications of the same fundamental concepts. Meteorology, physical
geography, alchemy, zoology, botany, agriculture, mineralogy, or
even medicine could all be explained by the four elements of the
ancients—earth, water, air and fire—and by the four elementary
qualities—hot, cold, dry and wet.

The belief that all nature was the result of various combinations of
these elements and qualities, and that nature could be changed by
the intensification or suppression of the appropriate ones, was shared
by all Arabic scientists. For instance, it was generally agreed that
earth could be produced by the correct combination of coldness,
dryness and 'substance'.

Similarly, water = coldness +humidity +substance; air = heat+
humidity +substance; fire = heat +dryness +substance; or heat =
fire −dryness; dryness = earth −coldness; coldness = water −humi-
dity; humidity = air −heat.

Alchemy and medicine were simply methods of discovering bodies
which repel one elementary quality while attracting another. Hence
there was born the idea that metals could be regenerated much like
diseased tissue, and that inorganic and organic matter were akin. The
term remedy (*adawiya*) was used by the alchemists as well as by the
physicians.

METEOROLOGY

Arabic meteorology was purely Aristotelian, and its leading exponent,
al-Kindī, did no more than simplify and rearrange the Peripatetic
model. However, Aristotle had put forward a number of incompatible
causal hypotheses, and al-Kindī reduced these to one principle: the
regular interaction between elementary qualities of varying intensity
and the motion of the sphere, which produced heat, compression, and
expansion. He never suspected the existence of other physical forces.

JABĪR AND THE FUNDAMENTAL CONCEPTS OF ALCHEMY

Since meteorology involves the study of physical phenomena, it is difficult to see how the ancients could have used it as a springboard for the fancies of alchemy. In fact, while holding fast to the elementary qualities, the alchemists introduced novel criteria for distinguishing between substances.

P. Kraus has discussed this subject at length in the course of his study of Jabīr, who classified substances into: (1) 'spirits', *i.e.* substances which completely evaporate when fired; (2) 'metals' *i.e.* substances which are fusible and malleable; (3) 'bodies' or mineral substances, *i.e.* fusible or non-fusible substances which are not malleable and can be pulverized.

The 'spirits' were sulphur, arsenic, mercury, ammonia and camphor; and the 'metals' were lead, tin, gold, silver, copper, iron and *karsini*, a substance which was undiscoverable, according to al-Rāzī, but which Qazwīnī identified as used for 'making pots and bells in some countries'. It might therefore have been an alloy like bronze. As for the 'bodies', they were complex substances containing varying degrees of 'spirit'. Most alchemists introduced personal variations into these classes, probably because they followed separate traditions.

What is important in the alchemical classification is the fact that nature was no longer divided by such perceptible qualities as hot, cold, dry and wet, but by operational qualities like evaporation, fusion, malleability, pulverization—in short, by purely physical factors. Admittedly, the alchemists also produced chemical transformations in their retorts and stills, but they paid little attention to them.[1] They concentrated on appearances and hence were unable to distinguish between apparently similar substances, and while they appreciated the difference between partial (*mujāvara*) and complete mixtures (*mizāj kullī*), they never formulated the idea of chemical compounds. Specific gravity was their main distinguishing criterion, and in this field al-Bīrūnī, al-Khazinī and Abū Manṣūr al Nazayrī continued and modified the work of the Alexandrians, obtaining fairly correct results for gold, lead, copper, *etc.* Altogether, al-Bīrūnī determined the specific gravity of some fifteen substances, but his evaluations had no other purpose than to establish in what proportions they could be mixed, much as Archimedes had investigated the proportion of gold and silver in Hieron's crown. The idea that specific gravity might be connected with purely chemical properties never occurred to the Arabs, though Jabīr, for instance, tried to measure the proportions of the different 'natures', or elementary substances, which went into various compounds. However, his 'natures' were extremely

[1] However, a 'synthetic' theory was being elaborated by Arabic philosophers. It was based on a 'formal cause' and introduced metaphysics into physics.

vague and the results, though based on measurements, failed to
reflect any kind of chemical reality.

THE CHARACTERISTICS OF ALCHEMY

In effect, what interested the alchemists above all was the intensity
of chemical reactions. Thus they realized that certain substances
reacted vigorously, while others were inert. They looked upon colour
changes as signs of the utmost importance but failed to appreciate
their true significance, which, as we now know, rests on complicated
ionic processes. Colour changes were chosen simply because they
were the most obvious, though, in fact, they are of subsidiary importance and were, in any case, beyond the capabilities of the investiga-
tors. In other words, Arabic alchemists adopted superficial concepts
which failed to describe any real phenomena. Thus Jabīr introduced
the concept of the 'potency' of substances, by which he referred to the
respective 'distances' of gold, silver, copper, tin, lead, iron and other
substances from the elixir governing the transmutation of metals.
Now, since no such elixir exists, the distances were obtained by
arithmological manipulations, and it is this sort of approach which
turned alchemy into an esoteric 'science'. Ignoring experiment and
observation, the alchemists were forced to rely on the most far-fetched
symbolic 'operations'.

AL-RĀZĪ

Al-Rāzī's *Sirr al-Asrār* (Secret of Secrets) avoided the worst of these
errors, and was therefore a somewhat more positive contribution to
science. He began with a classification of chemical substances similar
to Jabīr's, dividing minerals into stones, vitriols, borax and salts, and
examined their possible reactions in a host of apparatus. While we
agree with J. Ruska that al-Rāzī's substances and fundamental concepts have no equivalents in modern chemistry, it is important to
remember that al-Rāzī made a point of discarding number mysticism,
that he tried to carry out experiments, and that, by his descriptions of
the instruments and operations involved, he appreciated the importance of communicating his steps and helping others to repeat them.

CRITICS OF ALCHEMY: BĪRŪNĪ AND AVICENNA

Bīrūnī was not interested in alchemy as such, but discussed it, in
passing, in his *Kitāb al-Jamāhir fi'l-Jawāhir*, a treatise on mineralogy
in which he rejected all the facts that did not stand up to personal
investigation, and hence rid the lapidaries of his day of many of their
mythical illusions.

Avicenna carried out what in his time was a most original attack
on the very basis of alchemy. Though he did not abandon the idea of

transmutation outright, he realized fully that it was not by merely changing colours, one of many metallic properties, that chemists could change the nature of metals. These ideas were expressed clearly in a small work, the *Epistle on the Elixir*, whose authenticity has been proved by Ahmed Ates. 'I shall examine the natural facts,' the author begins, 'unlike the alchemists who are devoid of any of the arguments which are the basis of all science, and who offer nothing but idle chatter'. As for their apologists, they used 'the tenuous arguments of puny minds', instead of reason and experiment:

To assume that it is possible to turn silver the colour of gold, or copper the colour of silver, is tantamount to holding that there is a red dye which causes metals to become reddened and a white dye which causes metals to become bleached. Now we know that a mixture of colours of hard and stony bodies cannot be produced unless these bodies have first been softened and moulded. Moreover we obviously cannot soften and mould them unless they have been melted. Yet when they are melted it does not matter which red or white dye we use, since whenever colours are boiled over a fire they are destroyed and produce no effects; and whenever they fail to come to the boil they cannot be fixed by fire but evaporate, volatilize and escape, and are also of no use. Others neither boil nor subtilize and hence neither penetrate the metals nor mix with them and are again of no use. . . .

But instead of drawing the obvious conclusions from all these findings, Avicenna made great efforts to find a perfect dye which would meet all the alchemists' requirements.

In short, Arabic alchemy, while pursuing futile aims, nevertheless freed chemistry from its arithmological and magical shackles, and Avicenna's critique is evidence of the growing maturity of Moslem science in the eleventh century.

ALCHEMY AND THE STUDY OF ORGANIC MATTER
Apart from mineral substances, the alchemists also used vegetable and animal matter, mainly as reagents. But it would be wrong to conclude that the Arabs had begun to dabble in organic chemistry, for these substances, like minerals, were studied for their alchemical 'natures' and not for their chemical properties. To sum up, Arabic alchemy aimed at formulating the most general laws of all sorts of imaginary chemical processes, and at fitting the known facts to baseless assumptions.

BOTANY AND ZOOLOGY
Arabic studies of plants and animals were unsystematic and were never pursued for their own interest. Many biological texts, such as

Jāḥiẓ's *Book of Animals*, were simply collections of natural 'marvels', part legend and part fact, based largely on unsubstantiated tales of travellers. Others were linguistic exercises in naming various species. In fact, biology was always considered a subsidiary branch of agriculture and medicine, so that Arabic biology, like other branches of Arabic science, may be said to have been predominantly utilitarian in outlook.

AGRICULTURAL TEXTS

Arabic agricultural texts were mainly derived from Greek sources, and especially from the *Geoponics*. J. Ruska has shown that a work by Cassianos Bassos, which was translated into Arabic, had a tremendous influence on Moslem agriculturists, and so did Ibn Waḥshīya's *Nabataean Agriculture*, which P. Kraus has called 'one of the boldest falsehoods spread during the Middle Ages'. According to Martin Plessner, the book dealt with olive trees, springs and wells, the qualities of water and how to improve them, various plants and their possible varieties, changes in atmospheric conditions, vapours and winds, the causes of deforestation, the nature and improvement of soils, the cultivation of crops, horticulture, *etc.* Ibn Ḥajjaj and Ibn al-'Awwām acknowledge the book as their most important source.

We have already mentioned the influence of Dioscorides' *Materia Medica*, which inspired the most famous Arabian pharmacopoeias, those of Bīrūnī, of Maïmonides, and of Ibn al-Bayṭār. While al-Bayṭār recorded his predecessors' findings rather uncritically, Bīrūnī was far more selective and, like Maïmonides, verified the facts whenever he could. He was the first to suggest that flowers could be identified by the number of their parts:

All numbers are stamped on life and nature, above all on flowers, the number of whose petals, petioles and venules is a characteristic of each of their genera. . . . It is a strange fact that, whenever the petals of a flower have a circular base, their number generally obeys certain laws of mathematics, and most often corresponds to the number of equal chords that can be inscribed into circles by elementary geometry. . . . It is rarely indeed that we come across a flower with seven or nine petals, for the corresponding chords cannot be so inscribed. But there are arrangements of three, four, five, six, eight and ten petals. It is possible that, in time, genera of flowers with seven or nine petals may be discovered, or that these numbers are found in certain teratological specimens. Truly, nature limits her genera and species so that, should we count the seeds of a pomegranate, we are bound to find that another pomegranate from the same tree has the same number of seeds.

(Chronology, Sachau ed., 1878, p. 298.)

33 Casting a horoscope

34 Birth of a child

In other words, Bīrūnī was familiar with the idea of floral diagrams and saw that they could be used for purposes of classification.

TOXICOLOGY

Poisons were discussed by Ibn Waḥshīya, Jabīr, and by Maïmonides. In addition, most Arabic physicians referred to them in their medical textbooks. All these works were greatly influenced by Persian and, above all, by Indian ideas, and especially by the Indian *Book of Shanaq*. Shanaq may well have been the Arabic version of the Indian name Canakya (*c.* 320 B.C.), for Bettina Strauss has shown that the work is based on the *Caraka Samhita*, particularly in its identifications of poisonous substances and the distinction between 'mobile' poisons derived from animal products and 'immobile' poisons derived from mineral and vegetable substances. However, when it came to the actual preparation of poisons and treatment of cases of poisoning, the Arabs used Greek methods, which alone struck them as being rational and useful.

Arabic toxicology not only marked the advance from alchemy to rational medicine, but also emphasized the eminent place of medicine among all the other sciences. Arabic science, as we saw, was founded on the doctrine of elementary qualities. Now, these qualities were originally associated with only four elements, but the physicians gradually introduced more complex entities, for example the humours (black bile, blood, yellow bile, phlegm), food, drugs and poisons, all of which they endeavoured to keep in equilibrium. Moreover, each patient was said to have his own equilibrium, determined by his temperament, diet, medical history and even parental illness. All the great Arabic physicians insisted on these factors, and also on the inter-effects of mind and body. Al-Rāzī and Avicenna may therefore be called the forerunners of modern psychotherapy. In addition, their interest in nutrition made them very competent dieticians.

AL-ṬABARĪ'S *Paradise of Wisdom*

'Aly Rabban al-Ṭabarī's encyclopaedic *Paradise of Wisdom* (early ninth century) is a typical compendium of all the fundamental concepts of Arabic medicine, considered as the all-embracing science. From his study of matter, form and 'state' (*aḥwal*) Ṭabarī concluded that while original matter is the basis of quantity, derived matter is the basis of quality. Form is accidental to matter. 'Matter changes its form through a series of "states" (*ḥāl*) which affect the form but not matter itself.' This is an important reformulation of an Aristotelian idea; to alter the form, we must cause matter to change its quantity and quality.

All qualities are transformed according to their distribution, frequency or scarcity, the most widespread and strongest changing more slowly than the smaller and rarer.

Hence, in medical treatment, the physician must take stock of the state of the patient's body, or better still of each of his organs and humours. Ṭabarī no longer speaks of human temperament in general but of the temperament of the brain, the heart and the liver.

The signs of heat in the heart are, *inter alia*, good posture, good complexion, liveliness, a large chest, hairiness and an ample pulse. Heat and humidity in the heart are reflected in suppleness, moderate hirsuteness of the chest and a tendency to smile and to be gay; cold and dryness of the heart can be inferred from a narrow chest with little hair, a lack of real passion, resentment and a strong pulse. Cold and humidity of the heart result in indolence, idleness, lack of passion and a languid pulse.

Each organ has an ideal state of equilibrium (*i'tidāl*) which men can never attain, even in perfect health. Health is connected with habit, so that the health or disease of one man is no criterion for that of others.

Ibn Massawayh's Medical Aphorisms

The *Paradise of Wisdom* became the guide-book of all those physicians who obeyed the Koranic precept to place the welfare of their patients above all other concerns. Good physicians must make no precipitate judgments and deliver no long speeches, but listen attentively for the answers to skilfully worded questions. They must never apply their theories mechanically, but adapt their cures to each patient's individual needs. These ideas were epitomized in the *Aphorisms* of Ibn Massawayh, from which we quote the following sayings:

The constitution of living bodies is made up of numerous factors. Do not use brutal procedures which undermine the organism and attack, weaken and shake the body, so that its constitution becomes changed.

(Aphorism 26.)

Whenever possible, we must treat each organ with remedies resembling the organ's natural food; if the cure is a change of diet, so much the better.

(Aphorism 35.)

Patients whose main organs are impaired must not be given hot medicaments; you must control their diet until equilibrium is restored.

(Aphorism 61.)

The physician must copy the action of nature. *(Aphorism 64.)*

Finally, the most important aphorism:

In their treatment of diseases, physicians must aim to restore the body to its *normal* state of health, and not to perfect equilibrium. *(Aphorism 68.)*

Thus the best cures are those which are based on dietetic considerations, and drugs may be prescribed only in moderation, according to their potency with respect to the body's or organ's own 'temperamental strength'. In certain cases, poisons in small quantities may be administered. On the whole, Arabic therapy was therefore sound enough, even though it stuck to the cumbersome doctrine of humours and of elementary qualities.

Bīrūnī's *Book of Drugs*

The Arabic approach to diet and drugs was based on a classification of assimilable substances. According to the Introduction of al-Bīrūnī's *Book of Drugs*:

Everything that is absorbed, voluntarily or unconsciously, can be divided first of all into foods and poisons. Remedies are placed half-way between these two. Foods receive their qualities from active and passive forces, and primarily from their four degrees, so that the body, in equilibrium, has the power to transform nutriment into its own substance by complete digestion and by assimilation, thus replacing what part of the diet has been lost by disassimilation. That is the reason why the body must act on food before it can derive any benefit from it. As for poisons, they receive their qualities from the same forces but at their highest degree, which is the fourth, in such a way that they overpower the body and subject it to morbid and fatal transformations. . . . As for drugs, they are placed between the two, because they are corruptive with respect to food and curative with respect to poisons. Their (curative) action can be wrought only by skilful and scrupulous physicians. In addition, there are the medicinal foods, half-way between drugs and food, and the toxic medicaments, half-way between drugs and poisons. . . .

Diagnosis: Anatomical and Physiological Knowledge; Surgery

But before applying therapeutic measures, physicians had first to identify the diseases they wished to cure. The Arabs did not base their diagnoses on accurate anatomical and physiological criteria, chiefly because of the Koranic injunctions against human dissections. (There is no doubt, however, that some of the less orthodox physicians performed autopsies in secret.) The Arabs practised minor eye surgery with skill, and were familiar with the surgical methods of Antyllos of Alexandria, which al-Rāzī has described in his *Continens*. In his *Diseases of the Eyes*, Ibn Massawayh gave a description of the surgical treatment of pannus: the surgeon would lift the bloodvessels over the pupil with a small hook, and then sever them. Massawayh also described surgical operations on the eyelids and the sutures that were used. However, many physicians, including Avicenna, frowned upon the surgical treatment of eye diseases and, in general, despised all surgery as fit only for barbers and charlatans. The first great physician who treated surgery with respect was Abū'l Qāsim (Abulcasis, born near Cordova in 926). He devoted a section of his *Kitāb al-Taṣrīf* to cauterization, haemostasis, arterial ligatures, bone and eye surgery, *etc.*, and recommended the study of anatomy by dissection. But despite his and other contributions, the Arabs remained almost completely ignorant of the internal organs, since what surgery they practised was merely superficial.

DIAGNOSTICS

As Arabic diagnoses were based mainly on considerations of humoral and elemental balance, great attention was paid to such factors as heat, coldness, paleness, redness, emaciation, fatness, pulse-beat and the colour of the urine. Prognoses were commonly made in the Hippocratic manner, and the physicians recorded the subsequent course of the disease meticulously in order to check if their predictions had been correct. Historians are agreed that this keeping of case histories was one of the most important contributions of Arabic medicine. Meyerhof has given an account of thirty-three of al-Rāzī's cases, and their further scrutiny is bound to show to how great an extent Arabic medicine relied on practical experiments and observations, despite its formal adherence to Greek precepts.

The most important general medical texts were *The Treasure-book of Medical Science* by Abū'l Hasan Thābit ibn Qurrā ibn Marwān al-Harrānī, the *Continens* (*al-Hāwī*) and the *Kitāb al-Manṣūrī* by al-Rāzī, the *Kitāb al-Malakī* (*Liber Regius*) by 'Aly ibn 'Abbās al-Majūsī, and finally the famous *Canon* of Avicenna.

OPHTHALMOLOGY

Arabic physicians, like the surgeons, excelled in the treatment of eye diseases, which were very widespread in the entire East, particularly in Egypt. The treatment of trachoma and of pannus was described in a great number of works: by Ibn Massawayh (see above), by Ḥunayn ibn Ishāq, by Thābit ibn Qurrā, by al-Rāzī in the *Manṣūrī*, by 'Alq'ibn 'Abbās, by Avicenna, by Abū'l Qāsim, and by many others. Meyerhof was particularly impressed with the *Promptuary for Oculists* of 'Ali ibn 'Isā (tenth to eleventh century).

PULMONARY CIRCULATION

Last, we must mention the alleged discovery of the pulmonary circulation by Ibn al-Nafīs during the thirteenth century. As against Galen, al-Nafīs maintained that for the vital pneuma to be produced in the left ventricle, the blood must first be refined in the right ventricle and, since it cannot cross the walls of the heart, it must pass through the lungs. This pneumatic theory is, nevertheless, very different from the modern view of the nature of the pulmonary circulation.

CONCLUSION

What we have said about Arabic science should make it clear that, far from being mere transmitters of ancient notions, the Arabs reawakened scientific interest, exercised their critical faculties, and subjected Greek doctrines to the empirical test. As a result of their original concern with the practical applications of science, they invented remarkable instruments in astronomy, mechanics and chemistry, and set up the first great hospitals, the *maristans*, in which they not only treated diseases, but trained physicians and carried out scientific research.

The torch of learning, which the Barbarians had extinguished in the West, was kept alight by that other Mediterranean race, whose sons strove ceaselessly to praise Allah in all his manifestations.

BIBLIOGRAPHY

A very complete bibliography will be found in the *Introduction to the History of Science* by G. SARTON (Vol. I: *From Homer to Omar Khayyām*; Vol. II: *From Rabbi ben Ezra to Roger Bacon*, Baltimore, 1927–31) and in *La science arabe* by ALDO MIELI, Leyden, 1938. Important bibliographical data are found in various journals (*Isis, Archeion, etc.*). Here we shall merely mention the most important and accessible works, *viz.*:

B. CARRA DE VAUX, *Les penseurs de l'Islam*, Vol. II, Paris, 1921–26.

P. DUHEM, *Le système du monde . . .*, Vols. II and IV, Paris, 1914, 1916.

H. SUTER, Die Mathematiker und Astronomen der Araber und ihre Werke, *Abh. z. Gesch. d. math. Wissenschaft*, X, Leipzig, 1910.

S. PINÈS, Les précurseurs musulmans de la théorie de l'impetus, *Archeion*, XXI, 1938.

P. KRAUS, *Jābir Ibn Ḥayyān, Contribution à l'histoire des idées scientifiques en Islam*, 2 vols., Cairo, 1942–43. Particularly important.

L. LECLERC, *Histoire de la médecine arabe*, Paris, 1876.

E. BROWNE, *Arabian Medicine*, Cambridge, 1921.

D. CAMPBELL, *Arabian Medicine and its influence on the Middle Ages*, 2 vols., London, 1926.

DE L. O'LEARY, *How Greek Science Passed to the Arabs*, London, 1948.

CHAPTER 3

Science in Medieval India

THE INDIAN MIDDLE AGES began with the Moslem invasions which disturbed or paralysed the natural development of India's culture and introduced new ideas, particularly in Northern and Western India. On the other hand, Indonesia and Indo-China saw a great renewal of art at this time, and the Dravidian culture of Southern India, unaffected by the Arabic cultural expansion, absorbed Sanskrit Brahmanic ideas and discarded Buddhism, to become the hearth of a great religious, philosophic and artistic movement. In the course of this development, Southern India produced a scientific literature whose influence spread towards the East and at the same time enriched the scientific tradition of the North.

Hence the disruption of the Northern culture went hand in hand with the spreading of indigenous Indian ideas in and from the South. The Southern contribution was at first the elucidation of ancient texts, which Dravidian scholars considered to contain the sum total of knowledge. The eighth and ninth centuries saw a spate of scientific commentaries on these ancient texts and also some new contributions by the Tamils, who alone dared to take liberties with the older traditions.

MATHEMATICS AND ASTRONOMY

ŚRIPATI

Classical astronomy was pursued or extended in the eighth century by Lalla who amended the *Āryabhaṭa*, by Munjala in the tenth century, and by Śripati in the eleventh century. Śripati's work, the *Siddhānt-śekhara* ('Highest Solution', 1039), lost for centuries, has since been recovered in the South of India. Śripati based most of this work on Brahmagupta, and reached very nearly the same conclusions. For instance, his calculations of the number of planetary revolutions during one cosmic cycle were the same as Brahmagupta's, except for Mercury. Śripati was also influenced by Prthūdaka, a ninth-century commentator on Brahmagupta's work. While his own contribution

422

was therefore unoriginal, he did much to consolidate and to spread traditional ideas.

BHĀSKARA

Bhāskara, born in 1114, was a more important figure. His *Siddhānta-Śiromani* ('Head Jewel of Solutions'), written in 1150, was divided into four parts: (1) *Lilavata* ('The Beautiful'), which dealt with the rules of arithmetic, (2) *Vijaganita*, which dealt with root extraction and allied algebraic subjects, (3) *Grahagaṇitādhyaya*, which dealt with the motions of the planets, and (4) *Goladhyaya* ('Calculations of the Sphere').

Bhāskara's work may be called the critical continuation of that of his predecessors, including Brahmagupta, to whom his views were closest. His cosmology was based on the Sūrya Siddhānta, in conformity with which he attributed the motions of the planets to winds, distinguishing clearly between them and atmospheric currents. He explained the revolutions of the planets by developing a theory of epicycles, and analysed the motion of the sun by considering changes in longitude, not only from day to day as his predecessors had done, but over far shorter periods, so as to treat its motion as uniform during small intervals.

THE BHAKSHĀLĪ MANUSCRIPT

The Bhakshālī arithmetical manuscript discovered in Kashmir was at first considered to be of very ancient provenance, and became famous in the history of Indian mathematics. It is important chiefly for its many examples of practical calculations on which other texts are silent. It gives general solutions of numerous mathematical problems, including indeterminate quadratic equations, arithmetical progressions, and the method of false position.

Its precise date is not known, though from its script and style we may conclude that it could not have been written before the tenth century.

MATHEMATICAL CONTACTS WITH THE OUTSIDE WORLD

During the Middle Ages, Indian mathematicians and astronomers were thrown into contact with their Moslem and Chinese colleagues. Scientific contact with China had first been made during the first century A.D., when Buddhism began to spread in the Celestial Empire, and it seems to have been maintained during the Middle Ages. Much more important, however, were the contacts with Arabic science. Thus it is generally held that the Arabs took their decimal notation with nine figures and the zero symbol from India, though some scholars claim that 'Arabic' numerals are of Greek origin, and that they were transmitted to the Arabs by the Copts through the Neo-Platonists. In any case, the use of the decimal notation was widespread in India at the time of her first direct contact with Islam.

While the influence of Indian on Arabic algebra seems to have been small, the influence of Indian trigonometry was acknowledged by al-Battānī (died in 929).

CHEMISTRY

Indian chemistry is known to us mainly from medieval texts, even though its existence is vouched for by earlier writings which, in turn, are based on still older traditions. It may be divided into (1) alchemy, which appeared in India at about the same time as Greek astrology and may therefore have been based on Greek alchemy, (2) mineral pharmacology and (3) metallurgy, which made possible such achievements as the famous fourth-century Iron Pillar of Delhi. Moreover, Indian iron was described as desirable merchandise in the *Periplus of the Erythrean Sea* (first century A.D.), and the use of iron in the preparation of drugs was also mentioned by Suśruta as part of his discussion of caustic alkalis.

Alchemical speculations and also the general study of transmutations started with experiments on mercury (*raza*). Though most of these experiments were aimed at producing 'tantric' motions, *i.e.* marvellous transformations previously induced by ritual or magic, some manuals ignored Tantrism altogether and described the preparation of compounds by calcination and similar processes. Substances were classified as *mahārasa* or 'natural' products, such as cinnabar, as *uparasa* or derived products, as *loha*, metals and as *lavaṇa*, salts. In Tamil, chemical substances were traditionally divided into male and female.

Contacts between Indian and Taoist alchemy may be inferred from the fact that both shared Yoga practices in which Tantric or Taoist movements went hand in hand with alchemical speculations and procedures.

MEDICINE

From the Middle Ages to our day, Indian medical texts, commentaries on classical doctrines, special treatises and, above all, pharmacological compendia have poured forth in an unending stream.

THE COMPILERS

From early on, Indian physicians busied themselves with the compilation of ancient works, drawing upon their formulae and adding to them as they went along. Some scholars re-classified the subject-matter of the works of Suśruta, Caraka, and Vāghbata, particularly Mādhavakara who, probably in the seventh century, wrote the *Rugviniścaya* ('Study of Diseases'), also called the *Mādhavanidāna* ('Etiology according to Mādhava'), in which, quoting earlier authors, he discussed pathological symptoms and their causes. His work, which is far more systematic than that of his predecessors, became a standard text. It was subsequently amended, and its therapeutic section greatly augmented, by Vṛinda in the Siddhi Yoga ('Perfect Preparations'), and later still by Vangasena, who specified cures for all the listed conditions.

Śārngadhara (probably thirteenth but possibly eleventh century) wrote a most original *samhīta*, in which he not only drew on the classical *samhītas* but also adopted such Yoga notions as the effects of breathing, and suggested psycho-somatic techniques of influencing the diseased organism.

THE GREAT COMMENTATORS

The ancient texts, which were so often elliptical in their great concision, invited the work of commentators and of critics who added or amended as they went along. Thus Drdhabala completed the work of Caraka, and Nāgārjuna (?) added an appendix, the *Uttarasthāna*, to the Suśruta at an uncertain date. The main commentators of Suśruta were Gayadāsa, whose work is only partially preserved, and Dalhaṇa, who lived in Kashmir during the eleventh to twelfth centuries; the chief interpreter of Caraka was Cakrapāṇi who also wrote textbooks on therapy and *materia medica*; and finally, the leading commentators of Vāgbhata were Hemādri (twelfth century) and Aruṇadatta (thirteenth century). The work of an earlier commentator of Vāgbhata was translated into Tibetan (the *Pādārthacandrika* of Candranandana).

THE LEXICOGRAPHERS

Systematic dictionaries (*nighaṇṭu*) of drugs were compiled from early times, but particularly during the Middle Ages. The oldest of these, the *Dhanvantarinighaṇṭu*, seems to be older than even the first dictionary of classical Sanskrit, but the most widespread of all were the *Mandanavinoda* and the *Rajanighaṇṭu*, written in the fourteenth century.

TAMIL WORKS

The chemical works belonging to the Tamil tradition of extreme Southern India had a characteristic approach of their own. Unfortunately, they cannot be dated very accurately and have not been studied as fully as one might have hoped. These works are attributed either to Agastya, the mythical teacher of Sanskrit knowledge, to his pupil Tereiyar, or to a line of *sittars* (perfect men) some of whom had Moslem names.[1]

[1] For the bibliography of this chapter, the reader is referred to page 159 (Ancient Indian Science).

CHAPTER 4

Science in Medieval China

THE CHINESE MIDDLE AGES may be said to have begun with the
capture of the historic Northern capitals by the barbarians in A.D. 317,
which forced the Chinese to withdraw south of the Yangtze. They
set up their new capital in Nanking, colonized regions previously
held by tribal peoples (Miao, Ti), and acquired new geographical,
botanical and technological knowledge.

Meanwhile the barbarians established new dynasties which were
rapidly sinified, adapting and developing the cultural trends of
their hosts. While Taoism became an organized religion in 423,
Buddhism, which had reached China during the previous epoch,
made great strides under the Turkic dynasty of the Wei (386–557)
and became the basis of great artistic developments, for example
the monumental rock sculptures.

In 589, China was reunited by the Sui dynasty, under which the
previously rudimentary waterway linking the canal systems between the Yellow River and the Yangtze was greatly improved into
what became the Grand Canal. Another dynasty, the Tang (618–
907), restored China to the greatness she had enjoyed under the Han.
The Tang insisted that all state officials be appointed by written
examination and that the Confucian classics be taught in all schools.
They encouraged great poets like Li Po, Tu Fu, and Po Chu-yi, and
helped science to gain the upper hand over religious idealism.
China first came into contact with Islam during the Battle of the
Talas River in 751.

The fall of the Tang dynasty was followed by a period of anarchy,
lasting from 907–960, during which the country was split up. Unity
was re-established by the Sung dynasty in 960, which ushered in a
period of unprecedented achievements. The Neo-Confucian School
fused Taoist and Buddhist concepts into a doctrine which remained
classic until the nineteenth century. However, the economic basis
of the empire was extremely weak, and though the great reformer
Wang An-Shih tried to substitute money for the ancient system of
transporting tax grain to the capital in kind, his efforts came to
nothing. In 1125, the North was again invaded, this time by the

427

Jurchen, a Tungusic people from the Amur, who founded the Chin dynasty, while the Sung continued to govern the South until 1279.

It was then that, for the first time in her history, China was completely subjugated by barbarians, the Mongols, who having conquered all Central Asia, founded the Yuan dynasty, and invited foreign officials to their court. The most famous of these was the Venetian Marco Polo.

China did not recover her independence until 1368, when the Ming dynasty expelled the Mongols and attempted to restore the traditional empire by promulgating a new law code and overhauling the civil service. However, the reign of the Ming was short-lived, and in 1644 China was again subjugated by a new wave of barbarian invaders, the Manchus.

MATHEMATICS

CALCULATION

The 'Memoir on some Traditions of Mathematical Art' (*Shu Shu Chi-yi*), attributed to Hsü Yo of the Han though it may have been written by Chen Luan (*fl.* A.D. 570), contains descriptions of different types of the abacus. The first type consisted of a rectangular wooden frame with a number of parallel strings, each threading four balls representing one unit each, and a fifth ball of different colour representing five units, so that the total number of units represented by each string was nine. The second type was a frame with nine horizontal lines cut by vertical strings, each threading only one ball, the position of which on the frame showed what value it represented.

Figure 34 illustrates how the number 5,832 could be expressed by the two methods.

From the same period dates the 'Mathematical Manual of the Five Government Departments' (*Wu Tshao Suan Ching*) dealing with

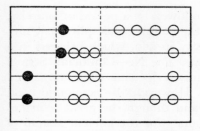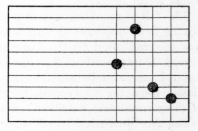

fig. 34 The number 5,832 represented on two different types of Chinese counting frame.

simple multiplication and division. At about 500, there appeared the book of Chang Chhiu-Chien, which gave examples of the modern rule of division—multiplying out—and also dealt with arithmetical and geometrical progressions connected with the weaving of textiles.

Even when applied to unrelated problems, mathematical progressions retained their original terminology: the number of terms was the number of days needed to weave an article, the common difference was the daily output, the first term was the amount woven on the first day, *etc.*

Towards 625, Wang Hsiao-Tung wrote the 'Continuation of Ancient Mathematics' (*Chhi Ku Suan Ching*), in which he considered quadratic equations and also cubic equations arising from such practical problems as, for instance, the need to calculate the lengths of the three sides of a right-angled triangle from the known sum of its two sides and from the known difference between the hypotenuse and one of its sides.

A story in the *Tang Chhüeh Shih* shows how equations of this kind were used in about 855 as a test for minor officials:

Once there were two clerks who held the same rank and had equal lengths of government service. They had even acquired the same commendations and the criticisms in their personal dossiers were identical. The responsible official of middle rank was quite baffled by the problem of their promotion and appealed to Yang Sun, who was his superior. Yang Sun thought the matter over and then said, 'One of the best merits of minor clerks is to be quick at computations. Let both candidates now listen to my question. Whoever first gets the right answer will obtain the advancement. The problem is this: Someone, when walking in the woods, overheard a number of robbers discussing how best to share the rolls of cloth which they had stolen. They said that if each had six rolls, there would be five rolls left, but if each had seven rolls, they would be eight rolls short. How many robbers were there, and what was the total number of rolls of cloth?' This problem was taken down by another minor clerk, and Yang Sun then asked the two candidates to reckon it out with counting-rods on the stone steps of the hall. After a short time one of them got the right answer. He was duly given the better position and the officials dispersed, having nothing to complain of or criticize in the decision.[1]

Only at the end of the thirteenth century did the abacus come into general use, and the decline of the counting-rod henceforth made the interpretation of earlier mathematical works increasingly difficult.

[1] J. Needham: *Science and Civilisation in China*, vol. III, p. 116.

ALGEBRAIC ADVANCES AND THE GREAT MATHEMATICIANS

The writings of the great mathematician Tsu Chung-Chih (430–501) are lost, but we know that his *Chui Shuh* had so great a reputation that it was still used for examinations in the seventh century. He gave two values of π—an 'excess value' of 3.1415927 and a 'deficit value' of 3.1415926.

In this connection, it must be noted that, in 635, 3.1415927 was still expressed by the corresponding (decimal) units of length, *viz.* 3 *chang*, 1 *chhih*, 4 *tshun*, 1 *fên*, 5 *li*, 9 *hao*, 2 *miao*, 7 *hu*. By 660, however, the astronomer Tshao Shih-Wei used a decimal system in which one word represented two places, so that 365.2448 was expressed as 365, *yü* 24, *chi* 48. At the end of the seventh century Han Yen simply wrote the word 'point' (*tuan*) behind the last integer. The zero symbol, which was introduced from India by Chhüthan Hsi Ta in the seventh or eighth century, was widely used during the ninth, when it was generally written as a small circle.

The Sung saw the birth of three great mathematicians, whose works have come down to us.

Chhin Chiu-Shao lived in the South and published his 'Notes on the Mathematical Treatise in Nine Sections' (*Shu Shu Chiu Chang*) in 1247. In it, he dealt with astronomical problems and the evaluation of complex areas and volumes. His algebraic calculations, unlike those of antiquity, were accompanied by explanatory figures, and he was the first to print negative numbers in black type and positive numbers in red. He also discussed indeterminate equations, and even gave solutions involving equations of the tenth degree.

Li Yeh (1178–1265) lived in Northern China at the time when the Mongols overthrew the Chin dynasty. In 1248, he wrote the 'Sea-Mirror of Circle Measurements' (*Tshî Yuan Hai Ching*), in which he dealt with the problem of inscribing circles in triangles. He wrote down the resulting equations, involving four unknowns, in vertical columns and horizontal rows. The centre compartment was occupied by the absolute term, if any; it was called *thai* (an abbreviation for *thai chi*, meaning pole-star, centre of heaven). *Jen* (man $= 3$ and its powers), was written to the right of *thai*; *ti* (earth $= y$ and its powers) to the left of it; *thien* (heaven $= x$ and its powers) was written below it. Proceeding outwards from *thai* in any straight direction, the first compartment was for the insertion of the simple term (coefficient of x, *etc.*), the second for the coefficient of x^2, *etc.* The coefficients of xy, x^2y and xy^2 were then entered into the squares corresponding to the respective powers of y on the top, and of x on the right. *Figure 35* shows how Li Yeh would have expressed the equation:

$$2y^3 - 8y^2 - xy^2 + 28y + 6xy - x^2 - 2x = 0$$

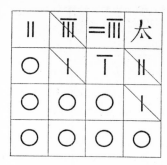

fig. 35 Li Yeh's method of expressing equations with two unknowns.

(*Thai* appears in the top right corner.)

Negative coefficients were expressed by diagonal strokes across the corresponding square and no longer by colour changes. When only one unknown was involved, Li Yeh would use only one row and write negative powers to the left of *thai*. Thus $x^2 + 2x + 3x^{-1} - 6x^{-2}$ would be expressed as shown in *fig. 36*.

fig. 36 Li Yeh's method of expressing equations with one unknown.

In his 'New Exercises' (*Yi Ku Yen Tuan*), published 1258, Li Yeh expressed equations containing absolute terms by placing the latter uppermost and all the other below.

Yang Hui published his 'Detailed Analysis of the Mathematical Rules in the "Nine Chapters" ' (*Hsiang Chieh Chiu Chang Suan Fa*) in 1261, and in his collected works (1275) he listed the sums of various series, for instance that of the squares of integers. He also solved simultaneous linear equations with up to five unknowns, and reduced all fractions to decimals. He criticized his predecessors for having used methods without working out their theoretical origin or principle. 'The men of old', he said, 'changed the name of their methods from problem to problem, so that as no specific explanation was given there is no way of telling their theoretical origin or basis.' He then proved his modern attitude by giving a theoretical demonstration that the complements of the parallelograms which are about the diameter of any given parallelogram are equal to one another. (In *fig. 37*, he proved that BP = PD.)

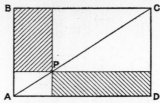

fig. 37 Geometric proof of Yang Hui (1261).

In 1299, finally, another famous mathematician, Chu Shih Chieh, published an 'Introduction to Mathematical Studies' (*Suan Hsüeh Chhi Mêng*), which forms a general introduction to algebra and contains a division table (expressed in words) suitable for use with the abacus. This work exercised an immense influence on Japanese mathematics. In his 'Precious Mirror of the Four Elements' (*Ssu Yuan Yü Chien*, 1303), Chu began with a diagram identical with Pascal's triangle, *i.e.* a device for finding the coefficients in the binomial theorem. Chu called his system a 'Diagram of the Old Method for finding Eighth and Lower Powers'. The 'Four Elements' of the title referred to the accessory unknowns which he used for solving indeterminate equations. He also discussed the summation of higher series of positive integers.

With these men, Chinese mathematics seems to have reached its apogee; only at the end of the medieval period was another important mathematical discovery made: the calculation of the equally tempered scale. Though Ho Chhêng Thien and Wang Phu had tried in the fifth century to produce a scale by the division of the octave into twelve equal intervals, it was only in 1584 that the Ming prince, Chu Tsai Yü, published the solution of the problem: the chromatic interval is $^{12}\sqrt{2}$.

ASTRONOMY AND GEOGRAPHY

Astronomy

During the fifth century, the Chinese did much to develop their astronomical instruments. Clepsydras were greatly improved and water power was used to drive armillary spheres, so that the instruments revolved in phase with the stars even during the actual observations. In 725, Yi Hsing invented the first escapement, thus opening the way for mechanical clocks, and in 1092 Su Sung gave a detailed description of a large astronomical clock which turned a celestial globe and an armillary sphere.

Some of the thirteenth-century instruments of Kuo Sho-Ching are still extant and are kept at the Purple Mountain Observatory

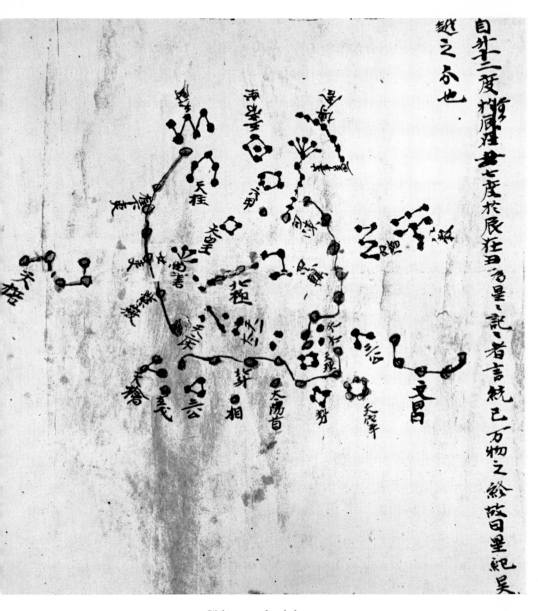

35 Chinese celestial map

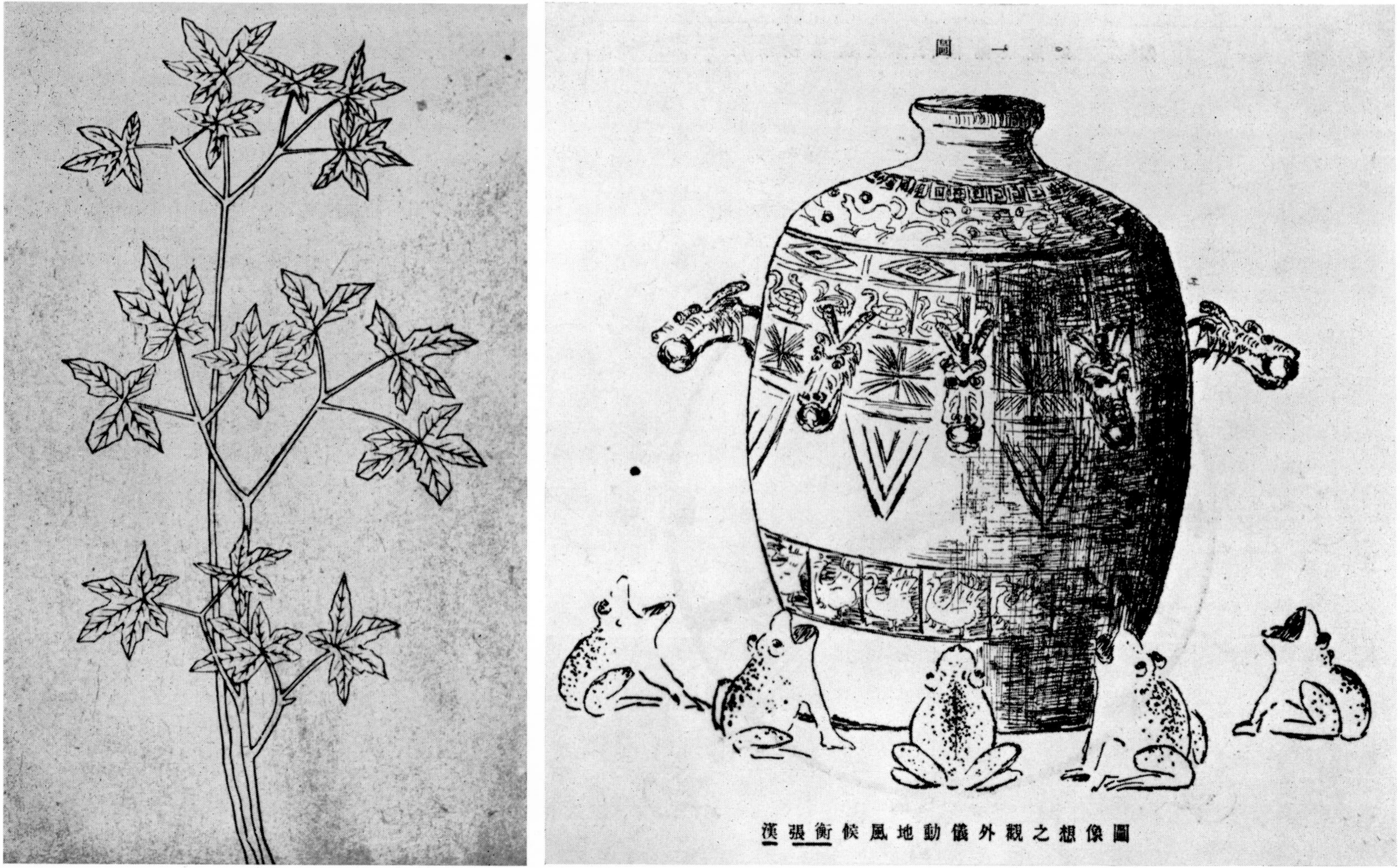

36 Chinese applied science: (a) page from a herbal; (b) seismograph

張衡候風地動儀外觀之想像圖

圖 一

1

north-east of Nanking; they include a simplified version of an Arabic *torquetum*, especially adapted to equatorial observations. This is one of the very rare signs of foreign influences on Chinese astronomy, for while many Indian astronomical and astrological texts were translated into Chinese during the seventh century, and though translations from the Arabic were frequent under the Mongols, the Chinese use of equatorial rather than ecliptic co-ordinates made their astronomy singularly immune from outside ideas.

GEOGRAPHY AND CARTOGRAPHY

Chinese cartography had its roots in antiquity, though no early maps have survived—not even the imperial map of the great Tang cartographer Chia Tan (730–785), which, we are told, measured 30 ft. by 33 ft. and was constructed on a scale of 1 inch to 100 *li*.

In his *Essays*, the engineer and high official, Shen Kua, explained the method by which he prepared his maps, including a relief map for the emperor. He determined the lengths of arcs of circles by adding the chord to twice the square of the sagitta divided by the diameter; he was familiar with the floating compass and knew that its needle did not point to the true north. He also predicted eclipses, thought that the moon and sun were spherical and not flat, and explained that they did not collide during eclipses because they were made of *chhi* (breath).

The astronomer Su Sung designed celestial globes in conjunction with his work on armillary spheres, and his globes must be the oldest printed Chinese star-charts still in existence. They were begun in 1088 and finished in 1095, and were five in number: one of the north polar region, two cylindrical 'Mercator' projections of the regions of declination about 50°N. and 60°S., and two polar projections, one of the northern and the other of the southern hemisphere. The most famous of Chinese planispheres, prepared in 1193 and engraved on stone in 1247, still exists as a stele in the Confucian temple at Suchow, Chiangsu. Two magnificent terrestrial maps, also engraved on stone and dating from 1137, now in the 'Forest of Steles' at Sian, were based on square grids and not on projections. The second, called the 'Map of the Tracks of Yü' (*Yü Chi Thu*), has a grid scale of 100 *li* to each square, and its accuracy is astonishing, particularly with respect to river systems. The oldest printed map, dated 1280, is preserved in the National Library at Peking. On all these maps, the north is at the top.

Under Mongol rule, geographical maps began to span the entire Asian continent. The geographer Chu Ssu-Pên (1273–1337) prepared a comprehensive map of China, and his successors added other known countries. An extant Korean revision dated 1402 gives more than a hundred European references (France and Germany are written phonetically) and thirty-five African places.

COSMOLOGY

The Neo-Confucian philosophers gave typical explanations of celestial phenomena. Thus Chang Tsai explains that the distant stars are carried endlessly by the rushing *chhi*, while the near planets are retarded by the *chhi* of the earth. The moon is more strongly retarded than the sun, since it is *yin* like the earth. Chu Hsi, who may be called the Thomas Aquinas of Chinese philosophy, considered the universe to consist of *chhi*—breath, energy, matter—and of *li*—structure, order. He gave a correct explanation of eclipses. His complete works were published in 1415 by the Ming emperor Yung Lo.

Chhi also figured largely in the theories of the fourteenth-century Ming biologist Wang Khuei, who classified nature in his 'The Beetle and the Sea' (*Li Hai Chi*) as follows: the heavens, rain and snow have *chhi* (breath); the earth has *chhi* and *hsing* (form); plants and some minerals have *chhi*, *hsing* and *hsing* (natural endowments); animals have *chhi*, *hsing*, *hsing* and *chhing* (sentiment). This work also contains a great many ecological and physiological comments.

NATURAL SCIENCE

As a rule, the different branches of Chinese medieval science did not develop independently, and references to scientific concepts can be found in all sorts of technical and biographical works and, above all, in medical literature.

At the beginning of the medieval period, the development of Taoism and its interest in alchemy, together with the growth of Buddhism and the introduction of Indian technical ideas, led to a great increase in observational activities.

FOSSILS

The progress of palaeontology illustrates this new trend particularly well. Fossil animals were first mentioned in A.D. 527, in Li Tao-Yuan's 'Commentary on the Waterways Classic' (*Shui Ching Chu*). The origins of extinct species of *Spirifer* (fossil brachiopods) were first explained in 375 by Lo Han. He stated that the Stone Swallow Mountain was so called because it harboured stone oysters which looked like swallows and used to fly about during thunderstorms. 'Now,' he added, 'these swallows do not fly about any more.' By

1133, Tu Wan, in his 'Cloud Forest Lapidary' (*Yün Lin Shih*) was no longer content with that explanation. He marked many of the swallow shapes on the rock face with his brush, and observed that the heat of the blazing sun and the rain cracked them, so that they fell through the air. 'They cannot really fly.'

fig. 38 The origins of the compass: Magnetite spoon resting on a polished bronze plate. (The Chinese characters which are engraved on the plate have been omitted.)

THE COMPASS

The origins of the compass must be sought in the attempts by Chinese diviners to foretell the future from the direction in which a spinning spoon came to rest. Chinese spoons have a short handle and are balanced about a central point. A south-pointing spoon made of magnetite and pivoting on a polished bronze plate is mentioned in the *Lun Hêng* ('Discourses weighed in the Balance', A.D. 83). It is also depicted on a bas-relief dated A.D. 114, which is kept in the Zürich Museum (*fig. 38*). Floating or pivoting magnetic needles are mentioned in ninth- to twelfth-century texts and were used for land surveying. It seems likely that sailors took over the compass from the Fu Kien geomancers. In 1125, a floating compass was carried during a voyage to Korea.

From Than Chhiao's 'Book of Transformations' (*Hua Shu*), written about 940, we know that four sorts of lenses were known at the time. The high Sung official, Shen Kua, was familiar with the camera obscura and the compass, and produced an artificial magnet by cooling a small trough of molten steel with its axis lying in a north–south direction. He also appreciated the significance of fossils. He prescribed naphtha as a substitute for wood-fuel and hence as a measure against deforestation. His writings on pharmacology, in particular, show how greatly knowledge of natural history had advanced over the past.

CHEMISTRY AND BOTANY

Mu Piao's 'Synonymic Dictionary of Minerals and Drugs' (808) listed 335 synonyms of sixty-two vegetable, animal and mineral substances. Developments of printing and wood-engraving techniques led to the publication, from the eleventh century onwards, of illustrated botanical texts. In the 'Pharmacopoeias of the Heavenly Husbandman' (*Pên Tshao*), the number of accurately described species increased up to the end of the sixteenth century, when Li Shih-Chen published his famous 'Great Pharmacopoeia' (*Pên Tshao Kang Mu*), containing 142 illustrations and descriptions of 1,074 vegetable, 443 animal and 217 mineral substances.

MEDICINE

Under the influence of Indian medicine, Chinese physicians adopted the theory of the four elements, air, water, earth and fire. This theory became the basis of Chao Yüan-Fang's 'Treatise on the Causes and Symptoms of Diseases' (610), in which the author gave the first definitive descriptions of variola, measles, bubonic plague, bacillary (hot) and amoebic (cold) dysentery, and mentioned cholera, leprosy and rickets. Altogether he listed 1,720 diseases, classified into 67 groups. In 652, a work entitled 'The Eight Golden Remedies' devoted separate chapters to diseases of women and children, and prescribed plantain seeds, mulberries and apricot kernels for beri-beri, the mollusc *Clemma japonica* for rickets, sheep's liver for nyctalopia, a salt-free diet for oedema, *Oryxa japonica* for malaria, and *Coptis japonica* for bacterial dysentery. No less than 717 drugs were enumerated. A medical text engraved on stone in 574 is preserved in Lung Mên (Honan). The 'Medical Secrets' of Wang Tao includes every branch of medicine and therapeutics and mentions the surgical removal of cataract. It was inspired by Indian ideas.

Under the Sung, medical theory was based on the five 'agents' and the six 'breaths' (*chhi*), the sexagesimal cycle and related ancient theories. We must recall that Chinese medicine was always looked upon as a public service and that its *codices* were promulgated by the state. Between 982 and 992, for instance, a government commission compiled the *Shêng Hui Fang* containing 16,834 recipes. The export of medical books was forbidden in 1006, and again in 1078, but there is a record of twenty-seven Arabic missions purchasing drugs and recipes. Medical examinations were set by the government and, in 1191, an examination was made up of questions of the type: 'What is the distance between the teeth and the lips? Are there three inches between the œsophagus and the teeth?'

In chronological order, the history of medieval Chinese medicine began in 973 with the publication of a larger edition of the *Pên*

Tshao books, the *Khai Pao Pên Tshao* (Khai-Pao reign-period pharmacopoeia). In 982, there is a record that haemorrhoids were being treated with arsenic, and in 1057 there appeared a new edition of the *Pên Tshao*. In 1061 local investigations were intensified and Su Sung published an illustrated pharmacopoeia, the *Pên Tshao Thu Ching*. In about 1110, there appeared a new pharmaceutical codex containing 790 formulae; in 1116 came a new revision of the Pharmacopoeia by Tshao Hiao Chung. A work on pediatrics by Ch'ien Yi mentioned six types of pulse. In 1134 appeared another work containing more than 3,000 formulae; in 1150 a new textbook on pediatrics was written by three authors; in 1174, Kuo Yung's 'Supplementary Treatise on Fevers' distinguished between variola, varicella, measles and German measles, and dealt particularly with differential diagnosis; in 1196 came an account of the treatment of ulcers of the back by Li Sung; in 1216 there appeared a remarkable (anonymous) work which criticized the theory that all diseases are caused by hot and cold, and indicated that pellagra was due to malnutrition. A work on diseases of women, published in 1237, had five chapters on obstetrics and three on gynaecology. A book on the pulse written in 1241 and containing 33 diagrams was translated into Arabic. Finally, in 1247 the first (illustrated) work on forensic medicine was written by Sung Tzhu. It consisted of two volumes describing types of death, three on poisons and four on symptoms.

From then on, Chinese medicine began to decline. True, medical schools continued under the Ming, but there were no further advances in medical knowledge or theories. In the fourteenth century, leprosy was first treated with chaulmugra oil, and in 1596 Li Shih-Chen published his 'Great Pharmacopoeia', which we have mentioned.

CONCLUSION

Chinese thought and science during the Middle Ages continued to follow along the paths they had entered under the Han dynasty. Foreign influences—Buddhism, Manichaeism, Nestorian Christianity —introduced novel conceptions which forced the Chinese to define their own philosophical views and led to the development of Neo-Confucianism under the Sung.

The resulting views strike us as far more correct than those holding sway in medieval Europe, even though it was in Europe that modern science was born with Copernicus, Bacon and Galileo.

Gunpowder, magnets and printing, three essential factors in changing medieval into modern society, were known in China centuries before they came to Europe.

This apparent paradox can be solved only by a close examination of Chinese society and politics. China was an agrarian country in which millions of peasants were governed by officials recruited by competitive examinations, which only the sons of the rich could afford to prepare for. For them, society was an autonomous organism, an objective reality with spontaneous laws of its own; their main function was to prevent these laws from being disturbed. Confucius had taught that the chief anti-social vices were selfishness (*ssu* and *li*) and rivalry (*ching* and *k'o*), and, in fact, it was the rise of the merchant class and commercial competition which threatened to undermine the Confucian structure of society. Hence the state did its utmost to halt this trend—under the Han the salt mines were nationalized and, in the fifteenth century, the Ming prohibited the maritime voyages which improvements in shipbuilding techniques and the invention of the rudder and the magnet had made possible.

In Europe, on the other hand, where the mercantile tradition of the Greek city-states was being continued, commerce exploited all technical advances, many of which had come from China. In the West, commercial transactions led to the treatment of commodities as mere abstractions expressed in monetary (mathematical) terms, while, in China, taxes and tithes were still being paid in kind. Though the Chinese made precise measurements of concrete objects, their scientific concepts were inherently qualitative and hence immeasurable. For instance, Chinese scholars held that earth-tremors could not be measured by means of the seismograph, invented in China during the second century, since tremors were due to unpredictable collisions between *Yin* and *Yang*.

Another consequence of mercantile development was the growth of towns and the greater contact between the inhabitants, particularly from the seventeenth century onwards. In China this process was far more gradual, so that although printing was known under the Sung, three great mathematicians did not know of one another's work and studied under different masters using different methods of notation. Moreover, two centuries later their works were completely forgotten, and it was not until the end of the eighteenth century that scholars brought them to light again. It is also remarkable that the discovery of the twelve-note scale, invented by Chu Tsai Yü and printed in 1594, was never used in China, while Europe learnt of it (though not of its real author), from Mersenne in 1636, and then used it widely. (The calculations involved were first set out in the unpublished papers of Simon Stevin, 1548–1620.)

Most Chinese printed texts dealt with arts and crafts, including medicine and politics. What we call science had little place in them.

Moreover, many texts fell quickly into oblivion, which might explain why Chinese science developed so slowly.

It seems that, starting from the Middle Ages, Chinese society became so unwieldy that it fell an easy prey first to the Mongol nomads and then to the Manchus, who became a military ruling caste. A feudal society superimposed on a bureaucratic system took root in the Far East at the very time when the West emerged from the medieval age. Nevertheless, long before the Renaissance and long before the rise of capitalist societies and the remarkable upsurge of scientific societies it brought in its wake, China was not only the greatest repository of detailed scientific knowledge, but also held the most accurate views about the scope of science.[1]

[1] For Bibliography, see Ancient Chinese Science, *p.* 177.

CHAPTER 5

Byzantine Science

BYZANTINE CIVILIZATION

From the beginning of the sixth to the middle of the fifteenth century, nine centuries rent by wars and invasions, it was Byzantium that kept Greek classical culture alive. The Byzantine age can be divided into the following three periods:

(1) *Origins and Development of Byzantine Civilization (330–565)*
Constantinople, or Byzantium, was founded by Constantine the Great on May 11th, 330. It was destined to become the capital of an empire which, while claiming to step into Rome's shoes, was, in fact, oriental rather than occidental. Between 330 and 518, Constantinople remained untouched by the Barbarians (Visigoths, Huns, Ostrogoths).

The reign of Justinian (518–565) marks the real beginning of Byzantine civilization, and of its artistic upsurge. Justinian looked upon himself as a true Roman and wrote most of his works ('The Justinian Code') in Latin. At its peak, his empire extended to Southern Spain, Italy, the Balkans, Asia Minor, Syria, Palestine, part of Egypt, and the coast of North Africa.

(2) *The Great Wars and the Consolidation of the Empire (565–1025)*
When Heraclius (610–641) vanquished the Persians, he tried to break with the Roman Empire completely and to found 'a truly Byzantine Empire, all of whose forces were concentrated on Constantinople' (C. Diehl). But the seventh century, in which the organization of the Eastern Empire went hand in hand with the increasing external pressure of Islam, was a dark period in the history of Byzantium. During that time, 'Greek fire', that formidable new weapon, was first deployed against the Arabs. The eighth century was the century of the Iconoclasts, who fought against the cult of icons and the abuses of the monks. The resulting religious quarrels led to the first schism between the Western and Eastern churches in 867, and to their final separation in 1054.

The Macedonian dynasty (ninth to eleventh centuries) marked the heyday of Byzantium, with emperors like Leo VI the Wise, Constantine VII Porphyrogenetos, Basil II, and Constantine IX Monomachos.

(3) *Decline of the Byzantine Empire* (1025–1453)

With the death of Basil II in 1025, Byzantium began to decline. Under the Ducas dynasty (1059–81), vacillations in foreign diplomacy led to the victory of the all-powerful Seljuks at the battle of Mantzikert in Asia Minor (1071).

Under the reign of Alexios I Comnenos (1081–1118) Byzantium was attacked by the Normans, the Patzinaks and the Bulgars, and its commercial predominance was seriously challenged by Venice.

But it was the Crusades that finished off the Eastern Empire. While the first three passed Byzantium by, thanks largely to the tactful diplomacy of the Emperors Alexios I, Manuel I and Isaac II Angelos, who managed to divert the Knights of the Cross into Asia Minor, the fourth Crusade, thwarted in its attempts to take Jerusalem, turned against Constantinople instead and sacked the city on April 13th, 1204. Baldwin of Flanders was elected Latin Emperor of Constantinople, while the Lascaris dynasty rallied the Greek elements of Byzantium in Cicaea (Asia Minor). Michael VIII Palaeologos succeeded Theodore II Lascaris as head of the Nicaean Empire, and recaptured Constantinople from the Latins in 1261.

However, the decline of Byzantium could no longer be halted. The Empire shrank further and further under the assaults of the Turks, so that by the beginning of the fifteenth century its territory was limited to Constantinople and its immediate environs. When no help was forthcoming from the rest of the Christian world, the Greeks were unable to resist the Turks any longer, and on May 29th, 1453, Constantinople itself fell to Muhammed II the Conqueror.

So much for the historical background. Before we discuss the scientific contribution of Byzantium itself, we must first look briefly at the way in which science was being taught in the Eastern Empire.

THE TEACHING OF SCIENCE

The exact sciences (arithmetic, geometry, musical theory, astronomy) made up the *quadrivium*, which was thought to be second in importance only to rhetoric. The Byzantines also taught 'physics', *i.e.* physics, chemistry, biology and medicine.

The University of Constantinople, founded by Constantine in 330, was reorganized and extended by Theodosos II in 425. Other universities existed at Antioch, Alexandria, Beyrut, Gaza and Athens, though Justinian closed the Athenian University in 529 because of its neo-Platonic views. From then on, all teachers had to be Christians.[1]

During the reign of Heraclius, Stephen of Alexandria taught philosophy and the *quadrivium* at the University of Constantinople. From the seventh to the ninth centuries, the Universities fell progressively under Church control and teaching declined. At the beginning of the ninth century, Theophilos restored a measure of freedom and, in 863, Bardas reorganized the University and charged Leo the mathematician with running it. Basil II probably suppressed all secular institutes of higher learning, and scholars like Psellos had to be taught by private instructors.

In 1045, Constantine IX founded a School of Law and a Faculty of Philosophy, of which Psellos became the head. Psellos, apart from teaching jurisprudence and metaphysics, also lectured on cosmography, geometry and musical theory. Constantine's schools continued to flourish until the fall of Constantinople in 1204.

During the Latin occupation, scientists like Nicephoros Blemmydes fled to the exiled court in Nicaea, where they continued to teach despite the absence of a University.

Under the Palaeologos dynasty, *i.e.* after the fall of the Latin empire, the University of Constantinople was reorganized by Andronicos II. It was placed under the direction of the Grand Logothetes (officials in charge of the entire civil service), the first of whom was Theodore Metochites. Under Manuel II (1391–1425) the University was reorganized once again; the various faculties were gathered into one single building and medical studies were pursued with far greater vigour than before.

We are now ready to look at the Byzantine contribution to scientific knowledge in greater detail.

THE EXACT SCIENCES

The Byzantines looked upon the study of the exact sciences, which were part of the *quadrivium*, as a kind of mental preparation for the study of philosophy.

In the early stages of the Eastern Empire (fourth to fifth century), Alexandria was its scientific capital and its renown was assured by great mathematicians and astronomers like Proclos (410–485), Marinos (end of fifth century) and Simplicios (beginning of sixth

[1] Some of the scientists concerned fled to Jundīshāpūr, where, after the Edessa School had been closed by the Emperor Zeno in 489, Nestorian scholars were already enjoying the protection of the Persian kings. (The Nestorians were disciples of the patriarch Nestor who had been found guilty of heresy by the Council of Ephesos in 431.) For Jundīshāpūr *see also p.* 397.

century), all of whom wrote commentaries on Euclid and Aristotle. At about the same time, John Philoponos wrote a commentary on the *Arithmetic* of Nicomachos of Gerasa, and a treatise on the astrolabe. He also put forward many original views on physics and mechanics, in which he questioned Aristotle's ideas on motion and vaguely anticipated the concept of inertia.

Cosmas Indicopleustes, a monk and traveller, presented a most ingenuous cosmology in his *Christian Topography* (547). According to him, the earth was a parallelogram surrounded by walls which converged to form the celestial vault. At the centre of the earth was found a high mountain behind which the sun disappeared every evening. The mere fact that such fantastic notions could be put forward shows clearly how much Greek science had degenerated since Ptolemy's time. Nor is this criticism tempered by the fact that Cosmas was one of the first European cosmographers who referred to China.

The *Madaba Mosaic*, the oldest known geographical map, gives a crude picture of the topography of Palestine and of the main towns; it was probably produced between A.D. 520 and 550.

In the sixth century still, the architects of the Church of St. Sophia (Hagia Sophia), Isidoros of Miletos and Anthemios of Tralles, gave evidence of their exceptional ability to use mathematics for practical purposes. Anthemios, the brother of the physician Alexander of Tralles, also wrote a work on burning-mirrors, of which some fragments are extant. Another scientist, Eutocios of Ascalon, wrote commentaries on various works of Archimedes and on Apollonios' *Conics*.

Domninos of Larissa, who lived at the same time, wrote a book on arithmetic, and Stephen of Alexandria, who lived under Heraclius, wrote a commentary on Aristotle's περὶ ἑρμηνείας, and a book on astronomy. The Akhmim arithmetical papyrus, a summary of Egyptian mathematics which was commonly used as an arithmetical handbook in Byzantium, was written in the seventh or eighth century, and the *Geodesy* of Heron the Younger (the 'anonymous surveyor of Byzantium') was written in about 938.

From tenth-century references we know that the Byzantines busied themselves with the construction of hydraulic and other machines based on the ingenious ideas of Heron of Alexandria.

Michael Psellos (1018–*c.* 1078), a polygraph, statesman, philosopher and historian, was one of the leaders of the Neo-Platonic Renaissance during the second half of the eleventh century. Apart from interesting letters in which he developed Diophantos' *Arithmetic*, he wrote some rather unoriginal works on musical theory, geometry (commentaries on Euclid), astronomy and medicine.

In the twelfth century, the Emperor Manuel encouraged mathematical studies for astrological reasons, though John Tzetzes (1110–1180) wrote some purely astronomical treatises during his reign.

The Palaeologoi (thirteenth to fifteenth centuries) presided over a new upsurge of mathematics and astronomy, thanks largely to Arab and Persian commentaries on the Greek masterpieces. The most famous of these were Shams al-Din of Samarkand's *Treatise on Dialectics* and *Risāla al-Riyādiyā* (which explained thirty-five propositions of the First Book of Euclid) and the translations of Persian astronomical texts by the physicians Gregory of Chioniades, Georgios Chrysococces and the monk Isaac Argyros.

The foremost thirteenth-century scholar, Georgios Pachymeres (1242–*c.* 1310), wrote an encyclopaedic treatise on the *quadrivium*, of which Part I contained a summary of the first book of Diophantos and extracts from Euclid and Nicomachos. Pachymeres, who was familiar with Indian numerals, was one of the first authors to solve a number of indeterminate equations. He discussed the progression of Anatolios as distinct from that of Diophantos, and commented on Pythagoras' theorem. Although somewhat unoriginal, his work is clear evidence of the very high level of mathematical teaching under the Palaeologoi.

During the fourteenth century, the chief Byzantine mathematicians were Maximos Planudes, Manuel Moschopulos and Nicholas Rhabdas. Planudes (d. 1310) wrote a commentary on the first two books of Diaphantos, in which he introduced the zero symbol (τζίφρα) together with the nine Arabic, or rather Indian, numerals. According to Paul Tannery, Arabic numerals reached Constantinople *via* Rome after 1204. The humanist Manuel Moschopulos, who lived during the reign of Andronicos II (1282–1328), wrote commentaries on a number of Greek and Roman authors, and also the first Western book on magic squares, no doubt based on Italian sources. Rhabdas wrote two letters (*c.* 1341) which are the only Byzantine texts to discuss arithmetical questions with any originality. In them he described, among other things, the Greek method of denoting very large numbers by literal symbols, the approximation $a+r/2a$ for $\sqrt{(a^2+r)}$, the rule of three, and the solution of eighteen original problems. Rhabdas apparently was not familiar with Arabic numerals and continued to use the Egyptian method of breaking down fractions into their unit parts.

The Calabrian monk Barlaam (d. *c.* 1350), whose real name was Bernardo of Seminara, spent much of his life in Constantinople and wrote a Greek *Logistica* in six books in which he discussed a host of mathematical questions. He was particularly well-versed in the Heronian method of approximating square roots.

Nicephores Blemmydes (d. 1272) who lived at Nicaea when Constantinople was occupied by the Latins, wrote an astronomical poem dedicated to the emperor John III Batatzes, and a treatise called *On the Heavens, the Earth, the Sun, the Moon, the Climate and the Days.*

Theodore Metochites (d. 1332), a philosopher and astronomer, wrote a commentary on Ptolemy, arriving at astronomy through the study of musical theory. He deserves credit for having opposed astrology when it was extremely popular and when a spate of astrological writings were appearing in the East. Nicephoros Gregoras, another encyclopaedic scholar and a pupil of Metochites, concentrated on the study of eclipses and, in about 1330, managed to predict two of them correctly. He wrote treatises on the astrolabe, one of which discussed the projection of great circles on plane maps, investigated musical theories (and particularly the theory of musical intervals) and the calendrical problem of fixing the date of Easter.

The monk Isaac Argyros, who was a mathematician, astronomer and theologian, was a pupil of Gregoras. He wrote astronomical books based mainly on Persian sources, commentaries on Euclid and Ptolemy and on Rhabdas' interpretation of Planudes' *Arithmetic*, a *Geodesy* modelled on that of Heron of Alexandria, a treatise on the extraction of square roots, and a table of the square roots of the numbers 1–102 expressed in sexagesimal fraction. In 1361, Theodore Meliteniotis, archdeacon and director of the patriarchal academy in Constantinople (*c*. 1360–88), wrote an astronomical treatise based on Ptolemy, Theon and Persian texts. Finally, Georgios Chrysococces, who flourished in Trebizond *c*. 1335–46, wrote a treatise on Persian astronomy.

We conclude with Bréhier that, 'While the sound doctrines of Metochites triumphed in the end, Byzantine, like Western, astronomy was unable to throw off the shackles of Ptolemy before the coming of Galileo.'

In musical theory, the most important Byzantine author was Manuel Bryemnios, who lived in the reign of Michael IX Palaeologos (1295–1320). He wrote a treatise on music ('Αρμονικά) which was a somewhat uncritical compilation of classical ideas.

Though a great many mathematical and astronomical texts were written at the turn of the fourteenth century, none of them deserves special mention. The humanist Gemistos Pletho (d. 1452), who was also interested in scientific questions, wrote a treatise on the calendar in which he proposed a reform based on the re-adoption of the lunisolar calendar. Being unusually well-informed on geographical matters, he believed in the sphericity of the earth. He ridiculed a great many current fables and superstitions and helped to spread the ideas of Strabo, whose writings were unknown in the West.

PHYSICS, CHEMISTRY AND MEDICINE

ALCHEMY AND CHEMISTRY
Alchemy, though of oriental origin, played a great role in Rome and Greece from the third century A.D. onwards. The writings of Zosimos of Constantinople (early fourth century) and other alchemists were widely read in Byzantium. In the sixth century, alchemy fell into the hands of the Syrians, and later of the Arabs, who transmitted it to Western Europe.

According to Berthelot, most Greek manuscripts dealing with alchemy were collated in Constantinople during the eighth and ninth centuries. There is also an important number of Byzantine alchemical texts dating from the tenth and eleventh centuries, when encyclopaedists like Psellos (*c.* 1040) and Blemmydes discussed the transformation of base metals into gold.

Stephanides claims that all these works were influenced by Alexandrian medical notions and must therefore be called chymeutic rather than alchemical, which term should be applied to the Arabic texts alone. His point of view is very questionable; in any case, the relevant Byzantine manuscripts interest the historian chiefly for their illustrations of the various instruments used—stills, pans, water baths, *etc.*

In fact, Byzantium was rightly famed for its development of chemical techniques. 'Greek Fire' was first used in 678 by Constantine Pogonatos in his campaign against, and victory over, the Arabs. Invented by the Syrian Callinicos, this new weapon also proved most effective during subsequent sieges of Constantinople, and historians have stressed its great importance in the preservation of the Eastern empire. This very inflammable liquid, which was showered upon the enemy by means of various war-machines, was made up of saltpetre, mineral oil, bitumen and other inflammable substances. Marc the Greek (date uncertain) has described various other pyrotechnic compounds used by the Byzantines, most of which had a saltpetre base. Byzantine mineralogy was an occult science related to alchemy. The writings on the virtues of stones by Psellos and Neilos Diasorenos (fourth century) are of purely historical interest.

BOTANY
Like the rest of medieval Europe, Byzantium was not seriously interested in botanical studies and Byzantine references to plants are made incidentally in medical or agricultural texts. According to F.

Brunet, Byzantine scholars before the sixth century concentrated on culling what medical applications they could from the botanical writings of Crateuas, Pliny the Elder and Dioscorides, and from other Greco-Roman sources. They went on to publish the findings of Egyptian rhizotomists and of Alexandrian physicians who had investigated the effects of a number of plants on their patients, slaves and condemned criminals.

This trend was continued until the fall of Constantinople, so that we find a vast number of references to medicinal plants in the writings of Alexander of Tralles, Simon Seth, Hierophilos, John Actuarios and Nicholas Myrepsos (who mentioned about 370 of them).

In addition, there was a large number of Byzantine dictionaries of medical botany, all anonymous except that of the monk Neophytos Prodromenos (fourth century), and all mere lists of plant-names. The only fairly important and truly scientific Byzantine contributions to botany were the admirable illustrations by sixth-century artists of the work of Dioscorides (the *Codex Aniciae Julianae* which was copied out and illustrated in Constantinople in 512).

In addition, Cosmas Indicopleustes described a number of Oriental plants including the pepper and the clove-tree. Finally, the *Geoponica*, a collection of ancient agricultural writings published during the reign of Constantine Porphyrogenetes, probably between 944 and 959, contained original passages on the cultivation of various vegetables and fruit-trees, and particularly of olives and grapes.

Zoology

Zoology was equally neglected in Byzantium. In about the year 500, Timothy of Gaza wrote a bestiary which was a completely uncritical compilation of the writings of ancient authors (Aristotle, Oppian of Apamea and Aelian).

In Book XI of his *Christian Topography*, Cosmas Indicopleustes described Ethiopian, Indian and Ceylonese animals with some objectivity (rhinoceros, wart-hog, giraffe, yak and various other vertebrates). The Byzantines published many compilations from Aristotle's *History of Animals*, the two most important of which appeared during the reigns of Constantine Porphyrogenetes (tenth century) and Constantine IX Monomachos (eleventh century). Finally, Manuel Philes (1275–1345) described fishes, birds and various quadrupeds in a long poem (περὶ ζῴων ἰδιότητος).

The Byzantines were familiar with some aspects of applied zoology, *e.g.* with sericulture, which was introduced during the reign of Justinian (*c.* 553–554) by two monks returning from the Far East.

The *Geoponica*, mentioned before, contains many references to crop pests, bees and cattle, and a number of physicians (Aëtios, Alexander of Tralles, Pepagomenos and John Actuarios) discussed poisonous snakes and parasites.

The medieval love for hunting, particularly during the twelfth and fourteenth centuries, led the Byzantines to rear hawks, falcons, dogs and cheetahs to help them capture rabbits, foxes, stags, wild boars, bears, *etc.* Their treatises on falconry and on cynegetics contained many accurate descriptions of the morphology and behaviour of hunting and hunted animals. One of the best of these was the textbook on falconry by the physician Pepagomenos (thirteenth century), who is also said to have written a book on dogs (κυνοσόφιον).

During the fourteenth century, literary works based on zoological notions were avidly read in Constantinople. Religious writings, like the *Physiologos*, which was particularly popular, used animals to express various Christian symbols. Following the Fathers of the Church (St. Cyril and St. Basil), many writers of poems about the Creation (*Hexaëmeron*) alluded to animals, and to Aristotelian ideas about them. Finally, Byzantine drawings of animals—and of plants— were very accurate whenever they were not too stylized under Sassanid influences.

MEDICINE

According to F. Brunet, the main sources of Byzantine medicine were Hippocrates, Celsos, Rufus, Aretaeos, Soranos, Galen and the physicians of the Alexandrian school.

Until Alexandria was captured by the Moslems in 640, Greek physicians went there to study anatomy, physiology, pathology, hygiene, *etc.*, and adopted Aristotelian and Neo-Platonic doctrines, together with the prevailing humoral, pneumatic and methodist theories of the empiricist and eclectic schools. Later, Greek physicians turned their attention to semeiology, diagnosis, therapy, dietetics, and pharmacology.

Christian doctrines, with their emphasis on miraculous cures, also had a great influence on Byzantine medicine, and so did Eastern ideas (Syrian, Armenian, Arabian and Persian).

We have already discussed the work of Oribasios, the first great physician of the Eastern Empire, and can now continue with Aëtios of Amida (late fifth century). He was born in Mesopotamia, studied at Alexandria, and was later appointed physician to Justinian's court. According to some authors he was the first Greek physician to adopt Christianity. His main work is a vast compilation in sixty books of the most important contributions of his predecessors. The work also contained the earliest reference to the cerebral centres as the seats of nervous conditions; according to Archigenes and Posidonios, Book VII gave a lucid account of eye diseases and Book XVI was an

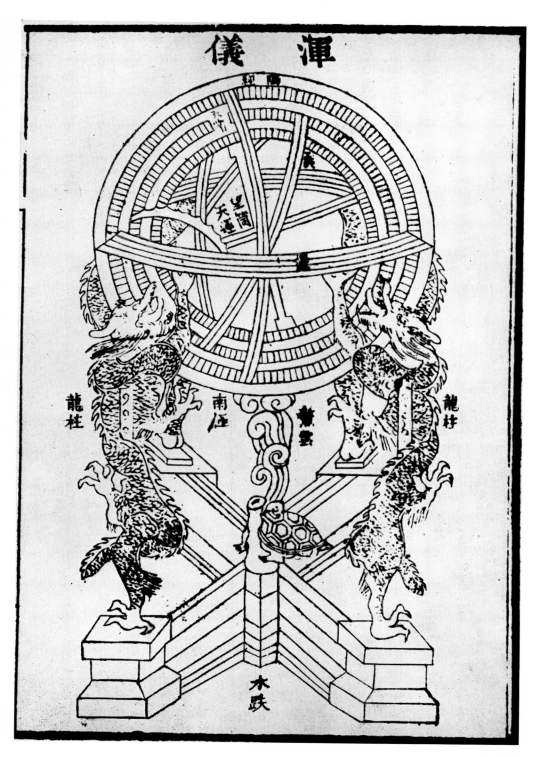

37 Chinese armillary sphere

38 Byzantine astrolabe

important treatise on gynaecology including—according to Leonides —a description of the surgical removal of tumours of the breast. Aëtios also described methods of invoking God's, or the saints', assistance for healing certain diseases.

Alexander of Tralles, another contemporary of Justinian, was the author of a well-known medical treatise in twelve books, in which he described many of his personal experiments and challenged a number of Hippocrates' and Galen's beliefs. The most interesting sections of his work dealt with diseases of the nervous system, of the respiratory tract (including very good descriptions of pleurisy and of its treatment), of the digestive tract and of gout. In a 'Letter on Intestinal Worms', he distinguished between the most important parasites and prescribed effective vermifuges.

According to F. Brunet, who has translated Alexander into French:

As a clinician, Alexander loved clarity, order, logic; he placed nothing higher than experiment and the peremptory clarity of the facts, which alone can justify theories. He was not a compiler, but a practitioner who appreciated the inadequacy of polished phrases at the patient's bedside.

Despite these great qualities, Alexander was still swayed by the superstitions of his time and prescribed incantations and the use of amulets whenever normal remedies failed.

During the reign of Justinian, there occurred the terrible plague of 542, the symptoms of which were described correctly by the historian Procopios in *c.* 560 (bubo of the groin, the armpits, behind the ears). Castiglioni was wrong to ascribe the plague to the decline of Byzantine civilization, for Byzantium continued to flourish for many centuries to come.

Paulos Aegineta, who lived during the first half of the seventh century, studied medicine in Alexandria. Of his works, most of which were quickly translated into Arabic, only a treatise on medicine in seven books has come down to us. The most interesting is Book VI, which dealt with surgery.

From some of its comments we can glean what great progress surgery had made since the time of Celsos, and that, despite their very poor anatomical knowledge, Byzantine surgeons had acquired enough technical skill to tackle very delicate and difficult operations. (Castiglioni.)

Besides his very cogent remarks on cancer, Paulos Aegineta also gave clear indications of how to cauterize liver abscesses and how to perform lithotomies. His surgical treatment of inguinal hernia remained the standard procedure until the end of the seventeenth century.

Two other seventh-century physicians, Theophilos Protospatharios and his pupil Stephen of Athens, wrote compilations of earlier medical works, and John and Stephen of Alexandria wrote commentaries on the work of Hippocrates and Galen.

During the reign of Theophilos (829–842), Leo the Iatrosophist wrote a medical encyclopaedia. From that time onwards the influence of Arabic physicians on Byzantine medicine began to grow rapidly. During the tenth century, which, thanks to the active support of the Emperor Constantine Porphyrogenetes, became the heyday of Byzantine science, Theophanos Nonnos wrote another famous medical encyclopaedia. It was based on Orabasios, and attacked the superstitions of the time.

In the eleventh century, Simon Seth, personal physician to the Emperor Michael VII Ducas, wrote a small book on the properties of food, in which he repeated Galen's ideas on the medical virtues of various plants and animals, and described a number of new remedies of Eastern origin. Another treatise on dietetics was written by Hierophilos the Sophist (middle of twelfth century).

The next medical authors of any importance lived during the thirteenth and fourteenth centuries. Demetrios Pepagomenos was commissioned to write what turned out to be an important work on gout by Michael VIII Palaeologos, and at the same time (end of thirteenth century) Nicholas Myrepsos published a medical treatise in forty-eight chapters. During the reign of Andronicos III (1328–1341), John Actuarios wrote an excellent medical treatise based on Galen and on other Greek and Arabic medical authors. He also wrote an unusually comprehensive treatise on the urine. At the end of the fourteenth and the beginning of the fifteenth century, Byzantine medical literature fell into a steep decline, although medical studies continued to be pursued and though hospitals flourished on an unprecedented scale.[1]

VETERINARY SCIENCE
The main Greco-Roman texts on hippiatry were joined into the *Hippiatrica* during the ninth and tenth centuries. During the thirteenth century, the physician Pepagomenos described diseases of falcons and dogs in his zoological writings, and similar descriptions were given by various anonymous treatises on falconry from about the same period.

PHARMACOLOGY
Byzantine authors wrote no specific pharmaceutical texts of any importance, and it was only within the framework of their medical writings that they mentioned remedies, generally borrowed from

[1] Byzantine infirmaries were first organized in the sixth century; one of the most important was that of Pontocrator founded in the twelfth century under John Comnenus. Byzantium also had asylums, leper institutes and almshouses.

Hellenistic sources and particularly from Dioscorides, Asclepiades and Rufus.

Alexander of Tralles, whom F. Brunet considers the first clinical author on psychotherapy, listed a great number of vegetable, animal and mineral remedies, and mentions that James Psychrestes, the trusted friend of the Emperor Leo I (457–474), used colchicum in the treatment of gout. Pharmacology is also discussed at some length in the works of Simon Seth, Nicholas Myrepsos and many other physicians. During the last stages of the Eastern Greek Empire (fourteenth to fifteenth century) a number of popular books on medicine and pharmacology added the most improbable remedies to those of classical authors.

Byzantium's role in the history of medicine and pharmacology is nevertheless important, since the translation of Byzantine texts into both Arabic and Latin helped to spread Greek ideas throughout the civilized world, so that the work of Nicholas Myrepsos remained the principal pharmaceutical code of the Parisian medical faculty until 1651.

CONCLUSION

No one could maintain that Byzantine scientific texts were of outstanding scientific value, or that most of them were more than poor compilations of earlier Greek or Hellenistic works or commentaries. One of the main reasons for this deficiency was the total subordination of science to the Church and the concentration on Platonic and Neo-Platonic doctrines, and thus on abstract speculations. Hence the Byzantine predilection for mathematics. Paradoxically enough, they also paid attention to the practical problems arising in agricultural and veterinary matters, hospital services, the use of Greek fire, *etc.*

It is only when we view Byzantine science in historical perspective that we come to look upon the Eastern Greek Empire as the torchbearer of Hellenism, at the very time when the West allowed itself to be plunged into utter darkness.

Byzantine science reached its highest peaks in the sixth century under Justinian, in the tenth century under Constantine Porphyrogenetes, and in the fourteenth century under the Palaeologoi, when it produced such encyclopaedic writers as Psellos, Pachymeres, Metochites and Gregoras. Despite the theological atmosphere in which they lived, these men were quick to appreciate the immense philosophical and scientific worth of the works of Plato, Aristotle, Euclid and Ptolemy. Hence they tried to preserve and, whenever possible, to advocate the Greeks' characteristic love of knowledge.

Byzantine scientists have earned the gratitude of later generations for their systematic compilations of Greek and Oriental masterpieces, and for their annotations, translations and illustrations of these works.

In this way, they helped to spread the ideas of Hellenic science not only to the Syrians, the Persians and, after the flight of the Nestorian scientists, to the Arabs, but also to the West, first during the Crusades and again after the capture of Constantinople, when Byzantine scientists fled to the West taking their books and manuscripts with them. Their arrival in Italy is rightly considered an important factor in preparing Europe for the Renaissance.

BIBLIOGRAPHY

M. BERTHELOT, *Introduction a l'étude de la chimie des Anciens et du Moyen Age*, Paris, 1938.

L. BRÉHIER, *La civilisation byzantine*, Paris, 1950.

F. BRUNET, *Œuvres médicales d'Alexandre de Tralles*, 4 vols., Paris, 1933–1935.

A. DELATTE, *Anecdota atheniensia et alia*, II: Greek texts on the history of science, Bibl. Fac. Lettres Univ. Liège, fasc. 88, 1939.

R. GUILLAND, Paper on *Nicéphore Grégoras. L'homme et l'œuvre*, Paris, 1926.

J. L. HEIBERG, Les sciences grecques et leur transmission, Part II: L'œuvre de conservation des Byzantins et des Arabes, *Scientia*, XXXI (1931), 97–104.

K. KRUMBACHER, *Geschichte der Byzantinischen Litteratur von Justinian bis zum Ende des Oströmischen Reiches (527–1453)*, Munich, 1897.

M. MERCIER, *Le feu grégeois; les feux de guerre depuis l'Antiquité; la poudre à canon*, Paris, 1952.

G. K. POURNAROPOULOS, Συμβολη εἰς την ἱστοριαν της βυζαντινης ἰατρικης, Athens, 1942.

M. STÉPHANIDÈS, Les savants byzantins et la science moderne. Renaissance et Byzance, *Archeion*, XIV (1932), 492–6.

P. TANNERY, *Science exactes chez les Byzantins*, Paris, 1920.

Quadrivium de Georges Pachmère (revised text by E. STEPHANOU, preface by V. LAURENT), Vatican City, 1940.

B. TATAKIS, *La philosophie byzantine*, in *Histoire de la philosophie* by E. BRÉHIER, suppl. fasc. No. 2, Paris, 1949.

J. THÉODORIDÈS, *Introduction a l'étude de la zoologie byzantine*, proceedings VIIth Congr. Int. Hist. Sciences, 601–9, 1953.

M. H. THOMSON, *Textes grecs inédits relatifs aux plantes*, Paris, 1955.

CHAPTER 6

Medieval Jewish Science

MEDIEVAL JEWISH HISTORY began in A.D. 70, with the destruction of Jerusalem and the disappearance of the Jewish state.

At that time, the fragmentation (*diaspora*) of the Jewish people, which had started in the sixth century B.C., culminated in their almost total dispersion throughout the Near East and Europe. Anxious not to lose their identity, the exiles clung desperately to their religion, their language, their moral code and their national pride. Because of their intellectual and linguistic gifts the exiled Jews, more than any other people, helped to spread scientific ideas during the Middle Ages.

Jewish scholars at the beginning of the Middle Ages wrote no scientific texts comparable with those of Hippocrates, Aristotle or Galen. All their scientific knowledge was incorporated into two encyclopaedic works, the Jerusalem Talmud, compiled and completed towards the end of the fourth century, and the more comprehensive Babylonian Talmud, completed towards the end of the fifth century. After the fall of Jerusalem Jewish scholars continued to teach science and theology, first in the academies of Tiberias, then in those of Sura and Pumbedita, and later still in Spain, France, Egypt and Northern Africa.

The scientific ideas scattered in the sixty-three volumes of the Babylonian Talmud and in those of the Jerusalem Talmud are by no means all of equal worth, but some, at least, were of first-rate importance. Thus, the Talmud was the first work to introduce concepts of morbid anatomy and forensic medicine.

In the seventh century, Judaeus Asaph wrote a Hebrew treatise of medicine which was comparable with non-Jewish treatises on the subject. He was soon followed by other Jewish scientists who published works in Hebrew, Arabic, or Latin, and who, above all, excelled as translators, thus acting as links between East and West. Because most major scientific works were translated into Hebrew during the Middle Ages, Jewish scholars were in the enviable position of having all the main sources at their finger-tips. Their frequent migrations, voluntary or otherwise, enabled Jewish scientists to become the chief proponents and purveyors of medieval science, persecutions and professional restrictions notwithstanding.

453

ASTRONOMY AND MATHEMATICS

ASTRONOMY

Knowledge of astronomy was most important to the Jews, both for scientific and for ritual reasons. In particular, they needed a precise calendar for observing their seasonal festivals.

The Talmuds contain a host of astronomical references, one of which makes it clear that Johanan ben Zaqai was skilled in predicting solstices and the motions of the planets. From other passages we learn that the Jews used special instruments for observing the moon, one of which was called '*shefofereth*'. Among the best Jewish astronomers of that time was the physician Mar Samuel, who claimed that he was as familiar with 'the paths of the sky' as with the alleyways of Nahardea, his native village. He is believed to have been the author of the *Baraïta of Rabbi Samuel*. According to the Talmudists, the planets revolved about the sun, and each day of the week (the Sabbath excepted) corresponded with one of them: Shabbetai with Saturn, Zedek with Jupiter, Maadim with Mars, Hamma with the Sun, Kohebeth or Naga with Venus, Kohab with Mercury, and Lebanah with the Moon. The Milky Way was called *Nehar Dinur* ('Current of fire'). Rabbi Joshua ben Hananya mentioned a comet which appeared every seventy years, and some modern scholars take this as evidence that the Talmudists had recognized Halley's Comet.

Among subsequent Jewish authors we must mention Jacob ibn Ṭāriq, court-astronomer of the Sultan al-Manṣūr, and also Mashallah, who is said to have assisted in drawing up the plans for the building of Baghdad in 762; (Rabban) Sahl al-Ṭabarī (ninth century), who was the first translator of Ptolemy's *Almagest* into Arabic; and the physician Shabbethai Donnolo (tenth century), who wrote the first Hebrew astronomical treatise, the *Sepher Tashkemoni*. Abraham Ibn Ezra was the author of an introduction to astronomy, the *Principles of Wisdom*, in which he discussed the astrolabe and astronomical tables, and Abraham bar Hiyya (twelfth century) wrote a Hebrew treatise called the *Shape of the Earth and the Foundations of Astronomy*, and also prepared a number of very original astronomical tables.

Special mention must be made of Moses Maïmonides, whose theological and philosophical writings contain many interesting astronomical ideas, including accurate methods of determining the position of the sun and the phases of the moon, which are so important for Jewish religious observances.

Jacob ben Maḥir (Profatius) translated a number of astronomical treatises into Hebrew during the fourteenth century and constructed a quadrant for use as an astrolabe. His contemporary Levi ben Gerson (Leo of Bagnols or Leo Hebraeus) wrote a treatise on astronomy and invented an astronomical instrument, the *Megalleh Amukoth* ('Discoverer of Profound Things'), which was admired by Reuchlin, Kepler, and Pope Clement VI. He is also credited by some with the invention of the camera obscura.

The 'Principles of the World' (*Yessodeh Olam*) and the 'Gates of Heaven' (*Sepher Shaar Hashamayim*) of Isaac ben Joseph Israeli exerted a great deal of influence on medieval scholars.

Isaac, the son of Solomon al-Chadabe, the inventor of an astronomical instrument described in his book *Keli Hemda* ('Precious Instrument'), established astronomical tables, and so did David ben Yomtov Poël, Solomon ben Elijah and Abraham Zacuto, physician and teacher at Salamanca and one of the patrons of Vasco da Gama's voyages, for which he constructed a metallic astrolabe. Zacuto's astronomical treatise *Biur Lukoth* ('Explanation of the Tables') was translated into Latin by Vecinho, Councillor to the Court of King John II of Portugal, and the Latin version, the *Almanach perpetuum*, was consulted by Christopher Columbus. In 1480, the physician Joseph of Lisbon suggested that astrolabes be carried by all ships. Finally, Master Jacob, the son of Abraham Crescas, who taught at the nautical academy in Majorca, was one of the fathers of modern cartography.

The Tibbonid family, *i.e.* Kalonymus ben David, Jacob Anatoli, Jehudah ben Moses Cohen and Abraham de Balmes, were particularly distinguished translators. We end this brief list of Jewish luminaries with Rabbi Hamnuna, who in a book of the Cabbala, the *Zohar* or 'Book of Splendour', asserted that the 'inhabited earth turns round like a ball'.

MATHEMATICS

The ritual laws concerning the Sabbath distances (*i.e.* the distances which a Jew may walk without desecrating the Sabbath), and also the need for a strict calendar, forced the Jews to study mathematics. The Talmudic tractates *Erubin* ('Unifications'), *Kilayim* ('Instruments') and *Oholoth* ('Tents') contain a great number of arithmetical, geometrical and geodesic ideas.

The most ancient Hebrew mathematical text is the *Mishnath hamiddoth* ('Treatise of Mensurations'), attributed to Rabbi Nehemiah (second century). This work, discovered in 1862 and published by Steinschneider, discusses mathematical terminology and geometry, and gives $\pi = 3\frac{1}{7}$.

Jewish mathematicians divided mathematics into seven branches: arithmetic, algebra, geometry, astronomy, astrology, optics and music, after the manner of Arabic scientists, who were as often the Jews' teachers as they were their pupils. Mashallah, Sahl ibn Bishr and Sahl (Rabban) al-Tabarī wrote in Arabic, while Jacob ben Nissim wrote a work on Indian mathematics, the *Heshbon haavak* ('Calculation of Powders') in Hebrew.

One of the most famous Jewish geometers was Abraham bar Hiyya ha-Nasi (Savasorda, twelfth century) whose main works, *The Treatise on Mensuration and Fractions* and *The Foundations of Reason and Intelligence, and the Tower of Faith*, were recently studied by J. Millas-Vallicrosa. Abraham ibn Ezra was the author of the *Sepher hamispar* ('Treatise on Arithmetic') and of the *Sepher hayechad* ('Unique Book'). Many extracts from the *Elements* of Euclid were included in the encyclopaedic *Midrash hachochmah* ('Interpretation of Wisdom') of Judah ben Samuel Cohen, of Toledo. Mention must also be made of Levi ben Gerson, the author of a treatise on arithmetic and of another on algebra, of Mordecai Comtino and his pupil Eli ben Abraham Misrachi, whose *Treatise on Arithmetic*, based on the work of Ibn Ezra, was greatly admired. Delambre claims that Misrachi was the first mathematician to use the modern method of taking square roots.

The leading Jewish commentators and translators of the Middle Ages were Abba Mari of Marseilles, Abraham ben Solomon Vardi, Profatius, Abraham Finzi and, finally, the most important of all— Kalonymus ben Kalonymus (Master Calo) of Arles, translator of the works of Archimedes, of al-Fārābī, Ibn al-Haytham, Thabid ibn Qurra and others. Their translations into and from Hebrew, Latin and Arabic enabled Western and Eastern scientists alike to study the main medieval works in the language of their choice.

BIOLOGY

The Jerusalem and Babylonian Talmuds contain a host of references to wild and domestic animals, particularly in connection with ritual problems. The peculiar zoological classification of animals in the Bible into *kosher* (pure) and *treyfah* (impure) became the subject of many Talmudic commentaries which, not content with anatomical and morphological descriptions, delved into animal ecology and psychology.

The Talmud also studied the vegetable kingdom, with a view to separating edible, and particularly medicinal, from poisonous plants.

The first specific Hebrew work on biology appeared in the fourteenth century, though many Jewish authors had discussed the subject incidentally in the course of their exegetic, philosophic and medical writings from the fifth century onwards, *i.e.* from the end of the Talmudic period. In particular, there were a number of lexico-graphic works containing biological descriptions, so that Samuel Bochart, one of the greatest scientists of the Renaissance, based his *Hierozoïcon* directly on the work of medieval Jewish lexicographers.

Inevi ably, Assaph (seventh century) and Donnolo (tenth century) discussed zoological and botanical notions in their medical writings, and so did the Biblical commentators Saadia and Hai Gaon in their exegetic texts.

The traveller Eldad ha-Dani took an interest in hemp cultivation and described many of the plants he had seen in Northern Africa, Mesopotamia and the Indies. Zoology and botany were also men-tioned in the Talmudic commentaries of Rabbi Hananel ben Hushiel and in the exegetic texts of Rabbi Gershon ben Judah, who taught at Metz. The foremost of all Jewish writers on biology was the 'Prince of Talmudic Scholars', Rabbi Solomon ben Isaac (Rashi of Troyes), whose knowledge was truly encyclopaedic. His commentaries contained thousands of French terms from which non-Jewish scientists were able to identify a host of animals and plants.

Special mention must also be made of Joseph ben Isaac Zimhi (Riqam or Maistre Petit), who was a poet, a grammarian and an exegete, and of his son David Zimhi (Redaq), whose *Sepher Hasho-rashim* ('Book of Roots') enabled other scholars to identify numerous plants and animals, as did the commentaries of Abraham ben Ibn Ezra and the Hebrew lexicon *Aruch* by the Italian Jew Nathan ben Jehial, which gave translations of Hebrew zoological terms in Greek, Arabic, Turkish, Latin, Italian, Aramaic and Old Slavonic. Among other authors whose work bore on biology were the physician, poet and statesman Judah ha-Levi, author of the *Kitāb-al-Khazarī*; the physician, philosopher and exegete Maïmonides, who wrote a *Treatise on Poisons*; Judah ben Solomon Cohen, who wrote a *Treatise on Wisdom*; and Shemtov ben Joseph ibn Falaquéra, who wrote the *Deoth Hafilosophim* ('Ideas of the Philosophers'). Interesting biological comments are also found in Meir Aldabi's *Paths of Faith*, and in the writings of the travellers Benjamin of Tudela, Estori Farḥi, and Caleb Afendopulo.

Five of the fourteen treatises or 'gates' of the encyclopaedic work 'Gates of Heaven' (*Shaar Hashamayim*) by Levi ben Gerson (recently published in English translation by F. S. Bodenheimer) are devoted to the natural sciences. Once again, we must mention Kalonymus ben Kalonymus, whose interesting biological comments in the *Treatise on Plants* and *Treatise on Animals* were based on Aristotle.

The first traveller mentioned in the Talmud was Rabbi Akiba (second century), who visited Africa, Mesopotamia, Persia and Gaul. In the eighth century, Rabbi Simeon Kayyara and Jehudah

Gaon of Sura gave an ethnographic account of the people of Asia in their compendium *Halakoth guedoloth* ('Great Laws'). Eldad ha-Dani, whom we mentioned earlier, Rabbi Jacob ben Shēara, Ibrahim bin Ya'qūb, Ab Hiyya ha-Nasi, Ibn Ezra, Maïmonides, Judah Hadassi, Benjamin of Tudela, Petachiah ben Jacob, Samuel ben Simon, and Judah al-Ḥarizi gave interesting descriptions of the people, the fauna and the flora of the countries which they had visited.

PHARMACOLOGY AND MEDICINE

PHARMACOLOGY

At the beginning of the Middle Ages, Jewish ideas on medicinal plants were scattered in the different Talmudic texts. In the seventh century, these scattered comments were collated in the *Sepher Refuoth* (Book of Drugs) written by the Syro-Palestinian physician Assaph ha-Yehudi (Judaeus). This book, based also on the work of Dioscorides, gave an excellent description of more than a hundred medicinal plants with their synonyms in Aramaic, Latin, Greek and Persian. Three centuries later, when the physician and exegete Donnolo wrote his *Sepher Hayakar* ('Precious Book') based on Dioscorides and Assaph, he gave the Hebrew, Greek, Latin, Arabic, Persian and Italian names of 120 medicinal plants, whose therapeutic properties he specified. With the assistance of the Greek monk Nicholas, the physician Ḥasdai ibn Shapruth, also famed as a jurist and as financier to the Caliph Abd al-Raḥman III, translated Dioscorides' *Materia Medica* into Arabic, while the Judaeo-Persian physician Masarjawaï wrote a treatise called *Substitutes for Remedies* and another (which is lost) called *The Virtues of Drugs, their Usefulness and their Poisonous Effects*.

A host of pharmaceutical terms was contained in 'Aly Rabban al-Tabarī's *Paradise of Wisdom*, in the *Treatise of Compound Medicaments* by Moses ben Eleazar (Musa ibn Alizar), court-physician to the Caliph al Muizz, and in the *Materia Medica* and the *Book of Medicinal Herbs and Food* by Isaac Israeli, works which were often consulted by medieval physicians. Abū'l Merwan ibn Ganah's *Al Talhis* ('The Digest'), which contained a list of the weights and measures used in medicine, gave the names of drugs in Arabic, Persian, Syriac, Greek, Berber and Spanish. Unfortunately this work is known only from quotations by Maïmonides and Ibn al-Bayṭār. Nathaniel (Ḥibath Allah ibn Gumay), physician to the Sultan Saladin and *ňagid* (*i.e.* head) of the Jewish community of Cairo, wrote a work on *Royal Medicaments*. The *Treatise on Drugs* by his pupil David ibn Abi'l-Bayan became a standard work in Egypt, Syria and Iraq.

By far the most important medieval book on pharmacology was the *Discourse on Poisons and Antidotes against Mortal Drugs* by Abu 'Imran Mūsā ibn Maimūn ibn 'Abdallāh al-Qurtubi al-Isrā'ili, better known as Maïmonides. A copy of this work, executed by Ibn al-Bayṭār, author of the *Treatise on Simples*, was discovered in the library of the Hagia Sophia in Istanbul, and was published in Cairo together with a French translation by Mayerhof (1940). While the Bible mentions no more than 170 names of plants and the Talmud no more than 320, sixty of which are of Greek, Persian and Hindu origin, Maïmonides went much further:

'I shall not mention', Maïmonides wrote, 'any known and authentic remedies which all physicians agree to call by none but their common Arabic or foreign names, because the aim of this summary is neither to define the different types of remedy by simple descriptions, nor to discuss their uses, but only to render some of their names into others. I shall classify the remedies listed in alphabetical order, but I shall avoid repetitions. . . . My aim is to reduce the size of this summary so as to facilitate the task of those wishing to memorize it and hence to profit from it . . .

(Folio 74, v° of the original)

There follows a list of more than 1,800 drugs, in 405 sections.

The Aegypto-Jewish physician Cohen the Druggist (Abū'l Munā ibn Nasser al-Aṭṭar) wrote a 'Manual for the Officine' (*Minhaj al-dukkān*) which replaced the *Hospital Formulary* of Ibn Abi'l-Bayan. This manual contained a great number of practical hints on the collection, preparation and preservation of medicinal plants.

Nathan ben Joel Falaquéra wrote the *Balsam of the Body*, and Solomon Hakattan of Montpellier published a *Pharmacopoeia* and also a translation of Nicholas' *Antidotary*. Rabbi Todras of Cavaillon wrote a 'Treatise on Compounds' (*Shaareh haharkavoth*).

Finally, we must mention the *Compendium aromatorium* of the Jewish physician Saladino di Ascoli of Tarentum, which was, in fact, the first treatise on Galenic pharmacology, inasmuch as all previous works 'were mainly devoted to a description of therapeutic drugs and their physiological effects' (Reutter de Rosemont). Muntner published Saladino's Hebrew manuscripts in 1953.

The list of Jewish pharmacologists would be incomplete without some reference to Jewish spice traders and apothecaries, on the subject of whom Dr. Glésinger writes:

The medieval spice and drug trades were mainly in the hands of Jews who enjoyed a number of privileges under Charlemagne. In the towns of Speyer and Worms, Jews traded in drugs as early as 1090, and Frederick II granted Austrian Jews the right to traffic in medicaments towards 1238. Thanks to these Jewish traders, Western physicians became acquainted with some of the most important remedies. . . . They (Jewish apothecaries) were held in great repute during the Middle Ages; many princes of the church and of the court consulted Jewish physicians and apothecaries. . . . Archbishop Bruno I of Trier (who died in 1124) called his Jewish physician Joshua '*physicae artis eruditissimum compotistam peroptimum*'.

At the end of the Middle Ages, Jewish apothecaries could be found in all the countries of Europe. As was the custom, the art of the apothecary was handed down from father to son, so that certain drugs were handled exclusively by one and the same family for a number of generations.

MEDICAL KNOWLEDGE

While the Jews produced no important medical treatises before the Middle Ages, they nevertheless counted many famous physicians among their number.

The Bible contains many hygienic precepts, which the Jews were anxious to observe scrupulously. Thus every householder had to declare the appearance of suspicious spots; cases and places of infection had to be disinfected and isolated; and leprosy and other 'impurities' had to be dealt with in special ways (*cf.* Leviticus XIII–XV). Above all, Jews had to distinguish between *kosher* (pure) and *treyfah* (impure) foods.

The Talmud re-examined all these problems in the light of medieval knowledge. Many questions of *kashrut* (dietary purity) were settled by experiment, and *shechitah* (ritual slaughter of animals) was greatly improved. *Shechitah* practices, which were based on the time-honoured method of severing the carotid artery and thus draining away the animal's blood very quickly, showed that the carotid contains blood and not air, and that sudden drainage of blood from the brain minimized the animal's suffering.

The Jews also realized that bloodless meat kept better and longer. Their inspections of the entrails and the meat of slaughtered animals (*bedikah*) in order to detect lesions (tumours, abscesses, adhesions, fractures, *etc.*) made the Jews the first comparative pathologists. Talmudic scholars studied and explained physiological ideas arising out of *shechitah* practices, and even applied this knowledge to surgery. Thus, the Talmud refers to a surgical intervention in a case of extreme obesity, and describes the first recorded intubation of a sheep's larynx. It also mentions the killing and autopsy of a paralysed sheep, and its account of a successful Caesarean section (*yozeh dopheneh*) is the only one of its kind in medieval medical literature. In forensic medicine, the Talmudists identified blood-spots by means of seven reagents, a procedure that was not mentioned elsewhere until the seventeenth century. Finally, Talmudic scholars carried out osteological examinations and, in the first century A.D., Rabbi Elishah and his pupils dissected the corpse of a prostitute.

It was only in the seventh century that the first treatise on medicine was written in the Hebrew language. This was the *Sepher Refuoth* ('Book of Drugs') of Assaph ha-Yehudi, which we mentioned earlier and which has come down to us in manuscript form. Assaph based his work on Greco-Roman sources and on the Talmud, but his *Medicina Pauperum* was original in that it was written with the express purpose of teaching poor patients to 'care for themselves without the help of a physician'. Lacking an adequate Hebrew terminology, he invented a great number of medical terms which are used to this day.

Assaph also drafted the first Hebrew medical oath (*Shevuath Assaph*), which all his pupils had to swear before they were handed their diplomas. The oath included the injunctions: 'Thou shalt not charge thyself with blood in thy practice' and 'Thou shalt not cause any man an injury'.

After this Hebrew-speaking physician, the torch of medical learning passed into the hands of Judaeo-Arabic scholars. Masarjawaï wrote an Arabic treatise on the *Force and Usefulness of Foods and their Disadvantages* and another on *Plants, their Advantages and Impediments*. One of the best-known physicians of the Middle Ages was Isaac ben Solomon Israeli (Isaac, Isaacus, or Judaeus), private physician to the Caliph Ziyudat Allah t'Agh and to the Fatimite 'Ubaidallāh al-Mahdī. His *On Fevers*, *On the Urine*, and *On Diets*, were translated by Constantine the African, who published them under the title of *Opera omnia Isaaci*. The Hebrew version of the *On Diets*, the *Sepher Hamissadim*, was one of the standard medical texts of the Middle Ages and of the Renaissance. Other leading physicians of that era were Dunash ben Tamim (a pupil of Isaac Israeli), Hasdaï ibn Shapruth, Ephraim ibn al-Zafaran, the poet and traveller Judah Hal-arizi, Moses ben Ṣadaka and Rabbi Nathaniel, author of the *Introduction to the Healing of the Body and the Spirit*.

But, beyond doubt, the greatest of them all was Maïmonides. This famous philosopher, theologian and physician was one of the main exponents of what we would call psycho-somatic medicine. He wrote—almost invariably at the behest of his royal patron, the Sultan Saladin—a score of books on such varied subjects as diet, regimen, haemorrhoids, conjugal life, poisons and their antidotes, asthma, the causes of accidents, Hippocrates' Aphorisms, and the sixteen books of Galen. The most popular of his works was his own book of aphorisms, the *Fuṣul Mūsa* ('Moses' Aphorisms').

All these books, and also his *Materia Medica*, were written in

Arabic and most of them were soon afterwards translated into Hebrew, Latin, French, German and English. Maïmonides was greatly influenced by the Talmud, by Greco-Roman authors and by Rhazes. Like Rhazes, he was a firm believer in the healing power of nature and he consequently stressed the importance of hygiene not only in prophylaxis but also in therapy. The great medieval surgeons Guy of Chauliac, Arnold of Villanova and Henry of Mondeville often quoted Maïmonides, to whom they referred as 'Rabbi Moses'.

THE PRACTITIONERS

A great many Spanish and Portuguese physicians of Jewish extraction played a distinguished role either as authors or as court physicians. Thus Alfonso VI of Castile, Alfonso X, Alfonso XI, Henry III and others chose Jewish physicians. The private physician of John II of Portugal was the Jewish astronomer Joseph Vecinho, and Christopher Columbus was accompanied on his voyages by two Jewish practitioners, the naval physician Bernal and the surgeon Marco.

During the persecution in Spain (1391), the physician Don Profiaṭ Duran (Efodi) was the moral mainstay of his Jewish co-religionists. At the same time, Rabbi Ẓemaḥ Duran, who had fled to Algiers, wrote his *Magen Aboth* ('The Shield of the Fathers'), which contained a number of chapters devoted to obstetrics and gynaecology. With the expulsion of the Jews from Spain in 1492 and from Portugal in 1497, there ended one of the most remarkable chapters in the history of Jewish medicine and science.

In Germany, too, Jews were often chosen as court physicians, and even as private physicians to the Princes of the Church. Though these men enjoyed great privileges, they, like their co-religionists, were often humiliated and sometimes persecuted. The first Jewish women to practice medicine were Doctor Sarah, who was given a special licence to work in Wurzburg by Archbishop John II (in 1490), and her colleague Doctor Zerlin, who worked in Frankfort.

Though there were few Jewish physicians in Austria, Bohemia, Rumania and Switzerland, some of them nevertheless attained prominent positions. Thus Stephen the Great of Moldavia appointed a Spanish Jew as his court physician.

In Italy, Jewish physicians played an important role as practitioners, as authors, and as translators of medical texts. Amongst the best known were Donnolo, an astronomer and pharmacologist whom we have mentioned before; Nathan Hameati, who translated Avicenna's *Canon* and a number of Galen's and Maïmonides' works; the astronomer and naturalist Kalonymus ben Kalonymus, who was court physician to Robert of Anjou; the physician Abraham Conat of Mantua, who was one of the first Jews to own a printing works;

Messer Leo and Elias Delmedigo, practitioners and rabbis (Delmedigo taught philosophy to the famous Pico della Mirandola); Vidal Balsom and Benjamin of Porta Leone, who wrote textbooks on therapy; and Moses of Palermo, who translated a work on hippiatry. Popes Boniface IX, Innocent VII, Alexander VI, Julius II and Leo X chose Jews as personal physicians.

THE SCHOOL OF SALERNO

While there is no evidence to support the legendary account that the School of Salerno was founded by one Helinus who taught in Hebrew, there is no doubt that the school was greatly influenced by Jewish thought and teachers. Some scholars believe that Donnolo taught there in the second half of the tenth century, and the school is mentioned by the famous twelfth-century Jewish traveller, Benjamin of Toledo, in his 'Itinerary' (*Maassoth*). Among the textbooks used at Salerno were the works of Isaac Israeli, translated into Latin by Constantine the African. A number of Salerno's Jewish physicians became famous, *e.g.* Moses ben Solomon and the eminent Latin scholar Ferrarius (Faradj ben Solomon), whom Charles of Anjou commissioned to translate Rhazes' *Continens*. (The translation contains a portrait of Ferrarius.)

THE MEDICAL SCHOOLS OF MONTPELLIER AND AVIGNON

Jews first settled in France during Roman days, a fact mentioned by Rabbi Akiba in the second century and by Dom Polycarp of the Riviera in about A.D. 300.

The activities of Jewish scientists in medieval France are best known from Rabbi Maḥir's Jewish settlement, the *Villa judaica*, in Narbonne. Rabbi Maḥir, who was sent to France by Hārūn al-Rashīd at the request of Charlemagne, taught Talmudic studies at the school which he founded, and his lectures dealt with veterinary science and probably with medicine as well. Talmudic schools were also founded at Béziers, Arles, Lunel, Nîmes, Toulouse, Carcassonne and other towns of Southern France, and later farther north in Paris, Sens, Évreux and Troyes. The head of the school in Troyes was the famous Talmudist Rabbi Solomon ben Isaac (Rashi). According to a number of medical historians, one of the pupils of Rabbi Abbon of Narbonne moved to Montpellier to teach medicine at a school which he set up, in which case an anonymous Talmudist would have been one of the founders of the famous Montpellier Medical School (*c.* 1021). Other Jewish and non-Jewish (Moslem?) scientists are said to have joined him there, to teach in Hebrew, Arabic and Latin, and later in Provençal. When, on the occasion of the celebration of the seventh centenary of the official foundation of the

Montpellier Medical School, a number of scholars discussed the delicate question of its origins, Father Vires had this to say:

During the ninth century, rabbinical schools of medicine were founded at Lunel, Narbonne, Béziers, Arles and Nîmes, in the Lower Languedoc province. In about 1020–1030, Jewish and Arabic disciples of Avicenna brought with them the teachings of Arabic science, which was steeped in Greek medical thought. At that time, Salerno in Italy was at the peak of its fame, and Christian students from Montpellier travelled there at the end of the eleventh century in order to complete their locally acquired knowledge. They returned home as 'Salernians' to teach the medicine they had learned abroad. Montpellier therefore benefited from at least two groups of medical schools: the Judaeo-Arabic masters, and the Christian masters, *i.e.* the Salernians.

Father Forgues added:

What seems most probable is that, in the twelfth century, our school in Montpellier was a medico-surgical centre built largely with the help of Jewish and Arabic elements. In fact, the part played by Arabic and Jewish physicians during the first beginnings of our school is one of the most remarkable chapters in the history of a university which claims that the Roman Catholic Church was its godmother in 1220. The reason is that during the tenth, eleventh and twelfth centuries the Arabs and the Jews had become the sole repositories of medical knowledge; Moslem medical schools were flourishing in Spain and in Asia alike. . . . Moreover, Moslems, Christians and Jews who had fled from Spain to settle in the Languedoc were indispensable intermediaries, brilliant purveyors of thought and of merchandise, importers and translators of the main works of the Spanish Arabs into Hebrew; whence the language of the students returning from Montpellier became charged with 'barbarous words', according to Bishop Salisbury of Chartres.

Another remarkable fact was the degree of liberty, almost of anarchy, which marked the beginnings of our first schools at Montpellier and which was expressed officially in the famous edict of William VIII (dated January 1181) abolishing all restrictions and distinctions, and promising full liberty of teaching and medical practice. 'Come who may, of whatever country or of whatever faith, may teach in the seignorial town of William.' Teachers and practitioners alike were judged by their work alone, and by no other standards.

The role of Jewish scientists in founding the Montpellier School was also emphasized by Jean Astruc (eighteenth century):

We have seen that, in 1180, William, the son of Matilda, promised full liberty to all without exception to profess medicine. Since many Jews

39 Christ healing dropsy and leprosy

40 The sciences of the *quadrivium*

taught at Montpellier, it would appear that they took full advantage of William's promise. It must also be admitted quite frankly that it is to them that the Faculty of Montpellier owed much of its original reputation, because in the tenth, eleventh and twelfth centuries the Jews were the almost exclusive repositories of medical knowledge in Europe, and it is through them that knowledge was communicated from the Arabs to the Christians.

From Montpellier, we pass on to Avignon, where Jewish scientists played an equally prominent role. According to Victorin Laval, one of the foremost historians of the Avignon School of Medicine:

From all we have said, it is clear that it was from such various centres as Salerno, from Jewish schools at the coast, and from Montpellier, that Jewish scientists came also to Avignon bringing with them the medical knowledge of the Arabs. In the twelfth century, Jews had settled there in large enough number to form a community which the Emperor Frederick placed under the protection of the Bishop, by special diploma, in 1178. This influence continued apace, particularly when, persecuted by Philip the Fair, the Jews were forced to leave Languedoc and to emigrate to Avignon, a hospitable country where the good-will of the Popes ensured them of relative liberty and of effective protection. The Jews came to Avignon not so much to carry on trade, to open banks, to manufacture cloth, to rent state property, or to be the kings' brokers and financiers, as to practise medicine, in which they greatly excelled over Christians. They were even called to Avignon for that very purpose, for we know that when Alphonse of Poitiers fell ill at Avignon he summoned a Jewish ophthalmologist from Spain. Again, Nostradamus tells us (*Histoire de la Provence*, p. 427) that Jeanne de Navarre charged the Jew Baruch Akhin of Arles to restore her to health, and finally even Pope Benedict XIII appointed a converted Jew, Josué Halorqui who later became the papal nuncio to Spain under the name of Jerome de Sainte-Foy.

S. Bayle has shown that in the fourteenth and fifteenth centuries medicine in Avignon was almost entirely in the hands of the Jews.

The fact that a great number of Jewish physicians practised in France is borne out by Wickersheimer's *Dictionnaire biographique des médecins de France*, by notarial entries and other documents of the time; Louis the Pious, Charles the Bald, Hugh Capet, René the Good, and many other French kings and nobles were in the habit of consulting them. Many Jewish physicians in France also became distinguished as original authors or translators; among these the Tibbonid family must take pride of place.

The first of the Tibbonids to settle in Provence was Samuel ben Judah ibn Tibbon, famous for his translations of the works of

Maïmonides. The work was continued by his son, Moses ibn Tibbon, who translated Maïmonides' *On Poisons, On Haemorrhoids, On Sexual Intercourse* and *On Diet*. The last and also the most illustrious Tibbonid was Jacob ben Maḥir ibn Tibbon, Dean of the Faculty of Medicine of Montpellier (*c.* 1300), who was an astronomer of renown cited by Copernicus, Reinhold and Clavius.

Other famous Jewish translators were Shem-tov ben Isaac, who translated Aristotle, Averroës, Abulcasis and Rhazes; Moses of Narbonne (Maistre Vidal), who wrote his medical aphorisms *Derek Chayim* ('The Path of Life') in verse; and Rabbi Gerson ben Hezekiah, who wrote a medical treatise, the *Sepher af Hakmati* ('Book of my Wisdom'), also in verse.

CONCLUSION

Our brief survey has shown us that Jewish scholars pursued all branches of medieval science undaunted by frequent legal discriminations against them. In mathematics and astronomy they wrote original works, commentaries and translations, and invented instruments used to great advantage by the discoverers of the New World and other fifteenth-century voyagers. In the natural sciences their lexicographic works did much to identify and classify a host of animals and plants. In pharmacology, they excelled both by their original writings and also by their translations. In medicine, they helped to establish and to develop the medical schools of Salerno, Montpellier and Avignon, and bestowed the benefits of their art on the small and the great of the land alike. Kings, Sultans, Princes, Popes and other dignitaries of the Church often consulted them and heaped honours and privileges upon them. Beyond that, they were the authors of many original works, commentaries and translations. We may take it that it is largely because of Jewish translators that Greco-Roman science reached the Arab world. The Jews are therefore rightly held to have been the main scientific links between West and East.

BIBLIOGRAPHY

G. SARTON, *Introduction to the History of Science*, 3 vols. in 5 parts, Baltimore, 1927–48.

Universal Jewish Encyclopaedia, 10 vols., New York, 1939–48.

C. ROTH, *The Jewish Contribution to Civilisation*, London, 1938.

M. STEINSCHNEIDER, *Hebraïsche Übersetzungen des Mittelalters und die Juden als Dolmetscher*, Berlin, 1893.

E. R. BEVAN and C. SINGER, *The Legacy of Israel*, London, 1927.

W. M. FELDMANN, *Rabbinical mathematics and astronomy*, London, 1931.

M. STEINSCHNEIDER, *Die Jüdischen Mathematiker und die Jüdischen anonymen mathematischen Schriften*, Frankfort, 1901.

H. FRIEDENWALD, *The Jews and Medicine*, Baltimore, 1944; *Jewish Luminaries in Medical History*, Baltimore, 1946.

S. R. KAGAN, *Jewish Medicine*, Boston, 1952.

J. PREUSS, *Biblisch-Talmudische Medizin*, Berlin, 1911.

CHAPTER 7

Medieval Science in the Christian West

MEDIEVAL CHRISTIANITY and scientific progress strike the layman as two incompatible ideas. Most people believe that the 'Greek miracle' was completely forgotten during the Middle Ages, to be resuscitated during the Renaissance as a relic from the past. This false belief springs from an unwarranted comparison of science with literature. While poetry loses much of its savour when, as did happen, it is accessible only in translation, scientific texts do not suffer irretrievably in that way. Through the Arabs (and also through direct translations) Greek ideas were therefore within the grasp of scholars, and so were many Indian, Persian and Moslem concepts. Nor is there any reason to hold that the erudite concerns of the humanists were *a priori* more seminal than the theological pre-occupations of the scholastics; the greatest scholars of the sixteenth century were often 'unlettered' men, and, in any case, the real scientific revolution had to await the dawn of the seventeenth century.

*   *   *

The term 'Middle Ages' is very confusing, for it is a collective name covering four clearly distinct periods. The first medieval period extends from the close of classic times until the beginning of the eleventh century, and is generally called the Dark Ages. It was a time of economic recession, of political disorder and barbaric customs, to which the so-called Carolingian Renaissance brought no more than a slight amelioration.

In the eleventh and twelfth centuries Europe suddenly woke up from its nightmare. There was a tremendous shift of populations, leading to the clearing of new land, the growth of towns, the establishment of monastic orders, the Crusades, and the building of more spacious churches. Prices soared, money circulated more freely and, as the ruling monarchs managed to suppress the worst excesses of their feudal barons, commerce revived and led to international contact through which the West was made familiar with—among other things—the corpus of Arabic science.

468

The thirteenth century was the peak of the Middle Ages. It saw the quick rise of the great universities and of such brilliant scholars as Albert the Great, St. Thomas Aquinas and Roger Bacon.

The fourteenth century followed in the intellectual wake of the thirteenth, much as the eighteenth was later to follow the seventeenth. The bourgeoisie came to power, and a secular—though not anti-clerical—approach made itself felt in literature. Law and authority, including even that of the Pope, no longer commanded blind respect. Then came the 1320's, with their bad harvests, and the beginning of the Hundred Years War. The first bank-collapse with international ramifications occurred in 1345, and the Great Plague of 1347–48 decimated Europe and depopulated the monasteries. These disasters went hand in hand with an intellectual attack on the classic ideals of the preceding century, and with the adoption by the masses of the most absurd mystical and superstitious beliefs.

During the late Middle Ages (1350–1450) the economy and the population figures suffered serious setbacks. While the universities were as good as dead, science survived by trying to apply itself to the solution of practical problems (accountancy, medicine, voyages of discovery).

The Middle Ages can therefore be divided into:

(1) The Dark Ages (from the fifth to the tenth centuries).

(2) The awakening of Europe and the introduction of Moslem ideas (eleventh to twelfth centuries).

(3) The emergence of the universities and the golden age of 'scholastic' science (thirteenth century and beginning of fourteenth century).

(4) The decline of the universities and the transformation of science into technology (1350–1450).

THE DARK AGES AND THE
REMNANTS OF CLASSICAL SCIENCE

THE INVASIONS

The Middle Ages began with the invasion of the Roman Empire by the Germans, themselves harried by the Slavs, who in turn were being driven out by the Huns. Scholars are still arguing at length whether Rome was destroyed from without, or whether—consumed by an economic, social and moral cancer—she was ready to submit to the first invader. In science, there is no doubt that the decline of classical pursuits was the result of purely internal causes, namely the complete subordination of disinterested research to utilitarian objectives and the introduction of mystical, magical and Neo-Platonic notions.

Neither Christianity nor the Barbarians can therefore be considered the chief causes of the collapse of ancient science.

However, Odoacer's overthrow of the last of the Western Emperors (476) nevertheless had marked effects on scientific pursuits. The Roman Empire was split up, Latin was vulgarized through the introduction of German idioms, general insecurity led to the increasing neglect of literature, and even handwriting degenerated into an illegible script, particularly in Gaul.

THE FOUNDERS

Even so, a few men charged themselves with the onerous task of saving and transmitting the heritage of antiquity. Thus Boëtius (d. 524), who wrote manuals on arithmetic, music, geometry and astronomy, translations of Aristotelian works on logic, and the famous *Philosophical Consolations*, was not only the 'last of the Romans' but also the founder of medieval thought, second in importance only to St. Augustine. His pupil Cassiodorus, in addition to charging his monks with the copying of ancient manuscripts, wrote the famous *Institutions*, which, despite their many shortcomings, were a fairly good bibliographical introduction to the study of science. According to Martianus Capella, Cassiodorus was the first to divide the liberal arts into the *trivium* (logic, grammar, dialectics) and the *quadrivium* (arithmetic, geometry, music and astronomy).

His ideas were taken up and developed in a gigantic compilation, the *Etymologies* of Isidore, Bishop of Seville (*c.* 600), which, in the course of what were often spurious philological explanations, 'summed up' the contents of the liberal arts, geography, natural science, agriculture and technology. In the absence of any other source, medieval authors were often thrown back on this work.

Another systematic attempt to salvage classical ideas was made by the Venerable Bede (d. 735). Steeped in Pliny and Isidore, he was a lover of science and a specialist on computation and arithmetic (he assured the triumph of the method of reckoning years with a reference to the Christian era, introduced *c.* 525 by Dionysius Exiguus, and his *Loquela per gestum digitorum* became the basis of medieval finger-reckoning). He also studied the relationship between the tides and the motion of the moon, winds, solstices and equinoxes, and noted that the tides vary from one point of the English coast to the next.

THE SO-CALLED CAROLINGIAN RENAISSANCE

Though the moral and political repercussions of the accession of the Carolingian dynasty and the restoration of the Western Empire (800) may not have had marked effects on medieval living conditions or on the arrogance of the feudal barons, it has been argued that the literary revival encouraged by Charlemagne had direct repercussions on the development of science.

Charlemagne appreciated that it was impossible to establish the City of God on earth with a largely illiterate clergy, and his capitularium of 789 made provisions for opening schools in which the psalter, solfeggio, the chant, and the principles of ecclesiastic computation and grammar could be taught. At the same time, Alcuin was charged with the educational reorganization of the empire, and the famous Palatine school was founded.

Like its great successor, the little ninth-century Renaissance produced marked educational advances, including the adoption of a very small and very legible script and the restoration of good Latin. In the purely scientific field, however, little if any progress was made.

Alcuin's *Propositiones ad acuendos juvenes* was no more than a collection of entertaining parlour games (*e.g.* the problem of how three jealous and amorous couples could cross a river in a boat holding only two people). His disciple, Hrabanus Maurus (776–856), simply plagiarized the scientific writings of Isidore of Seville, adding some superficial ideas on the atomic hypothesis of Lucretius.

The Irish astronomer Dicuil wrote the *De Mensura Orbis Terrae* in 825, which repeated current travellers' tales. The only descriptions of any interest in it dealt with Egypt and the Northern Isles (probably Iceland and the Faroes).

JOHANNES SCOTUS ERIGENA

Another Irishman, Johannes Scotus Erigena, who was head of the court school of Charles the Bald from *c.* 843, was one of the most impressive personages of the entire Carolingian period. His fame rests mainly on his knowledge of Greek which, though poor, was exceptionally good for his time, and enabled him to produce Latin translations of the works of the Pseudo-Dionysios, manuscripts of which Michael II had sent to Louis the Pious in 827. It was from these manuscripts that he purloined the basic ideas of his *De Divisione Naturae*, a work which even his contemporaries found suspect, and which the Church condemned officially three and a half centuries later. The *De Divisione Naturae* interests the historian of science not so much for its general Neo-Platonic concepts as for its astronomical doctrine.

In the ninth century, Heraclides' planetary system, in which Venus and Mercury revolved about the sun, was generally known through Martianus Capella's *De Nuptiis*, through Chalcidius' commentary on the *Timaeos*, and, to a lesser extent, through Macrobios' meditations on Cicero's *Dream of Scipio*. Johannes Scotus Erigena extended this system to Mars and Jupiter.

'As for the planets which revolve about the sun,' he wrote, 'they assume different colours according to the quality of the regions which they cross: I am referring to Jupiter and Mars, Venus and Mercury, which ceaselessly circle the sun as Plato (read Chalcidius) has taught in the Timaeos. When the planets are above the sun, they show us their clear face, but they look red whenever they are below it.'

It would be a mistake, however, to look upon this system as an advance on earlier ideas. In fact, those medieval astronomers who adopted it were the most backward of all. Moreover, Erigena believed that the distance of the earth from the moon was equal to the earth's diameter, which he calculated by halving Eratosthenes' terrestrial circumference.

* * *

In conclusion, we may say that the Carolingian Renaissance did little to further the study of the *quadrivium*, which henceforth was to be governed by Neo-Platonic notions cruder even than those of Boëtius or Capella. As a result, much attention was paid to the interpretation of sacred texts by number-symbolism, to simple proportions as the explanation of the combination of the elements, and to the relationship between stellar distances and musical intervals.

On the other hand, the appearance of new schools and scriptoria saved the last remnants of ancient culture from utter destruction, at the very time when the Norman invasion was breaking up the Carolingian Empire.

WESTERN CONTACTS WITH MOSLEM SCIENCE

Gerbert and the School of Salerno

But what learning the Carolingian clerks managed to save from the shipwreck of their empire is insignificant in comparison with the great Hellenic and, to a lesser extent, Indian heritage of the Moslems. Many historians refuse to admit that between the battle of Poitiers (732) and the end of the tenth century—the time of the Carolingian revival—science stood absolutely still. They stress the importance of the contacts between the Caliph of Baghdad and Charlemagne, the missions sent to Cordova by Charles the Bald (864) and by Otto I, and speak of the influence of Moslem art and of the role of the Transpyrenean Jews, whose insolence Agobard had resented so strongly.

GERBERT

There have been, above all, many discussions about the authenticity and originality of the work of Gerbert whom, short of convincing evidence to the contrary, we must consider as the first great scientist to have introduced Arabic numerals and the astrolabe into Europe.

Gerbert was born between 940 and 945, served as a monk in Aurillac and was a teacher at the school of Rheims (972–982) before being appointed Abbot of Bobbio (982). He intrigued against Otto I and helped Hugh Capet to usurp the throne. He was made Archbishop of Rheims, then of Ravenna, and in 999 was elected Pope (Sylvester II). He died on May 12th, 1003, after he had laid the plans for a crusade.

The most important part of his life, however, was his stay in Spain (967–970) under Atto, Bishop of Vich. There is no need to assume that he must have gone to Cordova to become acquainted with Arabic science, since the teaching in the Catalan monastery of Santa Maria de Ripoll was based on a fusion of Arabic ideas with those of Isidore of Seville. From Vich, he wrote to his friend Lupitus (Llobet) of Barcelona asking for a treatise on astrology (possibly to explain the use of the astrolabe), and as late as 984 he asked Bishop Miro of Gerona to send him the *De Multiplicatione et Divisione Numerorum* of one Joseph Hispanus.

Gerbert's mathematical works, which were carefully edited by Bubnow, raise very complex questions, if only because the origin of the so-called Arabic numerals has remained the subject of heated controversies.

'ARABIC' NUMERALS

We, for our part, agree with Smith and Karpinski that our numerals are of Indian origin, and were transmitted to the West by the Arabs. They were first used in Europe in conjunction with the abacus, a table on which numerals assume different values according to their position in different columns. This device was completely different from the Roman abacus, and references to it in Boëtius' apocryphal *Geometria* must have been added at a much later date. Calculations on the abacus were made with buttons, or 'apices', on which the numbers 1–9 were expressed either by the first letters of the Greek alphabet or by symbols representing the words:

> *igin* (1), *andras* (2), *ormis* (3), *arbas* (4), *quimas* (5),
> *caletis* (6), *zenis* (7), *temenias* (8), *celentis* (9).

Palaeographic studies suggest that this new method of calculation was spread to the West not so much by written texts, as was formerly believed, as by oral teaching. Novices would carry their own apices, and have their operations checked by itinerant masters.

According to William of Malmesbury, Gerbert was the first to 'take the abacus from the Saracens and to formulate rules which

DIFFERENCE: $100 - 87 = 13$

DIVISOR: 87

DIVIDEND: 4019

$$\frac{4000}{100} = 40;\ 40 \times 13 = 520$$

Discard the 4 in 4000; $19 + 520 = 539$

$$\frac{500}{100} = 5;\ 5 \times 13 = 65$$

Discard the 5 in 500; $39 + 65 = 104$

$$\frac{100}{100} = 1;\ 13 \times 1 = 13$$

Discard the 1 in 100; thus $13 + 4 = 17$

PARTIAL QUOTIENTS: $40 + 5 + 1$

RESULT: 46

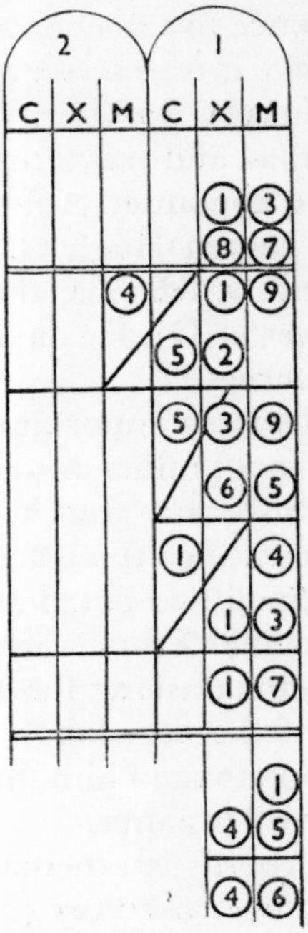

fig. 39 Division by Gerbert's abacus method.

abacists have to learn by the sweat of their brow'. Bernelinus, Hériger and Adalbold continued Gerbert's work.

The new arithmetic failed to reach more than a small select circle —its multiplication and division tables were so difficult that people preferred the 'difference' method illustrated in *fig. 39*.

Sometimes a blank button, called *sepos* (ψῆφος, tally), *cifra* (*al-sifr* = void) or zero (cypher), would be placed in an empty column. Gradually Europeans, like the Arabs, began to trace figures in the sand or dust and stopped engraving them on small buttons; the abacus made way for the algorithm. Compared with the complications of Greek logistics, these new arithmetical procedures were extremely simple and their introduction represents one of the greatest contributions of the Middle Ages to the progress of Western science.

THE ASTROLABE

At the same time as the abacus, and perhaps by the same path, the astrolabe made its first appearance in the Latin world.

This instrument consisted of projections on the equatorial plane of a celestial and a terrestrial sphere, and on it were marked the horizon and the latitude of the place where the astrolabe was used. The two discs (the spider and the tympanum) were fixed on a common pivot representing the axis of the world, so that the spider (the celestial map) could be turned to show, at any instant, the position of any point in the sky with respect to the observer. In this way, astronomical or astrological predictions, the daylight position of the stars, the risings and settings of the sun over a given town, or at a given period of the year, *etc.*, could be checked at a glance. But even when the astrolabe was combined with an alidade and a graduated circle, it was very rarely used for purely observational purposes.

First discovered in Catalonia by Gerbert (perhaps after reading a letter from Llobet of Barcelona), the astrolabe was popularized by the Benedictine abbot Herman the Lame of Reichenau.

During Gerbert's lifetime there was therefore a clear revival of interest in the *quadrivium*, which is also borne out by the most original works of St. Abbo of Fleury on arithmetic, the exchange of rather mediocre letters on mathematics between the schoolmen Ragimbold of Cologne and Radolf of Liège (*c.* 1025), the popular interest in *rithmomachy* (a kind of board-game in which odd numbers were played off against even numbers), and the many compilations of the works of the Roman agrimensors. With the encouragement of Bishop Fulbert this trend was pursued at the School of Chartres, whence it reached Oxford in the thirteenth century.

MEDICINE

The Barbarian laws and the Carolingian capitularies mention the existence of lay medical practitioners who taught their pupils by word of mouth what empirical knowledge they had acquired. Meanwhile, the Benedictine monasteries, as dispensers of Christian charity, built infirmaries set in beautiful gardens and preserved what ancient medical writings they could (Pliny, Caelius Aurelianus, Celsus, fragments of the Hippocratic *corpus*, of the writings of Galen and Dioscorides, and even some fragments of Paulos Aegineta and of Alexander of Tralles). Very often (at Monte Cassino, for instance) patients were given medical consultations while undergoing miraculous cures wrought by the holy relics.

The *Leech Book* of Bald is a good example of this mixture of ancient, Christian, and popular beliefs. Its cure for snake-bite, for instance, was a snake soaked in holy water.

THE SCHOOL OF SALERNO

Though scholars agreed that the School of Salerno had an appreciable influence on the subsequent development of science and of medicine, in particular, and though its doctrines were expounded in many extant texts, there is some doubt about its real history, especially since the most important documents (such as the *Antidotary* and the *Regimen*) have been radically altered over the years, so that their contents cannot always be attributed to their alleged authors. Though many have praised its secular character, the School seems to have had close links with Monte Cassino. Hence its true origins may well go back to the convalescent homes which the powerful Benedictine abbots had set up all round the enchanting bay, formerly a favourite watering place of the Romans.

The founders of the School are said to have been Salernus who taught in Latin, Pontos who taught in Greek, Adela who taught in Arabic, and Helinus who taught in Hebrew. While we need not give too much credence to the details of this legend, it does show to what extent Salerno was the meeting-place of Latin, Byzantine, Greek and Moslem ideas imported from nearby Sicily. A typical representative of the School was the Jew Donnolo of Otranto (Shabbethai ben Abraham ben Joel, 913–982), who was captured by the Saracens and taken to Palermo, and later wrote an antidotary in Hebrew.

However, the first teachers wrote manuals based on purely Greek or Latin ideas, and modern scholars have been unable to detect any Moslem influences in, for instance, the *Passionarius* of Gariopontus, the *Practica* of Petroncello, or Alphanus' translations of Nemesios of Emesa, let alone in the *Obstetrics* attributed to a woman-physician called Trotula.

CONSTANTINE THE AFRICAN

Constantine the African, a converted merchant from Carthage, is said to have collected manuscripts in Africa for the Salernian school, but to have lost a number of them when he suffered shipwreck. He became a monk in Monte Cassino, where he published all his works and died in 1087. Many of his writings were translations of unacknowledged Arabic sources. Since he was unfamiliar with the niceties of Latin grammar, his translations were crude, confusing and often completely wrong. Among the most important were the *Pantegni* of 'Aly ibn 'Abbās, the *Viaticus* of al-Ashaafar, the *Melancholy* of Ishāq ibn Imram, and a number of Galen's and Hippocrates' writings.

LATER HISTORY OF SALERNO

The School of Salerno was not organized as a university until fairly late in its history. Important advances were recorded in the twelfth century: better knowledge of anatomy, thanks to the methodical dissection of pigs (animals considered to be closest to man organically); the revival of surgery under Roger of Frugardo, who (*c.* 1170) gave sound advice on trepanation, cranial fractures, malignant tumours of the womb and the rectum, and, above all, on abdominal injuries (he mentioned a number of precautions that must be taken before placing cold intestines back into the abdominal cavity). According to R. J. Forbes, the Salernians were also the first to distil alcohol from grapes; the appearance of this new solvent (unknown to the Alexandrians and to the Arabs) had a profound effect on the manufacture of medicines and perfumes.

The Twelfth Century: the Age of the Great Translations

While Southern Italy continued to play its important part in teaching the rudiments of science, twelfth-century Spain, with such great scholars as Abubacer, Averroës and Maïmonides, became the great cultural centre of the time. Monks from all over Europe (including Italy) came to study the elements of Hellenic science from Arabic masters. Two of the pioneers of the twelfth-century scientific revival were Adelard of Bath and Constantine the African.

ADELARD OF BATH

Born in Bath *c.* 1170, Adelard studied at Tours, taught at Laon, and then visited Salerno, Sicily and Palestine. While his treatises on the abacus and the astrolabe make him one of Gerbert's successors, his translations of Euclid's *Elements* and of al-Khwārizmī's astronomical and trigonometrical writings make him a forerunner of the School of Toledo. His revised *Mappae Clavicula*, to which he added eighty-four original recipes, was a medieval masterpiece on the preparation of colours. His *Questiones Naturales*, a most important scientific work, preceded his great translations and hence lacks the breadth of his later knowledge. Written in the form of a dialogue between Adelard himself, a lover of Arabic science, and his young nephew, the product of the Christian school (*i.e.* an exponent of the prevailing Neo-Platonic views), the book first discussed questions of biology, ranging from plants to the human soul. It went on to consider hydrography, meteorology and astronomy. Though Adelard never came out frankly against Neo-Platonism, except to propound a superficial atomism, he strongly advocated the study of natural science. 'If it is the Creator's wish that plants spring from the earth, this process is not without a natural reason too.' Occasionally he would go much further than that:

What I myself have learned from the Arabic masters through reason is quite other than what you, seduced by a mask of authority, have allowed to ensnare you as in a halter. For what name fits authority better than that of halter? You allow yourself to be led by authority like a beast that knows not whither or why it is being driven.

THE CRUSADES

Stephen of Pisa, who gave a much better translation of 'Aly ibn 'Abbās' *Liber regalis* than Constantine the African's and who wrote a Greek-Arabic-Latin glossary to Dioscorides' *Materia Medica*, is, together with Adelard, almost our only source of information about the Crusades which, from 1095 to 1270, took so many Christian knights towards the East.

Because of their social origin, the Crusades had few repercussions on European intellectual life other than on military science (Greek fire) and on falconry (the hood supplanted the old method of lifting the bird's lower eyelid with a thread).

HELLENISM

Meanwhile, knowledge of Greek ideas spread, not only because of the interest in Hellenism shown by the monks of St. Denis, but also as a result of twelfth-century contacts between Italy and Byzantium. In 1136, for instance, John II Comnenos was asked to settle a dispute between champions of the Roman and the Orthodox Churches. James of Venice translated Aristotle's writings on logic directly from the Greek, and Burgundio of Pisa similarly translated Hippocrates, Galen, John of Damascus and an anonymous treatise on viniculture. Leo Tuscus gave the West the Byzantine version of Ahmed ibn Sirin's *Oneiromancy*. In Sicily, the home of the illustrious geographer al-Idrīsī, Aristippus of Catania produced an excellent version of Aristotle's *Meteors*, Book IV, and made personal observations of the eruptions of Etna (1157–58). Eugene of Palermo, who was perfect in Greek, Arabic and Latin, translated Ptolemy's *Almagest* and *Optics*.

Unfortunately the failure of the fourth Crusade, the pillage of Constantinople and the appearance of the Eastern Latin Empire (1204–61) were disastrous to this pre-humanism, of which the only great thirteenth-century representative was William of Moerbeke.

TRANSLATIONS IN SPAIN

Modern students, who are so much more familiar with Greek than with Arabic, are always astonished when they learn of the circuitous path by which ancient ideas reached the West. This strange route arose because, while Byzantium became lost in the subtleties of captious theological discussions, the Moslems alone forged ahead in the pursuit of knowledge.

Most twelfth-century translations were not the result of good dictionaries but of the collaboration of two people—often a Jew who translated from the Arabic into some common language and a Christian who produced the final, Latin version. Most of this work was done in Spain, where the division between the Moorish and Catholic kingdoms was not so strict as to exclude common contacts. In fact, from Gerbert onward, the Iberian peninsula was the main bridge between East and West.

PETER ALFONSO

Petrus Alphonsus, a Spanish Jew originally named Moses Sephardi, was born in 1062, at Huexa, Aragon. He became physician to Alfonso VI, King of Castile, and for a time to Henry I of England. He taught Walcher, prior of Malvern, the Arabic methods of predicting the orbits of the sun and the moon and the trepidation of the equinoxes (precession of eight degrees in 900 years and equal retrogradation during the next 900 years). In 1115, Peter Alfonso wrote an important treatise on al-Khwārizmī's Tables, which was used by Adelard of Bath. Finally, in his famous *Disciplina Clericalis*, he challenged the classification of the liberal arts and substituted a system in which the exact sciences figured more largely than before: (1) Logic, (2) Arithmetic, (3) Geometry, (4) Medicine (previously omitted), (5) Music, (6) Astronomy, (7) Philosophy and Grammar.

SAVASORDA

Another great Catalonian scholar, Abraham bar Ḥiyya of Barcelona, better known as Savasorda (chief of police) was the author of an important Hebrew work, whose purpose it was to acquaint the Jewish community of Southern France with the results of Arabic science. Together with Plato of Tivoli (1134–45) he introduced the West to Ptolemy's *Quadripartitum*, Theodosios' *Spherics* and al-Battānī's *De Motu Stellaris* (in which Regiomontanus later wrote a commentary). But the most fruitful result of the collaboration between these two scholars was Plato's Latin version (1145) of Savasorda's own Hebrew book, the *Liber Embadorum*. This was the first work in Latin to deal with quadratic equations and was one of the main mathematical source-books of Leonardo of Pisa. The book itself was written as a manual on surveying techniques and, while it dealt mainly with measurements of areas, it included Heron's formula expressing the area of a triangle (A) as a function of its three sides (a, b, c) and of s, where $s = \frac{1}{2}(a+b+c)$, viz.:

$$A = \sqrt{[s(s-a)(s-b)(s-c)]}.$$

Savasorda's approximate solutions included

$$\tfrac{13}{15} \text{ for } \sqrt{\tfrac{2}{3}}, \text{ and } 3\tfrac{1}{7} \text{ for } \pi,$$

though he added that astronomers would do better to use

$$\pi = 3 + \frac{8\frac{1}{2}}{60} = 3.141\dot{6}.$$

A concrete example will best illustrate his mathematical approach. To find the base b and the height h of an isosceles triangle from its area A and its equal sides a, he proceeded as follows:

$$A = \frac{bh}{2} \qquad\qquad a^2 = h^2 + \frac{b^2}{4}$$

$$\left.\begin{array}{l} a^2 = h^2 + \dfrac{b^2}{4} \\[2ex] 2A = bh \end{array}\right\} a^2 - 2A = \left(h - \frac{b}{2}\right)^2 \left\{\begin{array}{l} \dfrac{\sqrt{(a^2 - 2A)}}{2} = \dfrac{h}{2} - \dfrac{b}{4} \qquad [1] \\[2ex] \dfrac{a^2 - 2A}{4} = \left(\dfrac{h}{2} - \dfrac{b}{4}\right)^2 \\[2ex] \qquad\qquad A = \dfrac{bh}{2} \end{array}\right\}$$

$$\frac{a^2 - 2A}{4} + A = \left(\frac{h}{2} - \frac{b}{4}\right)^2 + \frac{bh}{2}$$

$$\frac{a^2 + 2A}{4} = \left(\frac{h}{2} + \frac{b}{4}\right)^2$$

$$\frac{\sqrt{(a^2 + 2A)}}{2} = \frac{h}{2} + \frac{b}{4} \qquad\qquad [2]$$

Addition and subtraction of [1] and [2] gives

$$\left.\begin{array}{l} h \\[1ex] b \\[1ex] \frac{}{2} \end{array}\right\} = \frac{\sqrt{(a^2 + 2A)} \pm \sqrt{(a^2 - 2A)}}{2}$$

THE SCHOOL OF TOLEDO

When Toledo, reconquered in 1085, became the capital of Castile, Bishop Raymond (1126–52) encouraged the converted Jew, John of Luna, and the Archdeacon Domingo Gondisalvo to translate a number of important texts. (Gondisalvo apparently translated John's Spanish versions into Latin.) Their *Liber Algorismi de Numero Indorum* (from al-Khwārizmī) was the main reason why algorithms, requiring neither columns nor sand, gradually replaced Gerbert's abacus. Herman the Dalmatian translated Ptolemy's *Planisphere* (of which the original has been lost), and Robert of Chester translated the Koran and al-Khwārizmī's algebraical writings (1245).

Crowning them all was Gerard of Cremona (1114–87), who translated Ptolemy's *Almagest*, Archimedes' *De Mensura Circuli*, Apollonios' *Conics* (?),[1] Diocles' *De Speculis Comburentibus*, the first three books of

---

[1] Most medieval quotations from this text seem to be extracts from Alhazen's *Optics*.

41 Finger reckoning

42 Nicole Oresme with his armillary sphere

Aristotle's *Meteorologia*, his *De Coelo et Mundo*, *De Generatione et Corruptione* and *Physics*, Avicenna's *Canon*, and various texts of Hippocrates, Galen, al-Kindī, Thābit ibn Qurra, Razī and al-Fārābī. It is because of Gerard's work and his direction of a team of collaborators that we can speak of the 'School of Toledo'.

Arabic Influences in the Thirteenth Century

In the thirteenth century, the decline of Islam and the rise of Christianity in Spain altered the character of the two great centres of translation in Spain and Sicily. Purely passive absorption of Arabic culture was abandoned in favour of a measure of independent research, thanks above all to the encouragement of two enlightened monarchs, Frederick II and Alfonso X of Castile.

FREDERICK II

The Emperor Frederick II (1194–1250), though a pupil and protégé of Pope Innocent III, was anti-clerical, pleasure-seeking, tyrannical and sceptical, and hence resembled a sixteenth- rather than a thirteenth-century prince. He kept up a scientific correspondence with Oriental kings, to whom he posed geometrical, astronomical, optical and philosophic problems which even the cleverest men of his court were unable to solve. He is accused of having performed such inhuman experiments as placing a prisoner in a closed barrel in order to see whether his soul departed when he died, of raising up children in absolute silence to find out what language they would speak spontaneously, or again of disembowelling two men to discover the respective effects of sleep and movement on their alimentary canal.

But it is not so much to these reprehensible investigations as to his famous treatise on falconry that Frederick owes his scientific reputation, for this book was a quite original attempt to combine book-learning with personal observation. Though Frederick commissioned Michael Scot to translate Aristotle's *History of Animals*, so that he might study it for himself, he never surrendered his independence of judgment:

We do not follow the prince of philosophers in all respects. He rarely went out hunting with birds of prey; while we, for our part, have always loved and practised this art. . . . Aristotle repeats hearsay evidence, but certainty is never born out of gossip.

Apart from its illustrations of almost nine hundred different birds, Frederick's treatise contained interesting observations on the way in which the beaks of birds are adapted to their feeding habits, on the cavities in their bones, on flight, and on the way in which wild ducks manage to deceive their pursuers by feigning injury. He made personal experiments on the artificial incubation of eggs, investigated whether vultures found their food by sight or smell, and rejected many Aristotelian and popular beliefs, such as that the barnacle goose is hatched from barnacles which grow on trees.

Frederick's private menagerie held lions, leopards, monkeys, camels, elephants, and also a giraffe—the first of its kind to be shown in Europe.

In addition, Frederick II was a great patron of the arts and sciences. Peter of Eboli dedicated his poem *The Waters of Pozzuoli* to him; in 1227 Adam of Cremona presented him with a list of hygienic rules to be observed during the Crusade. His veterinarian, Jordon Ruffo, wrote the most popular of all medieval hippiatries, and Jacob Anatoli translated Ptolemy and Averroës at Frederick's behest.

MICHAEL SCOT

Frederick's court astrologer, the translator Michael Scot (d. 1235), brought with him from Toledo al-Biṭrūjī's astronomy, Aristotle's zoology and Averroës' commentary on the *De Coelo et Mundo*. Moreover, he supplied Frederick with a number of texts on the occult sciences and on physiognomy, 'to enable the King to put his trust in the right people'.

In this cosmopolitan court, one man stood out above all the others: Leonardo Fibonacci of Pisa, the greatest mathematician of the Middle Ages.

LEONARDO OF PISA

His father, Guglielmo Bonaccio, was employed in the customs office at Buglia, on the Barbary Coast, where Leonardo was brought into touch with the East in 1192, at the age of twelve years. He was taught arithmetic and Arabic by a local grocer, and later his business activities and his search for manuscripts took him to Egypt, Syria, Greece, and Sicily.

When he returned to Pisa in 1202, he wrote his *Liber Abaci* (which he revised in 1228). This work, which, despite its title, had no connection with Gerbert's ideas, was divided into fifteen parts: Indian numerals, simple multiplication, addition, subtraction, division, multiplication of fractions, other operations with fractions, calculation of prices, barter and discount, partition, partnerships and money, progressions and proportions, methods of false positions (simple and double), square roots and cubic roots, algebra and geometry.

We cannot go into the details of the work, and shall merely look at one of its more curious aspects, namely the resolution of fractions into unit parts. It was the use of this Egyptian method which led Leonardo to the study of continuous fractions, for example:

$$\frac{13}{20} = \frac{1}{20} + \frac{1}{10} + \frac{1}{2} = \frac{1+5}{2}^{\;1+\frac{1}{2}}$$

or more generally:

$$\frac{1 + \dfrac{1 + \dfrac{1}{a_3}}{a_2}}{a_1} = \frac{1}{a_1} + \frac{1}{a_1 \cdot a_2} + \frac{1}{a_1 \cdot a_2 \cdot a_3}$$

For calculating the number of offspring of two rabbits, **Leonardo** devised the 'Fibonacci series':

$$0 \quad 1 \quad 1 \quad 2 \quad 3 \quad 5 \quad 8 \quad 13 \quad 21 \quad \ldots$$

which is made up of the terms $u_0, u_1, u_2, \ldots u_{n-1}, u_n$, so that

$$u_n = u_{n-1} + u_{n-2} = \frac{1}{\sqrt{5}}\left[\left(\frac{1+\sqrt{5}}{2}\right)^n - \left(\frac{1-\sqrt{5}}{2}\right)^n\right]$$

The algebraic part of the *Liber Abaci* is based on Euclid's *Elements* (geometric representation of quantities) and on Savasorda's *Liber Embadorum* (solution of quadratic equations). The use of abbreviations of the words *radix*, *census* and *numerus* to designate an unknown root, its unknown square and an unknown number, was a vague pointer in the direction of Vieta's algebraic symbols (1593).

Leonardo's *Practica Geometriae* (1220) shows considerable influence by Heron's *Metrica*. In connection with the solution of surveying problems by a method of approximation, similar to Archimedes', it gives $\pi = 3.141818$.

The *Flos Leonardi* is an analysis of fifteen determinate and indeterminate linear and quadratic equations, two of which were challenged by John of Palermo in the presence of the Emperor (1225). Leonardo solved

$$x^3 + 2x^2 + 10x = 20$$

by putting (in sexagesimal notation):

$$x = 1 \quad 22^{\mathrm{I}} \quad 7^{\mathrm{II}} \quad 43^{\mathrm{III}} \quad 33^{\mathrm{IV}} \quad 4^{\mathrm{V}} \quad 40^{\mathrm{VI}}$$

though he failed to say why and how.

One of the most curious problems he set himself was to take two symmetrical triangles from an isosceles triangle of sides 10, 10, and 12, so as to make up an equilateral pentagon.

In his *Epistola* to Theodore, Frederick's astrologer, Leonardo solved the equation:

$$x+y+z+u = 24 = \tfrac{1}{5}x+\tfrac{1}{3}y+2z+3u$$

by the groups of solutions:

$$x = 10 \quad y = 6 \quad z = 4 \quad u = 4$$
and
$$x = 5 \quad y = 12 \quad z = 2 \quad u = 5$$

The *Liber Quadratorum* was the result of another mathematical challenge by John of Palermo, namely to find a square number which, increased or diminished by five, would still be a perfect square. Leonardo assumed that $x^2 \pm N$ cannot be square unless N is a congruent number of the type $N = ab(a+b)(a-b)$, in which a and b are prime to each other, and their sum $(a+b)$ is even. These congruent numbers are all multiples of $24 = 3(3+1)(3-1)$. The first congruent number whose fifth part is a perfect square is:

$$720 = 12 \times 12 \times 5$$
$$41^2 - 720 = 31^2$$
$$41^2 + 720 = 49^2$$

The solution of the problem is therefore $\left(\tfrac{41}{12}\right)^2$, since $\left(\tfrac{41}{12}\right)^2$ increased or diminished by 5 gives the squares

$$\left(\tfrac{49}{12}\right)^2 \text{ and } \left(\tfrac{31}{12}\right)^2.$$

Leonardo was clearly a most brilliant mathematician, whose work was inspired not only by Euclid, Heron, Savasorda and the Arabs, but also by Diophantos, then completely unknown in the West.

After the death of Frederick II, the Sicilian court under Manfred and Charles of Anjou continued to be receptive to eastern influences. Thus Herman the German, like Michael Scot before him, lived and worked alternately in Sicily and Toledo.

Alfonso X

Under Alfonso X (1252–84), the Castilian like the Sicilian capital before it became a centre of original research.

A poet, musician, jurist, historian, astronomer, and a deplorable politician withal, Alfonso el Sabio (the 'Learned'—not the 'Wise', as he is often wrongly called) dreamt of a Spanish encyclopaedia of all human knowledge, and particularly of astronomy and astrology.

During his reign the four following works were published. The *Libros del Saber de Astronomia* (1280) contained a description of the celestial spheres, a list of the known stars and their co-ordinates, and an account of the main instruments (notably the plane and spherical astrolabes, the quadrant, the *saphaea Arzachelis*, and mercury, water, and other clocks), Abenragel's *Libro de los Juicios de las Estrellas*, Oviedala's *Libro de las Cruces*, and the *Lapidario*. The last three expounded the most far-fetched astrological and occult notions.

The *Alfonsine Tables*, however, remained the most important astronomical tables right up to the sixteenth century. They were published in Spanish in 1252, but unfortunately the 'canons' alone have survived. The classical edition of Rico y Sinobas misleads the reader by claiming that it represents the original text when in fact it is no more than a poor Spanish version of a Portuguese translation of an Arabic almanac. The Latin version, whose author and date are unknown, also differs from the original Castilian canons. It would therefore be a mistake to exaggerate the personal contribution of the King in the attempt to reconcile Ptolemy's theory of the precession of the equinoxes with the purely Arabic theory of trepidation.

In fact, the Alfonsine Tables were nothing but improvements of Arzachel's Toledan Tables established two centuries earlier, for, once the dates are suitably converted, the two are based on the same notions—mean solar, lunar and planetary orbits and equations; declination of the sun; the direct or retrograde motion of planets; ascension, opposition and conjunction of the sun and moon; visibility of the moon and of eclipses; trigonometrical theory of sines and chords; geographical latitudes; declination of stars; determination of the time from the position of stars; annual cycles; determination of shadows, *etc*. Because they were written in Spanish, the Alfonsine Tables did not reach the outside world until very much later, so much so that they were unknown in Paris before 1296.

The main and consistent traits of Iberian science up to the thirteenth century were improvements of numerical tables for astrological purposes, a strong Judaeo-Arabic influence, persistent Neo-Platonic trends, the early use of Spanish in writing scientific works, relative independence from the main scholastic currents, and the subsidiary role of the universities. These had therefore to be discussed consecutively, but we must now return to the eleventh-century scientific contributions of the rest of Europe.

SCIENCE, SCHOLASTICISM, AND THE UNIVERSITIES

The Eleventh- and Twelfth-Century Beginnings

While contacts between Christianity and Islam led to fruitful developments in Spain, Western Europe kept to itself and produced the scholastics.

In the eleventh and twelfth centuries there was increasing interest in the systematic application of dialectics to matters divine and in the scientific topics arising therefrom.

The Problem of Universals
In the quarrel about universals the Neo-Platonic realists (*e.g.* St. Anselm, William of Champeaux and most members of the School of Chartres) opposed the nominalists, the disciples of Roscelin, who held that the Platonic *idea* was no more than a word. Thus Abélard, the unhappy lover of Héloïse, preferred the reality of *particulars*, which alone could be grasped by positive knowledge, to that of *universals*, which represented no objective existents. Unfortunately he left it at that, and hence failed to convince his colleagues of the value of natural studies.

The Platonist, on the other hand, by asserting that *ideas* are reflected in genera and species, of which they are the eternal models, and that singular objects are too changeable to merit the name of 'substances', diverted their adherents from real observations to a study of numerical 'problems' (such as the correspondence of the four elements with the four humours, the four cardinal points and the four seasons, or of the seven planets with the seven musical intervals, the seven days of the week and the seven metals). They justified their conclusions with astrological, alchemical and magical hypotheses, and encouraged their disciples to 'transcend' common sense by a show of mathematical 'brilliance'.

The School of Chartres
The history of Chartres, which was founded at the beginning of the eleventh century by one of Gerbert's pupils, Bishop Fulbert (d. 1028), illustrates the influence on medieval thought of the Greco-Arabic concepts introduced by Constantine the African, Adelard of Bath and Herman the Dalmatian. The School was an advocate of Progress.

'We are', wrote Bernard of Chartres, 'like dwarfs placed upon the shoulders of giants, who can see better and further than giants, not because our vision is more acute and our stature greater, but because we have raised ourselves above them.'

Gilbert de la Porrée (1076–1164) distinguished between earth, water, air and fire, which could be grasped with the senses, and the four *sincere substances* of the same name, which existed outside nature and never intermingled with it. This philosophical subtlety became the leading thought of all alchemical writings.

The 'Father of Latin Scholars', Theodoric of Chartres, to whom Herman the Dalmatian dedicated his translation of Ptolemy's

Planisphere, is famed for his rationalist and mechanist cosmology. His *Hexameron* attempted to effect a non-symbolic reconciliation between the Book of Genesis and physics. God created the four elements and arranged them in concentric spheres; fire, being the lightest, quite naturally came to lie above all the others, which it enveloped by following its prescribed circular path. Fire illuminates and heats, evaporating the waters and thus setting free islands and continents. When it condenses, water produces the stars, which, by emitting additional heat, make possible the appearance of life on earth.

The Thirteenth Century

At the beginning of the thirteenth century, three new factors came to affect the development of medieval science. These were the founding of the universities, the rediscovery of Aristotle and the educational concerns of the mendicant orders.

THE UNIVERSITIES
The emergence of the universities was a direct result of the relaxation of feudal laws, of the increase in population and of the growth of towns. When students and teachers had so increased in number as to join guilds and to obtain legal privileges, it was but a short step to forming organized institutes of higher learning. However, there were tremendous differences among the various universities of the different towns. The secular and democratic character of Bologna arose from her concentration on legal studies, and was the main reason for her subsequent pre-eminence in anatomy and surgery. Paris was the constant object of papal concern and became the theological and Dominican centre of Europe. Montpellier was more exposed to Jewish and Arabian influences than any other, and hence pursued medical studies more rationally than even Bologna. Oxford again, whose teachers were mainly Fransciscans, continued to adhere more closely to Augustinian Neo-Platonism, a philosophy that struck them as more compatible with Franciscan views than with Aristotelian.

FAITH AND REASON
Previously philosophy had had little difficulty in remaining the servant of Christianity. Things changed radically in the thirteenth century, when the works of Aristotle were first introduced into the University of Paris. The study of physics, astronomy and physiology was resumed with renewed vigour and the Aristotelian dialectic came to be considered tantamount to science and reason. Unfortunately, this admirable doctrine failed to place God in a sufficiently exalted place

and in many respects (eternity, astrological fatalism, unity of the active intellect) was in flagrant opposition to Christian teaching.

Inside the universities, the Faculty of Arts, receptive as it was to the new ideas, was at loggerheads with the Faculty of Theology, the guardian of orthodoxy. Theologians were responsible for banishing Aristotle's natural philosophy and all commentaries on it from the University of Paris (1210–15), and for discriminating against its adherents. Later, official action was concentrated on only its most radical exponents, the Averroists (1270–77).

A similar development took place in dogmatics. Alexander of Hales and St. Bonaventura were still steeped in pure Augustinianism, but Albert the Great, who was a confirmed Aristotelian, thought that science and theology should be taught side by side. St. Thomas Aquinas, on the other hand, held firmly that all truth was one. According to him, philosophers and theologians alike must strive to reach a common meeting-point, but whenever natural science and theology spoke with different voices, the former had to be dismissed as false. It was wise, however, to find out where science had erred, for, wherever possible, actual knowledge was preferable to blind faith.

Meanwhile new ideas kept reaching the universities by way of a growing number of translations. This trend culminated in what has been called the thirteenth-century 'encyclopaedic' movement.

THE ENCYCLOPAEDIAS
The writings of Cassiodorus, of Isidore, of the Venerable Bede, of Rhaban Maur, and of Honorius had all been of an encyclopaedic nature, though their main object had been to solve what elementary scientific problems were raised in the interpretation of scripture. Their writings were later supplemented with the fables of the various bestiaries (all based on the *Physiologus*) and the lapidaries, the most famous of which was that of Marbode, Bishop of Rennes (d. 1123). Averse to their predecessors' gullibility, twelfth- and thirteenth-century writers felt it was their main task to eliminate all allegorical and mystical fantasies and to concentrate on the observed facts. St. Hildegarde (1098–1179) had set a precedent when he dealt with earlier authorities in a cavalier manner (possibly because of his poor knowledge of Latin) and preferred to use his own eyes. His observations on mushrooms and on river fish were unusually accurate.

The *De Naturis Rerum* of Alexander Neckam (1157–1217), which seems to have been influenced by the Arabs, contains one of the oldest Western descriptions of the compass. Brunetto Latini's *Treasure* is of no more than philological interest and Bartholomew the Englishman's *De Proprietatibus Rerum*, written in about 1240, was, according to the author himself, addressed to only the simple and ignorant.

The Flemish Dominican Thomas of Cantimpré, on the other hand, wrote a far more important work, the *De Naturis Rerum* (1230–50), which examined man (I–III), quadrupeds (IV), birds (V), the sea (VI), fishes (VII), reptiles, worms, insects, some molluscs and frogs (VIII–IX), trees (X–XI), herbs (XII), springs (XIII), stones (XIV), metals (XV), air (XVI), cosmography and the seven planets (XVII), meteorology (XVIII) and the four elements (XIX).

After 1526, Thomas added a treatise on bees and a book on the beauty of the sky and the motions of the stars. Though not completely uninterested in Christian symbolism, he had the typically medieval urge to look for the practical (and particularly medical) usefulness of things. His most interesting observations, which were inspired by his reading of Aristotle, bore on comparative anatomy. He wondered whether human monsters were descended from Adam and marvelled that bipeds and quadrupeds had blood while animals with more than four legs did not. He observed that all animals except man could move their ears, that quadrupeds with horns lacked upper incisors, and that all but the lion and the hare closed their eyes during sleep. Clearly the systematic search for final causes, which was so often pernicious in other fields, could lead to fruitful results in biology.

ALBERT THE GREAT

Although he was not himself an encyclopaedist, Albertus Magnus (1206–80) nevertheless earned his title of *Doctor Universalis*. He devoured the writings of Greek and Arabic scientists with an insatiable appetite. A great admirer of Aristotle, and anxious to reconcile Aristotelian with Christian thought, he paved the way for his great pupil St. Thomas Aquinas. Even so, he was never a slavish follower of the Stagirite and hence differed from those fifteenth-century schoolmen whose unquestioning acceptance of Aristotle's teaching brought all knowledge to a standstill. Albert's travels brought him into contact with all sorts and conditions of men, and he joined immense erudition to a love for facts and to great common sense.

His *De Vegetabilibus aut Plantis* was a commentary on a pseudo-Aristotelian text, and attempted to classify the vegetable kingdom in the manner of Theophrastos into leafless, cortical, tunicated and herbaceous plants; winged, campanulate and star-shaped flowers; and dry or fleshy fruits. He also studied plant physiology—triple position of the embryo in the cotyledon, relationship between bunches and tendrils in the vine, the influence of light and of heat on plant growth, the distinction between thorns and prickles, the relationship between wild and domesticated plants, *etc.* His practical advice was generally sound (vinification, preservation of manure and prevention of erosion by afforestation).

The *De Animalibus* consists of twenty-six books. The first nineteen follow Aristotle (History: I–X, Parts: XI–XIV, Reproduction: XV–XIX); the next two contain original physiological observations; and the last five (XXII–XXVI) resemble the zoological books of Thomas of Cantimpré. Albert dissected the eye of the mole; investigated the central nervous system of the scorpion and the crayfish; observed that an ant whose antennae were amputated was unable to return to its ant-heap by itself; he watched spiders spinning their webs and compared the eggs of fishes with those of birds, discovering the allantois. He rejected a number of current myths, such as that the barnacle goose was the fruit of a tree, that the phoenix rose up from its ashes, that the beaver threw its testicles at its pursuers, and that the eagle ensured the hatching of its eggs by covering them with the skin of a wolf before warming them in the sun. He did not believe that human monsters were devils and held that variations were produced by environmental factors. He gave a very meticulous account of the fauna of Germany, including some animals now extinct, *e.g.* the European bison.

In metallurgy, he believed that pure metals could be engendered only by the sublimation of a humid and a dry principle.

In fact, in their original state, namely in the depths of the earth, the two principles are mixed with impurities and hence are bound to prevent the formation of pure metals. But the smoke which rises up from the metal heated in the bowels of the earth is purer and becomes concentrated either in the pores of rocks or in separate veins.

Albert's views on alchemy are difficult to define, since a number of astrological treatises attributed to him seem to be apocryphal.

He appears to have looked upon transmutations as simple 'tinctures' of lower metals, but apparently he did not question the basic principles of alchemy, and even defined its different techniques (sublimation, distillation, pulverization, pounding, cooking, fermentation, solution, decomposition, liquefaction and coagulation).

Despite his catholic interests, Albert the Great must be considered the greatest naturalist rather than the greatest encyclopaedist of the Middle Ages. The latter title must go to his contemporary, Vincent of Beauvais, who compiled an encyclopaedia, the *Speculum Maius*, which, though failing in its claim to 'reflect all things of all times', nevertheless summarized the scientific knowledge of his day and enables historians to isolate the original views of scholastic writers.

THE FRANCISCAN SCHOOL OF OXFORD: ROBERT GROSSETESTE

While it would be wrong to speak of the Parisian Dominicans as pure Aristotelians and natural philosophers, and of the English Franciscans as pure Augustinian Neo-Platonists and mathematicians, there is no doubt that Robert Grosseteste (1175–1253) continued in the Augustinian tradition of Chartres: 'The truth of things consists in their fitness and in their correspondence with the *verbum* which is their eternal expression.' Grosseteste showed that this correspondence was based on the *corporicity* of light, which was both the first corporeal form and, by its instantaneous propagation, also the cause of material dimensions in space. It followed that the universe must have originated in the sources of light and that optics was the fundamental science. All natural phenomena could be explained by straight lines, angles and simple geometric figures.

Grosseteste, as Bishop of Lincoln, was the first medieval writer to deal with the fundamental methodological problem of *error*. He demanded the rejection of all conclusions that were logically incompatible with premises based on previous demonstrations, new observations, or on original intuitions. In this respect, his work was principally negative. For instance, his proof that the tails of comets could not be due to the 'concentration of many rays' setting inflammable things on fire, nor to the fact that 'many things close together may seem to be continuous when seen from a distance', nor yet to 'distortion of shapes by the intervening medium', led him to conclude that comets must be 'fires purified of terrestrial nature and endowed with celestial nature, especially that of the seven planets'.

Similarly, having criticized Aristotle's and Seneca's ideas on the rainbow, he put forward an unsatisfactory theory of his own involving double refraction from pure air to the cloud, and again from the rarer part of the cloud to the lower and denser mist. He added that the line joining the sun to the centre of the rainbow always passes through the observer's eye. Similarly vague were his ideas about lenses (the angle of refraction was said to vary with the angle of incidence), about colours (whose brightness was said to be produced by the transparency of the medium and the luminosity and concentration of rays), and about the heat of the sun (which was said to be due to the motion of its rays).

Though the actual 'discoveries' of Grosseteste were therefore negligible, we must remember that without him there might never have been an Oxford School.

ROGER BACON

The most famous of Grosseteste's disciples, Roger Bacon, the '*Doctor mirabilis*', has often been called 'the Father of Experimental Science', possibly by confusion with his great sixteenth-century namesake, Francis Bacon. Roger, unlike Francis, was above all a theologian.

Even so, some of his prophetic utterances, when divorced from their context, have an astonishingly modern sound: 'Nature cannot be known without mathematics', or 'Reasoning does not make a conclusion certain, unless the mind discover it by the method of experience (*via experientiae*).'

The Church was to assist him by mobilizing experimental science in its fight against the infidels, encouraging such ventures as the construction of mechanically-propelled ships, self-driven chariots, flying machines, submarines, suspension bridges and telescopes.

While Bacon obliged by supplying the required 'visions', he failed to combine them with original research, unlike his great successor Leonardo da Vinci. Even so, he seems to have been one of the first medieval scholars to speak of gunpowder, and though he did not himself invent them, he studied the possible combinations of lenses and concave mirrors into 'microscopes' and 'telescopes'. He also used the camera obscura for observing eclipses of the sun.

However, he failed to make any important theoretical contributions and the superiority of his optics over Grosseteste's may be attributed to his having read the work of Alhazen. Thus, he explained that rainbows cannot occur unless the sun is more than 42° above the horizon, and he defended the view of Albert the Great that rainbows resulted from individual droplets of rain behaving like small spherical mirrors. On the other hand, unlike Grosseteste, he failed to appreciate the importance of refraction.

DEVELOPMENT OF OPTICS

Alhazen's optics were made known to the West simultaneously by John Peckham (Archbishop of Canterbury in 1279) and by the Polish physicist Witelo, who was more than a mere compiler, for he constructed parabolic mirrors and used an instrument of his own invention to measure the angles of refraction of various colours in various media.

Between 1300 and 1310, the German Dominican, Theodoric of Freiburg, carried out methodical experiments on the rainbow and came to the following conclusions:

(1) The inner bow is caused when rays entering a particular raindrop are reflected internally once and emerge at points determined by the laws of reflection and refraction.

(2) The different colours seen by an observer come from different raindrops.

(3) The outer bow is separated by an angle of 11 degrees from the inner bow and its colours appear in the reverse order because of a further reflection before the second refraction.

Though Theodoric committed a number of avoidable errors (he made the angle between the sun, the inner rainbow and the eye 22°

instead of 42°, and he failed to appreciate that the sun's rays are parallel), he was nevertheless one of the leading experimental scholars of the Middle Ages and, as such, a forerunner of Descartes, who was greatly influenced by him.

PETER PEREGRINE OF MARICOURT

'One man I know', Roger Bacon wrote, 'and only one, who can be praised for his achievements in this (practical) science. . . . What others strive to see dimly and blindly, like bats in twilight, he gazes at in the full light of day, because he is a master of experiments. . . . He is ashamed that things should be known to laymen, old women, soldiers and ploughmen, of which he is ignorant.'

This man was Peter of Maricourt (*Petrus Peregrinus* or 'Peter Peregrine'), who is known only through his *Epistola de Magnete* written in 1269 at the siege of Lucera (where he possibly served as an engineer under Charles of Anjou).

After stressing the importance of manual skill in the work of the scientist, the book comes straight to its main point: the identification of the poles of the compass and the enunciation of the magnetic laws of attraction and repulsion. It contains a remarkable description of an experiment with a broken and repaired magnet, and explains that the swivelling of the magnetic needle is due neither to the presence of lodestone near the North Pole (since lodestone was mined in many parts of the world) nor to the Pole Star, since the north pole of the magnet does not point exactly towards the star but to the meeting point of the meridian circles. (Historians have wondered why, since he realized that the magnetic needle did not point to the true north, he failed to measure the magnetic declination, which was quite appreciable in Italy at the time.)

According to Peter Peregrine, it was the total effect of all four parts of the heavens (north, east, south, west), acting not on the poles alone but on the needle as a whole. He noted that a spherical lodestone pivoted on two sharp points, its axis lying north–south, followed the motions of the heavens.

These theoretical views led to such practical inventions as the floating magnet and the combination of the astrolabe with a magnet for measuring the azimuth of celestial bodies, and to many attempts to realize perpetual motion.

JORDANUS NEMORARIUS

The writings of Jordanus Nemorarius cannot be fitted into any school, nor can we state with certainty whether or not Jordanus Nemorarius and the Dominican Jordanus Saxo (General of the Dominican Order, 1222–37) were one and the same person.

His *Elementa Arithmeticae, Algorithmus Demonstratus* and *De Numeris Datis*, while not contributing anything original, were clear evidence of Jordanus' desire to extend the scope of Euclidean demonstrations. Jordanus was the first Western mathematician to make systematic use of the letters of the alphabet for designating algebraic quantities. His *De Triangulis* combines Greek with Arabic influences, *e.g.* in establishing that the side of a regular heptagon is half the side of the equilateral triangle inscribed in the same circle, a theorem which is attributed to Indian mathematicians but was used by Heron of Alexandria.

Jordanus' *Planisphere* is superior to Ptolemy's, and gives the first general formulation of the fundamental theorem of stereographic projection on which the construction of astrolabes is based (*i.e.* that circles are projected as circles).

The *Elementa super Demonstrationem Ponderis* are more than a mere summary of the *Mechanical Problems* and the *De Levi et Ponderosa*, attributed respectively to Aristotle and to Euclid. According to the axiom of Jordanus, that which can lift a certain weight up to a certain height can also lift a weight k times heavier to a height k times smaller. Hence, the axiom foreshadowed the principle of virtual work and could be used for solving lever problems.

Jordanus also investigated the problem of *gravitas secundum situm* (*i.e.* the component of gravity along the trajectory). He applied this concept to the curves described by the pans of a scale and this led him to consider infinitesimally small arcs, thus vaguely anticipating the infinitesimal calculus.

It is difficult to determine the real authorship of the *Liber Jordani de Ratione Ponderis*, which Duhem has called 'the precursor of Leonardo da Vinci'. This book studies inclined planes, establishes the quantitative laws governing *gravitas secundum situm* by introducing the concept of static *moment*, and applies it to the equilibrium of angular levers. This text, published in 1565 by Tartaglia, seems to have had a direct influence on Stevin and on Galileo.

THE STUDY OF CLASSICAL MATHEMATICS IN THE THIRTEENTH CENTURY

Great interest in Greek mathematics was also shown by John Campano of Novara, who wrote a near-classical commentary on Adelard of Bath's translation of Euclid's *Elements*. From it, it appears that the meaning of 'golden section' (the 'divine proportion' of Luca Pacioli)—though not the term itself—was well-known during the construction of the Gothic cathedrals.

Much more important was the work of the Dominican, William of Moerbeke, Archbishop of Corinth in 1276 and personal friend of

Albert the Great, of Witelo and of St. Thomas Aquinas. His translations of Proclos led to a revival of Platonism, and his rendering of Aristotle satisfied St. Thomas' constant wish to read the great philosopher without Arabic intermediaries. William's greatest claim to fame was his Latin translation (1269) of the original Greek version of the complete works of Archimedes (excepting only the *Arenarius* and the *Method*). This translation was an outstanding contribution to the development of science, for at the time the only Archimedean text known in the West was the *De Mensura Circulae*, translated by Plato of Tivoli and Gerard of Cremona. (Tartaglia's Latin edition of Archimedes, published in 1543, was an unacknowledged plagiarism of William's, and Maurolycus' translation did not appear until 1685.) Christian scholars, and especially the Parisian John of Murs, were still studying Archimedes in the fourteenth century.

THE SPANISH GROUP

No understanding of the variety of thirteenth-century scientific pursuits would be complete without a further account of scientific developments in the Iberian peninsula. In the last chapter we discussed the Arabic influences on Alfonso X. His contemporary, the Portuguese Peter of Spain, whose *Summulae Logicales* made him an undisputed master of dialectics, was a great champion of Avicenna's Augustinianism. When he became Pope (John XXI) he apparently used his personal influence to fight against the Averroist and Thomist trends of the Parisian school.

Peter of Spain—like Avicenna—was a physician. He tried to reconcile the *via experimenti* and the *via rationis*. In addition to numerous commentaries on Hippocrates, Galen and Isaac, he also wrote a treatise on eye diseases and a famous medical encyclopaedia called *The Treasure of the Poor*. He was particularly interested in problems of the soul (vegetative, sensitive and intellective).

Arnold of Villanova (d. 1311), a famous teacher at Montpellier and a court physician to the kings of Aragon and to the Pope, is said to have written nearly a hundred books (a great number of which are apocryphal or doubtful). Like many of his contemporaries, he was a convinced experimentalist, but he used his experiments to construct a vast cosmology dominated by the *spiritus*, or vital force—a sort of immaterial and cosmic fluid which could be poured from the spiritual into the vital domain, from one man into the next, and from planets into beings or things.

This philosophy opened wide the doors to astrology, alchemy and magic. Arnold soon afterwards adopted the most extravagant mystical beliefs and was promptly condemned by the Church. His views also brought him into conflict with the Salernian School, unlike which he prescribed simple diets, a minimum of drugs and psychological treatment.

Another Catalan, the *Doctor Illuminatus*, Raymond Lull of Majorca, was a logician first and foremost, whose main aim it was to construct tables and diagrams with movable parts, showing all the possible combinations of all the fundamental concepts. As a Franciscan mystic, he tried to apply his 'findings' to prove that God's perfection was at work in nature and even in mathematical principles. No wonder that his purely scientific, and particularly his geometrical, writings were nothing more than pedantic and useless justifications of the elementary knowledge of his time.

What we have said gives the lie to all those who equate medieval thought with Aristotelianism. To illustrate the non-conformity of the Catalan school, we need only mention that Arnold of Villanova saw fit to say of St. Thomas Aquinas that 'he does not behave himself like a theologian but like an ox'. Such outspokenness and the frequency with which it occurred show quite unequivocally how diverse were the opinions of fourteenth-century scholars, and how openly they could express them.

The Reaction against Aristotelian Physics

It is mainly because of their reaction against Aristotelian physics that a number of late medieval scholars have been called the precursors of Galileo. But it must be remembered that, even before the Parisian Nominalists began to challenge it, Aristotelianism had been questioned by the experimental school and condemned by many theologians. Moreover, the astronomers had simply discarded it.

Physicists and Astronomers
The differences between the physicists and the astronomers had their roots in antiquity. Aristotle, as we know, had adopted the system of Eudoxos, in which the spheres of the stars underwent uniform motion about a common centre, the spherical and immobile earth.

Ptolemy's eccentrics and epicycles therefore ran counter to Peripatetic physics and yet managed not only to 'save the appearances', but to provide the necessary astronomical tables needed by the computers and astrologers. However, Ptolemy's *Almagest* had ascribed no more than a symbolic value to the geometrical constructions which it introduced, and it was only in the Arabic version of the *Planetary Theory*, Book II, that these constructions were considered true reflections of real events. In disseminating this view, Thābit ibn Qurra emphasized the differences and the need to choose between Aristotle and Ptolemy.

43 Fourteenth-century sundial

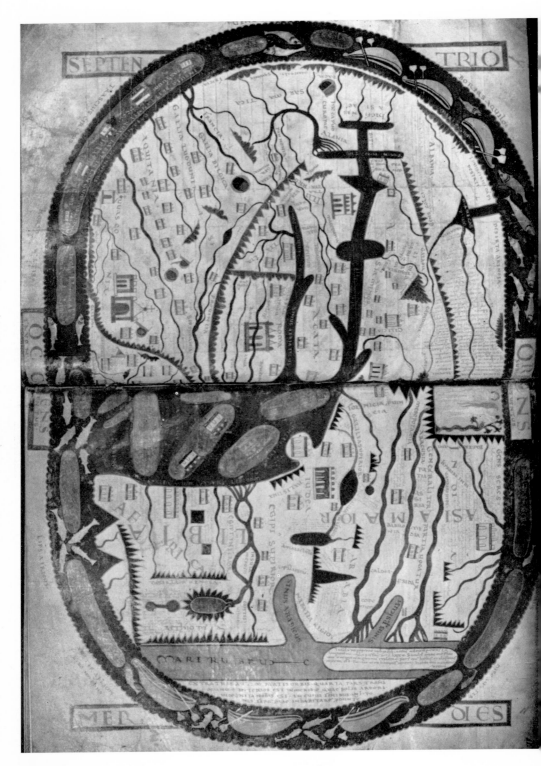

44 St. Sever monastic map

Peripatetic physics, though doomed, were given a brief new lease of life when Michael Scot's translation of al-Bitrūjī's *Planetary Theory* was published in 1217.

This new theory explained the motion of the planets by an extremely complicated arrangement of spheres, 'each imitating the other imperfectly'. While it did not run counter to Aristotle's doctrine, the theory explained the appearances qualitatively and crudely.

Al-Bitrūjī's system was adopted by William of Auvergne in about 1230, and shortly afterwards it exerted a profound influence on Robert Grosseteste. Albert the Great took an oversimplified view of it at first and finally rejected it altogether.

St. Thomas Aquinas, again, who was greatly impressed by Averroës' diatribe against the *Almagest*, later changed his mind and arrived at common-sense conclusions very much like those of Simplicios:

Although these (Ptolemy's) hypotheses seem to save the appearances, they must not be upheld as true, for the apparent motions of the stars might well be explained by some other hypothesis that men have not yet thought of.

Then, in 1267, there appeared a Latin translation of Alhazen's *Astronomical Summary*, in which the eccentrics and epicycles were fitted into a simple system of solid spheres. This work caused the balance of opinion to swing towards the Ptolemaic conception. The *imaginatio modernorum*, as it was called, made its entry into scholastic thought with Roger Bacon's *Opus Tertium*, though Bacon himself held that 'it is better to uphold the natural order of things, even if it contradicts the senses which are often unreliable in estimating great distances'. But with Bernard of Verdun and Richard of Middleton (shortly after 1281), Aristotle was banished from the heavens and his authority restricted to the sublunary world.

ADVANCES OF ASTRONOMY

Another problem dividing thirteenth-century scientists was that of the equinoxes. Very early on, astronomers had been forced to add a ninth sphere to the spheres of the seven planets and the fixed stars in order to explain the diurnal motion of the earth through a slowly revolving heaven (according to Aristotle, every sphere had an independent motion of its own). Some astronomers, such as Michael Scot, William of Auvergne and John Campano of Novara, added a tenth immobile sphere which they called the *Empyrean*.

The problem of the alleged variability of the equinoxes resulting from the discrepancy between the sidereal and the tropical year assumed great importance during the Middle Ages, when it appeared

32

that the Julian calendar had ceased to reflect the solar seasons. In these conditions it had become impossible to fix the date of Easter and of other festivals with any degree of accuracy.

In the middle of the thirteenth century, calendar makers were at one with Grosseteste, Sacrobosco and Campano in feeling that a reform was essential; Bacon even appealed to Pope Clement IV. However, nothing could be done until the choice was made between the theories of trepidation and precession. In 1337, John of Murs studied the problem in the light of the Alfonsine Tables, and in 1345 he wrote, on the order of Clement VI and in collaboration with Firmin of Belleval, the *Epistola super Reformatione Antiqui Kalendarii*, in which he suggested modifications which, two and a half centuries later (in 1582), were to redound to the glory of Gregory XIII.

How greatly interest in astronomy increased during the thirteenth century is shown by the incredible popularity of Sacrobosco's mediocre *Sphere*, and by the immense success of the rather more serious writings of John Campano and Prophatius.

The primitive astrolabe of Herman the Lame was gradually improved (azimuth markings, introduction of an *ostensor*, greater accuracy in dividing the ecliptic). This development was largely the result of translations of the works of Mashallah and of contributions by Raymond of Marseilles (*c.* 1140), John Campano and, later, by Geoffrey Chaucer.

A little after 1261, Peter Peregrine designed an astrolabe representing the entire universe. Henry Bate, of Malines, dedicated to William of Moerbeke an instrument for making astrological predictions which showed what stars rose and set at any given moment. This was similar to Arzachel's *saphea*, which was already known to others. Since it could be used in all latitudes, its use became widespread from 1263 onwards.

All these instruments were, as we have said, calculating devices rather than observational instruments; they assumed the kind of mathematical knowledge which we discussed in connection with Jordan's *Planisphere* and involved the prior preparation of celestial maps giving the co-ordinates of all the stars involved.

Angular measurements in the Middle Ages, as at the time of Tycho Brahe, were made by means of unwieldy quadrants, which were gradually improved. Thus the simple *quadrans vetustissimus*, marked with projection lines, made way for the *quadrans vetus*, marked with hour lines. A slide enabled astronomers to add (or subtract) the declination of the sun to the observed altitudes and thus to establish time and latitude without the use of tables.

Towards 1280, there appeared the *turquet*, attributed to Franco of Liège; it contained four graduated circles—three of which were provided with alidades—respectively parallel to the horizon, the equator, the ecliptic and the normal to the ecliptic. John Campano and William of St. Cloud also studied possible improvements to existing astronomical instruments. Finally, in 1342, Levi ben Gerson introduced the cross-staff, which may have been invented during the preceding century by Jacob ben Maḥir.

All these scholars also tried to compute increasingly accurate tables for astrological predictions, and so the pursuit of astrology led to fruitful results. Arzachel's *Toledan Tables* were the first of a long list, including the *Marseilles Tables* (1140), the *Canons* of Robert of Retines (Toledo 1149, London 1150), the *Tables* of Roger of Hereford (1178), the *London Tables* (1232), William the Englishman's treatise on Arzachel's Canons (Marseilles 1231), the almanacs for use with Robert the Englishman's quadrant, *etc.*

In 1292, William of St. Cloud made a vigorous attack on the so-called 'Toulouse Tables' (based on the Toledan), in which he put forward exceptionally accurate observational arguments. Two years later, he determined that the latitude of Paris was 48° 50′ and the obliquity of the ecliptic 23° 34′. He also found that the distance between the 'head' of Aries and the vernal equinox was 10° 13′ (in Thābit ibn Qurra's day it had been 9° 23′).

When the Alfonsine Tables reached Paris about 1296, astronomers recognized their superiority over the Toledan Tables, but only adopted them with reservations. John of Linières (1322) and John of Saxony (1355–56) tried to make them simpler to use; Geoffrey of Meaux attacked them (1320); and John of Murs tried to verify them by means of a large quadrant of ten feet radius (1318).

This concentration on astronomical measurements accelerated the progress of trigonometry. Though we cannot agree with the fairly widespread belief that trigonometry was introduced into Europe at the beginning of the fourteenth century—by which time al-Khwārizmī's and Arzachel's tables were well known in Latin translation—there is no doubt that the credit for having turned it into an independent discipline must go to three Englishmen: Richard Wallingford (*c.* 1326), John Mauduith and Simon Bredon (1380).

The Parisians, who had lagged behind at the time of John of Linières, quickly caught up with the Oxford masters, so that the sine tables eventually used by Regiomontanus were not the English tables but those of John Fusoris, a famous Parisian builder of astrolabes and canon of Notre Dame.

Astronomers preferred the so-called *physical*, *i.e.* sexagesimal, fractions to vulgar fractions; hence the extraction of square roots forced John of Gmunden, John of Murs, John of Linières and, above all, the Jewish astronomer Immanuel Bonfils of Tarascon, to work with decimal fractions for subsequent conversion into minutes and seconds, without, however, appreciating the importance of the step they had taken.

All these painstaking efforts were to bear fruit during the fifteenth century in the university of Vienna, and particularly in the work of Peurbach and Regiomontanus.

The history of Italian astronomy was far less straightforward. The controversy between the adherents of Aristotle and of Ptolemy left Italy unmoved until the middle of the fifteenth century, when Paul of Venice, Prodoximo of Beldomandi and Gaetano of Thiene began to examine the problems involved. It was then that the Averroist School in Padua was rent by the same arguments which the Parisians had dismissed as vain 150 years earlier. Hence Gilson could rightly assert that it was Averroism, and not scholasticism in general, which deserves to be called a narrow and obstinate kind of Aristotelianism.

THEOLOGIANS AND ARISTOTELIAN PHYSICS

Despite the intervention of St. Thomas Aquinas, Latin Aristotelians remained under the spell of Averroism and continued to embarrass Christian theologians in a number of important respects.

According to Aristotle, the gods were no more than 'unmoved movers' of the celestial spheres. Matter was eternal, hence there could not have been a creation *ex nihilo*, nor could the universe ever 'run down', for it was the preordained scene of ever-recurring stellar conjunctions and oppositions. Infected by Moslem fatalistic ideas and by its adherence to astrological notions, this doctrine left man with no more than an illusion of liberty: 'Everything possible will be; what will never be is impossible.' Averroism assumed explicitly that there was an *active intellect* shared by all men, and hence denied the existence of individual souls. Such views were bound to arouse the anger of the Church.

Since the fight against Averroism released God from the narrow prison in which Aristotle and his disciples had tried to confine him, it may be asked whether it did not also help science to discard the shackles of Aristotelianism and thus to pave the path for Galileo.

The question is best examined in connection with the doctrines condemned by Stephen Tempier, Bishop of Paris in 1277. Among the 219 'execrable errors which certain students of the Faculty of Arts have the temerity to study and discuss in the schools', there were at least two which interest the historian of science:

'God cannot impress translational motion on the heavens for the simple reason that such motion would produce vacuums', and 'The primary cause cannot create a multitude of worlds'.

From all the evidence, Stephen Tempier's counter-measures were drawn up in great haste. For instance, no one would have denied, as he claimed they did, that the celestial spheres underwent some translational motion. Even so, Pierre Duhem was able to write:

If we absolutely must give a date for the birth of modern science, there is no doubt that it was 1277. . . . It was the condemnation of Greek necessitarianism which led a number of theologians to affirm that, as a result of the omnipotence of the Christian God, those scientific or philosophical views which were traditionally judged incompatible with the essence of nature, were, in fact, *possible*. By allowing new mental experiences, the theological notion of an omnipotent God liberated the intellect from the finite field into which Greek thought had imprisoned the universe.

Now, though there is no doubt that the theologians encouraged a measure of independence from Aristotle, it is debatable whether they made more than this purely critical contribution.

Aristotelian (like Einsteinian) space was co-extensive with the universe: every motion involved a place; beyond the universe there was no place, and hence the plurality of worlds was an absurdity.

In attributing to God the power to create anything he likes outside the world, Stephen Tempier had replaced Aristotelian space with an infinite geometrical space, similar to that of Euclid or Descartes. Unfortunately, as A. Koyré has so clearly shown, the new field thrown open to mathematical and philosophical speculations was completely ignored, or else twisted into Augustinian Platonic channels—for instance by Thomas Bradwardine of Oxford, according to whom the divine essence was unlimited. God cannot exist without acting, nor act without existing (or even without being present). He is present and active in every creature, but He is also unchanging and hence immanent in the entire universe. While the Creation presupposes the prior existence of space, it would be absurd to imagine this space as void and limited, or to adopt the Pythagorean formula, 'God is a circle of which the centre is everywhere, and the circumference nowhere'.

Bradwardine's theory had been anticipated in substance by Robert Grosseteste, who, a hundred years earlier, had asserted that the universe was created from a point of light. Scholasticism did not, in effect, have to await the condemnation of 1277 to consider the problem of infinity in its most general form.

St. Thomas Aquinas opposed created to creative infinity, the existence of which he denied. Giles of Rome (1247–1316) claimed that the infinite must be viewed in three ways, according to whether magnitudes were manifested in the abstract, in substances in general, or in specific substance. Matter is not infinitely divisible, since beyond a given point it ceases to be matter. Medieval thought had thus returned to the atomic theory, though Roger Bacon pointed out that, since the side of a square and its diagonal have no common aliquot part, they can be divided *ad infinitum* and never produce an indivisible minimum. Peter of Spain intervened in the discussion by opposing categorical or active infinity with syncategorical infinity, *i.e.* infinity in the process of becoming.

In the middle of the fourteenth century, Albert of Saxony described a spiral whose successive steps were in the geometric progression $1, \frac{1}{2}, \frac{1}{4}, \frac{1}{16}, \ldots$ The spiral could therefore never be higher than 2, though the curve itself was syncategorically infinite. Albert thus had some inkling of the interconnection between the infinitely great and the infinitely small, a notion that was not developed until the seventeenth century.

Mathematical Interpretation of Physics

In Aristotle's sublunary world everything had its natural place; at the centre was the earth, surrounded by water, air and fire, in that order. Hence stones fall towards the earth while flames leap upwards; every motion is a disturbance of, or an attempt to re-establish, equilibrium—*actus existentis in potentia in quantum est in potentia*. Velocity varies directly with the force causing the motion and inversely with the resistance which tends to impede it, *i.e.*:

$$V = \frac{F}{R} \text{ or } \frac{V_2}{V_1} = \frac{F_2 R_1}{R_1 F_1}.$$

Averroës 'explained' these laws by stating that velocity was a function of the excess of the motive force over the resistance.

Thomas Bradwardine deserves great credit for having tried to produce a more mathematically satisfying formula in his *Tractatus Proportionum* (1328).

$V = F/R$ is absurd, he says, because if the force is equal to, or slightly smaller than, the resistance, there is no motion, even though V is greater than zero. Nor can we put:

$$\frac{V_2}{V_1} = (F_2 - R_2) - (F_1 - R_1)$$

or

$$\frac{V_2}{V_1} = \frac{F_2 - R_2}{F_1 - R_1}.$$

Instead, he suggested, if V_2 is double, triple or quadruple the value of V_1, the ratios F_2/R_2 and F_1/R_1 are equally in double, triple, or quadruple ratio, and so on.

This does not mean that one of the quotients will be 2, 3 or 4 times as great as the other. To understand Bradwardine's contention we may take the case of the proportion:

$$\frac{a}{b} = \frac{b}{c} = \frac{c}{d} = \frac{d}{e}, \text{ etc.}$$

Si fuerit proportio majoris inequalitatis primi ad secundum ut secundi ad tertium, erit proportio primi ad tertium precise dupla ad proportionem primi ad secundum.

$\dfrac{a}{c} = \left(\dfrac{a}{b}\right)^2$ is defined as 'dupla ad proportionem $\dfrac{a}{b}$'

$\dfrac{a}{d} = \left(\dfrac{a}{b}\right)^3$ is defined as 'tripla'

$\dfrac{a}{e} = \left(\dfrac{a}{b}\right)^4$ is defined as 'quadrupla'.

Bradwardine's proportions were therefore powers, and his mathematical interpretation of Aristotle's law was, in fact (in modern notation):

$$n\mathrm{V} = \log\left(\frac{\mathrm{F}}{\mathrm{R}}\right)^n$$

when $\dfrac{\mathrm{F}}{\mathrm{R}} = 1, e, e^2, e^3, \text{ etc.},$

$\mathrm{V} = 0, v, 2v, 3v, \text{ etc.}$

Naturally, if $V_2 = \dfrac{V_1}{n}$, $\dfrac{F_2}{R_2}$ must be $\sqrt[n]{\dfrac{F_1}{R_1}}$.

Bradwardine, though unfamiliar with logarithms, prepared for their discovery by relating an arithmetical to a geometric progression. Not very much later (1348–62) Nicole Oresme introduced the fractional exponents:

$\boxed{\begin{array}{cc} \mathrm{P} & \mathrm{I} \\ \hline \mathrm{I} & 2 \end{array}}$ 4, or $\boxed{\mathrm{I}\ p\ \tfrac{1}{2}}$ 4, for $4^{1\frac{1}{2}} = 8$.

Finally, in 1484, Nicholas Chuquet considered negative exponents of the type $a^{-n} = 1/a^n$.

From the very fact that his treatment of dynamics remained Aristotelian, Bradwardine's law was never incorporated into classical physics. Nevertheless his mathematical treatment of the absence of motion when resistance is equal to or slightly higher than the motor force, his astute suggestion that resistance increases rapidly with velocity and, above all, his introduction of quasi-logarithmic methods, are excellent examples of the fruitfulness of scholastic science in spite of its principles, which at first sight strike one as misconceptions.

INTENSITY AND FORM

Another interesting attempt to 'mathematize' physics was the endeavour to describe qualities by measurable quantities. Once again, the initiative was taken by the theologians. St. Thomas, for instance, wondered if one act could be said to be more or less charitable than another, and hence defined intensity by the degree of participation in immutable forms (whiteness, heat, charity, *etc.*), rather than by the addition of successive acts of participation (*e.g.* the number of individual charitable acts). Walter Burley, on the other hand, explained that variations in intensity were due to the replacement of an earlier form by a *forma totaliter nova*. For Henry of Ghent again, qualitative increases were 'infused into the form' and manifest themselves whenever potentiality is transformed into action.

Medieval scholars were much interested in the experiment of mixing two equal volumes of water at an equal temperature, from which they deduced a fundamental distinction between quantity of heat and temperature. They also dwelled on the relationship between a quality and its opposite, and wondered if the two were of the same nature or not, what were their respective maxima and minima, and whether they were complementary or else related by formulae of the type: heat = $1/$cold; cold = $1/$heat. The last assumption worried the mathematicians, because, being forced to consider the reciprocal of zero, they came up against infinite intensities.

Of the forms subject to 'intention' and 'remission' (*i.e.* to increases or decreases of intensity) there was one which seemed fairly simple, namely velocity, defined as the qualitative aspect of motion.

A disciple of Bradwardine, the Englishman Richard Swineshead, discussed the matter in his *Liber Calculationum* (written before 1350), in which he examined the increases in velocity produced when a constant force acts on a moving body. To do so, he proposed considering the time intervals:

$$\tfrac{1}{2} + \tfrac{1}{4} + \tfrac{1}{8} + \ldots 1/2^n + \ldots = 1.$$

He then assumed, quite gratuitously, that the velocity would increase by unit steps with each interval, so that:

$$\text{Velocity:} \quad 1 \quad 2 \quad 3 \quad 4 \ldots n$$

$$\text{Time:} \quad \frac{1}{2}+\frac{1}{4}+\frac{1}{8}+\frac{1}{16}\ldots+\frac{1}{2^n}+\ldots = 1$$

$$\text{Distance (Velocity} \times \text{Time):} \quad \frac{1}{2}+\frac{2}{4}+\frac{3}{8}+\frac{4}{16}\ldots+\frac{n}{2^n}+\ldots = 2$$

Hence he proved that with uniformly accelerated motion the distance covered in unit time is four times the distance covered during the first half of that time $(2 = \frac{1}{2} \times 4)$.

Despite his tenuous premises, Swineshead's law itself is correct, and many historians have therefore objected to Duhem's calling it 'the outcome of a senile science which had begun to drivel'. It must, however, be admitted that because of his *a priori* assumptions Swineshead encouraged his colleagues to propound the most extravagant notions. Nicole Oresme, for instance, 'improved' Swineshead's law by simply substituting Archimedes' series:

$$1+\frac{1}{4}+\frac{1}{16}+\frac{1}{64}\ldots+\frac{1}{4^{n-1}} = \frac{4}{3}$$

whence he obtained:

$$\text{Velocity:} \quad 1 \quad 2 \quad 3 \ldots \quad n$$

$$\text{Time:} \quad \frac{3}{4}+\frac{3}{16}+\frac{3}{64}\ldots+\frac{3}{4^n} = 1$$

$$\text{Distance (Velocity} \times \text{Time):} \quad \frac{3}{4}+\frac{6}{16}+\frac{9}{64}\ldots+\frac{n}{4} = \frac{4}{3}$$

He even considered motion accelerated during half the time, uniform during the next quarter, accelerated during the next eighth, uniform during the next sixteenth, *etc.*

Oresme's speculations encouraged fourteenth-century scientists to try their hand at summing all sorts of series, particularly since he had invented a graphical representation of the 'remission of forms'.

For instance, he represented uniformly accelerated motion by plotting velocity against time, obtaining the straight line AC (*fig. 40*). Hence he could prove geometrically that the space traversed by a body moving with uniformly accelerated velocity is equal to the space traversed by a body moving with a uniform velocity which is the mean of the initial and final velocities of the first body.

In *fig. 40*, if DB = AB/2, the area of the rectangle DBCE represents the distance covered by the second body, since DB × BC is the product of its velocity and time. Now DBCE is equal in area to the triangle ABC, which represents the distance covered by the first body.

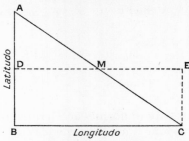

fig. 40 Oresme's representation of uniformly accelerated motion.

For his proof to be perfect, Oresme would have had to resolve the triangle ABC into the greatest possible number of small rectangles whose sides represent a series of extremely small intervals, and the corresponding *instantaneous* velocities. Unfortunately, Oresme preferred to take these steps for granted.

It has been pointed out that Oresme's rectangular co-ordinates were borrowed from classical cartographers (for instance from the *decumanus* and the *cardo* of the Roman surveyors), and that he cannot be considered the inventor of analytical geometry. Mlle. Anneliese Maier, in particular, has been outspoken on this subject:

'Oresme', she writes, 'constructed a diagram and could doubtless have used it for arriving at analytical geometry. But he failed to do so since he was not so much interested in curves and their relationship to co-ordinates, as in geometrical figures as such.'

In fact, Oresme's *configurationes intensionum* were meant to describe physical reality rather than the 'flux of forms'. According to the *figure* of the diagram describing its possible intentions or remissions, a quality was said to be sharp, soft, unstable, *etc.* The same method was also applied to sensitivity towards these qualities, so that, for instance, the response to 'heat' of man was plotted against that of woman, or that of a lion against that of an ass. Nicole Oresme used all these notions to present a theory of medical therapy and of sexuality.

These weird notions must not, however, blind us to Oresme's real greatness, or cause us to fall in with the very natural though excessive reaction against Duhem's eulogies on the Parisian scholars, by which Oxford has recently been accorded pride of place over them. One Oxford man, in particular, William of Heytesbury, does, however, deserve very special mention. In his *De Tribus Praedicamentis* (1335), he replaced *latitudo motus* (speed) with *velocitas intentionis vel remissionis*, changes in the rate of speed, and showed that they tend towards zero as the velocity approaches its maximum or minimum. Some historians consider this conception to be the forerunner of the derivative.

But whatever our views on the respective claims of France and England to pre-eminence, we must remember that despite his formal adherence to the Parisian nominalists, Nicole Oresme was opposed to the Occamist views of that school on motion; consciously or not, and no matter by what contemporary sources he was influenced, he was, above all, swayed by Platonic concepts.

THE NOMINALIST SCHOOL AND THE THEORY OF 'IMPETUS'
Steeped in the work of Bradwardine and Swineshead, the teacher of Nicole Oresme, John Buridan declared that '*quod istae regulae raro vel nunquam inventae sunt deduci ad effectum*'.

'We must not, however, say', he hastened to add, 'that such hypotheses are useless and artificial, since even if the conditions which they stipulate are not found in nature, it is possible that they could be implemented by the omnipotence of God.'

The approach of the strict nominalists went much further still. William of Occam denied that natural reason could ever arrive at metaphysical truths, and even held that faith, lacking demonstrative certainty, must be based on probability.

'In physics', he said, 'as in the other sciences there may be *demonstrationes propter quid*; in any case science demands that we begin with the best-known and simplest things, and hence we are generally forced to proceed from effects to causes. Thus we come to know matter, form and most things *a posteriori*, being unable to prove them *a priori*.'

Experiment and faith are the only remedies against scepticism. 'However, there exists', Nicholas of Autrecour wrote, 'a certain degree of certainty which men can attain if they apply their minds to the study of things and not to that of philosophy and of commentaries.' In short, there is nothing of absolute certainty in Aristotle.

While the Augustinian scholars in Oxford tackled Peripatetic dynamics with mathematics and with a desire to explain rather than to refute them, the Parisian Nominalists concentrated on experimental studies and had no respect for the authority of the great philosopher. John Buridan, in his turn, challenged (before 1352) Aristotle's view that the velocity of a body is proportional to the force acting upon it and inversely proportional to the resistance it meets.

This law, he claimed, was disproved by the fact that a stone does not stop moving the moment a thrower ceases to act upon it. The supplementary theory of *antiperistasis*, according to which the air, by rushing into the vacuum set up behind the moving projectile, acts as a motor force, was rejected by Buridan as being false, since, as he pointed out, straw carried by a ship was blown towards the stern and not in the direction of the ship's motion.

We must therefore assume that a mover in moving a body impresses on it a certain *impetus*, a certain power capable of moving the body in the direction in which the mover set it going. . . . It is by this *impetus* that the stone is moved after the thrower ceases to move it; but because of the resistance of the air and also because of the gravity of the stone, which inclines it to move in a direction opposite to that towards which the *impetus* tends to move it, this *impetus* is continually weakened.

A stone travels farther than a feather because 'the reception of all forms and natural dispositions is in matter and by reason of matter. Hence the greater quantity of matter a body contains, the more *impetus* it can receive.'

In these views, Duhem has seen the germs of the modern concept of inertia, but Mlle. Maier and M. Koyré have rightly challenged this view. They have recalled that, for Descartes and Newton, uniform motion in a straight line is a *state* equivalent to rest. The uniformly moving body perseveres in its state without any external force or cause. Just as external forces or causes are unnecessary to explain the state of rest, so there is no need to explain uniform motion by them. In other words, classical dynamics was not so much the result of more careful observations as of grasping the purely abstract idea of perpetual motion, independent of external forces and resistances.

Buridan, on the other hand, remained faithful to the Peripatetic conception that motion was caused and supported by the action of external forces; in the case of propulsion, he did no more than replace the external force with 'an intrinsic quality whose nature it is to move the body on which it has been impressed'. Even so, his formulation was a considerable improvement on Aristotle's, and we shall therefore look briefly into its antecedents.

THE CONCEPT OF 'IMPETUS' BEFORE BURIDAN

As early as 517, John Philoponos had put forward the idea that the instrument of projection imparted motive power to the projectile. While his view had no direct effects on scholastic thought, it was shared by Moslem scientists, particularly of the Baghdad School. Avicenna was interested in the violent tendency (*mayl qasrī*) of bodies 'to repel whatever impedes their motion in a given direction'. Unfortunately his views on the matter, at least in the Latin version, are almost unintelligible; hence scholars have had to look for possible links between Philoponos and Buridan in the writings of philosophers and theologians. Gilson, for instance, has cited the statement by Theodoric of Chartres (twelfth century) that:

If a stone is thrown, the *impetus projecti* is due to the thrower's standing on a support; the firmer his support the more powerful his throw

Thirteenth-century schoolmen (particularly St. Bonaventura and St. Thomas Aquinas) often compared the transmission of life, and of hereditary characters from father to son, with the impression of motor forces on projectiles. Again, Peter Olivi (1249–98) wondered how a simple 'formative force' could give rise to a living being:

Vis formativa non agit nisi sicut virtus instrumentalis alicujus principalis agentis . . . sicut, suo modo, impulsus seu inclinationes datae projectis a projectoribus movent ipsa projecta etiam in absentia projicientium.

But his impulsion was a far cry from Buridan's impetus, for it involved a final purpose. According to Olivi himself, the impulsion was the expression of the 'tendency of the projectile to move towards the end of the motion'. The whole problem was, in fact, the general problem of action impressed by an external agent. Francis de la Marche, for instance, wondered in 1320 'if the Sacraments did not contain a supernatural virtue, formally inherent in them'. This concern led him to investigate whether artificial instruments did not similarly receive their virtue from outside sources. His discussion of the case of a stone thrown violently into the air, as an illustration of his purely theological tenets, made him the first western scholar to oppose Aristotle's dynamics openly.

APPLICATIONS OF THE THEORY OF 'IMPETUS'

But though Buridan was not the first in the field, he was the first to formulate the new theory in scientific terms and to deduce from it a number of important consequences. He used it to explain the bouncing of tennis balls, the vibration of bells and also the free fall of bodies, which, he said, was due to the fact that the constant pull of the earth was continuously added to the impetus. This explanation led Albert of Saxony to suspect that velocity must be proportional either to the time or to the distance traversed, but he failed to choose between these two alternatives. Buridan, finally, followed Occam in denying Aristotle's view that the heavens and the sublunary world differed fundamentally both in their matter and in their laws. He proposed, instead, that the revolution of the celestial spheres was due to an impetus impressed upon them by God, after which, in the absence of all resistance, they continued to revolve perpetually. Hence there was no need to assume the existence of angels charged with the continuance of celestial motions.

Buridan went further still, and, in the *De Coelo et Mundo* (1328 or 1340), he questioned whether the earth was, in fact, the immobile centre of the universe. While he rejected the thesis that the earth rotates about its own axis, he agreed with Albert of Saxony that, because of continual surface changes, the earth's centre of gravity

could not be immobile and hence could not possibly occupy the
centre of the universe unless it described a compensating motion itself.

Nicole Oresme was much more strongly tempted than Buridan to
assume that the earth revolved through an immobile sky. In about
1377, he examined the theory of Heraclides of Pontos in the light of
Witelo's principle that it was impossible for a terrestrial observer to
tell whether the heavens or the earth was in motion. He refuted the
objection that, if the earth revolved, heavy objects would drop down
along a curved trajectory and not in a straight line, and summed up
somewhat abruptly: 'Considering everything that has been said, one
can then conclude that the earth is moved and the sky is not, and
there is no evidence to the contrary.'

*   *   *

Little though we know about them, medieval attempts to restore
Aristotle's physics force a number of conclusions upon us. First of all,
the fourteenth century witnessed no 'scientific revolution', and there
was no rupture of the 'union between finalist metaphysics and common-sense experience', by which Koyré has so rightly characterized
the Middle Ages. The Parisians were not the unswerving nominalists
they are generally believed to have been, and their role together with
that of Oxford has forced modern scholars to pay greater attention to
the influence of Neo-Platonism on the birth of modern science.

Averroism, despite its avowed differentiation between the truths of
faith and reason, now appears as a narrow and reactionary form of
conservatism. Its success in Italy largely explains the low level of
science in the fifteenth century, at the very time when, through
political circumstance, the University of Paris lost its former importance.

Medieval attempts to 'mathematicize' physics were thwarted by
the lack of suitable measuring instruments and, more generally, by
the lack of the kind of co-ordination between thought and manual
dexterity which Peter Peregrine had deplored in the thirteenth century. A rapid survey of the history of technology will show beyond
doubt that medieval craftsmen were not devoid of practical sense,
and that one of the greatest brakes on scientific progress was the
excessive lack of contact between the monks compiling manuscripts
in the seclusion of their cloisters, and the practically illiterate artisans,
navigators, military engineers and master builders.

SCIENCE AND PRACTICAL ACHIEVEMENTS AT THE END OF THE MIDDLE AGES

The Achievements of Medieval Technology

Though the study of medieval technology falls outside the province of this book, we must emphasize that, contrary to a widespread belief, medieval religious preoccupations were not entirely divorced from practical problems. Some scholars—for example, J. V. Nef—like to stress the contrast between Catholicism, with its love for *qualitative* perfection, and Protestantism, with its concern for *quantitative* achievements and science. Now this thesis is refuted by the fact that perhaps the most important technical revolution before the invention of the steam engine occurred during the late Middle Ages, when population movements in the tenth to twelfth centuries led to an unprecedented harnessing of natural forces (draught animal, water and wind).

THE HARNESSING OF POWER

Greece and Rome, which could rely on their slaves to perform all menial tasks, could afford to ignore other sources of power. By the ninth century, however, horses had become indispensable, and deeper saddles, nailed horseshoes and prick spurs and curbs were coming into increasing use. During the tenth to twelfth centuries the general introduction of rigid shaped collars allowed horses to take the weight on their shoulders instead of the neck as hitherto, and hence to pull with all their weight. Lateral traces for the tandem harness came into use, allowing horses to pull together. Roads made of stone cubes set in a bed of loose earth proved cheaper and more resistant to the weather than the famous Roman roads; the limber, for pulling the newly-invented artillery pieces, was first introduced in the fourteenth century.

When the water-mill, known in Illyria during the second century B.C., was introduced into feudal Europe, it was quickly put to an increasing number of uses (corn mills, oil mills, hop mills, wood mills, tanning mills, fulling mills, lifting machines, mechanical saws, trip-hammers, paper mills, *etc.*). As early as the tenth century lords of the manor began to claim a monopoly for their mills and may therefore be called the forerunners of modern monopoly capitalism.

The windmill, reported from Persia in the seventh century, reached Spain in the tenth century and thence the rest of Europe, but the originally vertical axle had become horizontal.

Anxious to use wind and water power to the best possible advantage, medieval technicians took a keen interest in the possible transformation of continuous into reciprocating motion and *vice versa*. They applied cams (which had been known to Heron) to trip-hammers, and their inventions, apart from improving milling methods, led to important engineering advances, illustrated by the appearance in early fifteenth-century Southern Germany of the pole-lathe.

THE INTRODUCTION OF NEW TECHNIQUES

In the heavy soil of north-western Europe improvements of harnessing methods alone were not enough to overcome the agricultural difficulties. Hence, during the thirteenth century successful efforts were made to introduce heavy wheeled ploughs with coulter, horizontal share and mouldboard. Crop rotation was improved by the division of land into three fields, of which one lay fallow, and new crops were introduced.

The first artesian well was drilled for the collegiate church of Lillers in 1126 (such wells were known in China very much earlier, and the subject had been studied by al-Birūnī in 1010). Other medieval innovations were sericulture (introduced into Sicily towards 1130), falconry, the pickling of herring, and the manufacture of champagne (Clairvaux, possibly in the fourteenth century). From 1280 onwards, the spinning-wheel began to replace the distaff and loose spindle.

Body linen began to appear in the fourteenth century, with consequent improvements in personal cleanliness and a decrease of leprosy. Linen was also a cheap source of raw material for the manufacture of paper, which seems to have begun in China in the first century and to have reached Western Europe in the thirteenth *via* Islam and Spain. Underwear therefore had a kinship with the history of book printing.

Hydraulic power was not only applied to the trip-hammer, but also to the forge bellows, which could now raise the temperature of furnaces sufficiently to allow metals to be cast. The first blast furnaces seem to have been opened at the beginning of the fifteenth century, though some historians claim that they have evidence of their existence in the Liège and Namur regions in about 1340.

Distilling methods, too, were greatly improved. The heart-shaped Alexandrian condenser, which used to be placed directly over the cucurbit and was laboriously cooled with moist ribbons, was abandoned in favour of the classical alembic, whose tubular outlet wound like a shell or serpent through a vessel of flowing water. Alcohol made its appearance in Salerno about 1100, and manufacturing methods were quickly improved by the introduction of dehydrating agents, *e.g.* potassium carbonate. The end-product was sold in two forms: *aqua ardens*, containing about 60 per cent, and *aqua vitae*, containing about 96 per cent of alcohol.

Mineral acids, previously known only from the colour of their vapours, which could not be condensed, were first produced in 1160 when a mixture of saltpetre, alum and vitriol was distilled into nitric acid, a substance used for breaking down alloys of silver and gold. Soon afterwards, sulphuric acid was obtained by the distillation of alum, or by boiling sulphur and leading the fumes into a glass bell inverted in water. Strangely enough, the end-products of these two methods were thought to be different. Hydrochloric acid was first produced in the fifteenth century, but the general use of all these acids depended on the replacement of metallic containers by appropriate glass vessels. Hence the history of Venetian glass is also the history of inorganic chemistry.

The principle of the lens had been described by Ibn al-Haytham and Grosseteste. When the first spectacles, made of rock-crystal and later of glass, appeared in 1285, they had converging lenses only; diverging lenses were introduced in the sixteenth century. Reading was also encouraged by the increasing use of tallow or wax candles.

Military science, too, was profoundly transformed during the Middle Ages: the new harness enabled the feudal lords to wear heavier armour and to charge with lowered lances. The new artillery was armed with mangonels and trebuchets, the Lateran Council of 1139 having forbidden the use of the arbalist as being too murderous a weapon for Christians to employ.

As early as the beginning of the Christian era, the Chinese were familiar with the explosive properties of mixtures of sulphur and saltpetre. Between the seventh and tenth centuries, they invented gunpowder, in 1231 they introduced the grenade, and in 1259–72 they manufactured the first cannon. Gunpowder reached the West in the thirteenth century (Roger Bacon is sometimes credited with its invention); the first cannon in Europe seems to date from 1319, the fuse from 1378, and the hand grenade from 1435; explosive mines arose from firework displays.

Weight-driven clocks (with no pendulum) were used widely from the end of the thirteenth century onwards, despite their unwieldy proportions.

The transition from the Roman to the Gothic style of architecture went hand in hand with technical advances, such as the reduction of the thrust exerted on the side walls by the nave roof. Building materials, which were previously carried by two men on a kind of stretcher, were now transported in wheelbarrows (first mentioned in China in A.D. 232). Civil engineers constructed bridges with segmented arches (China—A.D. 600, Italy—thirteenth century), sluice gates (Bruges 1180), dredgers (Middelburg 1435), Archimedean screws for drying polders (1408), *etc.*

33   24 pp.

THE CHINESE PROBLEM

These very brief remarks make it clear that the medieval peoples took a keen interest in concrete achievements and were receptive to all sorts of technical advances. It is extremely difficult to assess how many of these advances were original, how many were transmitted from China either directly or through the Arabs, and how many were made simultaneously, though independently.

We know that there were direct contacts between Europe and China in the thirteenth and fourteenth centuries. In 1235–37 the Hungarian Dominican Julian went to seek out his pagan compatriots who, he was told, lived somewhere between the Volga and the Urals. On his way he learned of the threat to his native land by the Tartars and he retraced his steps to warn the Holy See. In fact, the Mongols sacked Cracow, occupied Hungary and advanced to the Dalmatian coast (1241). Meanwhile, the Church had high hopes of turning them against Islam. John Pian del Càrpine was charged with taking a message from Innocent IV to the Great Khan (1245–47) and on his return he wrote the *Historia Mongolorum quos nos Tartaros Appelamus*, of which Vincent of Beauvais made a brief summary. St. Louis sent the Dominican, Andrew of Longjumeau, on a similar mission (1248–51) and, later, the Franciscan William Rubruquis (1253–54), of whom Roger Bacon spoke very highly.

As we saw, once the descendants of Ghengis Khan had conquered China, they succumbed to their hosts' superior civilization. The Yuan dynasty (1280–1368) which they founded was noted for its religious tolerance, and for its close relations with the Latin world. In 1287–88, the Nestorian of Peking, Rabban Ṣauma, called on Philip IV of France and on Pope Nicholas IV; in 1292 John of Montecorvino took up residence in the Chinese capital, and he founded the short-lived archbishopric of Khānbaliq in 1307. Marco Polo travelled right across Asia and returned along the coast between 1271 and 1295. In 1298, while leading a Venetian expedition against Genoa, he was taken prisoner and used his captivity to dictate an account of his travels to Rusticiano of Pisa. Other visitors to China included the missionaries Peregrino of Castello, Andrew of Perugia, Oderic of Pordenone (1318–28) and John of Marignolli (1339–53).

In addition, there were the many prisoners of war, merchants and craftsmen who had come into contact with the East. Among these were the Parisian goldsmith William Boucher, a woman from Metz whom William Rubruquis met at the court of the Great Khan, the merchant Peter of Lucalongo, and a surgeon from Lombardy whom John of Montecorvino discovered in Peking.

Hence, it would be wrong to conclude from the absence of medieval references to Chinese techniques that China had no influence on Western developments. What happened, rather, was that there was a great diffusion of stimulus. Once a missionary had come across wheelbarrows in China, he could not help but advise his compatriots to introduce similar means of transport.

Unfortunately, the conquest of Turkestan by Tamerlane, the expulsion of the Mongols from China and the beginning of the reign of the traditionalist Ming dynasty (1368) caused a violent nationalist reaction: the gate which had opened to the west was shut close for many centuries to come.

Technology and Science

Though we cannot ignore the possible external influences on medieval science, we must not exaggerate their importance either. During the Middle Ages the centre of European civilization shifted northward and many 'medieval achievements' were, in fact, developments of Mediterranean ideas that had previously been of little practical use (river navigation, timber construction, domestic heating, precautions against frost, *etc.*).

Modern students tend to over-emphasize what they call the insurmountable barriers between medieval technology and science. They should not forget that their own knowledge of the Middle Ages is based on two independent disciplines: literary history and archaeology, from which they know all that they do about scientific theories and medieval technology, respectively. Many of their objections can therefore be reduced to gaps in their own academic training.

THE APPLICATIONS OF THE QUADRIVIUM

After Hugh of St. Victor—from the twelfth century onwards—the practical usefulness of the *quadrivium* came to be generally recognized. Thus Fibonacci's *Liber Abaci* (1202) was used especially by merchants and remained the standard work until 1556–60 when Niccoló Tartaglia published his *Trattato Generale di Numero e Misure*. The *Liber Abaci* was translated into, and summarized in, the vernacular throughout the fourteenth and fifteenth centuries; the most famous version was probably that of Paolo Dagomari (Paolo dell' abaco). At the same time, and particularly in Italy, the growth of international trade changed business methods profoundly. Letters of exchange, which had originally been issued for single transactions, were gradually used for more and more complicated credit manipulations; commercial empires rose up with branches in all important trading centres and required simple book-keeping methods. The Italian double-entry system made its first appearance in Genoa in 1340; it was based on an earlier Venetian system using two columns. In the new system, every debit entry had to be offset by an equal credit entry so that, at all times, total debits balanced total credits. This meant the opening of 'impersonal' accounts (capital, depreciation, cash, stock, *etc.*).

According to Giovanni Villani, there were six abacus schools with over 1,000 students in Florence in 1338. Once qualified, the students were snapped up by the merchants. Luca Pacioli (1499) wrote a textbook on Italian book-keeping which became famous.

French manuals of commercial arithmetic, too, were widely read during the fourteenth and fifteenth centuries, first in the Mediterranean regions and in Flanders, and later in the rest of the country. The best of them all was Nicolas Chuquet's *Triparty*. But while French clerics taught the Italian system of calculating on paper (*fig. 42*), the universities continued to use Sacrobosco's algorithm, *i.e.* the Arab method of making successive corrections in the dust or sand (*fig. 41*).

All through the Middle Ages, from Boëtius to Hucbald of Saint Amand, Guido of Arezzo, John of Murs and Philip of Vitry, scholars

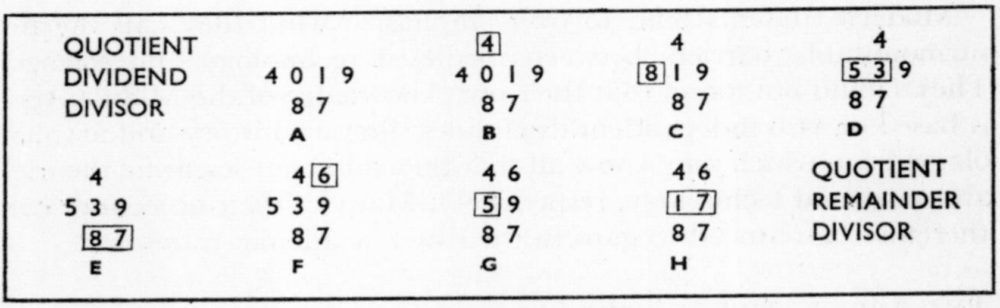

fig. 41 Division on a tray covered with sand (twelfth-century algorithm).

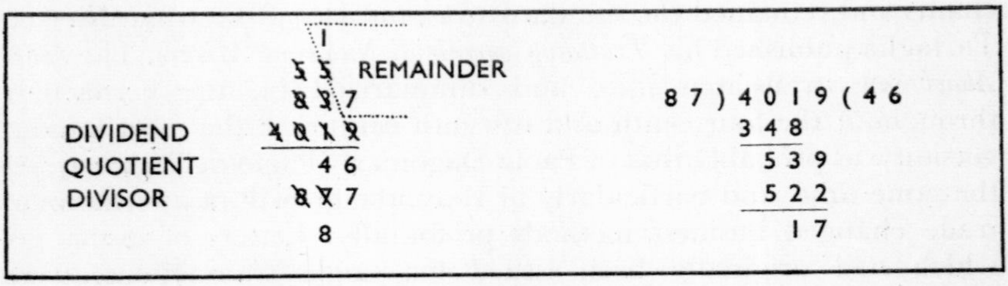

fig. 42 Division on paper (fifteenth- and sixteenth-century arithmetics). On the right: modern division of the same number.

looked upon harmony as an integral part of mathematics. But since chants were mainly liturgical, it was the Church that translated theory into practice, adopting Guido of Arezzo's method of naming the notes of the scale by the syllables *ut, re, mi, fa, so, la, te* (from the first syllables of a hymn to St. John the Baptist), and later introducing a mensural notation (twelfth century). The beauty of plainsong was enhanced by the introduction of the *organum*, a part sung as an accompaniment below or above the melody or plainsong, usually at an interval of a fourth or a fifth (tenth century). From this it was but a short step to the descant, based on strict counterpoint, and then to William of Machaut's polyphonic mass (fourteenth century).

A. C. Crombie tells us that, in the early twelfth century, Theophile the Priest gave the first European account of bell founding. Bells giving notes with intervals of the tonic, third, fifth and octave were produced by having diameters in the proportion of 30, 24, 20 and 15, and weights in the proportions of 80, 41, 24 and 10, respectively. These figures were obtained empirically.

At the beginning of the fourteenth century, Walter of Odington, a monk in the Benedictine abbey of Evesham, tried to formulate the 'law' governing these empirical findings, *viz.* that bells producing notes a whole tone apart must have weights in the ratio 9:8. Though he was wrong, his attempt is evidence of his desire to subordinate technology to science.

Another branch of the quadrivium, astronomy, could also be used for the 'practical' purposes of horoscopy. While astrology was the subject of heated controversies, especially during the fourteenth century, astrologers continued to couple their extravagant theories with a great deal of practical sense. A case in point is the work of John Fusoris, canon of Notre Dame.

He became first a Master of Arts, then a Master of Medicine and, finally, a Bachelor of Theology, in addition to having studied metal-founding under his father, who was a pewterer. He wrote theoretical treatises (particularly on cosmography) but also manufactured astrolabes, especially for Peter of Navarre and for the Pope. He cast the horoscope of Henry V of England, when the King was about to leave for France (1415), and for this was interned on the ground of having collaborated with the enemy. His technical prowess was recognized some years later, however, when he constructed an astronomical clock for the cathedral of Bourges (1423).

Medieval geometry was still intimately related to surveying, and even the best treatises (for example those of Savasorda and Fibonacci) were affected by this link. The golden mean was well-known from the many commentaries on Euclid's *Elements* (especially from that of

Campanus). Until the whole subject is investigated more closely, we cannot say to what extent medieval artists used it in their work.

Modern perspective was born in Florence at the turn of the fourteenth century and, from the start, it was altogether different from the perspective of Oxford, then almost synonymous with optics. Lorenzo Ghiberti, its first advocate and hence the forerunner of Leo Battista Alberti, Piero della Francesca and Leonardo da Vinci, followed in the tradition of Alhazen, John Peckham and Witelo. Lorenzo's influence can be fully appreciated only after a systematic study of Gothic *trompe l'œil*.

MEDICINE AND ALCHEMY

Just as some scientific theories were systematically applied to technology, technical knowledge led to a re-examination of ancient theoretical problems. This aspect of medieval science is best studied from the vast collections of medieval formularies, which, unfortunately, are too unwieldy to be examined by individual scholars. Even so, M. P. Cézard's recent research in the *Bibliothèque Nationale*, and similar attempts, are of great interest.

At a time when the edifice of ancient science was collapsing, day-to-day necessities forced people to cling to a number of ancient formulae, mixed with superstitions and local beliefs. We have seen that during the Dark Ages an empirical type of medicine was being practised by lay practitioners, and Salin has drawn attention to the existence of Merovingian medical methods that are far less primitive than one might have thought.

Marcelin Berthelot has shown conclusively that some recipes of the Greco-Egyptian Leyden papyrus found their way into the *Compositiones ad Tingenda Musiva*, published during the reign of Charlemagne, and into the tenth-century *Mappae Clavicula*. He also showed that the *Compositiones* are related to the *Liber Ignium* of Marcus Graecus and that the first eleven formulae of the *Clavicula* appear also in the *Schedula Diversarum Artium* of Theophile the Priest.

Hence, while practical men followed along familiar paths, the monks copied whatever interesting formulae they happened to come across. The two trends combined to produce valuable results, particularly in medicine.

From the twelfth century onwards medicine was again taught to students, first in Salerno and later in the Universities, and the formulae used are fairly easy to date. Chemistry, on the other hand, seems never to have been taught by the scholastics, though such works as the *Secretum Secretorum* and the *De Aluminibus* of al-Razī did much to increase knowledge of chemical ideas. The Arabs, through the pseudo-Geber, were also responsible for the growth of such mystical or allegorical notions as the production of gold from suitable combinations of sulphur and mercury. All such attempts, as typified in the *Tabula Smaragdina* and the *Turba Philosophorum*, were, moreover, based on misreadings of Aristotle and the Alexandrian Neo-Platonists.

In the thirteenth century, confusion increased when al-Razī's writings (*e.g.* the *Liber Claritas*) and even texts of Latin origin were published as the works of Geber. Similarly unwarranted was the attribution of numerous alchemical compilations to such leading schoolmen as Albert the Great, St. Thomas Aquinas, Vincent of Beauvais, Roger Bacon, Arnold of Villanova, Raymond Lull, *etc.*

It must be added that the formulae contained in all these works and those found in various manuscripts have not yet been classified methodically enough for scholars to date them or to identify their origins with any degree of certainty.

Moreover, medieval formulae cannot be verified in modern laboratories, since they generally failed to stipulate temperatures, reaction times and the nature or exact proportions of the substances involved. Some substances were used for their impurities alone (*e.g.* galena for traces of silver); the use of others was based on superstition, quackery, or the desire to deceive a gullible public. But it would be wrong to condemn medieval chemistry out of hand, since many of its techniques have stood the test of time, among them the illumination of manuscripts, the staining of glass, the dyeing of materials and the tempering of steel.

Attempts to transform base metals into gold and silver had theoretical as well as practical consequences. The theoretical part usually makes us smile; for example, the assumption that there was an elixir which would 'congeal' into the Philosophers' Stone (a sort of 'catalyst' aiding the combination of sulphur and mercury). Nor can we see any virtue in the subtle rationalizations by which the failure of attempts to change metals was explained away, or in the mystical attempts to combine the production of precious metals with the search for health, youth, strength and perfection. No wonder that Pope John XXII felt impelled to ban this type of alchemy in 1317.

Far more interesting were the purely empirical formulae for producing alloys or 'tinctures' of gold and silver—called *ad rubeum* and *ad album*, respectively. Money-changers and goldsmiths were forced to examine all metals, not only by eye and with the touchstone but also by testing their physical and chemical properties (density, ductility, malleability, ring, reaction to acids, *etc.*), and hence to increase their metallurgical knowledge.

But when all is said and done, medieval chemistry was never a real science; its symbols were useless, and its classification of various substances into smokes, spirits, waters, oils, stones, *etc.*, purely pragmatic. Much more valuable were the fairly accurate descriptions of laboratory techniques, such as those in the *Practica* (which, according to Miss Kibre, is rightly attributed to Albertus Magnus). These include distillation, sublimation, calcination, fixation, coagulation, fermentation, projection, multiplication (augmentation), *etc.* In fact, the main achievements of medieval chemistry were the manufacture of alcohol and of inorganic acids, made possible by the development of stills and glass vessels.

ARCHITECTS AND ENGINEERS

Historians have shown that Leonardo da Vinci, though ignorant of Greek and Latin, was yet influenced by Jordanus and Archimedes. To explain this paradox, Lucien Febvre has rightly observed that during the Renaissance men were still 'auditory' types who greatly preferred oral studies to book learning. Now his observation applies, *a fortiori*, to the Middle Ages, so that we cannot help wondering how much the great thirteenth-century cathedral-builders who, like Leonardo, neither studied at the universities nor sweated over polished theoretical treatises, knew of the classical heritage. What, in fact, was the scientific knowledge of the medieval architects and engineers?

A recent study by M. Pierre du Colombier on the building of medieval cathedrals supplies part of the answer. At the beginning of the Middle Ages, the 'patron' (bishop, abbot, or *custos fabricae*) took an active part in directing the stone-cutters. (One such was Suger of St. Denis.) By the middle of the thirteenth century, however, the work had become so complicated that one man could no longer handle both the financial and technical problems involved, and control of the practical work was put in the hands of an appointed director. Thus, in the time of St. Louis, the architect made his first appearance. Peter of Montreux called himself a 'Doctor of Masonry', while Nicholas of Biard, a great preacher, voiced his indignation:

> In great buildings, the master-in-chief orders his men about but rarely or never lends his own hand to the work; and yet he is paid much more than all the others. . . . The masonry masters, with walking sticks and gloves, say: 'Cut here and cut there' but they do no work themselves . . .

The emergence of architects went hand in hand with the production of an increasing number of plans and designs drawn on parchment. This increase, from 1250 onwards, has been explained by the fact that earlier manuscripts were exposed longer to the ravages of time, a view to which we cannot subscribe. In fact, there are extant only two such documents dated earlier than the reign of St. Louis:

45 Pepper harvest

Samterne cest bue herbe qui
est autrement appellee cresst
mum et est bue herbe dont les fluurs
ont tresfoues en deux et pour ce la
fent elles countre peruoisons et haul
te de cuer et confortent les mens
les de la poictrune lay en fait toill
que len appelle clenus faribracum
et le fait on de oile de oline on
fen met sure les fleurs dessus
dece ainsi que on fait oile vosas
ceste herbe entre en la recepte de
une medecine que len appelle crabia
mustata ceste herbe bault fembli
blement aux maladres dessusdres

dues comme bug doy et font espte
et non pas croutement herer mais
blenchastres ses fueilles outre et
mondrez sont harbondez le sant aux
femmes merueilbensement et curart
le font elles plus quant len les ont
mis lubulbee

Spinal cest bue maniere de char
don qui a la fueille large que
len appelle primeto

Spina benedicta est mame
de espine dont il croist
grang habondance en bretame et
aussi en autres pars et en fait
on les hayes ses fueilles ne sont
pont droitement onmes mais
bouchues et sont crespes et lon

the plan of the Abbey of St. Gall (ninth century) and that of the cloister in Canterbury (twelfth century). Quite suddenly there was a plethora of plans and sketches: Rheims Cathedral towards 1250, the face of the Strasbourg Cathedral in 1275, and plans for Cologne, Vienna, Ulm, Sienna, Orvieto, Milan, Florence and Cambridge in the fourteenth century. English tracing houses were opened in 1324.

Pierre du Colombier has shown that elevations were far more common than complete plans, that they were not true to any scale and were never fully implemented, but were rather used to give the bishops some ideas of the architects' intentions. Hence these drawings, far from being 'geometrical', were based on a rudimentary type of perspective.

It was at this stage that the Freemasons made their first appearance. They were itinerant builders who made themselves known as experts by secret signs, but had no other 'secret knowledge'. A unique document in the history of medieval architecture is an album of drawings made between 1235 and 1257 by the French architect, Vilard de Honnecourt. It is now generally agreed that his drawings were more than mere travel-sketches, but were meant to serve as models for craftsmen engaged in building-work. The thirty-three extant folios consist of plans, elevations, drawings of statues and designs of various machines (arbalist, hydraulic jack, hydraulic saw, clockwork mechanism for rotating an angel so that its finger kept pointing towards the sun, *etc.*). Villard was therefore an architect *cum* engineer, and his album may well have been the first of those innumerable technical treatises (many on military engineering) which flooded Southern Germany and Italy in the early fifteenth century.

The best known of these were the *Bellifortis* by Conrad Kyeser (1405), of which a later manuscript (1410) is kept in the library of Donaueschingen, the anonymous treatise on the Hussite Wars (1430), and the writings of Fontana (1420), Cennini (1437) and Meriano (1438). M. Bertrand Gille has shown that all these works were in the tradition begun by Villard de Honnecourt and culminating in the plates of the *French Encyclopaedia*. The sixteenth- to seventeenth-century 'theatrical machines' were but another aspect of the tradition. Thus the so-called 'precursors' of Leonardo da Vinci were not so much Duhem's Parisian schoolmen as the late medieval engineers.

This whole problem can be studied only in historical retrospect. True, a new type of man appeared in the middle of the thirteenth century, the architect or engineer (the latter especially at the court of Alfonso X), but he did not appear out of nowhere. The growing interest in statics, dynamics, hydrostatics and magnetism must have gone hand in hand with the increased social status of craftsmen, and men like Jordanus, Gerard of Brussels and William of Moerbeke,

32A

who translated Archimedes (or later, like Buridan or Albert of Saxony) are bound to have come into contact with many artisans. We know that Albert the Great sought out the company of craftsmen; we know that Roger Bacon was taught by Peter Peregrine and that Buridan, the chief upholder of the theory of impetus, was also a designer of trebuchets and cannons. On the other hand, there is no doubt that medieval craftsmen constructed cathedrals without being able to calculate the resistance of materials and that they fired their cannons without any knowledge of ballistics. It seems likely, therefore, that their practical concerns led them to new studies and new interests. Systematic research into technical references by schoolmen at the turn of the thirteenth century is bound to throw much fresh light on the details of these developments.

Cartography and the Voyages of Discovery

The history of cartography and of maritime discoveries has been so distorted by the chauvinism of many scholars, and by their ignorance of maritime problems, that it is difficult to write a reliable account of its phases.

The Norsemen who terrorized the coasts of the Carolingian Empire crossed the sea in *drakkars*, specimens of which have been dug up from Scandinavian peat bogs. Reconstructions show that they could reach a speed of 10–11 knots. The suggestion that the Norsemen generally sailed with the wind seems to be ruled out by their constant employment of oarsmen. In any case, the Vikings were not so much admirable for their alleged maritime discoveries as for their unquestioned courage and enterprise. They reached Iceland in 861, Greenland in 857 and America in A.D. 1000, when Leif Ericsson named the three regions on the Atlantic coast between Labrador and Massachusetts, calling the most northern Helluland (slate country), the mid-region Markland (wood country) and the southern region Vinland (wine country). Norsemen even tried to settle in these regions between 1003 and 1030.

The Norsemen are said by some historians to have been the first Europeans to sail by the compass. The *Historia Islandica* (1108) tells how one, Floki Vilgerdarson, sailed out in 868 with three ravens, in order to tell from their flight whether the mainland was near by, 'for sailors did not yet have a magnet'. This comment would be of capital importance had it been made in 1108; in reality it was added as an afterthought in about 1225, and is therefore later than the first French references to the compass.

When the compass first appeared in Europe at about the year 1200, it had been known to the Chinese for at least two centuries. Then, quite suddenly, it was mentioned by a large number of Western writers, including Guist of Provins, Alexander Neckam and James of Vitry.

The *marinette* or *calamite*, as they called it, was at first a magnetized needle fixed to a float; the pivoted needle must have been introduced very soon afterwards, since it was mentioned by Alexander Neckam and described by Peter Peregrine. The story that it was invented (or perfected) by one Plavio Gioja of Amalfi in 1302 has no real foundation.

The magnetic declination, still unknown to Peter Peregrine in 1269, was apparently recognized at the beginning of the fifteenth century. It was Christopher Columbus who first described its variation over different parts of the earth (13th–17th September, 1492).

However, more knowledge of what was the correct course was of little use if that course could not be followed. Hence it was a great boon to navigation when, simultaneously with the first appearance of the compass (early thirteenth century), the stern paddle of antiquity made way for the modern rudder fixed to the stern post, which allowed accurate steering. Lefebvre des Noettes holds that it was this development which made ocean travel possible, and that none of the great voyages of discovery could have been made without it.

In the thirteenth century there also appeared the first *portolani*. They contained written accounts of coasts and ports, navigational advice, tables of distances, and lists of obstructions and of navigable channels. The accompanying maps were of secondary importance. Quite different were the maritime charts first mentioned by William of Nangis in his account of an ocean crossing by St. Louis aboard a Genoese vessel in 1270. Of all extant portolani, the oldest is the famous *Carte Pisane* which is generally said to have been of Genoese origin, because the earliest signed portolan was that of the Genoese cartographer Giovanni di Carignano (*c.* 1300), and the earliest specimen, both signed and dated, that of another Genoese, Pietro Vesconte (1308).

These sparse references, taken from R. Almagia, do not, however, help to settle the difficult question whether the real origin of nautical charts goes back to the Arabs, the Byzantines, the Venetians, or the Genoese (who have much to support their claim).

Cartography reached Majorca and Catalonia some twenty years later. The oldest Majorcan marine map, dated 1339 and signed by Angelino Dulcert, is so similar to the earlier charts of the Italian Angellino Dalorto (dall'orto) that the two men have often been thought identical. In 1375, a magnificent *Atlas* was presented to

Charles V of France, and by a decree of 1354 Peter IV of Aragon ordered all ships under his command to carry two marine maps.

These maps were based on previous ocean crossings and gave distances and rhumb-lines (a rhumb-line is the line a vessel has to follow to cross the meridians at a constant angle). Now the rhumb-line, or loxodrome, was, in fact, no more than a crude approximation, since it was thought to be a straight line and distances were established by pure guess-work (the first recorded log was kept in 1577). Finally, the deflection of the magnetic needle from the true North was ignored, and the distortion of some ten degrees typical on fourteenth- and fifteenth-century marine maps is undoubtedly explained by the fact that there was a corresponding declination in Western Europe at the time.

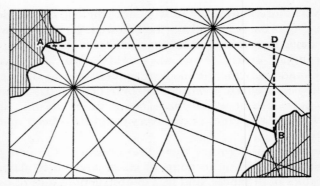

fig. 43 Marine chart used by fourteenth- and fifteenth-century navigators.

A vessel going from A to B (*fig. 43*) would follow the rhumb-line, using the scale of the map as a guide to distance. DB gave an indication of the difference in latitude, and AD of the difference in longitude between A and B. However, even the squared portolani had no meridians or parallels marked on them and cannot therefore be said to have been charts in the modern sense.

The end of the thirteenth century saw the first attempts to apply simple trigonometrical tables to navigation. Thus Raymond Lull declared in 1295–96 that sailors '*habent chartam, compassum, acum et stellam maris*', and that 'navigation is born and derived from geometry and arithmetic'. In particular, he dealt with the case of a ship driven south-eastwards by the wind while attempting to sail due east: 'If this ship travels eight miles, it has, in fact, travelled no more than six miles towards its real destination' (8 cos 45° = 5.64).

Strangely enough, at the very time when trigonometry was made an independent discipline at Oxford, sailors began to use *marteloio* or *martologio* tables, excellent examples of which can be found in Andrew Bianco's *Atlas* (1436) and in a manuscript dated 1444, though their invention undoubtedly goes back to the previous century. By means of these tables one could estimate not only how far a ship would have to travel along a given rhumb-line to regain its course after having been thrown off it by a persistent wind, but also the difference in latitude between two ports.

This brings us to the very controversial question of the origins of *astronomical* navigation. Nationalist passions and pedantic squabbles being what they are, we cannot pretend to be expressing more than a personal opinion on this matter, or on the history of medieval navigation in general.

(1) The nautical astrolabe of the Renaissance was a distant and extremely simplified derivation of the medieval astrolabe used for calculating *celestial* motions. Though the kings of Aragon commissioned nautical charts as well as astrological instruments throughout the fourteenth century, M. de Reparaz is wrong to read too much into this fact. In reality, from Arnold of Villanova and Raymond Lull onwards, and under the influence of Jewish writings, Catalonia and Majorca had largely succumbed to astrology. Astrologers rather than sailors were the main clients of the astrolabe makers.

(2) Astronomical navigation was not practised in the Mediterranean until the seventeenth century.

(3) The first ocean-going vessels were launched from the Atlantic coast of the African continent. The first ships hugged the coasts as they travelled southwards, and, driven along by favourable currents and the North East Trades, they were not long in reaching the Fortunate Islands (the Canaries). The return journey involved a north-westerly course which took the ships into the region of the variable winds (between the Canaries and the Azores). The farther north they went, the greater their chance of meeting the south-westerlies which would carry them to the Iberian peninsula. A. Cortesão has rightly remarked that it was during these return voyages that Madeira and the Azores were first reached. Once in the Sargasso Sea the ships ran the risk of being driven towards the Antilles. These were the main factors determining the birth of ocean navigation.

(4) Atlantic voyages were begun well before the fifteenth century, when the western coasts of Africa were first explored. Thus the Arabic geographer al-Idrīsī referred to eight adventurers who, in 1124, left Lisbon to seek out the western edges of the ocean, and gave up only after they had found Madeira and the Canaries.

Towards 1270–75, the Genoese Lanzarote Malocello rediscovered the most north-easterly of the Canaries, which still bears his name, and in 1292 two other Genoese sailors, the brothers Ugolino and

Vadino Vivaldo, went out in search of an Atlantic passage to India *'quod aliquis usque nunc minime attemptavit, per mare oceanum mercimonia utilia deferentes'*. However, their bold enterprise ended tragically in shipwreck.

During the fourteenth century, voyages to the Canaries became increasingly frequent. A Portuguese expedition with Italian backing was launched in 1341; Majorcan and Catalan expeditions sailed out in 1342, 1352, 1369, 1370 and 1386; an Andalusian expedition in 1393; and a French expedition in 1402, when attempts were made to colonize the islands by John of Béthancourt and Gadifer de La Salle.

The palm in this field, too, must be shared between the Genoese and the Catalans, for it was the former who, serving Portugal in great numbers from 1317 onwards, visited Madeira and the Azores before 1350, and the latter who went out in systematic search of new lands. James Ferrer explored the African coast beyond Cap Bayador in 1346, and in 1373 John of Aragon, who took a personal interest in this work, commissioned 'a complete navigator's map giving all the details and all other information needed for sailing from the Straits (of Gibraltar) into the Atlantic'.

(5) We still have no more than the vaguest notion about the construction and rigging of medieval ships, though it is generally agreed that the two common types of European ship were derived respectively from the Roman galley and the Norse longship, and that the square sail was gradually replaced by the triangular lateen sail. Shortly before 1420, there appeared the first caravel (probably in Portugal), a light ship with a square mizzen and three lateen sails. Caravels were particularly well-suited for tacking against the wind, and were probably derived from the *caravos* of the Arabs, based in turn on the *pangaios* of the Indian Ocean.

(6) Portugal takes pride of place among the great nations in oceanic exploration, both because of its favourable geographical position and because of Henry the Navigator's dogged determination to explore the African coasts (1415–60). Portugal's expansion was kept a great secret and hence our knowledge of nautical techniques during the first half of the fifteenth century is extremely hazy. Though historians have exaggerated the importance of the so-called naval 'School' or 'Academy' in Sagres, there is no doubt that Henry employed first-rate scientists. 'At great cost, he sent to Majorca for Master James, a man well-versed in the art of navigation, to produce maps and instruments . . . and to teach his science to the Portuguese officers.' Master James arrived between 1420 and 1427, and M. de Reparaz has identified him with Jafuda (the son of Abraham Cresques, the author of the *Catalan Mappemonde*, commissioned by Charles V). There is no conclusive evidence that navigation by the

pole was known in Portugal at that time, for it was only in 1462 that a sailor, Diego Gomes, first described the handling of a quadrant aboard ship (he might well have been referring to Martin Behaim's activities).

The determination of latitudes by measuring the meridian height of the sun was not commonly practised until 1480–85, when it may have been introduced as a result of Abraham Zacuto's teaching. The tables of Arzachel, of Alfonso of Castille, and fourteenth-century Arabic, Spanish and Portuguese almanacs provided the necessary theoretical data, but their practical application was delayed by the general illiteracy of the sailors, and by the very inadequacy of the marine charts then in use.

(7) Most students of the history of geography have paid insufficient attention to inland maps. Apart from the circular monastic maps (see Plate 44), the most important were those of Matthew Paris (England, *c.* 1250), of Opicinus de Canistris (Northern Italy, *c.* 1335–36), and the *Gough Map* (1325–30) kept in the Bodleian Library, Oxford. In addition, many medieval manuscripts contained long lists of towns accompanied with (generally correct) indications of their co-ordinates. We have noted the accuracy with which thirteenth-century geographers measured latitudes; the longitudes of the most important cities were subsequently established by eclipse comparisons. Nicole Oresme's rectangular co-ordinates were used to excellent effect by the makers of the famous Klosterneuburg maps (1425–30) which, as Dana Durand has shown, were free of any Ptolemaic influences.

We shall not enter into the controversial problem of the influence of Ptolemy's *Geography*, except to point out that this important work was never used by the leading Arab geographers (such as al-Khwārizmī and al-Mas'ūdī), nor did it reach the West *via* Islam. The first Latin translation of the *Geography* (from the Greek) by Giacomo d'Angelo was dedicated to Gregory XII in 1406, and to Alexander V in 1409, and maps first appeared in a manuscript presented to Cardinal Fillastre of Nancy in 1417. These maps were found to be inadequate and, in 1425, maps of Scandinavia and Greenland were added.

It also became clear that the map of the Mediterranean was elongated and far less accurate than the corresponding nautical maps, and that the Indian Ocean was not an 'inland Sea', since Southern Africa was not, in fact, joined to South-Eastern Asia. Simultaneously, the art of navigation was revolutionized by the theoretical study of various methods of projection and by drawing parallels and meridians on all maps. *Martelogio* was discarded in favour of the *regimento das leguas*, which gave the actual distances corresponding to a shift of one degree of latitude for the various wind regions.

'Positional' navigation thenceforth began to oust medieval guess-work, though the problem of determining longitudes could not be solved without accurate chronometers.

Medicine

We have already mentioned the survival of popular medicine at the beginning of the Middle Ages, the role of the School of Salerno, and of the Arabic translations, and the relationship between healing and scholastic philosophy (Peter of Spain and Arnold of Villanova). We have also discussed the invention of spectacles, the problems raised by the collections of formulae, and the influence on therapy of magic, astrology and holy relics. Subsequent medical advances, from the end of the thirteenth century to the dawn of the Renaissance, bore mainly on surgery and anatomy.

Classical Salernian surgeons (such as Roland and Roger) prescribed the lancing of wounds in order to eliminate what were believed to be the causes of infection. Two Italian physicians, Hugh of Lucca (d. 1252) and his son Theodoric (1205–98), were astute enough to realize that pus prevented the formation of scab; they therefore washed wounds with wine or allowed them to dry. Their method was introduced into France by Lanfranc of Milan, John Pitart and Henry of Mondeville.

Hugh of Lucca prescribed a compound of opium, henbane and mandragora to put patients to sleep before operations. Theodoric, though not the discoverer of narcotics, gave a particularly accurate description of the preparation of a 'somniferous' sponge, and added that, after use, it might be allowed to dry and then be immersed in tepid water to have its effectiveness restored.

Their contemporary, William of Saliceto, reintroduced the use of the knife (*c.* 1270) and abandoned the Arabic method of operating with a red-hot iron. He also described the treatment of hydrocephalic children by removing the fluid through a small hole in the head, made by a cautery.

From the fourteenth century onwards surgeons used more and more complicated instruments. Between 1306 and 1320, Henry of Mondeville used a magnet for extracting iron splinters; he invented a means of removing arrows from wounds and stressed the importance of carefully binding the arteries during amputations. Guy of Chaulliac (d. *c.* 1368) used a pulley and counter-weight to prevent fractured ribs from impeding respiration, and also studied the prevention of cerebro-spinal fluid-losses. His surgery was nevertheless not nearly as original as his great reputation might have led one to believe. Field surgery often went hand in hand with 'plastic' surgery, particularly

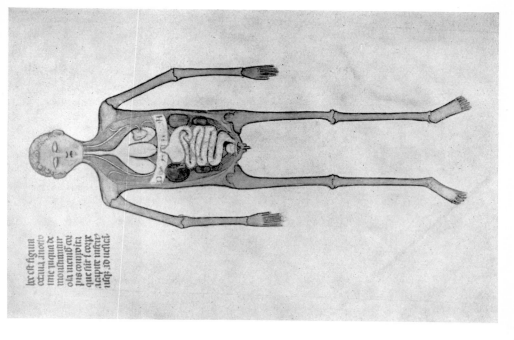

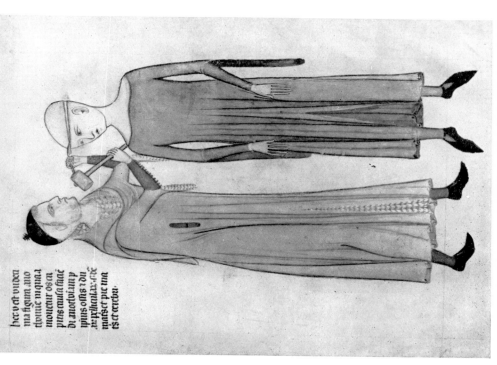

47 Anatomical drawings

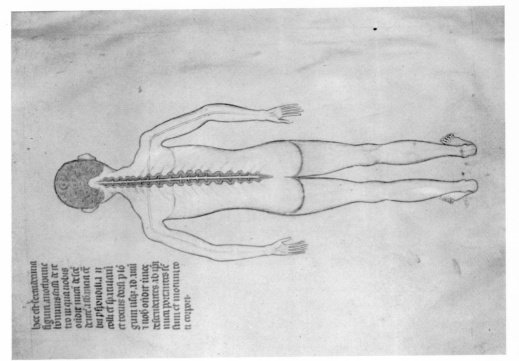

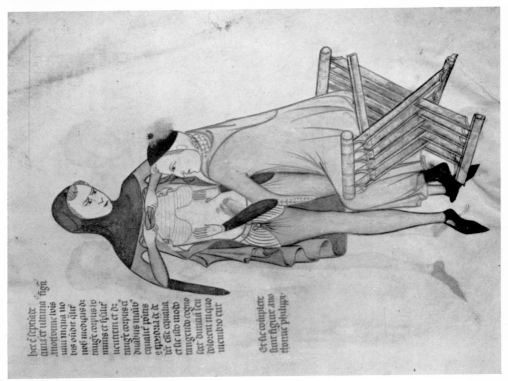

48 Anatomical drawings

of the nose. The Branca family of Catania (Sicily) were particularly famed for their tissue grafts (*c.* 1400).

It was said in the Middle Ages that a surgeon ignorant of anatomy sawed bones as a blind man might saw wood. But from the time of Erasistratos and Herophilos (third century B.C.), no surgeon had ever been allowed to perform human dissections; even the great Galen was forced to use monkeys and the Salernian masters had to make do with pigs. The results can be imagined!

The Emperor Frederick II is generally extolled for his 1241 edict, which precluded from surgical practice 'whosoever has not studied human anatomy in the school'. All he could have meant by such 'study', however, was book-learning joined to animal dissection.

It is also claimed that human dissections must have been practised at the beginning of the fourteenth century because a decree of the Great Council of Venice dated May 27th 1308 officially permitted one dissection per year. Actually, the real date of that decree was 1368, and it referred to autopsies rather than live dissections.

In any case, it was towards the end of the thirteenth century that the need for human rather than animal dissections made itself felt more strongly. This is borne out by numerous treatises on surgery (to be read *cum grano salis*) written at the time, and notably by William of Saliceto. At about the same time, there appeared the first open references to the performance of autopsies, first in Salimbene's *Chronicle* (1286) and later in Bologna (1302).

It was also in Bologna that Mondino de'Luzzi, having dissected two female bodies (January and March, 1316), published his findings in a small treatise on anatomy: '*non hic observans stylum altum, sed magis secundum manualem operationem*'. Since dissections are best begun with those organs which putrefy first, the student is introduced successively to the *venter inferior*, the *venter medius* (the thoracic cavity including the throat and the mouth), and finally to the *venter superior*, *i.e.* the head. On the whole, Mondino's treatise added little if anything to the anatomical knowledge contained in Book IV of William of Saliceto's, or in Part I of Henry de Mondeville's *Surgery*, no doubt because he was too steeped in traditional ideas to place enough reliance on his own observations and judgment. Thus, under the influence of Galen, he mistook the splenic vein for a duct pouring black bile or melancholy directly into the stomach (assumed to be spherical), and 'discovered' a central ventricle of the heart through which the lighter part of the blood passed from the right to the left chamber, there to form, by combining with pulmonary air, the vital *pneuma*. Though he was the first physician to notice that the uterus expands during menstruation, he continued to uphold the belief that it was seven-chambered. Again, while he observed that the liver moves upwards after death, he mistook it for the five-lobed organ of pigs. The main significance of Mondino's work is therefore that it shows us how low was the level of medieval anatomical studies even when dissections of human corpses had become more common.

It would be unfair to consider that the Church was chiefly responsible for this, since the Bull *De sepulturis* of Boniface VIII merely proscribed the common practice of boiling the corpses of those who had died in distant lands, so that their bones could be repatriated. The ecclesiastical prohibition to which Guy of Vigevano referred in his preface to his *Anatomy* (1345) may have been no more than a local measure by the Bishop of Paris; in fact, a manuscript in the Library of the Knights of Columbus describes how the ecclesiastical authorities ordered the cranium of a student who had died during an orgy to be cut open, in order to demonstrate to his fellow-pupils at St. Geneviève the justice of Avicenna's dictum that sexual excesses always produce a deterioration of the brain.

Nevertheless, the principle '*ecclesia abhorret a sanguine*' may well have discouraged the more pious surgeons from handling corpses themselves. Hence the classical paintings of the professor 'reading' Galen, while the *ostensor* points a rod at the organs laid bare by the *dissector*. Hence also the pre-eminence in anatomy of such lay universities as Bologna. In France, human dissections were not performed until much later. A start was made at Montpellier in 1314, and at Paris in 1407. (Systematic dissections were not begun in Paris until 1477.) However, we must agree with E. Wickersheimer that the dates mean very little, for discretion was the order of the day, particularly as the slightest scandal would have aroused the fury of the surgeons, who, in any case, resented the fact that physicians were teaching anatomy to the barbers, their competitors.

We lack the space to discuss the fight against the great epidemics, the reduction of the incidence of leprosy, the growth of hospital services, thermal balneology, or the medical and pharmacological practices taken over piecemeal from the Arabs, and conclude this section with an aside. Historians of medicine have paid too little attention to those commentators whose scholastic approach repels them. Future scholars will have to overcome this aversion and, taking a more objective view, determine whether Galen's authority was, in fact, as absolute as it is alleged to have been, or whether it was not tempered with ideas derived from Aristotle *via* Averroës. Only then will they be able to define the true nature of medieval medicine, of which Peter of Abano's *Conciliator* gives no more than a very superficial and ill-considered description.

Here is a rich field for those interested in doing original research into the history of science.

CONCLUSION

We cannot pretend that we have given systematic answers to all the many questions about medieval science raised alike by scientists, philosophers and theologians. All we have attempted to do is to set these problems in their historical perspective as best we could.

We question the truth of the double accusation against the Latin Middle Ages that they were both stagnant and sterile. While the classical heritage was often ignored and misused by the scholastics, and while such eminent men as Leonard of Pisa, Peter Peregrine and Theodoric of Freiburg had no worthy successors, it is nevertheless true to say that from one century to the next (and even from generation to generation) advances were made all along the scientific front.

The Church (whose attitude to science may have been an obstacle during other periods) encouraged rather than hindered science in the Middle Ages. Moreover, the Renaissance, though it acknowledged no masters other than those of classical antiquity, must, in fact, be regarded as the ungrateful daughter of the Middle Ages.

BIBLIOGRAPHY

The main references are mentioned in the following works:

G. SARTON, *Introduction to the History of Science*, Baltimore, 1927–48, 3 vols. in 5 parts.

L. THORNDIKE and P. KIBRE, *A Catalogue of incipits of Mediaeval scientific writings in Latin*, Cambridge, Mass., 1937; Supplements in *Speculum*, XIV, 1939; XVII, 1942; XXVI, 1951.

A. MIELI, *Panorama general de historia de la ciencia*, Vol. II: *El mundo islamico y el occidente medieval cristiano*. Vol. III: *La eclosion del Renacimiento*, Buenos Aires, 1946–51.

A. C. CROMBIE, *Augustine to Galileo*, London, 1960; *Robert Grosseteste and the experimental science*, Oxford, 1953; *Medieval and Early Modern Science*, Vol. I, New York, 1959.

A. MAIER, *Die Vorläufer Galileis im 14. Jahrhundert*, Rome, 1949; *Zwei Grundprobleme der scholastischen Naturphilosophie*, Rome, 1951; *An der Grenze von Scholastik und Naturwissenschaft*, Rome, 1952.

C. H. HASKINS, *Studies in the History of Medieval Science*, London, 1961.

R. M. PALTER, *Towards Modern Science*, Vol. I, New York, 1962.

In addition, we have particularly used the recent publications of the following authors:

On the Dark Ages: A. VAN DE VYVER and C. W. JONES.

On Arabic influences: J. M. MILLAS-VILLICROSA, J. VERNET.

On science and scholasticism: E. GILSON, M. D. CHENU, R. MCKEON, T. and J. CARRERAS Y ARTAU, M. CLAGETT, A. KOYRÉ, E. A. MOODY, E. J. KIJKSTERHUIS, P. KIBRE, H. BALSS, and E. FARAL.

On mathematics: J. E. HOFFMANN, C. B. BOYER, P. VER EECKE; on arithmetic and counting: K. VOGEL, G. BEAUJOUAN, R. DE ROOVER, A. FANFANI.

On astronomy: P. DUHEM (1954 ed.), J. M. MILLAS-VALLICROSA, F. CARMODY, E. ZINNER; on astrolabes: H. MICHEL, S. GARCIA-FRANCO, E. POULLE, D. J. PRICE.

On alchemy: L. THORNDIKE, F. SHERWOOD TAYLOR, J. R. PARTINGTON, P. KIBRE, P. CÉZARD, M. MERCIER, E. J. HOLMYARD.

On technology: B. GILLE, R. J. FORBES, J. NEEDHAM.

On architecture: F. M. LUND, P. DU COLOMBIER, F. D. PRAGER.

On cartography: G. DE REPARAZ, R. ALMAGIA, J. and A. CORTSÃO, M. DESTOMBES, D. B. DURAND; on navigation: G. COUTINHO, A. BARBOSA, S. GARCIA FRANCO, B. R. MOTZO, D. LEITE.

On biology and medicine: A. CASTIGLIONI, E. WICKERSHEIMER, H. SIGERIST, P. DIEPGEN, C. and D. W. SINGER, L. MCKINNEY, B. L. GORDON.

We have also been able to consult the papers of the late PIERRE BRUNET, the unedited theses of the Chartres School, the papers of P. CÉZARD on recipes and of E. POULLE on astrolabes. We must also acknowledge the help of J. THÉODORIDÈS on zoology and B. GILLE on mechanistic concepts. The journal *L'architecte des collectivités publiques* has kindly permitted us to use some of the plates it has published.

INDEX OF NAMES

Personal names appear in capital letters; geographical names and names of schools are in roman type; the titles of books are in italics.

SUBJECT INDEX

Abacus, 150, 166, 287, 405, 428, 473–4, 480
Acids, mineral, 513
Acoustics, 177, 215, 216, 241, 272, 299, 333
Acupuncture, 175, 177
Aether, 226, 232
Agriculture, 8, 9, 161, 162, 176, 181, 338, 352, 374, 416
Akkadian medical literature, 80–9, 156, 247
Alchemy, alchemists, 158, 159, 271, 336, 337, 366, 391, 394, 395, 413–15, 424, 446, 490, 518–19
Alcohol, 512
Alexandrian astronomy, 313
  engineers, 332, 333
  geographers, 323
  medical schools, 292, 341
  medicine, 344–9
  physicists, 333
Algebra, 26, 27, 303, 330, 403, 404, 407
  Babylonian, 95–101, 301
  Chinese, 167, 168, 177, 430–2
  geometric, 212, 213, 274, 276, 283, 290, 293, 299, 303
  Greek, 272, 301–3
  Indian, 150, 151
  medieval, 494
Algorithms, 276, 277, 284, 297, 474
Alphabet, 123, 129, 151
  Arab, 288, 404
  Greek, 287
Amber, 397
Anaesthetics, 174, 362, 528
Anatomy, 47, 48, 152, 153, 157, 250–2, 272, 337, 340, 341–5, 354, 356
  animal, 78, 152, 174, 175
  Galen, 357–9
  medieval, 489, 490
Angular measurement, 498–9
Anthropology, 228, 249, 251, 272, 338, 339, 340
Antiseptics, 362
Apeiron, 185, 190, 193, 197, 221
Arabic arithmetic, 405–8
  astronomy, 409–11
  botany, 415–16
  calendar, 410
  fractions, 405, 406
  geometry, 408, 409
  influence on the West, 481–5
  language, 133, 288, 319, 336, 386, 387, 392–5, 403
  mathematical notation, 151, 288, 405, 406
  medicine, 392, 419–21, 461
  meteorology, 412
  pharmacology, 395, 416
  philosophy, 390, 403, 404, 405, 408, 412
  physicians, 395, 421, 450

science and scientists, 396–402, 473, 477, 479
Aramaean mathematical notation, 150
  script, 128–30, 139
Archimedean screw, 513
Architecture, Byzantine, 443
  Egyptian, 15, 36, 37
  Etruscan, 268
  Hebrew, 122
  medieval, 513, 520–2
Area, measurement of, 19, 93, 105, 166, 280, 298
  circle, 30, 31, 105, 167, 207
  trapezium, 30
  triangle, 29, 30, 479–80
Arithmetic, 9, 10, 221, 473–4
  Arabic, 405–8
  Babylonian, 90–5
  Chinese, 167, 168
  Egyptian, 18–29
  Greek, 199–213, 218, 272, 276
  Indian, 150
  Roman, 269
Arithmo-geometry, 199–203, 211, 212
Aryan language, 403
Astrolabe, 294, 310, 312, 443, 445, 454, 473, 474–5, 494, 498
  nautical, 312, 455, 525
Astrology, 71, 72, 108–11, 123, 139, 146, 147, 169, 174, 271, 313, 318, 322, 366, 405, 410, 411, 498–9, 517
Astronomy, Amerindian, 377, 378
  Arabic, 409–11
  Assyrio-Babylonian, 108–20
  Byzantine, 443–4, 445
  Chaldean, 266
  Chinese, 165, 169–72, 432–3
  Egyptian, 9, 18–29, 32–44, 110, 170
  Greco-Roman, 305–22, 366
  Greek, 113, 119, 120, 138, 140, 141, 144, 146, 147, 171, 177, 180, 192–9, 213–15, 218, 228, 229, 241, 263, 264, 265, 270, 271, 299, 313, 343
  Indian, 136–48, 170, 422–4
  Jewish, 454–5
  medieval, 496, 497–500
  Mesopotamian, 33, 107–20, 126, 315, 317, 399
  Roman, 108, 110, 140
  Vedic, 136–48
Atmospheric refraction, 301, 316
Auscultation, 252

Babylonian algebra, 95–101, 301
  astronomy, 107–20, 125, 126, 138, 139, 140, 312, 313, 314, 317, 318
  mathematics, 90–9, 101–6, 205, 274, 286, 294, 299, 301, 303, 405–6
  Neo-Babylonian map, 77

543

A HISTORY OF SCIENCE

Edited by RENÉ TATON
of the Centre National de la Recherche Scientifique

The Contributors to this Volume:

ROGER ARNALDEZ Faculté des Lettres, Lyons (Arabic Science)
JEAN BEAUJEU Faculté des Lettres, Lille (Hellenistic and Roman Science)
GUY BEAUJOUAN Archives Nationales, Paris (Medieval Science in the Christian West)
RAYMOND BLOCH École des Hautes Études (Etruscan Science)
LOUIS BOURGEY Faculté des Lettres, Algiers (Hellenic Medicine)
PAUL DUPONT-SOMMER Sorbonne (Ancient Hebrew Science)
JEAN FILLIOZAT Collège de France (Indian Science)
RAYMOND FURON Muséum National d'Histoire Naturelle (Prehistoric Science)
ANDRÉ HAUDRICOURT Centre National de la Recherche Scientifique (Chinese Science)
JEAN ITARD Lycée Henry IV (Hellenistic and Roman Mathematics)
RENE LABAT Collège de France (Mesopotamia)
GUSTAVE LEFEBVRE Institut Français (Egyptian Science: general presentation and medicine)
LOUIS MASSIGNON Collège de France (Arabic Science)
P. H. MICHEL Bibliothèque mazarine (Hellenic Science)
J. NEEDHAM, F.R.S. Gonville and Caius College, Cambridge (Chinese Science)
I. SIMON Society for the History of Jewish Medicine (Medieval Jewish Science)
G. STRESSER-PÉAN École des Hautes Études (Pre-Columbian Science)
RENÉ TATON Centre National de la Recherche Scientifique (General co-ordination of the work)
JEAN THÉODORIDÈS Centre National de la Recherche Scientifique (Byzantine Science)
JEAN VERCOUTTER Director of Antiquities, Sudan (Egyptian Mathematics and Astronomy)
CHARLES VIROLLEAUD Institut Français (Phoenician Science)